Arithmetic and Prealgebra

An Accelerated Approach

1st Edition

Richard N. Aufmann | Joanne Lockwood

CENGAGE
Learning·

Australia • Brazil • Japan • Korea • Mexico • Singapore • Spain • United Kingdom • United States

**Arithmetic and Prealgebra
An Accelerated Approach
1st Edition**

Senior Project Development Manager:
 Linda deStefano

Market Development Manager:
 Heather Kramer

Senior Production/Manufacturing Manager:
 Donna M. Brown

Production Editorial Manager:
 Kim Fry

Sr. Rights Acquisition Account Manager:
 Todd Osborne

Basic College Mathematics, An Applied Approach, Tenth Edition
Richard N. Aufmann | Joanne Lockwood

© 2014, 2009 Cengage Learning. All rights reserved.

Library of Congress Control Number: 2012947144

For product information and technology assistance, contact us at
Cengage Learning Customer & Sales Support, 1-800-354-9706

For permission to use material from this text or product,
submit all requests online at **cengage.com/permissions**
Further permissions questions can be emailed to
permissionrequest@cengage.com

This book contains select works from existing Cengage Learning resources and was produced by Cengage Learning Custom Solutions for collegiate use. As such, those adopting and/or contributing to this work are responsible for editorial content accuracy, continuity and completeness.

Compilation © 2013 Cengage Learning

ISBN-13: 978-1-285-90709-3

ISBN-10: 1-285-90709-4

Cengage Learning
5191 Natorp Boulevard
Mason, Ohio 45040
USA
Cengage Learning is a leading provider of customized learning solutions with office locations around the globe, including Singapore, the United Kingdom, Australia, Mexico, Brazil, and Japan. Locate your local office at:
international.cengage.com/region.

Cengage Learning products are represented in Canada by Nelson Education, Ltd.
For your lifelong learning solutions, visit **www.cengage.com/custom.**
Visit our corporate website at **www.cengage.com.**

Printed in the United States of America

WebAssign Student Quick Start Guide

You can use WebAssign to access your homework, quizzes, and tests — whatever your instructor chooses — at any time of day or night, from any computer with a connection to the Internet and a Web browser. Your instructor creates your assignments, schedules them, and decides how many submissions you get. Your instructor also determines if you can have an extension, if you can save your work without submitting it at the time, and how much feedback you get after you submit an assignment.

The WebAssign support staff cannot change your username or password, give extensions, change your score, give you extra submissions, or help you with the content of your assignments.

Logging In

You can log in to WebAssign using any Web browser connected to the Internet. There are two different ways to log in to WebAssign. Each requires information from your teacher. If you are unsure about how to log in, please check with your teacher or another student in your class.

Go to the login page at http://webassign.net/login.html or the web address provided by your teacher. The way you log in depends on how your instructor set up the class:

- If your teacher created a WebAssign account for you, they will provide you with a **Username**, an **Institution** code and a **Password**. Simply enter this information in the boxes provided and click the **Log In** button.

WebAssign.

- If your teacher wants you to **Self-Enroll** in the WebAssign course they will provide you with a **Class Key**. You will create your own username and password. It is important that you remember this information so you can log in for the remainder of the class. In this case, just click the **I have a Class Key** button. You don't need to enter any other information on this page.

  Then, enter the **Class Key** your instructor provided and click **Submit**. Verify you are enrolling in the correct class on the next page.

Class Key

Enter the Class Key that you received from your instructor. You will only need to complete this once. After you have created your account, you can log in on the main page.

Class Key

[_____] [_____] [_____]

Class Keys generally start with an institution code, followed by two sets of four digits.

[Submit]

- Enter your preferred Login and Student information.

- Click the **Create My Account** button to complete the enrollment process.

- A review screen will display, showing your username, institution code, and password. **Retain a copy of this information.** You will need it to log into WebAssign.

Log In Information

Required fields are marked with an asterisk (*).

Preferred Username	* [_____] [Check Availability]
	Your username may contain letters, numbers, and the following characters: underscore (_), hyphen (-), period (.)
Institution Code	**webassign**
Password	* [_____]
Re-Enter Password	* [_____]
	Passwords are case-sensitive.

Student Information

Required fields are marked with an asterisk (*).

First Name	* [_____]
Last Name	* [_____]
Email Address	* [_____]
Student ID Number	[_____]

[Create My Account]

Access Codes

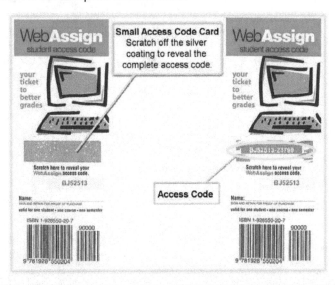

Once you log in, you may see a WebAssign Notice about entering an access code for your class. You can get an Access Code from any of the following places if you need to use one:

- A new textbook you purchased for the class.
- Your bookstore, which may sell Access Code cards.
- Online, where you can purchase an access code with a credit card.

You have a 14 day grace period to use WebAssign, starting with the WebAssign class start date. During this time you can work on and view your WebAssign assignments without registering a code.

After the grace period is over you will only see the code registration message until you submit or purchase a code.

There are two types of WebAssign access code cards. The small card requires you to scratch off the silver surface in order to reveal the complete access code.

Web**Assign.**

The larger security envelope card requires you to open the card to reveal the access code number.

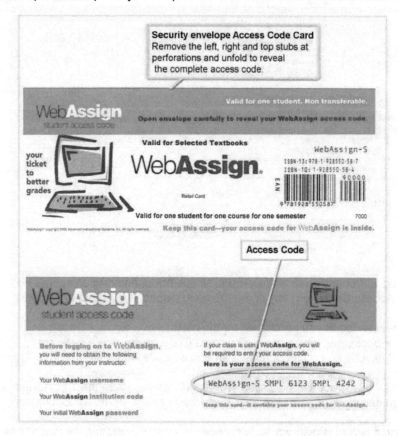

If you would like to purchase an access code directly from WebAssign online, you may do so with a credit card. Your code will be automatically registered to your WebAssign account as soon as the transaction is complete. You will receive an email confirmation. Please keep a copy for your records.

WebAssign.

Your WebAssign Home Page

Once you have successfully logged in you will see your WebAssign homepage. If you are taking more than one WebAssign class, you will need to select which class you wish to view first.

The upper right corner features links to a complete Student **Guide**, as well as a link to WebAssign Technical Support under **Help**. If you want to change your password or add or update your email address, simply click **My Options** in the upper right hand corner.

You will see your assignments and due dates listed, as well as any Communications, Grades, and Announcements posted by your teacher.

WebAssign
Wednesday, August 6, 2008 02:37 PM EDT

Home | My Assignments | Grades | Communication | Calendar

Demo Class, section 001, Fall 2009

Home

My Assignments

Current Assignments (13)

Name	Due
Basic Question Types with Practice (all)	Aug 13 2008 03:31 PM EDT
Intro to WebAssign 2008	Aug 15 2008 10:00 PM EDT
General Questions	Oct 25 2008 10:00 PM EDT

Past Assignments (4)

Communication

Class Forums

Homework	12 topics

Grades

My Grade : 92.40 (A)

David Thomson
Instructor: John Smith
Demo school

Announcements

Welcome

I hope you are all ready to learn in our class. I look forward to any questions you might have.

Archived Announcements

My Calendar

Jump to...

About this Class

Class Started: Wednesday, January 1, 2003
Class Ends: Thursday, January 14, 2010

Answering Questions

WebAssign has a variety of different question types, ranging from multiple choice to fill-in-the-blank to symbolic questions. Here are some things to keep in mind as you work through your assignments:

- Some questions may include numbers or words that appear in red. This signifies that the number or word has been randomized, so that you receive a different version of the same basic question from your classmates.

- Some WebAssign questions check the number of significant figures in your answer. If you enter the correct value with the wrong number of significant figures, you will not receive credit, but you will receive a hint that your number does not have the correct number of significant figures.

- Some questions require entering symbolic notation. Answer symbolic questions by using calculator notation. You must use the exact variables specified in the questions. The order is not important as long as it is mathematically correct. Clicking on the eye button previews the expression you enter in proper mathematical notation. Clicking on the symbolic formatting help button provides tips for using the correct keystrokes.

WebAssign.

- When you click on some WebAssign chemistry or math questions an input palette will open. These palettes, called chemPad and mathPad, will help you enter your answer in proper notation.

- Some questions may require the use of an Active Figure simulation. Active Figures require the free Macromedia Flash Player plug-in, downloadable from www.macromedia.com.

- If your instructor allows it, you can save your work without grading by selecting the Save Work button at the end of the question. After you save your work, it will be available to you the next time you click the assignment.

- Please note that WebAssign will **not** automatically submit your answers for scoring if you only **Save** your work. Your teacher will not be able to see your submissions. Please be sure to **Submit** prior to the due date and time.

- If your instructor allows it, you can submit answers by question part or for the entire assignment. To submit an individual question answer for grading, click the **Submit New Answers to Question __** button at the bottom of each question. To submit the entire assignment for grading, click the **Submit All New Answers** button at the end of the assignment.

Technical Support

If you are having difficulty logging in, please be sure to check with your teacher and verify whether an account has been created for you or whether you need to self-enroll. In either case your teacher needs to provide the appropriate information (username, institution code and password OR Class Key).

To email WebAssign Support go to http://www.webassign.net/info/support/report.html. This page also lists answers to **Common Problems**, and provides links to the **Student Guide**.

August 7, 2008

Contents

CHAPTER

4   Decimals   191

CHAPTER

5   Introduction to Linear Equations   247
and Variables

CHAPTER

6 Ratio and Proportion 301

AIM for Success

OBJECTIVES

SECTION A.1
- Get Ready
- Motivate Yourself
- Develop a "Can Do" Attitude Toward Math
- Strategies for Success
- Time Management
- Habits of Successful Students

SECTION A.2
- Get the Big Picture
- Understand the Organization
- Use the Interactive Method
- Use a Strategy to Solve Word Problems
- Ace the Test
- Ready, Set, Succeed!

Focus on Success

This important chapter describes study skills that are used by students who have been successful in this course. Chapter A covers a wide range of topics that focus on what you need to do to succeed in this class. It includes a complete guide to the textbook and how to use its features to become a successful student.

hxdbzxy/Shutterstock.com

Prep Test

Are you ready to succeed in this course?

1. Read this chapter. Answer all of the questions. Write down your answers on paper.

2. Write down your instructor's name.

3. Write down the classroom number.

4. Write down the days and times the class meets.

5. Bring your textbook, a notebook, and a pen or pencil to every class.

6. Be an active participant, not a passive observer.

A.1 | How to Succeed in This Course

Get Ready

We are committed to your success in learning mathematics and have developed many tools and resources to support you along the way.

DO YOU WANT TO EXCEL IN THIS COURSE?

Read on to learn about the skills you'll need and how best to use this book to get the results you want.

We have written this text in an *interactive* style. More about this later but, in short, this means that you are supposed to interact with the text. Do not just read the text! Work along with it. Ready? Let's begin!

WHY ARE YOU TAKING THIS COURSE?

Did you interact with the text, or did you just read the last question? Get some paper and a pencil or pen and answer the question. Really—you will have more success in math and other courses you take if you actively participate. Now, interact. Write down one reason you are taking this course.

_____

_____

Of course, we have no idea what you just wrote, but experience has shown us that many of you wrote something along the lines of "I have to take it to graduate" or "It is a prerequisite to another course I have to take" or "It is required for my major." Those reasons are perfectly fine. Every teacher has had to take courses that were not directly related to his or her major.

WHY DO YOU WANT TO SUCCEED IN THIS COURSE?

Think about why you want to succeed in this course. List the reasons here (not in your head . . . on the paper!):

_____

_____

One reason you may have listed is that math skills are important in order to be successful in your chosen career. That is certainly an important reason. Here are some other reasons.

- Math is a skill that applies across careers, which is certainly a benefit in our world of changing job requirements. A good foundation in math may enable you to more easily make a career change.
- Math can help you learn critical thinking skills, an attribute all employers want.
- Math can help you see relationships between ideas and identify patterns.

Motivate Yourself

Take Note
Motivation alone won't lead to success. For example, suppose a person who cannot swim is rowed out to the middle of a lake and thrown overboard. That person has a lot of motivation to swim, but most likely will drown without some help. You'll need motivation *and* learning in order to succeed.

You'll find many real-life problems in this book, relating to sports, money, cars, music, and more. We hope that these topics will help you understand how mathematics is used in everyday life. To learn all of the necessary skills and to understand how you can apply them to your life outside of this course, motivate yourself to learn.

One of the reasons we asked you why you are taking this course was to provide motivation for you to succeed. When there is a reason to do something, that task is easier to accomplish. We understand that you may not want to be taking this course but, to achieve your career goal, this is a necessary step. Let your career goal be your motivation for success.

MAKE THE COMMITMENT TO SUCCEED!

With practice, you will improve your math skills. Skeptical? Think about when you first learned to drive a car, ride a skateboard, dance, paint, surf, or any other talent that you now have. You may have felt self-conscious or concerned that you might fail. But with time and practice, you learned the skill.

List a situation in which you accomplished your goal by spending time practicing and perfecting your skills (such as learning to play the piano or to play basketball):

_____

_____

You do not get "good" at something by doing it once a week. **Practice** is the backbone of any successful endeavor—including math!

Develop a "Can Do" Attitude Toward Math

You can do math! When you first learned the skills you just listed above, you may not have done them well. With practice, you got better. With practice, you will get better at math. Stay focused, motivated, and committed to success.

We cannot emphasize enough how important it is to overcome the "I Can't Do Math" syndrome. If you listen to interviews of very successful athletes after a particularly bad performance, you will note that they focus on the positive aspects of what they did, not the negative. Sports psychologists encourage athletes always to be positive—to have a "can do" attitude. Develop this attitude toward math and you will succeed.

Change your conversation about mathematics. Do not say "I can't do math," "I hate math," or "Math is too hard." These comments just give you an excuse to fail. You don't want to fail, and we don't want you to fail. Write it down now: I can do math!

_____

_____

William Perugini/Shutterstock.com

Strategies for Success

PREPARE TO SUCCEED

There are a number of things that may be worrisome to you as you begin a new semester. List some of those things now.

Here are some of the concerns expressed by our students.

- **Tuition**
  Will I be able to afford school?
- **Job**
  I must work. Will my employer give me a schedule that will allow me to go to school?
- **Anxiety**
  Will I succeed?
- **Child care**
  What will I do with my kids while I'm in class or when I need to study?
- **Time**
  Will I be able to find the time to attend class and study?
- **Degree goals**
  How long will it take me to finish school and earn my degree?

These are all important and valid concerns. Whatever your concerns, acknowledge them. Choose an education path that allows you to accommodate your concerns. Make sure they don't prevent you from succeeding.

SELECT A COURSE

Many schools offer math assessment tests. These tests evaluate your present math skills. They don't evaluate how smart you are, so don't worry about your score on the test. If you are unsure about where you should start in the math curriculum, these tests can show you where to begin. You are better off starting at a level that is appropriate for you than starting with a more advanced class and then dropping it because you can't keep up. Dropping a class is a waste of time and money.

If you have difficulty with math, avoid short courses that compress the class into a few weeks. If you have struggled with math in the past, this environment does not give you the time to process math concepts. Similarly, avoid classes that meet once a week. The time delay between classes makes it difficult to make connections between concepts.

Some career goals require a number of math courses. If that is true of your major, try to take a math course every semester until you complete the requirements. Think about it this way. If you take, say, French I, and then wait two semesters before taking French II, you may forget a lot of material. Math is much the same. You must keep the concepts fresh in your mind.

Time Management

One of the most important requirements in completing any task is to acknowledge the amount of time it will take to finish the job successfully. Before a construction company starts to build a skyscraper, the company spends months looking at how much time each of the phases of construction will take. This is done so that resources can be allocated when appropriate. For instance, it would not make sense to schedule the electricians to run wiring until the walls are up.

MANAGE YOUR TIME!

wavebreakmedia ltd/Shutterstock.com

We know how busy you are outside of school. Do you have a full-time or a part-time job? Do you have children? Do you visit your family often? Do you play school sports or participate in the school orchestra or theater company? It can be stressful to balance all of the important activities and responsibilities in your life. Creating a time management plan will help you schedule enough time to do everything you need to do. Let's get started.

First, you need a calendar. You can use a daily planner, a calendar for a smartphone, or an online calendar, such as the ones offered by Google, MSN, or Yahoo. It is best to have a calendar on which you can fill in daily activities and be able to see a weekly or monthly view as well.

Start filling in your calendar now, even if it means stopping right here and finding a calendar. Some of the things you might include are:

- The hours each class meets
- Time for driving to and from work or school
- Leisure time, an important aspect of a healthy lifestyle
- Time for study. Plan at least one hour of study for each hour in class. This is a *minimum!*
- Time to eat
- Your work schedule
- Time for extracurricular activities such as sports, music lessons, or volunteer work
- Time for family and friends
- Time for sleep
- Time for exercise

Take Note

Be realistic about how much time you have. One gauge is that working 10 hours per week is approximately equivalent to taking one three-unit course. If your college considers 15 units a full load and you are working 10 hours per week, you should consider taking 12 units. The more you work, the fewer units you should take.

We really hope you did this. If not, please reconsider. One of the best pathways to success is understanding how much time it takes to succeed. When you finish your calendar, if it does not allow you enough time to stay physically and emotionally healthy, rethink some of your school or work activities. We don't want you to lose your job because you have to study math. On the other hand, we don't want you to fail in math because of your job.

If math is particularly difficult for you, consider taking fewer course units during the semesters you take math. This applies equally to any other subject that you may find difficult. There is no rule that you must finish college in four years. It is a myth—discard it now.

Now extend your calendar for the entire semester. Many of the entries will repeat, such as the time a class meets. In your extended calendar, include significant events that may disrupt your normal routine. These might include holidays, family outings, birthdays, anniversaries, or special events such as a concert or a football game. In addition to these events, be sure to include the dates of tests, the date of the final exam, and dates that projects or papers are due. These are all important semester events. Having them on your calendar will remind you that you need to make time for them.

CLASS TIME

To be successful, attend class. You should consider your commitment to attend class as serious as your commitment to your job or to keeping an appointment with a dear friend. It is difficult to overstate the importance of attending class. If you miss work, you don't get paid. If you miss class, you are not getting the full benefit of your tuition dollar. You are losing money.

If, by some unavoidable situation, you cannot attend class, find out as soon as possible what was covered in class. You might:

- Ask a friend for notes and the assignment.
- Contact your instructor and get the assignment. Missing class is no excuse for not being prepared for the next class.
- Determine whether there are online resources that you can use to help you with the topics and concepts that were discussed in the class you missed.

Going to class is important. Once you are there, participate in class. Stay involved and active. When your instructor asks a question, try to at least mentally answer the question. If you have a question, ask. Your instructor expects questions and wants you to understand the concept being discussed.

HOMEWORK TIME

In addition to attending class, you must do homework. Homework is the best way to reinforce the ideas presented in class. You should plan on at least one to two hours of homework and study for each hour you are in class. We've had many students tell us that one to two hours seems like a lot of time. That may be true, but if you want to attain your goals, you must be willing to devote the time to being successful in this math course.

You should schedule study time just as if it were class time. To do this, write down where and when you study best. For instance, do you study best at home, in the library, at the math center, under a tree, or somewhere else? Some psychologists who research successful study strategies suggest that just by varying where you study, you can increase the effectiveness of a study session. While you are considering where you prefer to study, also think about the time of day during which your study period will be most productive. Write down your thoughts.

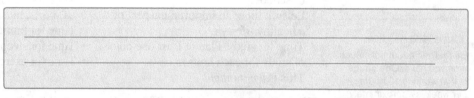

Look at what you have written, and be sure that you can consistently be in your favorite study environment at the time you have selected. Studying and homework are extremely important. Just as you should not miss class, do not miss study time.

Before we leave this important topic, we have a few suggestions. If at all possible, create a study hour right after class. The material will be fresh in your mind, and the immediate review, along with your homework, will help reinforce the concepts you are learning.

If you can't study right after class, make sure that you set aside some time *on the day of the class* to review notes and begin the homework. The longer you wait, the more difficult it will be to recall some of the important points covered during class. Study math in small chunks— one hour a day (perhaps not enough for most of us), every day, is better than seven hours in one sitting. If you are studying for an extended period of time, break up your study session by studying one subject for a while and then moving on to another subject. Try to alternate between similar or related courses. For instance, study math for a while, then science, and then back to math. Or study history for a while, then political science, and then back to history.

Meet some of the people in your class and try to put together a study group. The group could meet two or three times a week. During those meetings, you could quiz each other, prepare for a test, try to explain a concept to someone else in the group, or get help on a topic that is difficult for you.

After reading these suggestions, you may want to rethink where and when you study best. If so, do that now. Remember, however, that it is your individual style that is important. Choose what works for *you,* and stick to it.

Habits of Successful Students

Pattie Steib/Shutterstock.com

There are a number of habits that successful students use. Think about what these might be, and write them down.

What you have written is very important. The habits you have listed are probably the things you know you must do to succeed. Here is a list of some responses from successful students we have known.

- **Set priorities.** You will encounter many distractions during the semester. Do not allow them to prevent you from reaching your goal.

- **Take responsibility.** Your instructor, this textbook, tutors, math centers, and other resources are there to help you succeed. Ultimately, however, you must choose to learn. You must choose success.
- **Hang out with successful students.** Success breeds success. When you work and study with successful students, you are in an environment that will help you succeed. Seek out people who are committed to their goals.
- **Study regularly.** We have mentioned this before, but it is too important not to be repeated.
- **Self test.** Once every few days, select homework exercises from previous assignments and use them to test your understanding. Try to do these exercises without getting help from examples in the text. These self tests will help you gain confidence that you can do these types of problems on a test given in class.
- **Try different strategies.** If you read the text and are still having difficulty understanding a concept, consider going a step further. Contact the instructor or find a tutor. Many campuses have some free tutorial services. Go to the math or learning center. Consult another textbook. Be active and get the help you need.
- **Make flash cards.** This is one of the strategies that some math students do not think to try. Flash cards are a very important part of learning math. For instance, your instructor may use words or phrases such as *linear, quadratic, exponent, base, rational,* and many others. If you don't know the meanings of these words, you will not know what is being discussed.
- **Plod along.** Your education is not a race. The primary goal is to finish. Taking too many classes and then dropping some does not get you to the end any faster. Take only as many classes as you can successfully manage.

SECTION

A.2

How to Use This Text to Succeed in This Course

Helder Almeida/Shutterstock.com

Get the Big Picture

One of the major resources that you will have access to the entire semester is this textbook. We have written this text with you and your success in mind. The following is a guide to the features of this text that will help you succeed.

Actually, we want you to get the *really* big picture. Take a few minutes to read the table of contents. You may feel some anxiety about all the new concepts you will be learning. Try to think of this as an exciting opportunity to learn math. Now look through the entire book. Move quickly. Don't spend more than a few seconds on each page. Scan titles, look at pictures, and notice diagrams.

Getting this "big picture" view will help you see where this course is going. To reach your goal, it's important to get an idea of the steps you will need to take along the way.

As you look through the book, find topics that interest you. What's your preference? Racing? Sailing? TV? Amusement parks? Find the Index of Applications at the front of the book, and pull out three subjects that interest you. Write those topics here.

Understand the Organization

Look again at the Table of Contents. There are 12 chapters in this book. You'll see that every chapter is divided into sections, and each section contains a number of learning objectives. Each learning objective is labeled with a letter from A to D. Knowing how this book is organized will help you locate important topics and concepts as you're studying.

Before you start a new objective, take a few minutes to read the Objective Statement for that objective. Then, browse through the objective material. Especially note the words or phrases in bold type—these are important concepts that you'll need to know as you move along in the course. These words are good candidates for flash cards. If possible, include an example of the concept on the flash card, as shown at the left.

You will also see important concepts and rules set off in boxes. Here is one about multiplication. These rules are also good candidates for flash cards.

Flash Card

Rules for Multiplying Two Numbers

When two numbers have the same sign, the product is positive.
When two numbers have different signs, the product is negative.
Examples:
$(-12)(-8) = 96$ *and*
$9(-7) = -63$

Rules for Multiplying Two Numbers

For two numbers that have the same sign:

Multiply the absolute values of the factors. The product is positive.

EXAMPLES

1. $4 \cdot 9 = 36$ **2.** $(-12)(-8) = 96$

For two numbers that have different signs:

Multiply the absolute values of the factors. The product is negative.

EXAMPLES

3. $-7(6) = -42$ **4.** $9(-7) = -63$

Leaf through Section 1.2 of Chapter 1. Write down the words in bold and any concepts or rules that are displayed in boxes.

Use the Interactive Method

As we mentioned earlier, this textbook is based on an interactive approach. We want you to be actively involved in learning mathematics, and have given you many suggestions for getting "hands-on" with this book.

HOW TO Look on page 27. See HOW TO 2? A HOW TO introduces a concept (in this case, multiplying whole numbers) and includes a step-by-step solution of the type of exercise you will find in the homework.

HOW TO 2 Find the product of 47 and 23.

Multiply by the ones digit.	Multiply by the tens digit.	Add.

$$\begin{array}{r} 47 \\ \times\ 23 \\ \hline 141 \end{array} \quad (= 47 \times 3)$$

$$\begin{array}{r} 47 \\ \times\ 23 \\ \hline 141 \\ 940 \end{array} \quad (= 47 \times 20)$$

Writing the 0 keeps the columns aligned correctly.

$$\begin{array}{r} 47 \\ \times\ 23 \\ \hline 141 \\ 940 \\ \hline 1081 \end{array}$$

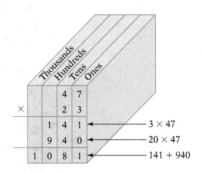

3×47
20×47
$141 + 940$

Grab paper and a pencil and work along as you're reading through the HOW TO. When you're done, get a clean sheet of paper. Write down the problem and try to complete the solution without looking at your notes or at the book. When you're done, check your answer. If you got it right, you're ready to move on.

Look through the text and find three instances of a HOW TO. Write the concept illustrated in each HOW TO here.

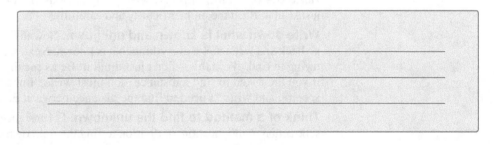

Example/You Try It Pair You'll need hands-on practice to succeed in mathematics. When we show you an example, work it out yourself, right beside the solution. Use the Example/You Try It pairs to get the practice you need.

Take a look at page 27. Example 2 and You Try It 2 are shown here.

EXAMPLE 2

Find 829 multiplied by 603.

Solution

$$\begin{array}{r} 829 \\ \times\ 603 \\ \hline 2487 \\ 49740 \\ \hline 499,887 \end{array}$$

- $3 \times 829 = 2487$
- Write a zero in the tens column for 0×829.
- $6 \times 829 = 4974$

YOU TRY IT 2

Multiply: 756×305

Your solution

Solution on p. S2

You'll see that each Example is fully worked out. Study the Example by carefully working through each step. Then, try to complete the You Try It. Use the solution to the Example as a model for solving the You Try It. If you get stuck, the solutions to the You Try Its are provided in the back of the book. There is a page number directly following the You Try It that shows you where you can find the completely-worked-out solution. Use the solution to get a hint for the step on which you are stuck. Then, try again!

When you've arrived at your solution, check your work against the solution in the back of the book. Turn to page S2 to see the solution for You Try It 2.

Remember that sometimes there is more than one way to solve a problem. But your answer should always match the answer we've given in the back of the book. If you have any questions about whether your method will always work, check with your instructor.

Use a Strategy to Solve Word Problems

Learning to solve word problems is one of the reasons you are studying math. This is where you combine all of the critical thinking skills you have learned to solve practical problems.

Try not to be intimidated by word problems. Basically, what you need is a strategy that will help you come up with the equation you will need to solve the problem. When you are looking at a word problem, try the following:

- **Read the problem.** This may seem pretty obvious, but we mean really read it. Don't just scan it. Read the problem slowly and carefully.

- **Write down what is known and unknown.** Now that you have read the problem, go back and write down everything that is known. Next, write down what it is you are trying to find. *Write* this—don't just think it! Be as specific as you can. For instance, if you are asked to find a distance, don't just write "I need to find the distance." Be specific and write "I need to find the distance between Earth and the moon."

- **Think of a method to find the unknown.** For instance, should you use addition, subtraction, multiplication, or division to find the unknown quantity? This is certainly the most difficult step.

- **Solve the problem.** Be careful as you solve the problem. There is no sense in getting to this point and then making a careless mistake. The unknown in most problems will include a unit such as feet, dollars, or miles per hour. When you write your answer, include a unit. An answer such as 20 doesn't mean much. Is it 20 feet, 20 dollars, 20 miles per hour, or something else?

- **Check your solution.** Now that you have an answer, go back to the problem and ask yourself whether it makes sense. This is an important step. For instance, if, according to your answer, the cost of a car is $2.51, you know that something went wrong.

In this text, the solution of every word problem is broken down into two steps, Strategy and Solution. The Strategy consists of the first three steps discussed above. The Solution is the last two steps. Here is an Example from page 28 of the text. Because you have not yet studied the concepts involved in the problem, you may not be able to solve it. However, note the detail in the Strategy. When you do the You Try It following an Example, be sure to include your own Strategy.

EXAMPLE 4

A pharmacist's assistant earns $640 for working a 40-hour week. This week the assistant also worked 7 hours of overtime at $26 an hour. Find the assistant's total pay for the week.

Strategy

To find the assistant's total pay for the week:
- Find the overtime pay by multiplying the hours of overtime (7) by the overtime rate of pay (26).
- Add the weekly salary (640) to the overtime pay.

Solution

$$
\begin{array}{r}
26 \\
\times\ 7 \\
\hline
182
\end{array}
\quad \text{overtime pay}
\qquad
\begin{array}{r}
640 \\
+\ 182 \\
\hline
822
\end{array}
$$

The assistant earned $822 this week.

YOU TRY IT 4

The buyer for Ross Department Store can buy 80 men's suits for $7600. Each sports jacket will cost the store $62. The manager orders 80 men's suits and 25 sports jackets. What is the total cost of the order?

Your strategy

Your solution

Solutions on p. S2

When you have finished studying a section, do the exercises your instructor has selected. Math is not a spectator sport. You must practice every day. Do the homework and do not get behind.

Ace the Test

There are a number of features in this text that will help you prepare for a test. These features will help you even more if you do just one simple thing: When you are doing your homework, go back to each previous homework assignment for the current chapter and rework two exercises. That's right—just *two* exercises. You will be surprised at how much better prepared you will be for a test by doing this.

Here are some additional aids to help you ace the test.

Chapter Summary Once you've completed a chapter, look at the Chapter Summary. The Chapter Summary is divided into two sections: Key Words and Essential Rules and Procedures. Flip to page 196 to see the Chapter Summary for Chapter 4. The summary shows all of the important topics covered in the chapter. Do you see the reference following each topic? This reference shows you the objective and page in the text where you can find more information on the concept.

Write down one Key Word and one Essential Rule or Procedure. Explain the meaning of the reference "4.1A, page 178."

Chapter Review Exercises Turn to page 197 to see the Chapter Review Exercises for Chapter 4. When you do the review exercises, you're giving yourself an important opportunity to test your understanding of the chapter. The answer to each review exercise is given at the back of the book, along with the objective the question relates to. When you're done with the Chapter Review Exercises, check your answers. If you had trouble with any of the questions, you can restudy the objectives and retry some of the exercises in those objectives for extra help.

Go to the Answer Section at the back of the text. Find the answers for the Chapter Review Exercises for Chapter 4. Write down the answer to Exercise 6. Explain the meaning of the reference "4.2B."

Chapter Test The Chapter Test for each chapter can be found after the Chapter Review Exercises and can be used to help you prepare for your exam. The answer to each question is given at the back of the book, along with both an objective reference and a reference to a HOW TO, Example, or You Try It that the question relates to. Think of these tests as "practice runs" for your in-class tests. Take the test in a quiet place, and try to work through it in the same amount of time that will be allowed for your actual exam.

The aids we have mentioned above will help you prepare for a test. You should begin your review *at least* two days before the test—three days is better. These aids will get you ready for the test.

Here are some suggestions to try while you are actually taking the test.

- **Try to relax.** We know that test situations make some students quite nervous or anxious. These feelings are normal. Try to stay calm and focused on what you know. If you have prepared as we have suggested, the answers will begin to come to you.
- **Scan the test.** Get a feeling for the big picture.
- **Read the directions carefully.** Make sure you answer each question fully.
- **Work the problems that are easiest for you first.** This will help you with your confidence and help reduce any nervous feelings you may have.

Ready, Set, Succeed!

It takes hard work and commitment to succeed, but we know you can do it! Doing well in mathematics is just one step you'll take on your path to success. Good luck. We wish you success.

Whole Numbers

Focus on Success

Have you read Chapter A, AIM for Success? It describes study skills used by students who have been successful in their math courses. It gives you tips on how to stay motivated, how to manage your time, and how to prepare for exams. Chapter A also includes a complete guide to the textbook and how to use its features to be successful in this course. It starts on page AIM-1.

Andresr/Shutterstock.com

Prep Test

Are you ready to succeed in this chapter? Take the Prep Test below to find out if you are ready to learn the new material.

1. Name the number of ◆s shown below.

   ◆ ◆ ◆ ◆ ◆ ◆ ◆

2. Write the numbers from 1 to 10.

   1 __ __ __ __ __ __ __ __ 10

3. Match the number with its word form.
   a. 4   A. five
   b. 2   B. one
   c. 5   C. zero
   d. 1   D. four
   e. 3   E. two
   f. 0   F. three

1

1.1 Introduction to Whole Numbers

OBJECTIVE A *To identify the order relation between two numbers*

The **whole numbers** are 0, 1, 2, 3, 4, 5, 6, 7, 8, 9, 10, 11, 12, 13, 14, ...

The three dots mean that the list continues on and on and that there is no largest whole number.

Just as distances are associated with the markings on the edge of a ruler, the whole numbers can be associated with points on a line. This line is called the **number line.** The arrow on the number line below indicates that there is no largest whole number.

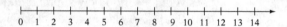

The **graph of a whole number** is shown by placing a heavy dot directly above that number on the number line. Here is the graph of 7 on the number line:

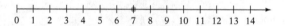

The number line can be used to show the order of whole numbers. A number that appears to the left of a given number **is less than (<)** the given number. A number that appears to the right of a given number **is greater than (>)** the given number.

Four is less than seven.
4 < 7

Twelve is greater than seven.
12 > 7

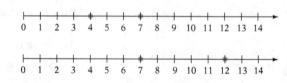

EXAMPLE 1

Graph 11 on the number line.

Solution

YOU TRY IT 1

Graph 6 on the number line.

Your solution

EXAMPLE 2

Place the correct symbol, < or >, between the two numbers.
a. 39 24
b. 0 51

Solution
a. 39 > 24
b. 0 < 51

YOU TRY IT 2

Place the correct symbol, < or >, between the two numbers.
a. 45 29
b. 27 0

Your solution
a.
b.

Solutions on p. S1

OBJECTIVE B   *To write whole numbers in words and in standard form*

Point of Interest

The Babylonians had a place-value system based on 60. Its influence is still with us in angle measurement and time:
60 seconds in 1 minute,
60 minutes in 1 hour. It appears that the earliest record of a base-10 place-value system for natural numbers dates from the 8th century.

When a whole number is written using the digits 0, 1, 2, 3, 4, 5, 6, 7, 8, and 9, it is said to be in **standard form.** The position of each digit in the number determines the digit's **place value.** The diagram below shows a **place-value chart** naming the first 12 place values. The number 37,462 is in standard form and has been entered in the chart.

In the number 37,462, the position of the digit 3 determines that its place value is ten-thousands.

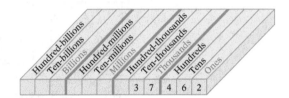

When a number is written in standard form, each group of digits separated from the other digits by a comma (or commas) is called a **period.** The number 3,786,451,294 has four periods. The period names are shown in red in the place-value chart above.

To write a number in words, start from the left. Name the number in each period. Then write the period name in place of the comma.

3,786,451,294 is read "three billion seven hundred eighty-six million four hundred fifty-one thousand two hundred ninety-four."

To write a whole number in standard form, write the number named in each period, and replace each period name with a comma.

Four million sixty-two thousand five hundred eighty-four is written 4,062,584. The zero is used as a place holder for the hundred-thousands place.

EXAMPLE 3

Write 25,478,083 in words.

Solution

Twenty-five million four hundred seventy-eight thousand eighty-three

YOU TRY IT 3

Write 36,462,075 in words.

Your solution

EXAMPLE 4

Write three hundred three thousand three in standard form.

Solution

303,003

YOU TRY IT 4

Write four hundred fifty-two thousand seven in standard form.

Your solution

Solutions on p. S1

OBJECTIVE C   *To write whole numbers in expanded form*

The whole number 26,429 can be written in **expanded form** as

$20,000 + 6000 + 400 + 20 + 9.$

The place-value chart can be used to find the expanded form of a number.

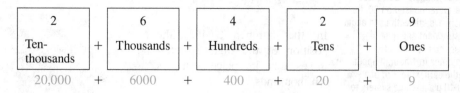

2 Ten-thousands	+	6 Thousands	+	4 Hundreds	+	2 Tens	+	9 Ones
20,000	+	6000	+	400	+	20	+	9

The number 420,806 is written in expanded form below. Note the effect of having zeros in the number.

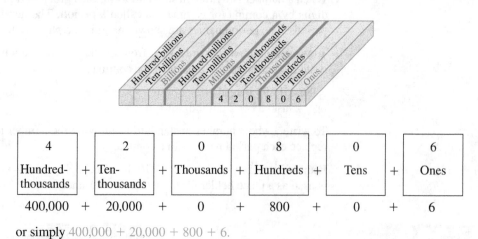

4 Hundred-thousands	+	2 Ten-thousands	+	0 Thousands	+	8 Hundreds	+	0 Tens	+	6 Ones
400,000	+	20,000	+	0	+	800	+	0	+	6

or simply 400,000 + 20,000 + 800 + 6.

EXAMPLE 5

Write 23,859 in expanded form.

Solution

20,000 + 3000 + 800 + 50 + 9

YOU TRY IT 5

Write 68,281 in expanded form.

Your solution

EXAMPLE 6

Write 709,542 in expanded form.

Solution

700,000 + 9000 + 500 + 40 + 2

YOU TRY IT 6

Write 109,207 in expanded form.

Your solution

Solutions on p. S1

OBJECTIVE D *To round a whole number to a given place value*

When the distance to the moon is given as 240,000 miles, the number represents an approximation to the true distance. Taking an approximate value for an exact number is called **rounding.** A rounded number is always rounded to a given place value.

37 is closer to 40 than it is to 30. 37 rounded to the nearest ten is 40.

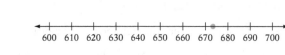

673 rounded to the nearest ten is 670. 673 rounded to the nearest hundred is 700.

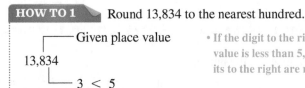

A whole number is rounded to a given place value without using the number line by looking at the first digit to the right of the given place value.

> **HOW TO 1** Round 13,834 to the nearest hundred.

Given place value

13,834

3 < 5

• If the digit to the right of the given place value is less than 5, that digit and all digits to the right are replaced by zeros.

13,834 rounded to the nearest hundred is 13,800.

> **HOW TO 2** Round 386,217 to the nearest ten-thousand.

Given place value

386,217

6 > 5

• If the digit to the right of the given place value is greater than or equal to 5, increase the digit in the given place value by 1, and replace all other digits to the right by zeros.

386,217 rounded to the nearest ten-thousand is 390,000.

EXAMPLE 7

Round 525,453 to the nearest ten-thousand.

Solution

Given place value

525,453

5 = 5

525,453 rounded to the nearest ten-thousand is 530,000.

YOU TRY IT 7

Round 368,492 to the nearest ten-thousand.

Your solution

EXAMPLE 8

Round 1972 to the nearest hundred.

Solution

Given place value

1972

7 > 5

1972 rounded to the nearest hundred is 2000.

YOU TRY IT 8

Round 3962 to the nearest hundred.

Your solution

Solutions on p. S1

1.1 EXERCISES

✔ Concept Check

1. Determine whether the statement is true or false.

   a. $23 > 48$ **b.** $0 < 14$ **c.** $15 > 0$ **d.** $47 < 74$

2. Name the place value of the digit 3 in each number.

   a. 83,479 **b.** 3,491,507 **c.** 2,634,958 **d.** 76,319,204

OBJECTIVE A *To identify the order relation between two numbers*

For Exercises 3 to 6, graph the number on the number line.

3. 3 ┤├─┼─┼─┼─┼─┼─┼─┼─┼─┼─┼─┼→
        0 1 2 3 4 5 6 7 8 9 10 11 12

4. 5 ┤├─┼─┼─┼─┼─┼─┼─┼─┼─┼─┼─┼→
        0 1 2 3 4 5 6 7 8 9 10 11 12

5. 9 ┤├─┼─┼─┼─┼─┼─┼─┼─┼─┼─┼─┼→
        0 1 2 3 4 5 6 7 8 9 10 11 12

6. 0 ┤├─┼─┼─┼─┼─┼─┼─┼─┼─┼─┼─┼→
        0 1 2 3 4 5 6 7 8 9 10 11 12

For Exercises 7 to 14, place the correct symbol, $<$ or $>$, between the two numbers.

7. 37   49
8. 58   21
9. 101   87
10. 245   158

11. 2701   2071
12. 0   45
13. 107   0
14. 815   928

15. 🗐 Do the inequalities $21 < 30$ and $30 > 21$ express the same order relation?

OBJECTIVE B *To write whole numbers in words and in standard form*

For Exercises 16 to 23, write the number in words.

16. 2675
17. 3790
18. 42,928
19. 58,473

20. 356,943
21. 498,512
22. 3,697,483
23. 6,842,715

For Exercises 24 to 29, write the number in standard form.

24. Eighty-five

25. Three hundred fifty-seven

26. Three thousand four hundred fifty-six

27. Sixty-three thousand seven hundred eighty

28. Six hundred nine thousand nine hundred forty-eight

29. Seven million twenty-four thousand seven hundred nine

30. 🖼 What is the place value of the first digit on the left in a seven-digit whole number?

OBJECTIVE C   *To write whole numbers in expanded form*

For Exercises 31 to 38, write the number in expanded form.

31. 5287   **32.** 6295   **33.** 58,943   **34.** 453,921

35. 200,583   **36.** 301,809   **37.** 403,705   **38.** 3,000,642

39. 🖼 The expanded form of a number consists of four numbers added together. Must the number be a four-digit number?

OBJECTIVE D   *To round a whole number to a given place value*

For Exercises 40 to 51, round the number to the given place value.

40. 926   Tens   **41.** 845   Tens   **42.** 1439   Hundreds

43. 3973   Hundreds   **44.** 43,607   Thousands   **45.** 52,715   Thousands

46. 389,702   Thousands   **47.** 629,513   Thousands   **48.** 647,989   Ten-thousands

49. 253,678   Ten-thousands   **50.** 36,702,599   Millions   **51.** 71,834,250   Millions

52. 🖼 True or false? If a number rounded to the nearest ten is less than the original number, then the ones digit of the original number is greater than 5.

Critical Thinking

53. If 3846 is rounded to the nearest ten and then that number is rounded to the nearest hundred, is the result the same as the result you get when you round 3846 to the nearest hundred? If not, which method is correct for rounding to the nearest hundred?

Projects or Group Activities

54. The U.S. House of Representatives has 435 members. The number of representatives that each state sends to the House of Representatives is based on the population of the state. State populations are determined every 10 years by the Census Bureau. Use the Census Bureau's Internet site to determine which states gained or lost a seat in the House of Representatives after the 2010 census.

1.2 Addition of Whole Numbers

OBJECTIVE A   *To add whole numbers*

Addition is the process of finding the total of two or more numbers.

APPLY THE CONCEPT

Maryka carried 4 soccer balls from her car to the soccer field. She returned to her car and carried 3 more balls to the field. By counting, the total of 4 balls and 3 balls is 7 balls. Maryka carried a total of 7 balls from her car to the field.

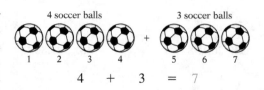

$$4 + 3 = 7$$

Addend + Addend = Sum

Here is a table of basic addition facts. These facts should be memorized.

Basic Addition Facts

+	1	2	3	4	5	6	7	8	9
1	1 + 1 = 2	1 + 2 = 3	1 + 3 = 4	1 + 4 = 5	1 + 5 = 6	1 + 6 = 7	1 + 7 = 8	1 + 8 = 9	1 + 9 = 10
2	2 + 1 = 3	2 + 2 = 4	2 + 3 = 5	2 + 4 = 6	2 + 5 = 7	2 + 6 = 8	2 + 7 = 9	2 + 8 = 10	2 + 9 = 11
3	3 + 1 = 4	3 + 2 = 5	3 + 3 = 6	3 + 4 = 7	3 + 5 = 8	3 + 6 = 9	3 + 7 = 10	3 + 8 = 11	3 + 9 = 12
4	4 + 1 = 5	4 + 2 = 6	4 + 3 = 7	4 + 4 = 8	4 + 5 = 9	4 + 6 = 10	4 + 7 = 11	4 + 8 = 12	4 + 9 = 13
5	5 + 1 = 6	5 + 2 = 7	5 + 3 = 8	5 + 4 = 9	5 + 5 = 10	5 + 6 = 11	5 + 7 = 12	5 + 8 = 13	5 + 9 = 14
6	6 + 1 = 7	6 + 2 = 8	6 + 3 = 9	6 + 4 = 10	6 + 5 = 11	6 + 6 = 12	6 + 7 = 13	6 + 8 = 14	6 + 9 = 15
7	7 + 1 = 8	7 + 2 = 9	7 + 3 = 10	7 + 4 = 11	7 + 5 = 12	7 + 6 = 13	7 + 7 = 14	7 + 8 = 15	7 + 9 = 16
8	8 + 1 = 9	8 + 2 = 10	8 + 3 = 11	8 + 4 = 12	8 + 5 = 13	8 + 6 = 14	8 + 7 = 15	8 + 8 = 16	8 + 9 = 17
9	9 + 1 = 10	9 + 2 = 11	9 + 3 = 12	9 + 4 = 13	9 + 5 = 14	9 + 6 = 15	9 + 7 = 16	9 + 8 = 17	9 + 9 = 18

Some special properties of addition that are used frequently are given below.

Commutative Property of Addition

Two numbers can be added in either order; the sum will be the same.

EXAMPLES

1. $4 + 8 = 8 + 4$
$12 = 12$

2. $9 + 6 = 6 + 9$
$15 = 15$

Associative Property of Addition

Grouping an addition in any order gives the same result. Parentheses are grouping symbols that mean "Do operations inside parentheses first."

EXAMPLES

1. $(3 + 2) + 4 = 3 + (2 + 4)$
$5 + 4 = 3 + 6$
$9 = 9$

2. $(3 + 6) + 2 = 3 + (6 + 2)$
$9 + 2 = 3 + 8$
$11 = 11$

Addition Property of Zero
Zero added to any number does not change the number.

EXAMPLES

1. $4 + 0 = 4$ **2.** $0 + 7 = 7$

Point of Interest

The plus sign first appeared in 1489 in *Mercantile Arithmetic.* It was used to indicate a surplus, not as the symbol for addition. That use did not occur until about 1515.

To add large numbers, begin by arranging the numbers vertically, keeping the digits of the same place value in the same column.

HOW TO 1   Add: $321 + 6472$

```
        THOUSANDS HUNDREDS TENS ONES
              3   2   1
          + 6   4   7   2
            6   7   9   3
```

• Add the digits in each column.

There are several words or phrases in English that indicate the operation of addition. Here are some examples:

added to	3 added to 5	$5 + 3$
more than	7 more than 5	$5 + 7$
the sum of	the sum of 3 and 9	$3 + 9$
increased by	4 increased by 6	$4 + 6$
the total of	the total of 8 and 3	$8 + 3$
plus	5 plus 10	$5 + 10$

Integrating Technology

Most scientific calculators use *algebraic logic:* the add (+), subtract (−), multiply (×), and divide (÷) keys perform the indicated operation using the number in the display and the next number keyed in. For instance, for HOW TO 2 at the right, enter 24 + 71 = . The display reads 95.

When the sum of the digits in a column exceeds 9, the addition will involve **carrying.**

HOW TO 2   What is the sum of 487 and 369?

```
    HUNDREDS TENS ONES
            1
      4   8   7
    + 3   6   9
              6
```

• The phrase *the sum of* means to add.
• Add the ones column.
  $7 + 9 = 16$ (1 ten + 6 ones).
  Write the 6 in the ones column and carry the 1 ten to the tens column.

```
      1   1
      4   8   7
    + 3   6   9
          5   6
```

• Add the tens column.
  $1 + 8 + 6 = 15$ (1 hundred + 5 tens).
  Write the 5 in the tens column and carry the 1 hundred to the hundreds column.

```
      1   1
      4   8   7
    + 3   6   9
      8   5   6
```

• Add the hundreds column.
  $1 + 4 + 3 = 8$ (8 hundreds).
  Write the 8 in the hundreds column.

The sum is 856.

EXAMPLE 1

Find the total of 17, 103, and 8.

Solution

$$\begin{array}{r} \overset{1}{1}7 \\ 103 \\ +8 \\ \hline 128 \end{array}$$

• 7 + 3 + 8 = 18
Write the 8 in the ones column. Carry the 1 to the tens column.

YOU TRY IT 1

What is 347 increased by 12,453?

Your solution

EXAMPLE 2

Find the sum of 89, 36, and 98.

Solution

$$\begin{array}{r} \overset{2}{8}9 \\ 36 \\ +98 \\ \hline 223 \end{array}$$

• 9 + 6 + 8 = 23
Write the 3 in the ones column. Carry the 2 to the tens column.

YOU TRY IT 2

Add: 95 + 88 + 67

Your solution

EXAMPLE 3

Add: 41,395
        4,327
      497,625
    + 32,991

Solution

$$\begin{array}{r} \overset{1\,1\,2\ 2\,1}{4}1,395 \\ 4,327 \\ 497,625 \\ +32,991 \\ \hline 576,338 \end{array}$$

YOU TRY IT 3

Add: 392
        4,079
       89,035
    +   4,992

Your solution

Solutions on p. S1

Integrating Technology

This example illustrates that estimation is important when one is using a calculator.

ESTIMATION: Estimation and Calculators

At some places in the text, you will be asked to use your calculator. Effective use of a calculator requires that you estimate the answer to the problem. This helps ensure that you have entered the numbers correctly and pressed the correct keys.

For example, if you use your calculator to find 22,347 + 5896 and the answer in the calculator's display is 131,757,912, you should realize that you have entered some part of the calculation incorrectly. In this case, you pressed $\times$ instead of $+$. By estimating the answer to a problem, you can help ensure the accuracy of your calculations. There is a special symbol for **approximately equal to: ≈.**

For example, to estimate the answer to 22,347 + 5896, round each number to the same place value. In this case, we will round to the nearest thousand. Then add.

$$\begin{array}{r} 22,347 \approx \ 22,000 \\ +5,896 \approx +6,000 \\ \hline 28,000 \end{array}$$

The sum 22,347 + 5896 is approximately 28,000. Knowing this, you would know that 131,757,912 is much too large and is therefore incorrect.

To estimate the sum of two numbers, first round each number to the same place value, and then add. Compare this answer with the calculator's answer.

OBJECTIVE B   *To solve application problems*

trekandshoot/Shutterstock.com

To solve an application problem, first read the problem carefully. Devising a **strategy** involves identifying the quantity to be found and planning the steps that are necessary to find that quantity. Finding the **solution of an application problem** involves performing each operation stated in the strategy and writing the answer.

HOW TO 3

🥧 The table below displays the Walmart store count and square footage in the United States as reported in the Walmart 2011 Annual Report.

	Discount Stores	Supercenters	Sam's Clubs	Neighborhood Markets
Number of units	629	3029	611	168
Square footage (in millions)	68	560	81	7

Find the total number of Walmart discount stores and Supercenters in the United States.

Strategy   To find the total number of Walmart discount stores and Supercenters in the United States, read the table to find the number of each type of store in the United States. Then add the numbers.

Solution
$$\begin{array}{r} 629 \\ +\ 3029 \\ \hline 3658 \end{array}$$

Walmart has a total of 3658 discount stores and Supercenters in the United States.

EXAMPLE 4

Use the table above to find the total number of Sam's Clubs and neighborhood markets that Walmart owns in the United States.

Strategy

To determine the total number of Sam's Clubs and neighborhood markets, read the table to find the number of Sam's Clubs and the number of neighborhood markets. Then add the two numbers.

Solution
$$\begin{array}{r} 611 \\ +\ 168 \\ \hline 779 \end{array}$$

Walmart owns a total of 779 Sam's Clubs and neighborhood markets.

YOU TRY IT 4

Use the table above to determine the total square footage of Walmart stores in the United States.

Your strategy

Your solution

Solution on p. S1

1.2 EXERCISES

✔ Concept Check

For Exercises 1 to 6, identify the property on page 8 or 9 that justifies the statement.

1. $347 + 0 = 347$

2. $6 + (8 + 1) = (6 + 8) + 1$

3. $(3 + 7) + 4 = 3 + (7 + 4)$

4. $13 + 302 = 302 + 13$

5. $(9 + 8) + 3 = (8 + 9) + 3$

6. $23 + (0 + 9) = 23 + 9$

OBJECTIVE A   *To add whole numbers*

For Exercises 7 to 36, add.

7.
$$\begin{array}{r} 17 \\ + 11 \\ \hline \end{array}$$

8.
$$\begin{array}{r} 25 \\ + 63 \\ \hline \end{array}$$

9.
$$\begin{array}{r} 83 \\ + 42 \\ \hline \end{array}$$

10.
$$\begin{array}{r} 63 \\ + 94 \\ \hline \end{array}$$

11.
$$\begin{array}{r} 77 \\ + 25 \\ \hline \end{array}$$

12.
$$\begin{array}{r} 63 \\ + 49 \\ \hline \end{array}$$

13.
$$\begin{array}{r} 56 \\ + 98 \\ \hline \end{array}$$

14.
$$\begin{array}{r} 86 \\ + 68 \\ \hline \end{array}$$

15.
$$\begin{array}{r} 658 \\ + 831 \\ \hline \end{array}$$

16.
$$\begin{array}{r} 842 \\ + 936 \\ \hline \end{array}$$

17.
$$\begin{array}{r} 735 \\ + 93 \\ \hline \end{array}$$

18.
$$\begin{array}{r} 189 \\ + 50 \\ \hline \end{array}$$

19.
$$\begin{array}{r} 859 \\ + 725 \\ \hline \end{array}$$

20.
$$\begin{array}{r} 637 \\ + 829 \\ \hline \end{array}$$

21.
$$\begin{array}{r} 36{,}925 \\ + 65{,}392 \\ \hline \end{array}$$

22.
$$\begin{array}{r} 56{,}772 \\ + 51{,}239 \\ \hline \end{array}$$

23.
$$\begin{array}{r} 50{,}873 \\ + 28{,}453 \\ \hline \end{array}$$

24.
$$\begin{array}{r} 34{,}872 \\ + 46{,}079 \\ \hline \end{array}$$

25.
$$\begin{array}{r} 878 \\ 737 \\ + 189 \\ \hline \end{array}$$

26.
$$\begin{array}{r} 768 \\ 461 \\ + 669 \\ \hline \end{array}$$

27.
$$\begin{array}{r} 319 \\ 348 \\ + 912 \\ \hline \end{array}$$

28.
$$\begin{array}{r} 292 \\ 579 \\ + 315 \\ \hline \end{array}$$

29.
$$\begin{array}{r} 9409 \\ 3253 \\ + 7078 \\ \hline \end{array}$$

30.
$$\begin{array}{r} 8188 \\ 8020 \\ + 7104 \\ \hline \end{array}$$

31.
$$\begin{array}{r} 2038 \\ 2243 \\ + 3139 \\ \hline \end{array}$$

32.
$$\begin{array}{r} 4252 \\ 6882 \\ + 5235 \\ \hline \end{array}$$

33.
$$\begin{array}{r} 67{,}428 \\ 32{,}171 \\ + 20{,}971 \\ \hline \end{array}$$

34.
$$\begin{array}{r} 52{,}801 \\ 11{,}664 \\ + 89{,}638 \\ \hline \end{array}$$

35.
$$\begin{array}{r} 76{,}290 \\ 43{,}761 \\ + 87{,}402 \\ \hline \end{array}$$

36.
$$\begin{array}{r} 43{,}901 \\ 98{,}301 \\ + 67{,}943 \\ \hline \end{array}$$

For Exercises 37 to 44, add.

37. 20,958 + 3218 + 42

38. 80,973 + 5168 + 29

39. 392 + 37 + 10,924 + 621

40. 694 + 62 + 70,129 + 217

41. 294 + 1029 + 7935 + 65

42. 692 + 2107 + 3196 + 92

43. 97 + 7234 + 69,532 + 276

44. 87 + 1698 + 27,317 + 727

45. What is 9874 plus 4509?

46. What is 7988 plus 5678?

47. What is 3487 increased by 5986?

48. What is 99,567 increased by 126,863?

49. What is 23,569 more than 9678?

50. What is 7894 more than 45,872?

51. What is 479 added to 4579?

52. What is 23,902 added to 23,885?

53. Find the total of 659, 55, and 1278.

54. Find the total of 4561, 56, and 2309.

55. Find the sum of 34, 329, 8, and 67,892.

56. Find the sum of 45, 1289, 7, and 32,876.

For Exercises 57 to 60, use a calculator to add. Then round the numbers to the nearest hundred, and use estimation to determine whether the sum is reasonable.

57. 1234 + 9780 + 6740

58. 919 + 3642 + 8796

59. 241 + 569 + 390 + 1672

60. 107 + 984 + 1035 + 2904

For Exercises 61 to 64, use a calculator to add. Then round the numbers to the nearest thousand, and use estimation to determine whether the sum is reasonable.

61.	**62.**	**63.**	**64.**
32,461	29,036	25,432	66,541
9,844	22,904	62,941	29,365
+ 59,407	+ 7,903	+ 70,390	+ 98,742

For Exercises 65 to 68, use a calculator to add. Then round the numbers to the nearest ten-thousand, and use estimation to determine whether the sum is reasonable.

65.
```
   67,421
   82,984
   66,361
   10,792
 + 34,037
```

66.
```
   21,896
    4,235
   62,544
   21,892
 +  1,334
```

67.
```
  281,421
    9,874
   34,394
  526,398
 + 94,631
```

68.
```
  542,698
   97,327
    7,235
   73,667
 + 173,201
```

69. Which property of addition (see pages 8 and 9) allows you to use either arrangement shown at the right to find the sum of 691 and 452?

```
  691      452
+ 452    + 691
```

OBJECTIVE B   *To solve application problems*

70. Use the table of Walmart data on page 11. What does the sum 68 + 560 represent?

71. **Demographics**   In a recent year, according to the Centers for Disease Control and Prevention, there were 138,660 twin births in this country, 5877 triplet births, 345 quadruplet deliveries, and 46 quintuplet and other higher-order multiple births. Find the total number of multiple births during the year.

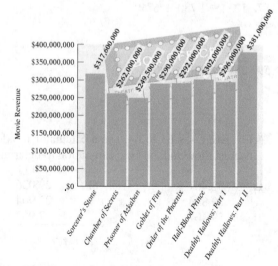

Melissa King/Shutterstock.com

72. **Demographics**   The Census Bureau estimated that the U.S. population would grow by 296 million people from 2000 to 2100. Given that the U.S. population in 2000 was 281 million, find the Census Bureau's estimate of the U.S. population in 2100.

The Film Industry   The graph at the right shows the domestic box-office gross income from the first eight *Harry Potter* movies. Use this information for Exercises 73 to 75.

73. Find the total gross income from the eight *Harry Potter* movies.

74. Find the total gross income from the two lowest-grossing *Harry Potter* movies.

75. Find the total gross income from the two highest-grossing *Harry Potter* movies.

(*Source:* www.the-numbers.com/movies/series/HarryPotter.php)

76. Geometry   The perimeter of a triangle is the sum of the lengths of the three sides of the triangle. Find the perimeter of a triangle that has sides that measure 12 inches, 14 inches, and 17 inches.

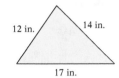

77. Travel   The odometer on a moving van reads 68,692. The driver plans to drive 515 miles the first day, 492 miles the second day, and 278 miles the third day.
a. How many miles will be driven during the three days?
b. What will the odometer reading be at the end of the trip?

78. ● Internet   Thirty-seven million U.S. households do not have broadband Internet access. Seventy-eight million U.S. households do have broadband Internet access. How many households are there in the United States? (*Source:* U.S. Department of Commerce)

79. ● Energy   In a recent year, the United States produced 5,633,000 barrels of crude oil per day and imported 9,003,300 barrels of crude oil per day. Find the total number of barrels of crude oil produced and imported per day in the United States. (*Source:* Energy Information Administration)

eyeidea/Shutterstock.com

Critical Thinking

80. If you roll two ordinary six-sided dice and add the two numbers that appear on top, how many different sums are possible?

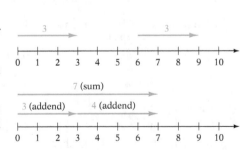

81. If you add two *different* whole numbers, is the sum always greater than either one of the numbers? If not, give an example.

82. If you add two whole numbers, is the sum always greater than either one of the numbers? If not, give an example. (Compare this with Exercise 81.)

83. ◣ Make up a word problem for which the answer is the sum of 34 and 28.

84. Call a number "lucky" if it ends in a 7. How many lucky numbers are less than 100?

Projects or Group Activities

The size, or magnitude, of a number can be represented on the number line by an arrow.

The number 3 can be represented anywhere on the number line by an arrow that is 3 units in length.

To add on the number line, place the arrows representing the addends head to tail, with the first arrow starting at zero. The sum is represented by an arrow starting at zero and stopping at the tip of the last arrow.

85. Represent the sum of 2 and 6 using arrows on the number line.

86. Represent the sum of 5 and 4 using arrows on the number line.

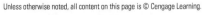

SECTION

1.3 Subtraction of Whole Numbers

OBJECTIVE A *To subtract whole numbers without borrowing*

Subtraction is the process of finding the difference between two numbers.

APPLY THE CONCEPT ·······

A store had 7 iPads in stock. Nathan sold 3 iPads from the stock. By counting, the difference between 7 iPads and 3 iPads is 4. There are 4 iPads remaining in stock.

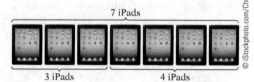

7 iPads

3 iPads   4 iPads

7 iPads	−	3 iPads	=	4 iPads
Minuend	**−**	**Subtrahend**	**=**	**Difference**

Subtraction can be related to addition as shown at the right. This relationship can be used to check a subtraction.

$$\begin{array}{r} \text{Subtrahend} \quad 3 \\ + \text{Difference} \quad + 4 \\ \hline = \text{Minuend} \quad 7 \end{array}$$

Point of Interest

The minus sign dates from the same period as the plus sign, around 1515.

To subtract large numbers, begin by arranging the numbers vertically, keeping the digits that have the same place value in the same column. Then subtract the digits in each column.

HOW TO 1 Subtract 8955 − 2432 and check.

THOUSANDS	HUNDREDS	TENS	ONES
8	9	5	5
− 2	4	3	2
6	5	2	3

$$\begin{array}{lr} \textit{Check:} \quad \text{Subtrahend} & 2432 \\ + \text{Difference} & + 6523 \\ \hline = \text{Minuend} & 8955 \end{array}$$

EXAMPLE 1

Subtract 6594 − 3271 and check.

Solution

$$\begin{array}{r} 6594 \\ - 3271 \\ \hline 3323 \end{array} \qquad \textit{Check:} \begin{array}{r} 3271 \\ + 3323 \\ \hline 6594 \end{array}$$

YOU TRY IT 1

Subtract 8925 − 6413 and check.

Your solution

EXAMPLE 2

Subtract 15,762 − 7541 and check.

Solution

$$\begin{array}{r} 15{,}762 \\ - 7{,}541 \\ \hline 8{,}221 \end{array} \qquad \textit{Check:} \begin{array}{r} 7{,}541 \\ + 8{,}221 \\ \hline 15{,}762 \end{array}$$

YOU TRY IT 2

Subtract 17,504 − 9302 and check.

Your solution

Solutions on p. S1

OBJECTIVE B   *To subtract whole numbers with borrowing*

In all the subtraction problems in the preceding objective, for each place value, the lower digit was smaller than the upper digit. When the lower digit is larger than the upper digit, subtraction will involve **borrowing.**

HOW TO 2   Subtract: 692 − 378

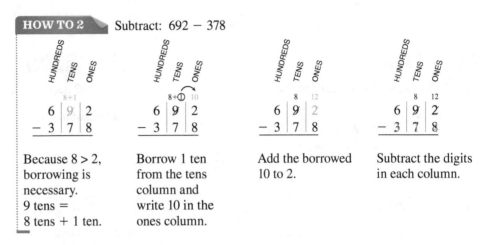

Because 8 > 2, borrowing is necessary.
9 tens = 8 tens + 1 ten.

Borrow 1 ten from the tens column and write 10 in the ones column.

Add the borrowed 10 to 2.

Subtract the digits in each column.

The phrases below are used to indicate the operation of subtraction. An example is shown at the right of each phrase.

minus	8 minus 5	8 − 5
less	9 less 3	9 − 3
less than	2 less than 7	7 − 2
the difference between	the difference between 8 and 2	8 − 2
decreased by	5 decreased by 1	5 − 1

Take Note
"The difference between 1234 and 485" means 1234 − 485.

HOW TO 3   Find the difference between 1234 and 485, and check.

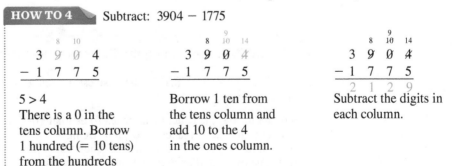

Tips for Success
The HOW TO feature indicates an example with explanatory remarks. Using paper and pencil, you should work through the example. See *AIM for Success* at the front of the book.

Subtraction with a zero in the minuend involves repeated borrowing.

HOW TO 4   Subtract: 3904 − 1775

$$
\begin{array}{r}
\overset{8}{\cancel{3}}\ \overset{10}{\cancel{9}}\ 0\ 4 \\
-\ 1\ 7\ 7\ 5 \\
\end{array}
$$

5 > 4
There is a 0 in the tens column. Borrow 1 hundred (= 10 tens) from the hundreds column and write 10 in the tens column.

Borrow 1 ten from the tens column and add 10 to the 4 in the ones column.

Subtract the digits in each column.

EXAMPLE 3

Subtract 4392 − 678 and check.

Solution

$$
\begin{array}{r}
\overset{3}{\cancel{4}}\ \overset{13}{\cancel{3}}\ \overset{8}{\cancel{9}}\ \overset{12}{\cancel{2}} \\
-\quad 6\ 7\ 8 \\
\hline
3\ 7\ 1\ 4
\end{array}
\qquad
\begin{array}{r}
Check:\quad 678 \\
+\ 3714 \\
\hline
4392
\end{array}
$$

YOU TRY IT 3

Subtract 3481 − 865 and check.

Your solution

EXAMPLE 4

Find 23,954 less than 63,221 and check.

Solution

$$
\begin{array}{r}
\overset{5}{\cancel{6}}\ \overset{12}{\underset{2}{\cancel{3}}},\ \overset{11}{\underset{1}{\cancel{2}}}\ \overset{11}{\underset{1}{\cancel{2}}}\ \overset{11}{\cancel{1}} \\
-\ 2\ 3,9\ 5\ 4 \\
\hline
3\ 9,2\ 6\ 7
\end{array}
\qquad
\begin{array}{r}
Check:\quad 23,954 \\
+\ 39,267 \\
\hline
63,221
\end{array}
$$

YOU TRY IT 4

Find 54,562 decreased by 14,485 and check.

Your solution

EXAMPLE 5

Subtract 46,005 − 32,167 and check.

Solution

$$
\begin{array}{r}
4\ \overset{5}{\cancel{6}},\ \overset{10}{\cancel{0}}\ 0\ 5 \\
-3\ 2,\ 1\ 6\ 7
\end{array}
$$

• There are two zeros in the minuend. Borrow 1 thousand from the thousands column and write 10 in the hundreds column.

$$
\begin{array}{r}
4\ \overset{5}{\cancel{6}},\ \overset{9}{\underset{10}{\cancel{0}}}\ \overset{10}{\cancel{0}}\ 5 \\
-3\ 2,\ 1\ 6\ 7
\end{array}
$$

• Borrow 1 hundred from the hundreds column and write 10 in the tens column.

$$
\begin{array}{r}
4\ \overset{5}{\cancel{6}},\ \overset{9}{\underset{10}{\cancel{0}}}\ \overset{9}{\underset{10}{\cancel{0}}}\ \overset{15}{\cancel{5}} \\
-3\ 2,\ 1\ 6\ 7 \\
\hline
1\ 3,\ 8\ 3\ 8
\end{array}
$$

• Borrow 1 ten from the tens column and add 10 to the 5 in the ones column.

$$
\begin{array}{r}
Check:\quad 32,167 \\
+\ 13,838 \\
\hline
46,005
\end{array}
$$

YOU TRY IT 5

Subtract 64,003 − 54,936 and check.

Your solution

Solutions on pp. S1–S2

ESTIMATION: Estimating the Difference Between Two Whole Numbers

Calculate 323,502 − 28,912. Then use estimation to determine whether the difference is reasonable.

Subtract to find the exact difference. To estimate the difference, round each number to the same place value. Here we have rounded to the nearest ten-thousand. Then subtract. The estimated answer is 290,000, which is very close to the exact difference 294,590.

$$
\begin{array}{r}
323,502 \approx \quad 320,000 \\
-\quad 28,912 \approx -\ 30,000 \\
\hline
294,590 \qquad\quad 290,000
\end{array}
$$

OBJECTIVE C *To solve application problems*

The table at the right shows the populations of the four regions of the United States. Use this table for Example 6 and You Try It 6.

Region	Population
Northeast	55,317,240
Midwest	66,927,001
South	114,555,744
West	71,945,553

Source: U.S. Census Bureau

EXAMPLE 6

Find the difference between the population of the most populous region and the population of the least populous region.

Strategy

To find the difference:

• Identify the most populous region (the South) and the least populous region (the Northeast).
• Subtract the population of the Northeast (55,317,240) from the population of the South (114,555,744).

Solution   114,555,744
              − 55,317,240
              59,238,504

There are 59,238,504 more people living in the South than in the Northeast.

YOU TRY IT 6

Find the difference between the population of the Midwest and the population of the Northeast.

Your strategy

Your solution

EXAMPLE 7

You had a balance of $415 on your student debit card. You then used the card, deducting $197 for books, $48 for art supplies, and $24 for theater tickets. What is your new student debit card balance?

Strategy

To find your new debit card balance:

• Add to find the total of the three deductions (197 + 48 + 24).
• Subtract the total of the three deductions from the original balance (415).

Solution

  197   415
   48   − 269
 + 24   146
 269 total deductions

Your new debit card balance is $146.

YOU TRY IT 7

Your total weekly salary is $638. Deductions of $127 for taxes, $18 for insurance, and $35 for savings are taken from your pay. Find your weekly take-home pay.

Your strategy

Your solution

Solutions on p. S2

1.3 EXERCISES

✔ Concept Check

For Exercises 1 to 4, find the difference. Then write the related addition problem using Subtrahend + Difference = Minuend.

1. $9 - 5$ **2.** $7 - 2$ **3.** $11 - 0$ **4.** $8 - 8$

OBJECTIVE A   *To subtract whole numbers without borrowing*

For Exercises 5 to 34, subtract.

5. $\begin{array}{r} 12 \\ -\ 8 \\ \hline \end{array}$ **6.** $\begin{array}{r} 11 \\ -\ 4 \\ \hline \end{array}$ **7.** $\begin{array}{r} 15 \\ -\ 6 \\ \hline \end{array}$ **8.** $\begin{array}{r} 19 \\ -\ 8 \\ \hline \end{array}$ **9.** $\begin{array}{r} 25 \\ -\ 3 \\ \hline \end{array}$

10. $\begin{array}{r} 16 \\ -\ 7 \\ \hline \end{array}$ **11.** $\begin{array}{r} 68 \\ -\ 8 \\ \hline \end{array}$ **12.** $\begin{array}{r} 55 \\ -\ 4 \\ \hline \end{array}$ **13.** $\begin{array}{r} 89 \\ -\ 23 \\ \hline \end{array}$ **14.** $\begin{array}{r} 77 \\ -\ 3 \\ \hline \end{array}$

15. $\begin{array}{r} 88 \\ -\ 57 \\ \hline \end{array}$ **16.** $\begin{array}{r} 54 \\ -\ 21 \\ \hline \end{array}$ **17.** $\begin{array}{r} 1305 \\ -\ 404 \\ \hline \end{array}$ **18.** $\begin{array}{r} 1202 \\ -\ 701 \\ \hline \end{array}$ **19.** $\begin{array}{r} 1497 \\ -\ 706 \\ \hline \end{array}$

20. $\begin{array}{r} 1763 \\ -\ 801 \\ \hline \end{array}$ **21.** $\begin{array}{r} 2836 \\ -\ 1711 \\ \hline \end{array}$ **22.** $\begin{array}{r} 8974 \\ -\ 3972 \\ \hline \end{array}$ **23.** $\begin{array}{r} 9273 \\ -\ 6142 \\ \hline \end{array}$ **24.** $\begin{array}{r} 8976 \\ -\ 7463 \\ \hline \end{array}$

25. $129 - 82$ **26.** $77 - 36$ **27.** $969 - 44$ **28.** $132 - 61$ **29.** $4865 - 304$

30. $1347 - 103$ **31.** $9999 - 6794$ **32.** $1525 - 702$ **33.** $8843 - 7621$ **34.** $7806 - 3405$

For Exercises 35 and 36, find two whole numbers with the given difference and sum.

35. Difference = 2; sum = 8   **36.** Difference = 5; sum = 9

OBJECTIVE B   *To subtract whole numbers with borrowing*

For Exercises 37 to 80, subtract.

37. $\begin{array}{r} 71 \\ -\ 18 \\ \hline \end{array}$ **38.** $\begin{array}{r} 93 \\ -\ 28 \\ \hline \end{array}$ **39.** $\begin{array}{r} 47 \\ -\ 18 \\ \hline \end{array}$ **40.** $\begin{array}{r} 44 \\ -\ 27 \\ \hline \end{array}$

41. $\begin{array}{r} 37 \\ -\ 29 \\ \hline \end{array}$ **42.** $\begin{array}{r} 50 \\ -\ 27 \\ \hline \end{array}$ **43.** $\begin{array}{r} 70 \\ -\ 33 \\ \hline \end{array}$ **44.** $\begin{array}{r} 993 \\ -\ 537 \\ \hline \end{array}$

45.   250
        − 192

46.   840
        − 783

47.   768
        − 194

48.   770
        − 395

49. 674 − 337

50. 3526 − 387

51. 1712 − 289

52. 4350 − 729

53. 1702 − 948

54. 1607 − 869

55. 5933 − 3754

56. 7293 − 3748

57. 9407 − 2918

58. 3706 − 2957

59. 8605 − 7716

60. 8052 − 2709

61. 80,305 − 9176

62. 70,702 − 4239

63. 10,004 − 9306

64. 80,009 − 63,419

65. 70,618 − 41,213

66. 80,053 − 27,649

67. 70,700 − 21,076

68. 80,800 − 42,023

69.   2600
        − 1972

70.   8400
        − 3762

71.   9003
        − 2471

72.   6004
        − 2392

73.   8202
        − 3916

74.   7050
        − 4137

75.   7015
        − 2973

76.   4207
        − 1624

77.   7005
        − 1796

78.   8003
        − 2735

79.   20,005
        − 9,627

80.   80,004
        − 8,237

81. Which of the following phrases represent the subtraction 673 − 571?

(i) 571 less 673   (ii) 571 less than 673   (iii) 673 decreased by 571

82. Find 10,051 less 9027.

83. Find 17,031 less 5792.

84. Find the difference between 1003 and 447.

85. What is 29,874 minus 21,392?

86. What is 29,797 less than 68,005?

87. What is 69,379 less than 70,004?

88. What is 25,432 decreased by 7994?

89. What is 86,701 decreased by 9976?

For Exercises 90 to 93, use the relationship between addition and subtraction to complete the statement.

90. ___ + 39 = 104   **91.** 67 + ___ = 90   **92.** ___ + 497 = 862   **93.** 253 + ____ = 4901

For Exercises 94 to 99, use a calculator to subtract. Then round the numbers to the nearest ten-thousand and use estimation to determine whether the difference is reasonable.

94. 80,032
$-$ 19,605

95. 90,765
$-$ 60,928

96. 32,574
$-$ 10,961

97. 96,430
$-$ 59,762

98. 567,423
$-$ 208,444

99. 300,712
$-$ 198,714

OBJECTIVE C   *To solve application problems*

100. **Banking**   You have $304 in your checking account. If you write a check for $139, how much is left in your checking account?

101. **Insects**   The table at the right shows the number of taste genes and the number of smell genes in the mosquito, fruit fly, and honey bee.
   a. How many more smell genes does the honey bee have than the mosquito?
   b. How many more taste genes does the mosquito have than the fruit fly?
   c. Which of these insects has the best sense of smell?
   d. Which of these insects has the worst sense of taste?

	Mosquito	Fruit Fly	Honey Bee
Taste genes	76	68	10
Smell genes	79	62	170

Source: www.sciencedaily.com
Images: mosquito, © iStockphoto.com/Henrik Larsson; fruit fly, © iStockphoto.com/arlindo71; honey bee, © iStockphoto.com/beti gorse

102. **Electric Car Sales**   The graph at the right shows the projected sales of electric cars in the United States from 2015 to 2020.
   a. Are sales of electric cars projected to increase for the years shown?
   b. How many more electric cars are projected to be sold in 2020 than in 2015?
   c. Between which two consecutive years is the number of electric cars sold projected to increase the most?

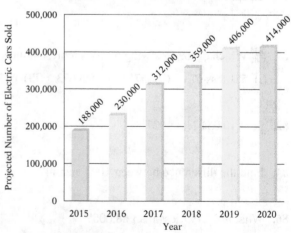

Projected Sales of Electric Cars in the United States
(*Source: An Analysis of Battery Electric Vehicle Production Projections;* Cunnigham, John; MIT, 2009)

103. 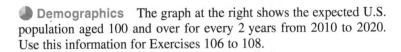 Earth Science   Use the graph at the right to find the difference between the maximum heights to which the Great Fountain and Valentine geysers erupt.

104. 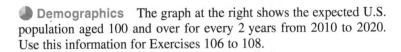 Earth Science   According to the graph at the right, how much higher is the eruption of the Giant than that of Old Faithful?

105. 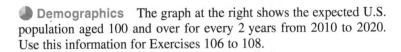 Education   In a recent year, 775,424 women and 573,079 men earned a bachelor's degree. How many more women than men earned a bachelor's degree that year? (*Source:* The National Center for Education Statistics)

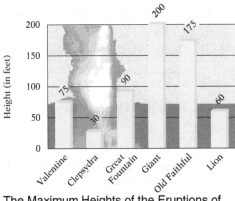

The Maximum Heights of the Eruptions of Six Geysers at Yellowstone National Park

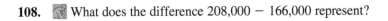 Demographics   The graph at the right shows the expected U.S. population aged 100 and over for every 2 years from 2010 to 2020. Use this information for Exercises 106 to 108.

106. What is the expected growth in the population aged 100 and over during the 10-year period?

107. **a.** Which 2-year period has the smallest expected increase in the number of people aged 100 and over?
b. Which 2-year period has the greatest expected increase?

108. What does the difference 208,000 − 166,000 represent?

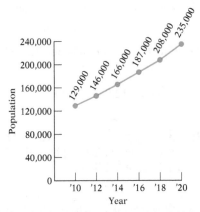

Expected U.S. Population Aged 100 and Over

Source: U.S. Census Bureau

109. Finances   You had a credit card balance of $409 before you used the card to purchase books for $168, CDs for $36, and a pair of shoes for $97. You then made a payment to the credit card company of $350. Find your new credit card balance.

Critical Thinking

110. Answer true or false.
a. 9 − (5 − 3) = (9 − 5) − 3
b. Subtraction is an associative operation. *Hint:* See part (a) of this exercise.

111. Make up a word problem for which the difference between 15 and 8 is the answer.

Projects or Group Activities

112. Write down a five-digit number in which all of the digits are different. Now reverse the order of the digits to form a new five-digit number. Subtract the smaller number from the larger one. Add the digits of the difference. If the result is a two-digit number, add the digits again. What is the result? Try this with a four-digit or six-digit number. Is the result always the same?

✔ CHECK YOUR PROGRESS: CHAPTER 1

1. Graph 7 on the number line.

0 1 2 3 4 5 6 7 8 9 10 11 12 13 14

2. Place the correct symbol, < or >, between the two numbers.
107   97

3. Write 82,743 in words.

4. Write 2,530,021 in words.

5. Write twenty-three thousand four hundred one in standard form.

6. Write nine hundred three thousand three in standard form.

7. Write 63,291 in expanded form.

8. Round 592,455 to the nearest thousand.

9. Round 45,962 to the nearest ten-thousand.

10. Add: 90,361 + 2955 + 750,679

11. Find the sum of 2034 and 12,598.

12. Find 40,781 increased by 156,742.

13. Subtract: 12,045 − 4987

14. Find 823 less than 9361.

15. ⬤ **National Debt**   An estimate of the national debt is fourteen trillion seven hundred fifty-eight billion dollars. Round this number to the nearest hundred billion.

16. ⬤ **Waterfalls**   The height of Yosemite Falls is 2425 feet, and the height of Colonial Falls is 2585 feet. How much higher is Colonial Falls than Yosemite Falls?

17. **Charity**   Janice decided to donate some money to a charity. Her contributions for a six-month period were $25, $30, $13, $15, $20, and $27. Find the total amount of her contribution for the six months.

⬤ **Health Statistics**   The table at the right shows the median height, in centimeters (cm), from birth to age 5 for boys and girls. Use this chart for Exercises 18 and 19. (*Source:* National Center for Health Statistics)

18. How many centimeters do boys grow from birth to age 5?

19. Between which two consecutive years do girls grow the most?

Age	Height of Girls (cm)	Height of Boys (cm)
Birth	49	50
1	74	75
2	84	87
3	95	91
4	100	102
5	108	110

20. **Sports**   The scores for a professional golfer for four rounds of golf were 68, 72, 69, and 66. What was the total score for the golfer for the four rounds of golf?

1.4 Multiplication of Whole Numbers

OBJECTIVE A *To multiply a number by a single digit*

Multiplication is used to find the total number of objects in several groups when each group contains the same number of objects.

APPLY THE CONCEPT

Sebastian purchased 8 six-packs of soda for a party. The total number of cans of soda he purchased can be found by adding 6 eight times. Sebastian purchased 48 cans of soda.

$$6 \;+\; 6 \;+\; 6 \;+\; 6 \;+\; 6 \;+\; 6 \;+\; 6 \;+\; 6 \;=\; 48$$

The number of cans can also be found by using multiplication.

$$6 \quad \times \quad 8 \quad = \quad 48$$

Multiplicand $\times$ Multiplier $=$ Product

The **multiplicand** is the number of objects in each group (6 cans in each six-pack); the **multiplier** is the number of groups (8 six-packs); the **product** is the total number of objects (48 cans). Frequently we will discuss the *factors* of a product. A **factor** is one of the numbers that are multiplied to obtain a product. 6 and 8 are factors of 48.

Here is a table of basic multiplication facts. These facts should be memorized.

Basic Multiplication Facts

×	1	2	3	4	5	6	7	8	9
1	$1 \times 1 = 1$	$1 \times 2 = 2$	$1 \times 3 = 3$	$1 \times 4 = 4$	$1 \times 5 = 5$	$1 \times 6 = 6$	$1 \times 7 = 7$	$1 \times 8 = 8$	$1 \times 9 = 9$
2	$2 \times 1 = 2$	$2 \times 2 = 4$	$2 \times 3 = 6$	$2 \times 4 = 8$	$2 \times 5 = 10$	$2 \times 6 = 12$	$2 \times 7 = 14$	$2 \times 8 = 16$	$2 \times 9 = 18$
3	$3 \times 1 = 3$	$3 \times 2 = 6$	$3 \times 3 = 9$	$3 \times 4 = 12$	$3 \times 5 = 15$	$3 \times 6 = 18$	$3 \times 7 = 21$	$3 \times 8 = 24$	$3 \times 9 = 27$
4	$4 \times 1 = 4$	$4 \times 2 = 8$	$4 \times 3 = 12$	$4 \times 4 = 16$	$4 \times 5 = 20$	$4 \times 6 = 24$	$4 \times 7 = 28$	$4 \times 8 = 32$	$4 \times 9 = 36$
5	$5 \times 1 = 5$	$5 \times 2 = 10$	$5 \times 3 = 15$	$5 \times 4 = 20$	$5 \times 5 = 25$	$5 \times 6 = 30$	$5 \times 7 = 35$	$5 \times 8 = 40$	$5 \times 9 = 45$
6	$6 \times 1 = 6$	$6 \times 2 = 12$	$6 \times 3 = 18$	$6 \times 4 = 24$	$6 \times 5 = 30$	$6 \times 6 = 36$	$6 \times 7 = 42$	$6 \times 8 = 48$	$6 \times 9 = 54$
7	$7 \times 1 = 7$	$7 \times 2 = 14$	$7 \times 3 = 21$	$7 \times 4 = 28$	$7 \times 5 = 35$	$7 \times 6 = 42$	$7 \times 7 = 49$	$7 \times 8 = 56$	$7 \times 9 = 63$
8	$8 \times 1 = 8$	$8 \times 2 = 16$	$8 \times 3 = 24$	$8 \times 4 = 32$	$8 \times 5 = 40$	$8 \times 6 = 48$	$8 \times 7 = 56$	$8 \times 8 = 64$	$8 \times 9 = 72$
9	$9 \times 1 = 9$	$9 \times 2 = 18$	$9 \times 3 = 27$	$9 \times 4 = 36$	$9 \times 5 = 45$	$9 \times 6 = 54$	$9 \times 7 = 63$	$9 \times 8 = 72$	$9 \times 9 = 81$

 Tips for Success

Some students think that they can "coast" at the beginning of this course because the topic of Chapter 1 is whole numbers. However, this chapter lays the foundation for the entire course. Be sure you know and understand all of the concepts presented. For example, study the properties of multiplication presented in this lesson.

The times sign "$\times$" is only one symbol that is used to indicate multiplication. Each of the expressions that follow represents multiplication.

$$7 \times 8 \qquad 7 \cdot 8 \qquad 7(8) \qquad (7)(8) \qquad (7)8$$

As with addition, there are some useful properties of multiplication.

Commutative Property of Multiplication

Two numbers can be multiplied in either order; the product will be the same.

EXAMPLES

1. $4 \times 3 = 3 \times 4$

$12 = 12$

2. $9 \times 7 = 7 \times 9$

$63 = 63$

Associative Property of Multiplication

Grouping numbers to be multiplied in any order gives the same result. Do the multiplication inside the parentheses first.

EXAMPLES

1. $(4 \times 2) \times 3 = 4 \times (2 \times 3)$
$\quad\quad 8 \quad\times 3 = 4 \times \quad 6$
$\quad\quad\quad\quad 24 = 24$

2. $3 \times (2 \times 5) = (3 \times 2) \times 5$
$\quad 3 \times \quad 10 \quad = \quad 6 \quad \times 5$
$\quad\quad\quad\quad 30 = 30$

Multiplication Property of One

Multiplying a number by 1 does not change the number.

EXAMPLES

1. $8 \times 1 = 8$
2. $1 \times 6 = 6$

Multiplication Property of Zero

A number multiplied by zero is zero.

EXAMPLES

1. $7 \times 0 = 0$
2. $0 \times 4 = 0$

⭐ **Tips for Success**

One of the key instructional features of this text is the Example/You Try It pairs. Each Example is completely worked. You are to solve the You Try It problems. When you are ready, check your solution against the one given in the Solutions section. The solution for You Try It 1 below is on page S2 (see the reference at the bottom right of the You Try It). See *AIM for Success* at the front of the book.

Multiplication of larger numbers requires repeated use of the basic multiplication facts.

HOW TO 1 Multiply: 37×4

$$\begin{array}{r} \overset{2}{37} \\ \times\ 4 \\ \hline 8 \end{array}$$

• $4 \times 7 = 28$ (2 tens + 8 ones)
Write the 8 in the ones column and carry the 2 to the tens column.

$$\begin{array}{r} \overset{2}{37} \\ \times\ 4 \\ \hline 148 \end{array}$$

• The 3 in 37 is 3 tens.
4×3 tens $=\ \ 12$ tens
Add the carry digit. $\underline{+\ 2\ \text{tens}}$
$\quad\quad\quad\quad\quad 14$ tens

The product is 148.

The phrases below are used to indicate the operation of multiplication. An example is shown at the right of each phrase.

times	7 times 3	$7 \cdot 3$
the product of	the product of 6 and 9	$6 \cdot 9$
multiplied by	8 multiplied by 2	$8 \cdot 2$

EXAMPLE 1

Find the product of 735 and 9.

Solution

$$\begin{array}{r} \overset{3\ 4}{735} \\ \times\ \ 9 \\ \hline 6615 \end{array}$$

• $9 \times 5 = 45$
Write the 5 in the ones column.
Carry the 4 to the tens column.
$9 \times 3 = 27,\ 27 + 4 = 31$
$9 \times 7 = 63,\ 63 + 3 = 66$

YOU TRY IT 1

Multiply: 648×7

Your solution

Solution on p. S2

OBJECTIVE B   *To multiply larger whole numbers*

Note the pattern in the products shown at the right.

Multiply the nonzero parts of the factors.

Then attach the same number of zeros to the product as the total number of zeros in the factors.

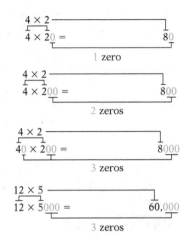

HOW TO 2   Find the product of 47 and 23.

Multiply by the ones digit.	Multiply by the tens digit.	Add.
47	47	47
× 23	× 23	× 23
141 (= 47 × 3)	141	141
	940 (= 47 × 20)	940
		1081

Writing the 0 keeps the columns aligned correctly.

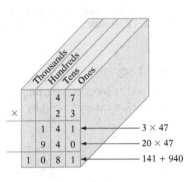

The place-value chart on the right above illustrates the placement of the products.

Note the placement of the products when multiplying by a factor that contains a zero.

HOW TO 3   Multiply: 439 × 206

439
× 206
─────
2634
000   0 × 439
878
─────
90,434

When working the problem, we usually write only one zero. Writing this zero ensures the proper placement of the products.

439
× 206
─────
2634
8780
─────
90,434

EXAMPLE 2

Find 829 multiplied by 603.

Solution

829
×   603
─────
2487
49740
─────
499,887

• 3 × 829 = 2487
• Write a zero in the tens column for 0 × 829.
• 6 × 829 = 4974

YOU TRY IT 2

Multiply: 756 × 305

Your solution

Solution on p. S2

ESTIMATION: Estimating the Product of Two Whole Numbers

Calculate 3267 × 389. Then use estimation to determine whether the product is reasonable.

Multiply to find the exact product.   3267 × 389 = 1,270,863

To estimate the product, round each number so that it has only one nonzero digit. Then multiply. The estimated answer is 1,200,000, which is very close to the exact product 1,270,863.

$$\begin{array}{r} 3267 \approx 3000 \\ \times\; 389 \approx \times\;400 \\ \hline 1{,}200{,}000 \end{array}$$

OBJECTIVE C   *To solve application problems*

EXAMPLE 3

A state park forester receives a salary of $1050 each week. How much does the forester earn in 4 weeks?

Strategy

To find the forester's earnings for 4 weeks, multiply the weekly salary (1050) by the number of weeks (4).

Solution

$$\begin{array}{r} 1050 \\ \times\;\;\; 4 \\ \hline 4200 \end{array}$$

The forester earns $4200 in 4 weeks.

YOU TRY IT 3

An elephant will eat approximately 150 pounds of food each day. How many pounds of food will an elephant eat in a 365-day year?

Your strategy

Your solution

EXAMPLE 4

A pharmacist's assistant earns $640 for working a 40-hour week. This week the assistant also worked 7 hours of overtime at $26 an hour. Find the assistant's total pay for the week.

Strategy

To find the assistant's total pay for the week:
- Find the overtime pay by multiplying the hours of overtime (7) by the overtime rate of pay (26).
- Add the weekly salary (640) to the overtime pay.

Solution

$$\begin{array}{r} 26 \\ \times\; 7 \\ \hline 182 \end{array} \text{ overtime pay} \qquad \begin{array}{r} 640 \\ +\; 182 \\ \hline 822 \end{array}$$

The assistant earned $822 this week.

YOU TRY IT 4

The buyer for Ross Department Store can buy 80 men's suits for $7600. Each sports jacket will cost the store $62. The manager orders 80 men's suits and 25 sports jackets. What is the total cost of the order?

Your strategy

Your solution

Solutions on p. S2

1.4 EXERCISES

Concept Check

For Exercises 1 to 4, write the expression as a product.

1. 2 + 2 + 2 + 2 + 2 + 2   **2.** 4 + 4 + 4 + 4 + 4   **3.** 7 + 7 + 7 + 7   **4.** 18 + 18 + 18

For Exercises 5 to 8, identify the property on pages 25–26 that justifies the statement.

5. $1 \times 23 = 23$ **6.** $(9 \times 5) \times 7 = 9 \times (5 \times 7)$ **7.** $8 \times 12 = 12 \times 8$ **8.** $(9 \times 5) \times 7 = (5 \times 9) \times 7$

OBJECTIVE A   *To multiply a number by a single digit*

For Exercises 9 to 43, multiply.

9. 3
× 4

10. 2
× 8

11. 5
× 7

12. 6
× 4

13. 5
× 5

14. 7
× 7

15. 0
× 7

16. 8
× 0

17. 8
× 9

18. 7
× 6

19. 66
× 3

20. 70
× 4

21. 67
× 5

22. 127
× 9

23. 623
× 4

24. 802
× 5

25. 607
× 9

26. 300
× 5

27. 600
× 7

28. 906
× 8

29. 703
× 9

30. 127
× 5

31. 632
× 3

32. 559
× 4

33. 632
× 8

34. 524
× 4

35. 337
× 5

36. 841
× 6

37. 6709
× 7

38. 3608
× 5

39. 8568
× 7

40. 5495
× 4

41. 4780
× 4

42. 3690
× 5

43. 9895
× 2

44. True or false? The product of two one-digit whole numbers must be a two-digit whole number.

45. Find the product of 5, 7, and 4.

46. Find the product of 6, 2, and 9.

47. What is 3208 multiplied by 7?

48. What is 5009 multiplied by 4?

49. What is 3105 times 6?

50. What is 8957 times 8?

OBJECTIVE B   *To multiply larger whole numbers*

For Exercises 51 to 82, multiply.

51.
$$\begin{array}{r} 16 \\ \times\ 21 \\ \hline \end{array}$$

52.
$$\begin{array}{r} 18 \\ \times\ 24 \\ \hline \end{array}$$

53.
$$\begin{array}{r} 35 \\ \times\ 26 \\ \hline \end{array}$$

54.
$$\begin{array}{r} 27 \\ \times\ 72 \\ \hline \end{array}$$

55.
$$\begin{array}{r} 693 \\ \times\ 91 \\ \hline \end{array}$$

56.
$$\begin{array}{r} 581 \\ \times\ 72 \\ \hline \end{array}$$

57.
$$\begin{array}{r} 419 \\ \times\ 80 \\ \hline \end{array}$$

58.
$$\begin{array}{r} 727 \\ \times\ 60 \\ \hline \end{array}$$

59.
$$\begin{array}{r} 8279 \\ \times\ 46 \\ \hline \end{array}$$

60.
$$\begin{array}{r} 9577 \\ \times\ 35 \\ \hline \end{array}$$

61.
$$\begin{array}{r} 6938 \\ \times\ 78 \\ \hline \end{array}$$

62.
$$\begin{array}{r} 8875 \\ \times\ 67 \\ \hline \end{array}$$

63.
$$\begin{array}{r} 7035 \\ \times\ 57 \\ \hline \end{array}$$

64.
$$\begin{array}{r} 6702 \\ \times\ 48 \\ \hline \end{array}$$

65.
$$\begin{array}{r} 3009 \\ \times\ 35 \\ \hline \end{array}$$

66.
$$\begin{array}{r} 6003 \\ \times\ 57 \\ \hline \end{array}$$

67.
$$\begin{array}{r} 809 \\ \times\ 530 \\ \hline \end{array}$$

68.
$$\begin{array}{r} 607 \\ \times\ 460 \\ \hline \end{array}$$

69.
$$\begin{array}{r} 800 \\ \times\ 325 \\ \hline \end{array}$$

70.
$$\begin{array}{r} 700 \\ \times\ 274 \\ \hline \end{array}$$

71.
$$\begin{array}{r} 987 \\ \times\ 349 \\ \hline \end{array}$$

72.
$$\begin{array}{r} 688 \\ \times\ 674 \\ \hline \end{array}$$

73.
$$\begin{array}{r} 312 \\ \times\ 134 \\ \hline \end{array}$$

74.
$$\begin{array}{r} 423 \\ \times\ 427 \\ \hline \end{array}$$

75.
$$\begin{array}{r} 379 \\ \times\ 500 \\ \hline \end{array}$$

76.
$$\begin{array}{r} 684 \\ \times\ 700 \\ \hline \end{array}$$

77.
$$\begin{array}{r} 985 \\ \times\ 408 \\ \hline \end{array}$$

78.
$$\begin{array}{r} 758 \\ \times\ 209 \\ \hline \end{array}$$

79.
$$\begin{array}{r} 3407 \\ \times\ 309 \\ \hline \end{array}$$

80.
$$\begin{array}{r} 5207 \\ \times\ 902 \\ \hline \end{array}$$

81.
$$\begin{array}{r} 4258 \\ \times\ 986 \\ \hline \end{array}$$

82.
$$\begin{array}{r} 6327 \\ \times\ 876 \\ \hline \end{array}$$

83. Find a one-digit number and a two-digit number whose product is a number that ends in two zeros.

84. What is 5763 times 45?

85. What is 7349 times 27?

86. Find the product of 2, 19, and 34.

87. Find the product of 6, 73, and 43.

88. What is 376 multiplied by 402?

89. What is 842 multiplied by 309?

For Exercises 90 to 97, use a calculator to multiply. Then use estimation to determine whether the product is reasonable.

90.
$$\begin{array}{r} 8745 \\ \times\ \ 63 \\ \hline \end{array}$$

91.
$$\begin{array}{r} 4732 \\ \times\ \ 93 \\ \hline \end{array}$$

92.
$$\begin{array}{r} 2937 \\ \times\ 206 \\ \hline \end{array}$$

93.
$$\begin{array}{r} 8941 \\ \times\ 726 \\ \hline \end{array}$$

94.
$$\begin{array}{r} 3097 \\ \times\ 1025 \\ \hline \end{array}$$

95.
$$\begin{array}{r} 6379 \\ \times\ 2936 \\ \hline \end{array}$$

96.
$$\begin{array}{r} 32{,}508 \\ \times\ \ \ 591 \\ \hline \end{array}$$

97.
$$\begin{array}{r} 62{,}504 \\ \times\ \ \ 923 \\ \hline \end{array}$$

OBJECTIVE C *To solve application problems*

98. Geometry The perimeter of a square is equal to four times the length of a side of the square. Find the perimeter of the square herb box garden shown at the right.

8 ft

99. Geometry The area of a rectangle is equal to the product of the length and the width. Find the area of the rectangular tennis court shown at the right.

36 ft

78 ft

100. The price of grapes is $3 per pound, and the price of cherries is $5 per pound. Which of the following represents the price of 4 pounds of grapes and 2 pounds of cherries?
(i) $(4 \times 3) + (4 \times 5)$ **(ii)** $(2 \times 3) + (4 \times 5)$
(iii) $5 \times (3 + 5)$ **(iv)** $(4 \times 3) + (2 \times 5)$

101. Fuel Efficiency Rob Hill owns a compact car that averages 43 miles on 1 gallon of gas. How many miles could the car travel on 12 gallons of gas?

102. Fuel Efficiency A plane flying from Los Angeles to Boston uses 865 gallons of jet fuel each hour. How many gallons of jet fuel were used on a 6-hour flight?

103. Matchmaking Services See the news clipping at the right.
a. How many marriages occur between eHarmony members each week?
b. How many marriages occur each year? Use a 365-day year.

In the NEWS!

Find Your Match Online

eHarmony, the online matchmaking service, boasts marriages among its members at the rate of 542 a day.
Source: www.eharmony.com

104. College Education See the news clipping at the right.
 a. Find the average cost of tuition, room, and board for 4 years at a public university.
 b. Find the average cost of tuition, room, and board for 4 years at a private university.
 c. Find the difference in the average cost of tuition, room, and board for 4 years at a private university and 4 years at a public university.

> ## In the NEWS!
>
> **Comparing Tuition Costs**
>
> The average annual cost of tuition, room, and board at a four-year public university is $15,875. At a four-year private university, the average cost is $42,841.
>
> *Source:* National Center for Education Statistics

Construction The table at the right below shows the hourly wages for four types of jobs at a small construction company. Use this table for Exercises 105 to 107.

105. The owner of this company wants to provide the electrical installation for a new house. On the basis of the architectural plans, it is estimated that the installation will require 3 electricians, each working 50 hours, to complete the job. What is the estimated cost for the electricians' labor?

106. Carlos Vasquez, a plumbing contractor, hires 4 plumbers from this company at the hourly wage given in the table. If each plumber works 23 hours, what are the total wages paid by Carlos?

Type of Work	Wage per Hour
Electrician	$34
Plumber	$30
Clerk	$16
Bookkeeper	$20

107. The owner of this company estimates that a kitchen remodel will require 1 electrician working 30 hours and 1 plumber working 33 hours. This project also requires 3 hours of clerical work and 4 hours of bookkeeping. What is the total cost for these four components of the remodel?

Critical Thinking

108. Determine whether each statement is always true, sometimes true, or never true.
 a. A whole number times zero is zero.
 b. A whole number times 1 is the whole number.
 c. The product of two whole numbers is greater than either of the numbers.

109. Safety According to the National Safety Council, in a recent year, a death resulting from an accident occurred at the rate of 1 every 5 minutes. At this rate, how many accidental deaths occurred each hour? Each day? Throughout the year? Explain how you arrived at your answers.

110. Demographics According to the Population Reference Bureau, in the world today, 267 people are born every minute and 108 people die every minute. Using this statistic, what is the increase in the world's population every hour? Every day? Every week? Every year? Use a 365-day year. Explain how you arrived at your answers.

Tiplyashin Anatoly/Shutterstock.com

Projects or Group Activities

111. What multiplication problem is shown at the right? The letters S, T, R, A, and W stand for five different digits.

$$\begin{array}{r} \text{STRAW} \\ \times 4 \\ \hline \text{WARTS} \end{array}$$

SECTION

1.5   Division of Whole Numbers

OBJECTIVE A   *To divide by a single digit with no remainder in the quotient*

Division is used to separate objects into equal groups.

APPLY THE CONCEPT ....

Four friends want to share equally in the cost of a $24 birthday present for their friend Bianca. From the diagram below, each friend's share of the cost is $6.

Cost of the present
$24

| Gina's share | Jason's share | Michelle's share | Isaiah's share |
| $6 | $6 | $6 | $6 |

The solution of this division problem is written as follows:

Each friend's share

Number of friends   6 ← **Quotient**

Divisor ——→ 4$\overline{)24}$

Cost of the present
Dividend

Note that the quotient multiplied by the divisor equals the dividend.

$$\frac{6}{4\overline{)24}}$$ because $\boxed{\begin{array}{c}6\\ \text{Quotient}\end{array}} \times \boxed{\begin{array}{c}4\\ \text{Divisor}\end{array}} = \boxed{\begin{array}{c}24\\ \text{Dividend}\end{array}}$

$$\frac{6}{9\overline{)54}}$$ because $\quad 6 \quad \times \quad 9 \quad = \quad 54$

$$\frac{5}{8\overline{)40}}$$ because $\quad 5 \quad \times \quad 8 \quad = \quad 40$

Property of One in Division

Any whole number, except zero, divided by itself is 1.

EXAMPLES

1. $8\overline{)8}$ with quotient 1

2. $14\overline{)14}$ with quotient 1

Property of Zero in Division

Zero divided by any whole number other than zero is zero.

EXAMPLES

1. $7\overline{)0}$ with quotient 0

2. $13\overline{)0}$ with quotient 0

Note that the Property of Zero in Division states that zero divided by any whole number *other than zero* is zero. Division by zero is not allowed. Here is an example of why this is so.

Suppose we try to divide 0 into 8, and write $0\overline{)8}^{?}$. The quotient—the number that replaces the question mark—times the divisor, 0, must equal the dividend, 8. In other words, $\boxed{?} \times 0$ would have to be 8. However, any number times zero is zero. There is no number whose product with 0 is 8, and therefore no number that can replace the question mark to make a true statement.

When the dividend is a larger whole number, the digits in the quotient are found in steps.

HOW TO 1   Divide $4\overline{)3192}$ and check.

$$
\begin{array}{r}
7 \\
4\overline{)3192} \\
-28 \\
\hline
39
\end{array}
$$

- Think $4\overline{)31}^{7}$. Place 7 in the quotient.
- Multiply 7×4.
- Subtract: $31 - 28 = 3$. Bring down the 9.

$$
\begin{array}{r}
79 \\
4\overline{)3192} \\
-28 \\
\hline
39 \\
-36 \\
\hline
32
\end{array}
$$

- Think $4\overline{)39}^{9}$. Place 9 in the quotient.
- Multiply 9×4.
- Subtract: $39 - 36 = 3$. Bring down the 2.

$$
\begin{array}{r}
798 \\
4\overline{)3192} \\
-28 \\
\hline
39 \\
-36 \\
\hline
32 \\
-32 \\
\hline
0
\end{array}
$$

Check:
$$
\begin{array}{r}
798 \\
\times \quad 4 \\
\hline
3192
\end{array}
$$

- Think $4\overline{)32}^{8}$. Place 8 in the quotient.
- Multiply 8×4.
- Subtract: $32 - 32 = 0$.

The place-value chart can be used to show why this method works.

$$
\begin{array}{r}
\text{HUNDREDS} \; \text{TENS} \; \text{ONES} \\
7 \quad 9 \quad 8 \\
4\overline{)\;3 \quad 1 \quad 9 \quad 2} \\
-\;2 \quad 8 \quad 0 \quad 0 \\
\hline
3 \quad 9 \quad 2 \\
-\;3 \quad 6 \quad 0 \\
\hline
3 \quad 2 \\
-\;3 \quad 2 \\
\hline
0
\end{array}
$$

7 hundreds $\times$ 4

9 tens $\times$ 4

8 ones $\times$ 4

There are other ways of expressing division.

54 divided by 9 equals 6.

54   ÷   9 equals 6.

$$\frac{54}{9} \text{ equals } 6.$$

EXAMPLE 1

Divide $7\overline{)56}$ and check.

Solution

$$7\overline{)56}^{\,8}$$

Check: $8 \times 7 = 56$

YOU TRY IT 1

Divide $9\overline{)63}$ and check.

Your solution

EXAMPLE 2

Divide $2808 \div 8$ and check.

Solution

$$
\begin{array}{r}
351 \\
8\overline{)\,2808} \\
-24 \\
\hline
40 \\
-40 \\
\hline
08 \\
-8 \\
\hline
0 \\
\end{array}
$$

Check: $351 \times 8 = 2808$

YOU TRY IT 2

Divide $4077 \div 9$ and check.

Your solution

EXAMPLE 3

Divide $7\overline{)2856}$ and check.

Solution

$$
\begin{array}{r}
408 \\
7\overline{)\,2856} \\
-28 \\
\hline
05 \\
-0 \\
\hline
56 \\
-56 \\
\hline
0 \\
\end{array}
$$

- Think $7\overline{)5}^{\,0}$. Place 0 in the quotient.
- Multiply 0×7.
- Subtract: $5 - 0 = 5$. Bring down the 6.

Check: $408 \times 7 = 2856$

YOU TRY IT 3

Divide $9\overline{)6345}$ and check.

Your solution

Solutions on pp. S2–S3

OBJECTIVE B *To divide by a single digit with a remainder in the quotient*

Sometimes it is not possible to separate objects into a whole number of equal groups.

APPLY THE CONCEPT

A baker has 14 muffins to pack into 3 boxes. Each box holds 4 muffins. From the diagram, we see that after the baker places 4 muffins in each box, there are 2 left over. The 2 leftover muffins represent the **remainder.**

The baker's division problem can be written as follows.

$$\underset{\substack{\textbf{Divisor} \\ \text{(Number of boxes)}}}{\longrightarrow} 3\overline{)\,14\,} \leftarrow \textbf{Dividend}$$

Quotient (Number in each box)
Dividend (Total number of muffins)
Remainder (Number left over)

$$\begin{array}{r} 4 \\ 3\overline{)\,14\,} \\ -12 \\ \hline 2 \end{array}$$

The answer to a division problem with a remainder is frequently written

$$3\overline{)14}^{\,4\ r2}$$

Note that $\boxed{\underset{\text{Quotient}}{4}} \times \boxed{\underset{\text{Divisor}}{3}} + \boxed{\underset{\text{Remainder}}{2}} = \boxed{\underset{\text{Dividend}}{14}}$.

EXAMPLE 4

Divide $4\overline{)2522}$ and check.

Solution

$$\begin{array}{r} 630 \ r2 \\ 4\overline{)\,2522\,} \\ -24 \\ \hline 12 \\ -12 \\ \hline 02 \\ -0 \\ \hline 2 \end{array}$$

• Think $4\overline{)2}$. Place 0 in the quotient.
• Multiply 0×4.
• Subtract: $2 - 0 = 2$.

Check: $(630 \times 4) + 2 =$
$\quad\quad 2520 \ + 2 = 2522$

YOU TRY IT 4

Divide $6\overline{)5225}$ and check.

Your solution

Solution on p. S3

EXAMPLE 5

Divide 9)27,438 and check.

Solution

```
      3,048 r6
9) 27,438
  −27
    0 4        • Think 9)4. Place 0 in the quotient.
   −0          • Multiply 0 × 9.
    43         • Subtract: 4 − 0 = 4. Bring down the 3.
   −36
    78
   −72
     6
```

Check: (3048 × 9) + 6 =
27,432 + 6 = 27,438

Divide 7)21,409 and check.

Your solution

Solution on p. S3

OBJECTIVE C   *To divide by larger whole numbers*

When the divisor has more than one digit, estimate at each step by using the first digit of the divisor. If that product is too large, lower the guess by 1 and try again.

HOW TO 2   Divide 34)1598 and check.

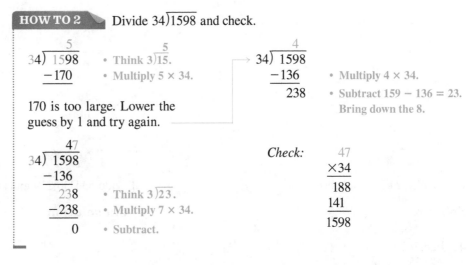

```
     5
34) 1598       • Think 3)15.
  −170         • Multiply 5 × 34.

170 is too large. Lower the
guess by 1 and try again.

     47
34) 1598
  −136
    238        • Think 3)23.
  −238         • Multiply 7 × 34.
     0         • Subtract.
```

```
     4
34) 1598
  −136         • Multiply 4 × 34.
    238        • Subtract 159 − 136 = 23.
                 Bring down the 8.
```

Check:
```
      47
    ×34
     188
     141
    1598
```

The phrases below are used to indicate the operation of division. An example is shown at the right of each phrase.

the quotient of	the quotient of 9 and 3	9 ÷ 3
divided by	6 divided by 2	6 ÷ 2

Find 7077 divided by 34 and check.

Solution

$$
\begin{array}{r}
208 \text{ r5} \\
34)\overline{7077} \\
-68 \\
\hline
27 \\
-0 \\
\hline
277 \\
-272 \\
\hline
5
\end{array}
$$

• Think $34)\overline{27}$ with 0. Place 0 in the quotient.
• Multiply 0×34.
• Subtract: $27 - 0 = 27$. Bring down the 7.

Check: $(208 \times 34) + 5 =$
$7072 + 5 = 7077$

Divide $4578 \div 42$ and check.

Your solution

Find the quotient of 21,312 and 56, and check.

Solution

$$
\begin{array}{r}
380 \text{ r32} \\
56)\overline{21,312} \\
-16\,8 \\
\hline
4\,51 \\
-4\,48 \\
\hline
32 \\
-0 \\
\hline
32
\end{array}
$$

• Think $5)\overline{21}$. 4×56 is too large. Try 3.

Check: $(380 \times 56) + 32 =$
$21,280 + 32 = 21,312$

Divide $18,359 \div 39$ and check.

Your solution

Divide $427)\overline{24,782}$ and check.

Solution

$$
\begin{array}{r}
58 \text{ r16} \\
427)\overline{24,782} \\
-21\,35 \\
\hline
3\,432 \\
-3\,416 \\
\hline
16
\end{array}
$$

Check: $(58 \times 427) + 16 =$
$24,766 + 16 = 24,782$

Divide $534)\overline{33,219}$ and check.

Your solution

EXAMPLE 9

Divide 386)206,149 and check.

Solution

```
        534 r25
386) 206,149
    −1930
     13 14
    −11 58
      1 569
     −1 544
         25
```

Check: $(534 \times 386) + 25 =$
$206,124 \quad + 25 = 206,149$

YOU TRY IT 9

Divide 515)216,848 and check.

Your solution

Solution on p. S3

ESTIMATION: Estimating the Quotient of Two Whole Numbers

Calculate 38,772 ÷ 54. Then use estimation to determine whether the quotient is reasonable.

Divide to find the exact quotient.   38,772 ÷ 54 = 718

To estimate the quotient, round each number so that it contains one nonzero digit. Then divide. The estimated answer is 800, which is close to the exact quotient 718.

$38,772 \div 54 \approx$
$40,000 \div 50 = 800$

OBJECTIVE D   *To solve application problems*

The **average** of several numbers is the sum of all the numbers divided by the number of those numbers.

A student has six test grades in a Spanish class. They are 81, 87, 80, 85, 79, and 86. To find the student's average of test score, divide the sum of the six test scores by 6.

$$\text{Average test score} = \frac{81 + 87 + 80 + 85 + 79 + 86}{6} = \frac{498}{6} = 83$$

The student's average test score in the Spanish class is 83.

HOW TO 3

🔵 The table below shows how much a median-income family can expect to spend raising a child to the age of 17 years. Find the average amount spent each year. Round to the nearest dollar.

Expenses to Raise a Child	
Housing	$70,020
Food	$35,970
Transportation	$28,590
Child care/education	$37,740
Clothing	$13,260
Health care	$17,760
Other	$19,030

Source: Department of Agriculture, *Expenditures on Children by Families*

Julie Keen/Shutterstock.com

Strategy

To find the average amount spent each year:

• Add all the numbers in the table to find the total amount spent during the 17 years.
• Divide the sum by 17.

Solution

$$
\begin{array}{r}
70,020 \\
35,970 \\
28,590 \\
37,740 \\
13,260 \\
17,760 \\
+\;\;19,030 \\
\hline
222,370
\end{array}
$$
• Sum of all the costs

$$
\begin{array}{r}
13,080 \text{ r}10 \\
17\overline{)\,222,370} \\
-17 \\
\hline
52 \\
-51 \\
\hline
13 \\
-\;0 \\
\hline
137 \\
-136 \\
\hline
10 \\
-\;0 \\
\hline
10
\end{array}
$$

• When rounding to the nearest whole number, compare twice the remainder to the divisor. If twice the remainder is less than the divisor, drop the remainder. If twice the remainder is greater than or equal to the divisor, add 1 to the units digit of the quotient and drop the remainder.

• Twice the remainder is 2 × 10 = 20. Because 20 > 17, add 1 to the units digit of the quotient.

The average amount spent each year to raise a child to the age of 17 is $13,081.

EXAMPLE 10

Ngan Hui, a freight supervisor, shipped 35,640 bushels of wheat in 9 railroad cars. Find the amount of wheat shipped in each car.

Strategy

To find the amount of wheat shipped in each car, divide the number of bushels (35,640) by the number of cars (9).

Solution

$$
\begin{array}{r}
3\ 960 \\
9{\overline{\smash{\big)}\,35{,}640}} \\
-27 \\
\hline
86 \\
-81 \\
\hline
54 \\
-54 \\
\hline
0
\end{array}
$$

Each car carried 3960 bushels of wheat.

YOU TRY IT 10

Suppose a Michelin retail outlet can store 270 tires on 15 shelves. How many tires can be stored on each shelf?

Your strategy

Your solution

EXAMPLE 11

The used car you are buying costs $11,216. A down payment of $2000 is required. The remaining balance is paid in 48 equal monthly payments. What is the monthly payment?

Strategy

To find the monthly payment:

• Find the remaining balance by subtracting the down payment (2000) from the total cost of the car (11,216).
• Divide the remaining balance by the number of equal monthly payments (48).

Solution

$$
\begin{array}{r}
11{,}216 \\
-\ 2{,}000 \\
\hline
9{,}216
\end{array}
$$
• **Remaining balance**

$$
\begin{array}{r}
192 \\
48{\overline{\smash{\big)}\,9216}} \\
-48 \\
\hline
441 \\
-432 \\
\hline
96 \\
-96 \\
\hline
0
\end{array}
$$

The monthly payment is $192.

YOU TRY IT 11

A soft-drink manufacturer produces 12,600 cans of soft drink each hour. Cans are packed 24 to a case. How many cases of soft drink are produced in 8 hours?

Your strategy

Your solution

Solutions on pp. S3–S4

1.5 EXERCISES

✔ Concept Check

For Exercises 1 to 4, find the quotient. Then write the related multiplication problem using Quotient × Divisor = Dividend.

1. 4)8   **2.** 3)12   **3.** 5)30   **4.** 9)63

For Exercises 5 to 8, use the relationship between multiplication and division to complete the multiplication problem.

5. __ × 9 = 54   **6.** 12 × __ = 60   **7.** 8 × __ = 96   **8.** __ × 15 = 90

OBJECTIVE A   *To divide by a single digit with no remainder in the quotient*

For Exercises 9 to 24, divide.

9. 7)49   **10.** 5)80   **11.** 6)96   **12.** 6)480

13. 4)840   **14.** 3)690   **15.** 7)308   **16.** 7)203

17. 9)6327   **18.** 4)2120   **19.** 8)7280   **20.** 9)8118

21. 7)35,042   **22.** 4)28,032   **23.** 9)54,450   **24.** 8)25,632

25. What is 7525 divided by 7?   **26.** What is 32,364 divided by 4?

27. 🖑 If the dividend and the divisor in a division problem are the same number, what is the quotient?

OBJECTIVE B   *To divide by a single digit with a remainder in the quotient*

For Exercises 28 to 50, divide.

28. 4)9   **29.** 2)7   **30.** 5)27   **31.** 9)88   **32.** 3)40

33. 6)97   **34.** 8)83   **35.** 5)54   **36.** 7)632   **37.** 4)363

38. 4)921   **39.** 7)845   **40.** 8)1635   **41.** 5)1548   **42.** 7)9432

43. 7)8124   **44.** 3)5162   **45.** 5)3542   **46.** 8)3274

47. $4\overline{)15{,}301}$ **48.** $7\overline{)43{,}500}$ **49.** $6\overline{)34{,}263}$ **50.** $7\overline{)21{,}495}$

51. What is 45,738 divided by 4? Round to the nearest ten.

52. What is 37,896 divided by 9? Round to the nearest hundred.

53. What is 3572 divided by 7? Round to the nearest ten.

54. What is 78,345 divided by 4? Round to the nearest hundred.

55. True or false? When a three-digit number is divided by a one-digit number, the quotient can be a one-digit number.

OBJECTIVE C   *To divide by larger whole numbers*

For Exercises 56 to 83, divide.

56. $27\overline{)96}$ **57.** $44\overline{)82}$ **58.** $42\overline{)87}$ **59.** $67\overline{)93}$

60. $41\overline{)897}$ **61.** $32\overline{)693}$ **62.** $23\overline{)784}$ **63.** $25\overline{)772}$

64. $74\overline{)600}$ **65.** $92\overline{)500}$ **66.** $70\overline{)329}$ **67.** $50\overline{)467}$

68. $36\overline{)7225}$ **69.** $44\overline{)8821}$ **70.** $19\overline{)3859}$ **71.** $32\overline{)9697}$

72. $88\overline{)3127}$ **73.** $92\overline{)6177}$ **74.** $29\overline{)14{,}721}$ **75.** $63\overline{)44{,}653}$

76. $22\overline{)98{,}654}$ **77.** $77\overline{)83{,}629}$ **78.** $57\overline{)114{,}545}$ **79.** $73\overline{)365{,}566}$

80. $206\overline{)3097}$ **81.** $504\overline{)6504}$ **82.** $654\overline{)1217}$ **83.** $546\overline{)2344}$

84. Find the quotient of 5432 and 21.

85. Find the quotient of 8507 and 53.

86. What is 37,294 divided by 72?

87. What is 76,788 divided by 46?

88. Find 23,457 divided by 43. Round to the nearest hundred.

89. Find 341,781 divided by 43. Round to the nearest ten.

90. True or false? If the remainder of a division problem is 210, then the divisor was less than 210.

For Exercises 91 to 102, use a calculator to divide. Then use estimation to determine whether the quotient is reasonable.

91. $76\overline{)389{,}804}$ **92.** $53\overline{)117{,}925}$ **93.** $29\overline{)637{,}072}$ **94.** $67\overline{)738{,}072}$

95. $38\overline{)934{,}648}$ **96.** $34\overline{)906{,}304}$ **97.** $309\overline{)876{,}324}$ **98.** $642\overline{)323{,}568}$

99. $209\overline{)632{,}016}$ **100.** $614\overline{)332{,}174}$ **101.** $179\overline{)5{,}734{,}444}$ **102.** $374\overline{)7{,}712{,}254}$

OBJECTIVE D *To solve application problems*

103. **Salaries** Melissa's annual starting salary as a chemical engineer is $69,048. What is her monthly salary?

104. **Cooking** A chef is making 120 meatballs from 6 pounds of hamburger. Six pounds of hamburger contain 7200 calories.
a. How many calories are in one meatball?
b. How many calories are in one pound of hamburger?

105. **Jewelry** A jeweler is making 15 identical gold necklaces from 30 ounces of a gold alloy that costs $375 per ounce. What is the cost of the gold alloy in each necklace?

106. **Manufacturing** It costs a manufacturer of the energy drink Z-ENG $126,000 to make 63,000 bottles of the drink. The manufacturer packages the Z-ENG in cartons of four bottles. What is the cost of a carton of four bottles of Z-ENG?

107. **Education** A nursing student received scores of 86, 94, 79, and 93 on four anatomy exams. What was the nursing student's average score for the four exams?

108. **Education** To receive an A grade in a Spanish course, a professor requires a minimum score of 450 points on the five semester exams. If Richard receives a score of 82 on the first exam, what average score must Richard receive on the remaining four tests to achieve the minimum total of 450 points?

109. **Electronics** The cost of a 3D television that you are purchasing is $3180. If you make a down payment of $1620 and agree to pay off the remaining balance in 12 equal monthly payments, what is the monthly payment?

110. **Wages** A sales associate earns $440 for working a 40-hour week. Last week, the associate worked an additional 9 hours at $13 an hour. What is the difference between the associate's hourly overtime pay rate and the regular hourly pay rate?

Insurance The table at the right shows the sources of insurance claims for losses of laptop computers in a recent year. Claims have been rounded to the nearest ten thousand dollars. Use this information for Exercises 111 and 112.

111. What was the average monthly claim for theft?

112. For all sources combined, find the average claim per month.

Source	Claims
Accidents	$560,000
Theft	$300,000
Power surge	$80,000
Lightning	$50,000
Transit	$20,000
Water/flood	$20,000
Other	$110,000

Source: Safeware, The Insurance Company

Work Hours The table at the right shows, for different countries, the average numbers of hours per year that employees work. Use this information for Exercises 113 to 115. Use a 50-week year. Round answers to the nearest whole number.

113. What is the average number of hours worked per week by employees in the United Kingdom?

114. On average, how many more hours per week do employees in the United States work than employees in France?

115. On average, how many more hours per week do employees work in the country with the most hours worked per year than in the country with the least hours worked per year?

Country	Annual Number of Hours Worked
France	1554
Germany	1390
Greece	2119
United Kingdom	1646
United States	1768

Source: Organization for Economic Cooperation and Development

116. **Weather** The daily low temperatures, in degrees Fahrenheit, for 9 consecutive summer days in Fargo, North Dakota, were 66, 55, 55, 61, 62, 66, 65, 52, and 58. What was the average low temperature for those 9 days?

117. **U.S. Postal Service** Use the information in the news clipping at the right to determine, on average, how many pieces of mail the U.S. Postal Service processed per day this year. Assume there are 300 working days in a year.

In the NEWS!

Decline in USPS Mail Volume

This year, the U.S. Postal Service processed 117 billion pieces of mail. This is a decline of 6 billion pieces from last year.
Source: www.usps.com

118. Which problems below require division to solve?
  (i) Four friends want to share a restaurant bill of $48 equally. Find the amount that each friend should pay.
  (ii) On average, Sam spends $30 a week on gas. Find Sam's average yearly expenditure for gas.
  (iii) Emma's 12 phone bills for last year totaled $660. Find Emma's average monthly phone bill.

Critical Thinking

119. **Payroll Deductions** Your paycheck shows deductions of $225 for savings, $98 for taxes, and $27 for insurance. Find the total of the three deductions.

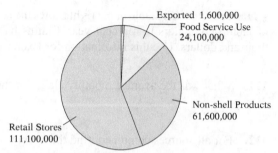

Exported 1,600,000
Food Service Use
24,100,000

Non-shell Products
61,600,000

Retail Stores
111,100,000

Eggs Produced in the United States (in cases)
Source: American Egg Board

Dairy Products The topic of the graph at the right is the eggs produced in the United States during a recent year. It shows where the eggs that were produced went or how they were used. Use this graph for Exercises 120 and 121.

120. Use the graph to determine the total number of cases of eggs produced during the year.

121. How many more cases of eggs were sold by retail stores than were used for non-shell products?

Finances The graph at the right shows the annual expenditures, for a recent year, of an average household in the United States. Use this information for Exercises 122 to 124. Round answers to the nearest whole number.

122. What is the total amount spent annually by an average household in the United States?

123. What is the average monthly expense for housing?

124. What is the difference between the average monthly expense for food and the average monthly expense for health care?

125. **Finances** You purchase a used car with a down payment of $2500 and monthly payments of $195 for 48 months. Find the total amount paid for the car.

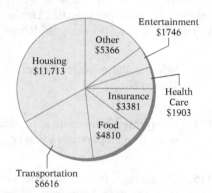

Entertainment
$1746

Other
$5366

Housing
$11,713

Insurance
$3381

Health
Care
$1903

Food
$4810

Transportation
$6616

Average Annual Household Expenses
Source: Bureau of Labor Statistics
Consumer Expenditure Survey

Projects or Group Activities

126. A **factor** of a given number is a number that divides the given number evenly. For instance, 6 is a factor of 54 but 8 is not a factor of 54.
a. Find all the factors of 48.
b. Find all the factors of 144.
c. Find all the factors of 97.

For Exercises 127 to 130, state which operation—addition, subtraction, multiplication, or division—you would use to solve the problem. Do not solve.

127. Mary and Jose are building a brick walkway. They have 35 bricks, 7 of which are unusable. How many usable bricks do they have?

128. Mary and Jose are building a brick walkway. They want to have a walkway that has 7 bricks in each row and 35 rows. How many bricks do they need?

129. Mary and Jose are building a brick walkway. They have 35 bricks and want a walkway that is 7 bricks wide. How many rows of bricks can they make?

130. Mary and Jose are building a brick walkway. They have 7 bricks and purchase 35 more bricks. How many bricks do they now have?

1.6

Exponential Notation and the Order of Operations Agreement

OBJECTIVE A *To simplify expressions that contain exponents*

Repeated multiplication of the same factor can be written in two ways:

$$3 \cdot 3 \cdot 3 \cdot 3 \cdot 3 \quad \text{or} \quad 3^5 \leftarrow \textbf{Exponent}$$

The **exponent** indicates how many times the factor occurs in the multiplication. The expression 3^5 is in **exponential notation.**

It is important to be able to read numbers written in exponential notation.

$6 = 6^1$ is read "six to the first power" or just "six." Usually the exponent 1 is not written.

$6 \cdot 6 = 6^2$ is read "six squared" or "six to the second power."

$6 \cdot 6 \cdot 6 = 6^3$ is read "six cubed" or "six to the third power."

$6 \cdot 6 \cdot 6 \cdot 6 = 6^4$ is read "six to the fourth power."

$6 \cdot 6 \cdot 6 \cdot 6 \cdot 6 = 6^5$ is read "six to the fifth power."

Each place value in the place-value chart can be expressed as a power of 10.

$$\begin{aligned}
\text{Ten} &= 10 &= 10 &= 10^1 \\
\text{Hundred} &= 100 &= 10 \cdot 10 &= 10^2 \\
\text{Thousand} &= 1000 &= 10 \cdot 10 \cdot 10 &= 10^3 \\
\text{Ten-thousand} &= 10{,}000 &= 10 \cdot 10 \cdot 10 \cdot 10 &= 10^4 \\
\text{Hundred-thousand} &= 100{,}000 &= 10 \cdot 10 \cdot 10 \cdot 10 \cdot 10 &= 10^5 \\
\text{Million} &= 1{,}000{,}000 &= 10 \cdot 10 \cdot 10 \cdot 10 \cdot 10 \cdot 10 &= 10^6
\end{aligned}$$

Integrating Technology

A calculator can be used to evaluate an exponential expression. The y^x key (or, on some calculators, an x^y or $\wedge$ key) is used to enter the exponent. For instance, for the example at the right, enter 4 y^x 3 $=$. The display reads 64.

To simplify a numerical expression containing exponents, write each factor as many times as indicated by the exponent, and then carry out the indicated multiplication.

$$4^3 = 4 \cdot 4 \cdot 4 = 64$$
$$2^2 \cdot 3^4 = (2 \cdot 2) \cdot (3 \cdot 3 \cdot 3 \cdot 3) = 4 \cdot 81 = 324$$

EXAMPLE 1

Write $3 \cdot 3 \cdot 3 \cdot 5 \cdot 5$ in exponential notation.

Solution

$3 \cdot 3 \cdot 3 \cdot 5 \cdot 5 = 3^3 \cdot 5^2$

YOU TRY IT 1

Write $2 \cdot 2 \cdot 2 \cdot 2 \cdot 3 \cdot 3 \cdot 3$ in exponential notation.

Your solution

Solution on p. S4

EXAMPLE 2

Write as a power of 10: $10 \cdot 10 \cdot 10 \cdot 10$

Solution
$10 \cdot 10 \cdot 10 \cdot 10 = 10^4$

YOU TRY IT 2

Write as a power of 10: $10 \cdot 10 \cdot 10 \cdot 10 \cdot 10 \cdot 10 \cdot 10$

Your solution

EXAMPLE 3

Simplify $3^2 \cdot 5^3$.

Solution
$$3^2 \cdot 5^3 = (3 \cdot 3) \cdot (5 \cdot 5 \cdot 5)$$
$$= 9 \cdot 125$$
$$= 1125$$

YOU TRY IT 3

Simplify $2^3 \cdot 5^2$.

Your solution

Solutions on p. S4

OBJECTIVE B *To use the Order of Operations Agreement to simplify expressions*

More than one operation may occur in a numerical expression. The answer may be different depending on the order in which the operations are performed. For example, consider $3 + 4 \times 5$.

Multiply first, then add.
$$3 + \underbrace{4 \times 5}$$
$$\underbrace{3 + 20}$$
$$23$$

Add first, then multiply.
$$\underbrace{3 + 4} \times 5$$
$$\underbrace{7 \times 5}$$
$$35$$

An Order of Operations Agreement is used so that only one answer is possible.

Integrating Technology

Many scientific calculators have an x^2 key. This key is used to square the displayed number. For example, after the user presses 4 x^2 =, the display reads 16.

Order of Operations Agreement

Step 1. Perform operations inside grouping symbols such as parentheses.
Step 2. Simplify exponential expressions.
Step 3. Do multiplication and division as they occur from left to right.
Step 4. Do addition and subtraction as they occur from left to right.

EXAMPLES

1. $3(7 - 2) = 3(5)$ — • Perform operations inside grouping symbols. [Step 1]
      $= 15$ — • Multiply. [Step 3]
2. $5 \cdot 4^2 = 5 \cdot 16$ — • Simplify exponential expressions. [Step 2]
      $= 80$ — • Multiply. [Step 3]
3. $18 \div 9 \cdot 4 = 2 \cdot 4$ — • Do multiplication and division from left to right. [Step 3]
      $= 8$
4. $12 - 2 \cdot 4 = 12 - 8$ — • Do multiplication and division from left to right. [Step 3]
      $= 4$ — • Do addition and subtraction from left to right. [Step 4]

HOW TO 1 Simplify: $3 \times (2 + 1) - 2^2 + 4 \div 2$

Use the Order of Operations Agreement.

$3 \times (2 + 1) - 2^2 + 4 \div 2$

$3 \times 3 - 2^2 + 4 \div 2$ **1.** Perform operations inside parentheses.

$3 \times 3 - 4 + 4 \div 2$ **2.** Simplify expressions with exponents.

$9 - 4 + 4 \div 2$ **3.** Do multiplication and division as they occur from left to right.

$9 - 4 + 2$

$5 + 2$ **4.** Do addition and subtraction as they occur from left to right.

7

One or more of the steps of the Order of Operations Agreement may not be needed to simplify an expression. In that case, proceed to the next step in the Order of Operations Agreement.

HOW TO 2 Simplify $5 + 8 \div 2$.

There are no parentheses or exponents, so Steps 1 and 2 of the Order of Operations Agreement are not needed. Proceed to Step 3 of the agreement.

$5 + 8 \div 2$

$5 + 4$ **3.** Do multiplication or division.

9 **4.** Do addition or subtraction.

EXAMPLE 4

Simplify: $64 \div (8 - 4)^2 \cdot 9 - 5^2$

Solution

$64 \div (8 - 4)^2 \cdot 9 - 5^2$

$= 64 \div 4^2 \cdot 9 - 5^2$ • Parentheses

$= 64 \div 16 \cdot 9 - 25$ • Exponents

$= 4 \cdot 9 - 25$ • Division and multiplication

$= 36 - 25$

$= 11$ • Subtraction

YOU TRY IT 4

Simplify: $5 \cdot (8 - 4)^2 \div 4 - 2$

Your solution

Solution on p. S4

1.6 EXERCISES

✔ Concept Check

1. How many times does 7 occur as a factor in the expression 7^5?

2. Using the Order of Operations Agreement, does $8 \cdot (4 \cdot 2) = (8 \cdot 4) \cdot 2$? If so, what Property of Multiplication does this show? See pages 25 and 26 for the Properties of Multiplication.

3. Which expressions below have the same value?
   (i) $8 \div 4 \div 2$ **(ii)** $8 \div (4 \div 2)$ **(iii)** $(8 \div 4) \div 2$?

4. Which expressions below have the same value?
   (i) $8 - 4 - 2$ **(ii)** $(8 - 4) - 2$ **(iii)** $8 - (4 - 2)$

OBJECTIVE A *To simplify expressions that contain exponents*

For Exercises 5 to 16, write the number in exponential notation.

5. $2 \cdot 2 \cdot 2$

6. $7 \cdot 7 \cdot 7 \cdot 7 \cdot 7$

7. $6 \cdot 6 \cdot 6 \cdot 7 \cdot 7 \cdot 7 \cdot 7$

8. $6 \cdot 6 \cdot 9 \cdot 9 \cdot 9 \cdot 9$

9. $2 \cdot 2 \cdot 2 \cdot 3 \cdot 3 \cdot 3$

10. $3 \cdot 3 \cdot 10 \cdot 10$

11. $5 \cdot 7 \cdot 7 \cdot 7 \cdot 7 \cdot 7$

12. $4 \cdot 4 \cdot 4 \cdot 5 \cdot 5 \cdot 5$

13. $3 \cdot 3 \cdot 3 \cdot 6 \cdot 6 \cdot 6 \cdot 6$

14. $2 \cdot 2 \cdot 5 \cdot 5 \cdot 5 \cdot 8$

15. $3 \cdot 3 \cdot 3 \cdot 5 \cdot 9 \cdot 9 \cdot 9$

16. $2 \cdot 2 \cdot 2 \cdot 4 \cdot 7 \cdot 7 \cdot 7$

For Exercises 17 to 41, simplify.

17. 2^3

18. 2^6

19. $2^4 \cdot 5^2$

20. $2^6 \cdot 3^2$

21. $3^2 \cdot 10^2$

22. $2^3 \cdot 10^4$

23. $6^2 \cdot 3^3$

24. $4^3 \cdot 5^2$

25. $5 \cdot 2^3 \cdot 3$

26. $6 \cdot 3^2 \cdot 4$

27. $2^2 \cdot 3^2 \cdot 10$

28. $3^2 \cdot 5^2 \cdot 10$

29. $0^2 \cdot 4^3$

30. $6^2 \cdot 0^3$

31. $3^2 \cdot 10^4$

32. $5^3 \cdot 10^3$ **33.** $2^2 \cdot 3^3 \cdot 5$ **34.** $5^2 \cdot 7^3 \cdot 2$ **35.** $2 \cdot 3^4 \cdot 5^2$ **36.** $6 \cdot 2^6 \cdot 7^2$

37. $5^2 \cdot 3^2 \cdot 7^2$ **38.** $4^2 \cdot 9^2 \cdot 6^2$ **39.** $3^4 \cdot 2^6 \cdot 5$ **40.** $4^3 \cdot 6^3 \cdot 7$ **41.** $4^2 \cdot 3^3 \cdot 10^4$

42. Rewrite the expression using the numbers 3 and 5 exactly once. Then simplify the expression.
   a. $3 + 3 + 3 + 3 + 3$
   b. $3 \cdot 3 \cdot 3 \cdot 3 \cdot 3$

OBJECTIVE B   *To use the Order of Operations Agreement to simplify expressions*

For Exercises 43 to 81, simplify by using the Order of Operations Agreement.

43. $4 - 2 + 3$

44. $6 - 3 + 2$

45. $6 \cdot 3 + 5$

46. $5 \cdot 9 + 2$

47. $14 - 2 \cdot 4$

48. $12 + 3 \cdot 5$

49. $3 + 6 \div 3$

50. $12 + 8 \div 4$

51. $2 \cdot 3^2$

52. $5 \cdot 2^3$

53. $4 \cdot (5 - 3) + 2$

54. $3 + (4 + 2) \div 3$

55. $5 + (8 + 4) \div 6$

56. $8 - 2^2 + 4$

57. $16 \cdot (3 + 2) \div 10$

58. $12 \cdot (1 + 5) \div 12$

59. $10 - 2^3 + 4$

60. $5 \cdot 3^2 + 8$

61. $16 + 4 \cdot 3^2$

62. $12 + 4 \cdot 2^3$

63. $16 + (8 - 3) \cdot 2$

64. $7 + (9 - 5) \cdot 3$

65. $2^2 + 3 \cdot (6 - 2)^2$

66. $3^3 + 5 \cdot (8 - 6)^3$

67. $2^2 \cdot 3^2 + 2 \cdot 3$

68. $4 \cdot 6 + 3^2 \cdot 4^2$

69. $3 \cdot (6 - 2) + 4$

70. $5 \cdot (8 - 4) - 6$ **71.** $8 - (8 - 2) \div 3$ **72.** $12 - (12 - 4) \div 4$

73. $8 + 2 - 3 \cdot 2 \div 3$ **74.** $10 + 1 - 5 \cdot 2 \div 5$ **75.** $3 \cdot (4 + 2) \div 6$

76. $(7 - 3)^2 \div 2 - 4 + 8$ **77.** $20 - 4 \div 2 \cdot (3 - 1)^3$ **78.** $12 \div 3 \cdot 2^2 + (7 - 3)^2$

79. $(4 - 2) \cdot 6 \div 3 + (5 - 2)^2$ **80.** $18 - 2 \cdot 3 + (4 - 1)^3$ **81.** $100 \div (2 + 3)^2 - 8 \div 2$

By placing parentheses at various places in the expression $2 \cdot 3 + 8 \cdot 4 - 2$, it is possible to change the value of the expression. For Exercises 82 to 85, insert parentheses in the above expression so that the value is the given number.

82. 22   **83.** 54   **84.** 44   **85.** 66

Critical Thinking

For Exercises 86 to 89, determine whether the two expressions are equal.

86. $(2 + 3)^5$ and $2^5 + 3^5$

87. $(2 + 3)^5$ and $2^5 + 3^5$

88. $(12 \div 3)^4$ and $12^4 \div 3^4$

89. $(6 - 4)^4$ and $6^4 - 4^4$

Projects or Group Activities

90. Recall that the Associative Property of Addition states that grouping an addition in any order gives the same result.
   a. Is subtraction an associative operation? Explain your answer.
   b. Is division an associative operation? Explain your answer.

91. Evaluate **a.** $(3^4)^2$ and **b.** $3^{(4^2)}$.
   c. According to the Order of Operations Agreement, what is the value of 3^{4^2}?

SECTION

1.7 | Prime Numbers and Factoring

OBJECTIVE A | *To factor numbers*

Whole-number **factors** of a number divide that number evenly (there is no remainder).

1, 2, 3, and 6 are whole-number factors of 6 because they divide 6 evenly.

$$\frac{6}{1)\overline{6}} \quad \frac{3}{2)\overline{6}} \quad \frac{2}{3)\overline{6}} \quad \frac{1}{6)\overline{6}}$$

Note that both the divisor and the quotient are factors of the dividend.

To find the factors of a number, try dividing the number by 1, 2, 3, 4, 5, ... Those numbers that divide the number evenly are its factors. Continue this process until the factors start to repeat.

HOW TO 1 Find all the factors of 42.

$42 \div 1 = 42$	1 and 42 are factors.
$42 \div 2 = 21$	2 and 21 are factors.
$42 \div 3 = 14$	3 and 14 are factors.
$42 \div 4$	Will not divide evenly
$42 \div 5$	Will not divide evenly
$42 \div 6 = 7$	6 and 7 are factors. $\}$ Factors are repeating; all the
$42 \div 7 = 6$	7 and 6 are factors. $\}$ factors of 42 have been found.

1, 2, 3, 6, 7, 14, 21, and 42 are the factors of 42.

The following rules are helpful in finding the factors of a number.

2 is a factor of a number if the last digit of the number is 0, 2, 4, 6, or 8.

436 ends in 6; therefore, 2 is a factor of 436. ($436 \div 2 = 218$)

3 is a factor of a number if the sum of the digits of the number is divisible by 3.

The sum of the digits of 489 is $4 + 8 + 9 = 21$. 21 is divisible by 3. Therefore, 3 is a factor of 489. ($489 \div 3 = 163$)

5 is a factor of a number if the last digit of the number is 0 or 5.

520 ends in 0; therefore, 5 is a factor of 520. ($520 \div 5 = 104$)

EXAMPLE 1

Find all the factors of 30.

Solution

$30 \div 1 = 30$
$30 \div 2 = 15$
$30 \div 3 = 10$
$30 \div 4$ • Will not divide evenly
$30 \div 5 = 6$
$30 \div 6 = 5$ • Factors are repeating.

1, 2, 3, 5, 6, 10, 15, and 30 are the factors of 30.

YOU TRY IT 1

Find all the factors of 40.

Your solution

Solution on p. S4

> **OBJECTIVE B**   *To find the prime factorization of a number*

 Point of Interest

Prime numbers are an important part of cryptology, the study of secret codes. To make it less likely that codes can be broken, cryptologists use prime numbers that have hundreds of digits.

A number is a **prime number** if its only whole-number factors are 1 and itself. 7 is prime because its only factors are 1 and 7. If a number is not prime, it is called a **composite number.** Because 6 has factors of 2 and 3, 6 is a composite number. The number 1 is not considered a prime number; therefore, it is not included in the following list of prime numbers less than 50.

$$2, 3, 5, 7, 11, 13, 17, 19, 23, 29, 31, 37, 41, 43, 47$$

The **prime factorization** of a number is the expression of the number as a product of its prime factors. In the example below, we use a "T-diagram" to find the prime factors of 60. Begin with the smallest prime number as a trial divisor, and continue with prime numbers as trial divisors until the final quotient is 1.

$$
\begin{array}{c|c}
\multicolumn{2}{c}{60} \\
\hline
2 & 30 \\
2 & 15 \\
3 & 5 \\
5 & 1 \\
\end{array}
\qquad
\begin{array}{l}
60 \div 2 = 30 \\
30 \div 2 = 15 \\
15 \div 3 = 5 \\
5 \div 5 = 1 \\
\end{array}
$$

The prime factorization of 60 is $2 \cdot 2 \cdot 3 \cdot 5$.

Finding the prime factorization of larger numbers can be more difficult. Try each prime number as a trial divisor. Stop when the square of the trial divisor is greater than the number being factored.

> **HOW TO 2**   Find the prime factorization of 106.

$$
\begin{array}{c|c}
\multicolumn{2}{c}{106} \\
\hline
2 & 53 \\
53 & 1 \\
\end{array}
$$

• 53 cannot be divided evenly by 2, 3, 5, 7, or 11. Prime numbers greater than 11 need not be tested because 11^2 is greater than 53.

The prime factorization of 106 is $2 \cdot 53$.

EXAMPLE 2

Find the prime factorization of 315.

Solution

$$
\begin{array}{c|c}
\multicolumn{2}{c}{315} \\
\hline
3 & 105 \\
3 & 35 \\
5 & 7 \\
7 & 1 \\
\end{array}
$$

• $315 \div 3 = 105$
• $105 \div 3 = 35$
• $35 \div 5 = 7$
• $7 \div 7 = 1$

$315 = 3 \cdot 3 \cdot 5 \cdot 7$

YOU TRY IT 2

Find the prime factorization of 44.

Your solution

EXAMPLE 3

Find the prime factorization of 201.

Solution

$$
\begin{array}{c|c}
\multicolumn{2}{c}{201} \\
\hline
3 & 67 \\
67 & 1 \\
\end{array}
$$

• Try only 2, 3, 5, 7, and 11, because $11^2 > 67$.

$201 = 3 \cdot 67$

YOU TRY IT 3

Find the prime factorization of 177.

Your solution

Solutions on p. S4

1.7 EXERCISES

✔ Concept Check

1. Which of the following numbers are factors of 72?
   (i) 0   (ii) 1   (iii) 9   (iv) 14   (v) 24   (vi) 72

2. Which of the following numbers are prime factors of 210?
   (i) 2   (ii) 5   (iii) 7   (iv) 11   (v) 30   (vi) 35

OBJECTIVE A   *To factor numbers*

For Exercises 3 to 42, find all the factors of the number.

3. 4	**4.** 6	**5.** 10	**6.** 20	**7.** 7
8. 12	**9.** 9	**10.** 8	**11.** 13	**12.** 17
13. 18	**14.** 24	**15.** 56	**16.** 36	**17.** 45
18. 28	**19.** 29	**20.** 33	**21.** 22	**22.** 26
23. 52	**24.** 49	**25.** 82	**26.** 37	**27.** 57
28. 69	**29.** 48	**30.** 64	**31.** 95	**32.** 46
33. 54	**34.** 50	**35.** 66	**36.** 77	**37.** 80
38. 100	**39.** 96	**40.** 85	**41.** 90	**42.** 101

43. ✏ True or false? A number can have an odd number of factors.

44. ✏ True or false? If a number has exactly four factors, then the product of those four factors must be the number.

OBJECTIVE B   *To find the prime factorization of a number*

For Exercises 45 to 88, find the prime factorization.

45. 6	**46.** 14	**47.** 17	**48.** 83

49. 24   **50.** 12   **51.** 27   **52.** 9

53. 36   **54.** 40   **55.** 19   **56.** 37

57. 90   **58.** 65   **59.** 115   **60.** 80

61. 18   **62.** 26   **63.** 28   **64.** 49

65. 31   **66.** 42   **67.** 62   **68.** 81

69. 22   **70.** 39   **71.** 101   **72.** 89

73. 66   **74.** 86   **75.** 74   **76.** 95

77. 67   **78.** 78   **79.** 55   **80.** 46

81. 120   **82.** 144   **83.** 160   **84.** 175

85. 216   **86.** 400   **87.** 625   **88.** 225

89. True or false? The prime factorization of 102 is $2 \cdot 51$.

Critical Thinking

90. All prime numbers greater than 10 end in one of four digits. What are these digits?

91. Not every number that ends in one of the digits you found in Exercise 90 is a prime number. Give examples of numbers that end in each of these digits but are not prime numbers.

92. There are three digits such that any two of them will form a two-digit prime number. What are these three digits? Give an example of a prime number that uses all three digits. Give an example of a number that uses all three digits but is not a prime number.

Projects or Group Activities

93. What is the Sieve of Eratosthenes? Use this method to find all prime numbers less than 100.

1 | Summary

Key Words	Examples

The **whole numbers** are 0, 1, 2, 3, 4, 5, 6, 7, 8, 9, 10, ... [1.1A, p. 2]

The **graph of a whole number** is shown by placing a heavy dot directly above that number on the number line. [1.1A, p. 2]

This is the graph of 4 on the number line.

0 1 2 3 4 5 6 7 8 9 10 11 12

The symbol for **is less than** is $<$. The symbol for **is greater than** is $>$. These symbols are used to show the order relation between two numbers. [1.1A, p. 2]

$3 < 7$
$9 > 2$

When a whole number is written using the digits 0, 1, 2, 3, 4, 5, 6, 7, 8, and 9, it is said to be in **standard form.** The position of each digit in the number determines the digit's **place value.** The place values are used to write the expanded form of a number. [1.1B, p. 3]

The number 598,317 is in standard form. The digit 8 is in the thousands place. The number 598,317 is written in expanded form as $500,000 + 90,000 + 8000 + 300 + 10 + 7$.

Addition is the process of finding the total of two or more numbers. The numbers being added are called **addends.** The result is the **sum.** [1.2A, p. 8]

$$\begin{array}{r} \overset{1\ \ 11}{8,762} \\ +\ 1,359 \\ \hline 10,121 \end{array}$$

Subtraction is the process of finding the difference between two numbers. The **minuend** minus the **subtrahend** equals the **difference.** [1.3A, p. 16]

$$\begin{array}{r} 4\ \ \overset{11}{\cancel{1}}\ \ 11\ \ 6\ \ 13 \\ \cancel{5}\ \ 2, \cancel{1}\ \ 7\ \ 3 \\ -\ 3\ \ 4, 9\ \ 6\ \ 8 \\ \hline 1\ \ 7, 2\ \ 0\ \ 5 \end{array}$$

Multiplication is repeated addition of the same number. The numbers that are multiplied are called **factors**. The result is the **product**. [1.4A, p. 25]

$$\begin{array}{r} {\scriptstyle 4\ 5} \\ 358 \\ \times\ \ 7 \\ \hline 2506 \end{array}$$

Division is used to separate objects into equal groups. The **dividend** divided by the **divisor** equals the **quotient**. [1.5A, p. 33]

For any division problem,
(**quotient** · **divisor**) + **remainder** = **dividend**. [1.5B, p. 36]

$$\begin{array}{r} 93\ \text{r}3 \\ 7\overline{)654} \\ -63 \\ \hline 24 \\ -21 \\ \hline 3 \end{array}$$

Check: $(7 \cdot 93) + 3 = 651 + 3 = 654$

The expression 4^3 is in **exponential notation**. The **exponent**, 3, indicates how many times 4 occurs as a factor in the multiplication. [1.6A, p. 47]

$5^4 = 5 \cdot 5 \cdot 5 \cdot 5 = 625$

Whole-number **factors** of a number divide that number evenly (there is no remainder). [1.7A, p. 53]

$18 \div 1 = 18$
$18 \div 2 = 9$
$18 \div 3 = 6$
$18 \div 4$ 4 does not divide 18 evenly.
$18 \div 5$ 5 does not divide 18 evenly.
$18 \div 6 = 3$ The factors are repeating.

The factors of 18 are 1, 2, 3, 6, 9, and 18.

A number greater than 1 is a **prime number** if its only whole-number factors are 1 and itself. If a number is not prime, it is a **composite number**. [1.7B, p. 54]

The prime numbers less than 20 are 2, 3, 5, 7, 11, 13, 17, and 19.
The composite numbers less than 20 are 4, 6, 8, 9, 10, 12, 14, 15, 16, and 18.

The **prime factorization** of a number is the expression of the number as a product of its prime factors. [1.7B, p. 54]

$$\begin{array}{r} 42 \\ 2\,|\,\overline{21} \\ 3\,|\,\overline{7} \\ 7\,|\,\overline{1} \end{array}$$

The prime factorization of 42 is $2 \cdot 3 \cdot 7$.

Essential Rules and Procedures

Examples

To round a number to a given place value: If the digit to the right of the given place value is less than 5, replace that digit and all digits to the right by zeros. If the digit to the right of the given place value is greater than or equal to 5, increase the digit in the given place value by 1, and replace all other digits to the right by zeros. [1.1D, p. 4]

36,178 rounded to the nearest thousand is 36,000.

4592 rounded to the nearest thousand is 5000.

Properties of Addition [1.2A, p. 8]

Commutative Property of Addition
Two numbers can be added in either order; the sum will be the same.

$8 + 3 = 3 + 8$

Associative Property of Addition
Grouping an addition in any order gives the same result.

$(2 + 4) + 6 = 2 + (4 + 6)$

Addition Property of Zero
Zero added to a number does not change the number.

$7 + 0 = 7$

To estimate the answer to an addition calculation: Round each number to the same place value. Perform the calculation using the rounded numbers. [1.2A, p. 8]

$$\begin{array}{r} 39{,}471 \\ 12{,}586 \end{array} \qquad \begin{array}{r} 40{,}000 \\ + \ 10{,}000 \\ \hline 50{,}000 \end{array}$$

50,000 is an estimate of the sum of 39,471 and 12,586.

Properties of Multiplication [1.4A, pp. 25–26]

Commutative Property of Multiplication
Two numbers can be multiplied in either order; the product will be the same.

$2 \cdot 8 = 8 \cdot 2$

Associative Property of Multiplication
Grouping numbers to be multiplied in any order gives the same result.

$(2 \cdot 4) \cdot 6 = 2 \cdot (4 \cdot 6)$

Multiplication Property of Zero
A number multiplied by zero is zero.

$3 \cdot 0 = 0$

Multiplication Property of One
Multiplying a number by 1 does not change the number.

$6 \cdot 1 = 6$

Division Properties of Zero and One [1.5A, p. 33]
Any whole number, except zero, divided by itself is 1.
Zero divided by any whole number other than zero is zero.

$3 \div 3 = 1$
$0 \div 3 = 0$

Order of Operations Agreement [1.6B, p. 48]

Step 1. Perform operations inside grouping symbols such as parentheses.

Step 2. Simplify exponential expressions.

Step 3. Do multiplication and division as they occur from left to right.

Step 4. Do addition and subtraction as they occur from left to right.

$$5^2 - 3(2 + 4) = 5^2 - 3(6)$$
$$= 25 - 3(6)$$
$$= 25 - 18$$
$$= 7$$

1 | Review Exercises

1. Simplify: $3 \cdot 2^3 \cdot 5^2$

2. Write 10,327 in expanded form.

3. Find all the factors of 18.

4. Find the sum of 5894, 6301, and 298.

5. Subtract: 4926
              $-\ 3177$

6. Divide: $7\overline{)14{,}945}$

7. Place the correct symbol, $<$ or $>$, between the two numbers: 101   87

8. Write $5 \cdot 5 \cdot 7 \cdot 7 \cdot 7 \cdot 7 \cdot 7$ in exponential notation.

9. What is 2019 multiplied by 307?

10. What is 10,134 decreased by 4725?

11. Add: 298
              461
           $+\ 322$

12. Simplify: $2^3 - 3 \cdot 2$

13. Round 45,672 to the nearest hundred.

14. Write 276,057 in words.

15. Find the quotient of 109,763 and 84.

16. Write two million eleven thousand forty-four in standard form.

17. What is 3906 divided by 8?

18. Simplify: $3^2 + 2^2 \cdot (5 - 3)$

19. Simplify: $8 \cdot (6 - 2)^2 \div 4$

20. Find the prime factorization of 72.

21. What is 3895 minus 1762?

22. Multiply: 843
                  $\times\ \ 27$

23. Wages   Vincent Meyers, a sales assistant, earns $480 for working a 40-hour week. Last week, Vincent worked an additional 12 hours at $24 an hour. Find Vincent's total pay for last week's work.

24. Fuel Efficiency   Louis Reyes, a sales executive, drove a car 351 miles on 13 gallons of gas. Find the number of miles driven per gallon of gasoline.

25. Consumerism   A car is purchased for $29,880, with a down payment of $3000. The balance is paid in 48 equal monthly payments. Find the monthly car payment.

26. Compensation   An insurance account executive received commissions of $723, $544, $812, and $488 during a 4-week period. Find the total income from commissions for the 4 weeks.

27. Banking   You had a balance of $516 in your checking account before making deposits of $88 and $213. Find the total amount deposited, and determine your new account balance.

28. Car Payments   You have a car payment of $246 per month. What is the total of the car payments over a 12-month period?

College Enrollment   The table at the right shows the approximate numbers of males and females enrolled in U.S. colleges in 2005 and 2009. Use this information for Exercises 29 to 32.

Year	Males	Females
2005	7,455,925	10,031,550
2009	8,769,504	11,658,207

Source: National Center for Education Statistics

29. In which year, 2005 or 2009, were more males enrolled in U.S. colleges?

30. What is the difference between the number of males and the number of females enrolled in U.S. colleges in 2005?

31. Find the increase in the number of males enrolled in U.S. colleges from 2005 to 2009.

32. How many more students were enrolled in U.S. colleges in 2009 than in 2005?

1 | TEST

1. Simplify: $3^3 \cdot 4^2$

2. Write 207,068 in words.

3. Subtract: 23,006
           $-$ 7,937

4. Find all the factors of 20.

5. Multiply: 9736
            $\times$ 704

6. Simplify: $4^2 \cdot (4 - 2) \div 8 + 5$

7. Write 906,378 in expanded form.

8. Round 74,965 to the nearest hundred.

9. Divide: $97\overline{)108{,}764}$

10. Write $3 \cdot 3 \cdot 3 \cdot 7 \cdot 7$ in exponential form.

11. Find the sum of 8756, 9094, and 37,065.

12. Find the prime factorization of 84.

13. Simplify: $16 \div 4 \cdot 2 - (7 - 5)^2$

14. Find the product of 8 and 90,763.

15. Write one million two hundred four thousand six in standard form.

16. Divide: $7\overline{)60{,}972}$

17. Place the correct symbol, $<$ or $>$, between the two numbers: 21   19

18. Find the quotient of 5624 and 8.

19. Add: 25,492
            $+71,306$

20. Find the difference between 29,736 and 9814.

Education The table at the right shows the projected enrollment in public and private elementary and secondary schools for the fall of 2013 and the fall of 2016. Use this information for Exercises 21 and 22.

Year	Pre-Kindergarten through Grade 8	Grades 9 through 12
2013	41,873,000	16,000,000
2016	43,097,000	16,684,000

Source: The National Center for Education Statistics

21. Find the difference between the projected total enrollment in 2016 and in 2013.

22. In 2016, how many students are projected to be enrolled in pre-kindergarten through grade 12?

23. Farming A farmer harvested 48,290 pounds of lemons from one grove and 23,710 pounds of lemons from another grove. The lemons were packed in boxes with 24 pounds of lemons in each box. How many boxes were needed to pack the lemons?

Matt Jones/Shutterstock.com

24. Biology A hummingbird beats its wings approximately 52 times per second. How many times will a hummingbird beat its wings in 900 seconds (15 minutes)?

25. Traffic A radar detector was set up on a highway to determine the average speed of motorists on a certain segment of the highway. The recorded speeds, in miles per hour, for 12 cars were 68, 73, 59, 77, 65, 52, 71, 68, 76, 64, 59, and 60. What was the average speed for these 12 cars?

Fractions

OBJECTIVES

SECTION 2.1

A To find the least common multiple (LCM)

B To find the greatest common factor (GCF)

SECTION 2.2

A To write a fraction that represents part of a whole

B To write an improper fraction as a mixed number or a whole number, and a mixed number as an improper fraction

SECTION 2.3

A To find equivalent fractions by raising to higher terms

B To write a fraction in simplest form

SECTION 2.4

A To add fractions with the same denominator

B To add fractions with different denominators

C To add whole numbers, mixed numbers, and fractions

D To solve application problems

SECTION 2.5

A To subtract fractions with the same denominator

B To subtract fractions with different denominators

C To subtract whole numbers, mixed numbers, and fractions

D To solve application problems

Focus on Success

Have you formed or are you part of a study group? Remember that a study group can be a great way to stay focused on succeeding in this course. You can support each other, get help and offer help on homework, and prepare for tests together. (See Homework Time, page AIM-5.)

© iStockphoto.com/Christoper Futcher

Prep Test

Are you ready to succeed in this chapter? Take the Prep Test below to find out if you are ready to learn the new material.

For Exercises 1 to 6, add, subtract, multiply, or divide.

1. 4×5

2. $2 \cdot 2 \cdot 2 \cdot 3 \cdot 5$

3. 9×1

4. $6 + 4$

5. $10 - 3$

6. $63 \div 30$

7. Which of the following numbers divide evenly into 12?
1 2 3 4 5 6 7 8 9 10 11 12

8. Simplify: $8 \times 7 + 3$

9. Complete: $8 = ? + 1$

10. Place the correct symbol, $<$ or $>$, between the two numbers.
44   48

SECTION

2.1 The Least Common Multiple and Greatest Common Factor

OBJECTIVE A *To find the least common multiple (LCM)*

 Tips for Success

Before you begin a new chapter, you should take some time to review previously learned skills. One way to do this is to complete the Prep Test. See page 65. This test focuses on the particular skills that will be required for the new chapter.

The **multiples of a number** are the products of that number and the numbers 1, 2, 3, 4, 5, ...

$$3 \times 1 = 3$$
$$3 \times 2 = 6$$
$$3 \times 3 = 9$$
$$3 \times 4 = 12 \qquad \text{The multiples of 3 are 3, 6, 9, 12, 15, ...}$$
$$3 \times 5 = 15$$

A number that is a multiple of two or more numbers is a **common multiple** of those numbers.

The multiples of 4 are 4, 8, 12, 16, 20, 24, 28, 32, 36, ...
The multiples of 6 are 6, 12, 18, 24, 30, 36, 42, ...
Some common multiples of 4 and 6 are 12, 24, and 36.

The **least common multiple (LCM)** is the smallest common multiple of two or more numbers.

The least common multiple of 4 and 6 is 12.

Listing the multiples of each number is one way to find the LCM. Another way to find the LCM uses the prime factorization of each number.

To find the LCM of 450 and 600, find the prime factorization of each number and write the factorization of each number in a table. Circle the greatest product in each column. The LCM is the product of the circled numbers.

	2	3	5
450 =	2	(3 · 3)	(5 · 5)
600 =	(2 · 2 · 2)	3	5 · 5

• In the column headed by 5, the products are equal. Circle just one product.

The LCM is the product of the circled numbers.
The LCM = 2 · 2 · 2 · 3 · 3 · 5 · 5 = 1800.

EXAMPLE 1

Find the LCM of 24, 36, and 50.

Solution

	2	3	5
24 =	(2 · 2 · 2)	3	
36 =	2 · 2	(3 · 3)	
50 =	2		(5 · 5)

The LCM = 2 · 2 · 2 · 3 · 3 · 5 · 5 = 1800.

YOU TRY IT 1

Find the LCM of 12, 27, and 50.

Your solution

Solution on p. S4

OBJECTIVE B   *To find the greatest common factor (GCF)*

Recall that a number that divides another number evenly is a factor of that number. The number 64 can be evenly divided by 1, 2, 4, 8, 16, 32, and 64, so the numbers 1, 2, 4, 8, 16, 32, and 64 are factors of 64.

A number that is a factor of two or more numbers is a **common factor** of those numbers.

The factors of 30 are 1, 2, 3, 5, 6, 10, 15, and 30.

The factors of 105 are 1, 3, 5, 7, 15, 21, 35, and 105.

The common factors of 30 and 105 are 1, 3, 5, and 15.

The **greatest common factor (GCF)** is the largest common factor of two or more numbers.

The greatest common factor of 30 and 105 is 15.

Listing the factors of each number is one way of finding the GCF. Another way to find the GCF is to use the prime factorization of each number.

To find the GCF of 126 and 180, find the prime factorization of each number and write the factorization of each number in a table. Circle the least product in each column that does not have a blank. The GCF is the product of the circled numbers.

	2	3	5	7
$126 =$	(2)	(3 · 3)		7
$180 =$	2 · 2	3 · 3	5	

• In the column headed by 3, the products are equal. Circle just one product. Columns 5 and 7 have a blank, so 5 and 7 are not common factors of 126 and 180. Do not circle any number in these columns.

The GCF is the product of the circled numbers.
The GCF = 2 · 3 · 3 = 18.

EXAMPLE 2

Find the GCF of 90, 168, and 420.

Solution

	2	3	5	7
$90 =$	(2)	3 · 3	5	
$168 =$	2 · 2 · 2	(3)		7
$420 =$	2 · 2	3	5	7

The GCF = 2 · 3 = 6.

YOU TRY IT 2

Find the GCF of 36, 60, and 72.

Your solution

EXAMPLE 3

Find the GCF of 7, 12, and 20.

Solution

	2	3	5	7
$7 =$				7
$12 =$	2 · 2	3		
$20 =$	2 · 2		5	

Because no numbers are circled, the GCF = 1.

YOU TRY IT 3

Find the GCF of 11, 24, and 30.

Your solution

Solutions on p. S4

2.1 EXERCISES

✔ Concept Check

For Exercises 1 to 4, list the first four multiples of the given number.

1. 5
2. 7
3. 10
4. 15

5. List the first ten multiples of 6 and the first ten multiples of 8. What are the common multiples of 6 and 8 in the lists? What is the least common multiple of 6 and 8?

For Exercises 6 to 9, list the factors of the given number.

6. 12
7. 20
8. 23
9. 28

10. List the factors of 18 and the factors of 24. What are the common factors of 18 and 24? What is the greatest common factor of 18 and 24?

OBJECTIVE A　　*To find the least common multiple (LCM)*

For Exercises 11 to 40, find the LCM.

11. 5, 8
12. 3, 6
13. 3, 8
14. 2, 5
15. 4, 6

16. 6, 8
17. 8, 12
18. 12, 16
19. 5, 12
20. 3, 16

21. 8, 14
22. 4, 10
23. 8, 32
24. 7, 21
25. 9, 36

26. 14, 42
27. 44, 60
28. 120, 160
29. 102, 184
30. 123, 234

31. 4, 8, 12
32. 5, 10, 15
33. 3, 5, 10
34. 2, 5, 8
35. 3, 8, 12

36. 5, 12, 18
37. 9, 36, 64
38. 18, 54, 63
39. 3, 7, 20
40. 4, 9, 35

41. True or false? If two numbers have no common factors, then the LCM of the two numbers is their product.

42. True or false? If one number is a multiple of a second number, then the LCM of the two numbers is the second number.

OBJECTIVE B *To find the greatest common factor (GCF)*

For Exercises 43 to 72, find the GCF.

43. 3, 5   **44.** 5, 7   **45.** 6, 9   **46.** 18, 24   **47.** 15, 25

48. 14, 49   **49.** 25, 100   **50.** 16, 80   **51.** 32, 51   **52.** 21, 44

53. 12, 80   **54.** 8, 36   **55.** 16, 140   **56.** 48, 144   **57.** 44, 96

58. 18, 32   **59.** 3, 5, 11   **60.** 6, 8, 10   **61.** 7, 14, 49   **62.** 6, 15, 36

63. 10, 15, 20   **64.** 12, 18, 20   **65.** 24, 40, 72   **66.** 3, 17, 51   **67.** 17, 31, 81

68. 14, 42, 84   **69.** 25, 125, 625   **70.** 12, 68, 92   **71.** 32, 56, 72   **72.** 24, 36, 48

73. True or false? If two numbers have a GCF of 1, then the LCM of the two numbers is their product.

74. True or false? If the LCM of two numbers is one of the two numbers, then the GCF of the numbers is the other of the two numbers.

Critical Thinking

75. Work Schedules Joe Salvo, a lifeguard, works 3 days and then has a day off. Joe's friend Raya works 5 days and then has a day off. How many days after Joe and Raya have a day off together will they have another day off together?

76. Find the LCM of each of the following pairs of prime numbers: 2 and 3, 5 and 7, and 11 and 19. Based on these examples, what is the LCM of two prime numbers?

77. Find the GCF of each of the following pairs of prime numbers: 3 and 5, 7 and 11, and 29 and 43. Based on these examples, what is the GCF of two prime numbers?

Projects or Group Activities

78. Using the pattern for the first two triangles shown below, determine the center number of the last triangle.

79. Two numbers are called *coprime* if the GCF of the two numbers is 1. Determine whether each pair of numbers is coprime.
    a. 48, 50   **b.** 25, 36   **c.** 22, 27   **d.** 71, 73

SECTION

2.2 Introduction to Fractions

OBJECTIVE A *To write a fraction that represents part of a whole*

 Take Note
The *fraction bar* separates the numerator from the denominator. The *numerator* is the part of the fraction that appears above the fraction bar. The *denominator* is the part of the fraction that appears below the fraction bar.

 Point of Interest
The fraction bar was first used in 1050 by al-Hassar. It is also called a vinculum.

A **fraction** can represent the number of equal parts of a whole.

The shaded portion of the circle is represented by the fraction $\frac{4}{7}$. Four of the seven equal parts of the circle (that is, four-sevenths of it) are shaded.

Each part of a fraction has a name.

Fraction bar $\rightarrow \dfrac{4}{7} \begin{array}{l} \leftarrow \textbf{Numerator} \\ \leftarrow \textbf{Denominator} \end{array}$

A **proper fraction** is a fraction less than 1. The numerator of a proper fraction is smaller than the denominator. The shaded portion of the circle can be represented by the proper fraction $\frac{3}{4}$.

A **mixed number** is a number greater than 1 with a whole-number part and a fractional part. The shaded portion of the circles can be represented by the mixed number $2\frac{1}{4}$.

An **improper fraction** is a fraction greater than or equal to 1. The numerator of an improper fraction is greater than or equal to the denominator. The shaded portion of the circles can be represented by the improper fraction $\frac{9}{4}$. The shaded portion of the square can be represented by $\frac{4}{4}$.

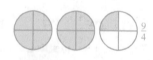

EXAMPLE 1

Express the shaded portion of the circles as a mixed number.

Solution $3\frac{2}{5}$

YOU TRY IT 1

Express the shaded portion of the circles as a mixed number.

Your solution

EXAMPLE 2

Express the shaded portion of the circles as an improper fraction.

Solution $\dfrac{17}{5}$

YOU TRY IT 2

Express the shaded portion of the circles as an improper fraction.

Your solution

Solutions on p. S4

OBJECTIVE B   *To write an improper fraction as a mixed number or a whole number, and a mixed number as an improper fraction*

 Point of Interest

Archimedes (c. 287–212 B.C.) is the person who calculated that $\pi \approx 3\frac{1}{7}$. He actually showed that $3\frac{10}{71} < \pi < 3\frac{1}{7}$. The approximation $3\frac{10}{71}$ is more accurate but more difficult to use.

Note from the diagram that the mixed number $2\frac{3}{5}$ and the improper fraction $\frac{13}{5}$ both represent the shaded portion of the circles, so $2\frac{3}{5} = \frac{13}{5}$.

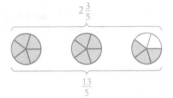

An improper fraction can be written as a mixed number or a whole number.

HOW TO 1   Write $\frac{13}{5}$ as a mixed number.

Divide the numerator by the denominator.	To write the fractional part of the mixed number, write the remainder over the divisor.	Write the answer.
$\begin{array}{r} 2 \\ 5\overline{)13} \\ -10 \\ \hline 3 \end{array}$	$\begin{array}{r} 2\frac{3}{5} \\ 5\overline{)13} \\ -10 \\ \hline 3 \end{array}$	$\dfrac{13}{5} = 2\frac{3}{5}$

To write a mixed number as an improper fraction, multiply the denominator of the fractional part by the whole-number part. The sum of this product and the numerator of the fractional part is the numerator of the improper fraction. The denominator remains the same.

HOW TO 2   Write $7\frac{3}{8}$ as an improper fraction.

$$7\frac{3}{8} = \frac{(8 \times 7) + 3}{8} = \frac{56 + 3}{8} = \frac{59}{8} \qquad 7\frac{3}{8} = \frac{59}{8}$$

EXAMPLE 3

Write $\frac{21}{4}$ as a mixed number.

Solution
$$\begin{array}{r} 5 \\ 4\overline{)21} \\ -20 \\ \hline 1 \end{array} \qquad \frac{21}{4} = 5\frac{1}{4}$$

YOU TRY IT 3

Write $\frac{22}{5}$ as a mixed number.

Your solution

EXAMPLE 4

Write $\frac{18}{6}$ as a whole number.

Solution $\dfrac{18}{6} = 18 \div 6 = 3$

YOU TRY IT 4

Write $\frac{28}{7}$ as a whole number.

Your solution

EXAMPLE 5

Write $21\frac{3}{4}$ as an improper fraction.

Solution $21\frac{3}{4} = \dfrac{84 + 3}{4} = \dfrac{87}{4}$

YOU TRY IT 5

Write $14\frac{5}{8}$ as an improper fraction.

Your solution

Solutions on pp. S4–S5

2.2 EXERCISES

✔ Concept Check

For Exercises 1 to 4, identify the fraction as a proper fraction, an improper fraction, or a mixed number. State whether the fraction is less than 1, equal to 1, or greater than 1.

1. $\dfrac{12}{7}$

2. $5\dfrac{2}{11}$

3. $\dfrac{29}{40}$

4. $\dfrac{13}{13}$

OBJECTIVE A   *To write a fraction that represents part of a whole*

For Exercises 5 to 8, express the shaded portion of the circle as a fraction.

5.

6.

7.

8.

For Exercises 9 to 14, express the shaded portion of the circles as a mixed number.

9.

10.

11.

12.

13.

14.

For Exercises 15 to 20, express the shaded portion of the circles as an improper fraction.

15.

16.

17.

18.

19.

20.

21. Shade $1\dfrac{2}{5}$ of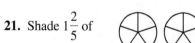

22. Shade $1\dfrac{3}{4}$ of

23. Shade $\dfrac{6}{5}$ of

24. Shade $\dfrac{7}{3}$ of

25. 🔲 True or false? The fractional part of a mixed number is an improper fraction.

OBJECTIVE B *To write an improper fraction as a mixed number or a whole number, and a mixed number as an improper fraction*

For Exercises 26 to 49, write the improper fraction as a mixed number or a whole number.

26. $\dfrac{11}{4}$ **27.** $\dfrac{16}{3}$ **28.** $\dfrac{20}{4}$ **29.** $\dfrac{18}{9}$ **30.** $\dfrac{9}{8}$ **31.** $\dfrac{13}{4}$

32. $\dfrac{23}{10}$ **33.** $\dfrac{29}{2}$ **34.** $\dfrac{48}{16}$ **35.** $\dfrac{51}{3}$ **36.** $\dfrac{8}{7}$ **37.** $\dfrac{16}{9}$

38. $\dfrac{7}{3}$ **39.** $\dfrac{9}{5}$ **40.** $\dfrac{16}{1}$ **41.** $\dfrac{23}{1}$ **42.** $\dfrac{17}{8}$ **43.** $\dfrac{31}{16}$

44. $\dfrac{12}{5}$ **45.** $\dfrac{19}{3}$ **46.** $\dfrac{9}{9}$ **47.** $\dfrac{40}{8}$ **48.** $\dfrac{72}{8}$ **49.** $\dfrac{3}{3}$

For Exercises 50 to 73, write the mixed number as an improper fraction.

50. $2\dfrac{1}{3}$ **51.** $4\dfrac{2}{3}$ **52.** $6\dfrac{1}{2}$ **53.** $8\dfrac{2}{3}$ **54.** $6\dfrac{5}{6}$ **55.** $7\dfrac{3}{8}$

56. $9\dfrac{1}{4}$ **57.** $6\dfrac{1}{4}$ **58.** $10\dfrac{1}{2}$ **59.** $15\dfrac{1}{8}$ **60.** $8\dfrac{1}{9}$ **61.** $3\dfrac{5}{12}$

62. $5\dfrac{3}{11}$ **63.** $3\dfrac{7}{9}$ **64.** $2\dfrac{5}{8}$ **65.** $12\dfrac{2}{3}$ **66.** $1\dfrac{5}{8}$ **67.** $5\dfrac{3}{7}$

68. $11\dfrac{1}{9}$ **69.** $12\dfrac{3}{5}$ **70.** $3\dfrac{3}{8}$ **71.** $4\dfrac{5}{9}$ **72.** $6\dfrac{7}{13}$ **73.** $8\dfrac{5}{14}$

74. True or false? If an improper fraction is equivalent to 1, then the numerator and the denominator are the same number.

Critical Thinking

75. Name three situations in which fractions are used. Provide an example of a fraction that is used in each situation.

Projects or Group Activities

76. Using a denominator of 5, write improper fractions that represent the numbers 1, 2, 3, and 4.

77. Using a denominator of 8, write an improper fraction that represents a number greater than 2 but less than 3. *Hint*: There is more than one answer.

2.3   Writing Equivalent Fractions

OBJECTIVE A   *To find equivalent fractions by raising to higher terms*

Equal fractions with different denominators are called **equivalent fractions.**

$\frac{4}{6}$ is equivalent to $\frac{2}{3}$.

Remember that the Multiplication Property of One states that the product of a number and 1 is the number. This is true for fractions as well as whole numbers. This property can be used to write equivalent fractions.

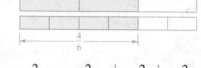

$$\frac{2}{3} \times 1 = \frac{2}{3} \times \frac{1}{1} = \frac{2 \cdot 1}{3 \cdot 1} = \frac{2}{3}$$

$$\frac{2}{3} \times 1 = \frac{2}{3} \times \boxed{\frac{2}{2}} = \frac{2 \cdot 2}{3 \cdot 2} = \frac{4}{6} \qquad \frac{4}{6} \text{ is equivalent to } \frac{2}{3}.$$

$$\frac{2}{3} \times 1 = \frac{2}{3} \times \boxed{\frac{4}{4}} = \frac{2 \cdot 4}{3 \cdot 4} = \frac{8}{12} \qquad \frac{8}{12} \text{ is equivalent to } \frac{2}{3}.$$

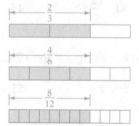

$\frac{2}{3}$ was rewritten as the equivalent fractions $\frac{4}{6}$ and $\frac{8}{12}$.

HOW TO 1   Write a fraction that is equivalent to $\frac{5}{8}$ and has a denominator of 32.

$32 \div 8 = 4$ • Divide the larger denominator by the smaller.

$$\frac{5}{8} = \frac{5 \cdot 4}{8 \cdot 4} = \frac{20}{32}$$

• Multiply the numerator and denominator of the given fraction by the quotient (4).

$\frac{20}{32}$ is equivalent to $\frac{5}{8}$.

EXAMPLE 1

Write $\frac{2}{3}$ as an equivalent fraction that has a denominator of 42.

Solution $42 \div 3 = 14, \dfrac{2}{3} = \dfrac{2 \cdot 14}{3 \cdot 14} = \dfrac{28}{42}$

$\frac{28}{42}$ is equivalent to $\frac{2}{3}$.

YOU TRY IT 1

Write $\frac{3}{5}$ as an equivalent fraction that has a denominator of 45.

Your solution

EXAMPLE 2

Write 4 as a fraction that has a denominator of 12.

Solution   Write 4 as $\frac{4}{1}$.

$$12 \div 1 = 12, \ 4 = \frac{4 \cdot 12}{1 \cdot 12} = \frac{48}{12}$$

$\frac{48}{12}$ is equivalent to 4.

YOU TRY IT 2

Write 6 as a fraction that has a denominator of 18.

Your solution

Solutions on p. S5

OBJECTIVE B *To write a fraction in simplest form*

Writing the **simplest form of a fraction** means writing it so that the numerator and denominator have no common factors other than 1.

The fractions $\frac{4}{6}$ and $\frac{2}{3}$ are equivalent fractions.

$\frac{4}{6}$ has been written in simplest form as $\frac{2}{3}$.

The Multiplication Property of One can be used to write fractions in simplest form. Write the numerator and denominator of the given fraction as a product of factors. Write factors common to both the numerator and denominator as an improper fraction equivalent to 1.

$$\frac{4}{6} = \frac{2 \cdot 2}{2 \cdot 3} = \boxed{\frac{2}{2}} \cdot \frac{2}{3} = \boxed{\frac{2}{2}} \cdot \frac{2}{3} = 1 \cdot \frac{2}{3} = \frac{2}{3}$$

The process of eliminating common factors is displayed with slashes through the common factors as shown at the right.

To write a fraction in simplest form, eliminate the common factors.

An improper fraction can be changed to a mixed number.

$$\frac{4}{6} = \frac{2 \cdot \overset{1}{\cancel{2}}}{\underset{1}{\cancel{2}} \cdot 3} = \frac{2}{3}$$

$$\frac{18}{30} = \frac{\overset{1}{\cancel{2}} \cdot \overset{1}{\cancel{3}} \cdot 3}{\underset{1}{\cancel{2}} \cdot \underset{1}{\cancel{3}} \cdot 5} = \frac{3}{5}$$

$$\frac{22}{6} = \frac{\overset{1}{\cancel{2}} \cdot 11}{\underset{1}{\cancel{2}} \cdot 3} = \frac{11}{3} = 3\frac{2}{3}$$

EXAMPLE 3

Write $\frac{15}{40}$ in simplest form.

Solution $\qquad \frac{15}{40} = \frac{3 \cdot \overset{1}{\cancel{5}}}{2 \cdot 2 \cdot 2 \cdot \underset{1}{\cancel{5}}} = \frac{3}{8}$

YOU TRY IT 3

Write $\frac{16}{24}$ in simplest form.

Your solution

EXAMPLE 4

Write $\frac{6}{42}$ in simplest form.

Solution $\qquad \frac{6}{42} = \frac{\overset{1}{\cancel{2}} \cdot \overset{1}{\cancel{3}}}{\underset{1}{\cancel{2}} \cdot \underset{1}{\cancel{3}} \cdot 7} = \frac{1}{7}$

YOU TRY IT 4

Write $\frac{8}{56}$ in simplest form.

Your solution

EXAMPLE 5

Write $\frac{8}{9}$ in simplest form.

Solution $\qquad \frac{8}{9} = \frac{2 \cdot 2 \cdot 2}{3 \cdot 3} = \frac{8}{9}$

$\frac{8}{9}$ is already in simplest form because there are no common factors in the numerator and denominator.

YOU TRY IT 5

Write $\frac{15}{32}$ in simplest form.

Your solution

EXAMPLE 6

Write $\frac{30}{12}$ in simplest form.

Solution $\qquad \frac{30}{12} = \frac{\overset{1}{\cancel{2}} \cdot \overset{1}{\cancel{3}} \cdot 5}{\underset{1}{\cancel{2}} \cdot 2 \cdot \underset{1}{\cancel{3}}} = \frac{5}{2} = 2\frac{1}{2}$

YOU TRY IT 6

Write $\frac{48}{36}$ in simplest form.

Your solution

Solutions on p. S5

2.3 EXERCISES

✔ Concept Check

1. Is there a fraction equivalent to $\frac{3}{5}$ with a denominator of 7? Explain.

2. If a fraction is in simplest form, what is the GCF of the numerator and denominator of the fraction?

OBJECTIVE A   *To find equivalent fractions by raising to higher terms*

For Exercises 3 to 37, write an equivalent fraction with the given denominator.

3. $\dfrac{1}{2} = \dfrac{}{10}$ 4. $\dfrac{1}{4} = \dfrac{}{16}$ 5. $\dfrac{3}{16} = \dfrac{}{48}$ 6. $\dfrac{5}{9} = \dfrac{}{81}$ 7. $\dfrac{3}{8} = \dfrac{}{32}$

8. $\dfrac{7}{11} = \dfrac{}{33}$ 9. $\dfrac{3}{17} = \dfrac{}{51}$ 10. $\dfrac{7}{10} = \dfrac{}{90}$ 11. $\dfrac{3}{4} = \dfrac{}{16}$ 12. $\dfrac{5}{8} = \dfrac{}{32}$

13. $3 = \dfrac{}{9}$ 14. $5 = \dfrac{}{25}$ 15. $\dfrac{1}{3} = \dfrac{}{60}$ 16. $\dfrac{1}{16} = \dfrac{}{48}$ 17. $\dfrac{11}{15} = \dfrac{}{60}$

18. $\dfrac{3}{50} = \dfrac{}{300}$ 19. $\dfrac{2}{3} = \dfrac{}{18}$ 20. $\dfrac{5}{9} = \dfrac{}{36}$ 21. $\dfrac{5}{7} = \dfrac{}{49}$ 22. $\dfrac{7}{8} = \dfrac{}{32}$

23. $\dfrac{5}{9} = \dfrac{}{18}$ 24. $\dfrac{11}{12} = \dfrac{}{36}$ 25. $7 = \dfrac{}{3}$ 26. $9 = \dfrac{}{4}$ 27. $\dfrac{7}{9} = \dfrac{}{45}$

28. $\dfrac{5}{6} = \dfrac{}{42}$ 29. $\dfrac{15}{16} = \dfrac{}{64}$ 30. $\dfrac{11}{18} = \dfrac{}{54}$ 31. $\dfrac{3}{14} = \dfrac{}{98}$ 32. $\dfrac{5}{6} = \dfrac{}{144}$

33. $\dfrac{5}{8} = \dfrac{}{48}$ 34. $\dfrac{7}{12} = \dfrac{}{96}$ 35. $\dfrac{5}{14} = \dfrac{}{42}$ 36. $\dfrac{2}{3} = \dfrac{}{42}$ 37. $\dfrac{17}{24} = \dfrac{}{144}$

38. 🖘 When you multiply the numerator and denominator of a fraction by the same number, you are actually multiplying the fraction by the number _____.

OBJECTIVE B   *To write a fraction in simplest form*

For Exercises 39 to 73, write the fraction in simplest form.

39. $\dfrac{4}{12}$ 40. $\dfrac{8}{22}$ 41. $\dfrac{22}{44}$ 42. $\dfrac{2}{14}$ 43. $\dfrac{2}{12}$

44. $\dfrac{50}{75}$ **45.** $\dfrac{40}{36}$ **46.** $\dfrac{12}{8}$ **47.** $\dfrac{0}{30}$ **48.** $\dfrac{10}{10}$

49. $\dfrac{9}{22}$ **50.** $\dfrac{14}{35}$ **51.** $\dfrac{75}{25}$ **52.** $\dfrac{8}{60}$ **53.** $\dfrac{16}{84}$

54. $\dfrac{20}{44}$ **55.** $\dfrac{12}{35}$ **56.** $\dfrac{8}{36}$ **57.** $\dfrac{28}{44}$ **58.** $\dfrac{12}{16}$

59. $\dfrac{16}{12}$ **60.** $\dfrac{24}{18}$ **61.** $\dfrac{24}{40}$ **62.** $\dfrac{44}{60}$ **63.** $\dfrac{8}{88}$

64. $\dfrac{9}{90}$ **65.** $\dfrac{144}{36}$ **66.** $\dfrac{140}{297}$ **67.** $\dfrac{48}{144}$ **68.** $\dfrac{32}{120}$

69. $\dfrac{60}{100}$ **70.** $\dfrac{33}{110}$ **71.** $\dfrac{36}{16}$ **72.** $\dfrac{80}{45}$ **73.** $\dfrac{32}{160}$

74. Suppose the denominator of a fraction is a multiple of the numerator. When the fraction is written in simplest form, what number is its numerator?

Critical Thinking

75. Make a list of five different fractions that are equivalent to $\frac{2}{3}$.

76. Show that $\frac{15}{24} = \frac{5}{8}$ by using a diagram.

Projects or Group Activities

77. **Geography**   **a.** What fraction of the states in the United States of America have names that begin with the letter M?
b. What fraction of the states have names that begin and end with a vowel?

2.4 Addition of Fractions and Mixed Numbers

OBJECTIVE A   *To add fractions with the same denominator*

Addition of Fractions with the Same Denominator

To add fractions with the same denominator, add the numerators and place the sum over the common denominator.

EXAMPLES

1. $\dfrac{2}{7} + \dfrac{3}{7} = \dfrac{2+3}{7} = \dfrac{5}{7}$

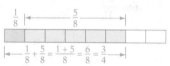

2. $\dfrac{1}{8} + \dfrac{5}{8} = \dfrac{1+5}{8} = \dfrac{6}{8} = \dfrac{3}{4}$

📝 **Take Note**

In Example 2 at the right, note that the answer is reduced to simplest form. Always write your answer in simplest form.

EXAMPLE 1

Add: $\dfrac{5}{18} + \dfrac{7}{18}$

Solution

$\dfrac{5}{18} + \dfrac{7}{18} = \dfrac{5+7}{18} = \dfrac{12}{18}$

$= \dfrac{2}{3}$

• The denominators are the same. Add the numerators. Place the sum over the common denominator.
• Write the answer in simplest form.

YOU TRY IT 1

Add: $\dfrac{3}{8} + \dfrac{7}{8}$

Your solution

Solution on p. S5

OBJECTIVE B   *To add fractions with different denominators*

 Integrating Technology

Some scientific calculators have a fraction key, **aᵇ/c** . It is used to perform operations on fractions. To use this key to simplify the expression at the right, enter

1 **aᵇ/c** 2 + 1 **aᵇ/c** 3 **=**

   $\dfrac{1}{2}$ $\dfrac{1}{3}$

Addition of Fractions with Different Denominators

To add fractions with different denominators, first rewrite the fractions as equivalent fractions with a common denominator. Then add the numerators and place the sum over the common denominator. The LCM of the denominators of the fractions is the **least common denominator (LCD).**

EXAMPLE

Add: $\dfrac{1}{2} + \dfrac{1}{3}$

The LCM of the denominators 2 and 3 is 6.

$\dfrac{1}{2} + \dfrac{1}{3} = \dfrac{3}{6} + \dfrac{2}{6}$ • Write equivalent fractions with 6 as the denominator.

$= \dfrac{3+2}{6} = \dfrac{5}{6}$ • Add the numerators.

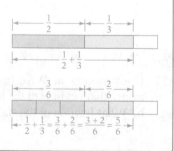

EXAMPLE 2

Add: $\dfrac{5}{8} + \dfrac{7}{9}$

Solution

Write equivalent fractions using 72 (the LCM of the denominators) as the common denominator. Then add.

$$\frac{5}{8} + \frac{7}{9} = \frac{45}{72} + \frac{56}{72} = \frac{45 + 56}{72} = \frac{101}{72} = 1\frac{29}{72}$$

YOU TRY IT 2

Add: $\dfrac{7}{9} + \dfrac{11}{15}$

Your solution

EXAMPLE 3

Find $\dfrac{7}{12}$ more than $\dfrac{3}{8}$.

Solution

Write equivalent fractions using 24 (the LCM of the denominators) as the common denominator. Then add.

$$\frac{3}{8} + \frac{7}{12} = \frac{9}{24} + \frac{14}{24} = \frac{9 + 14}{24} = \frac{23}{24}$$

YOU TRY IT 3

Find the sum of $\dfrac{5}{12}$ and $\dfrac{9}{16}$.

Your solution

EXAMPLE 4

Add: $\dfrac{2}{3} + \dfrac{3}{5} + \dfrac{5}{6}$

Solution

Write equivalent fractions using 30 (the LCM of the denominators) as the common denominator. Then add.

$$\frac{2}{3} + \frac{3}{5} + \frac{5}{6} = \frac{20}{30} + \frac{18}{30} + \frac{25}{30} = \frac{20 + 18 + 25}{30}$$

$$= \frac{63}{30} = 2\frac{3}{30} = 2\frac{1}{10}$$

YOU TRY IT 4

Add: $\dfrac{3}{4} + \dfrac{4}{5} + \dfrac{5}{8}$

Your solution

Solutions on p. S5

OBJECTIVE C   *To add whole numbers, mixed numbers, and fractions*

The sum of a whole number and a fraction is a mixed number.

 Take Note

The procedure at the right illustrates why $2 + \dfrac{2}{3} = 2\dfrac{2}{3}$.

You do not need to show these steps when adding a whole number and a fraction. Here are two more examples:

$$7 + \frac{1}{5} = 7\frac{1}{5}$$

$$6 + \frac{3}{4} = 6\frac{3}{4}$$

HOW TO 1   Add: $2 + \dfrac{2}{3}$

$$2 + \frac{2}{3} = \frac{6}{3} + \frac{2}{3} = \frac{8}{3} = 2\frac{2}{3}$$

To add a whole number and a mixed number, write the fraction and then add the whole numbers.

HOW TO 2   Add: $7\dfrac{2}{5} + 4$

Write the fraction.
$$\begin{array}{r} 7\dfrac{2}{5} \\ + 4 \\ \hline \dfrac{2}{5} \end{array}$$

Add the whole numbers.
$$\begin{array}{r} 7\dfrac{2}{5} \\ + 4 \\ \hline 11\dfrac{2}{5} \end{array}$$

Integrating Technology
Use the fraction key on a calculator to enter mixed numbers. For the example at the right, enter

$$5\frac{4}{9}$$

6 $a^{b/c}$ 14 $a^{b/c}$ 15 =

$$6\frac{14}{15}$$

To add two mixed numbers, add the fractional parts and then add the whole numbers. Remember to reduce the sum to simplest form.

HOW TO 3 What is $6\frac{14}{15}$ added to $5\frac{4}{9}$?

The LCM of the denominators 9 and 15 is 45.

Add the fractional parts.

$$5\frac{4}{9} = 5\frac{20}{45}$$
$$+6\frac{14}{15} = 6\frac{42}{45}$$
$$\overline{\qquad \frac{62}{45}}$$

Add the whole numbers.

$$5\frac{4}{9} = 5\frac{20}{45}$$
$$+6\frac{14}{15} = 6\frac{42}{45}$$
$$\overline{11\frac{62}{45} = 11 + \frac{62}{45} = 11 + 1\frac{17}{45} = 12\frac{17}{45}}$$

APPLY THE CONCEPT

A pastry chef is making a blueberry cake that requires $1\frac{1}{3}$ cups of flour for the streusel topping and $1\frac{1}{4}$ cups of flour for the cake. To find the total amount of flour the chef needs, add $1\frac{1}{3}$ and $1\frac{1}{4}$.

$$1\frac{1}{3} + 1\frac{1}{4} = 1\frac{4}{12} + 1\frac{3}{12} = 2\frac{7}{12}$$

The chef needs $2\frac{7}{12}$ cups of flour.

EXAMPLE 5

Add: $5 + \frac{3}{8}$

Solution $\quad 5 + \frac{3}{8} = 5\frac{3}{8}$

YOU TRY IT 5

What is 7 added to $\frac{6}{11}$?

Your solution

EXAMPLE 6

Find 17 increased by $3\frac{3}{8}$.

Solution $\quad 17 + 3\frac{3}{8} = 20\frac{3}{8}$

YOU TRY IT 6

Find the sum of 29 and $17\frac{5}{12}$.

Your solution

EXAMPLE 7

Add: $5\frac{2}{3} + 11\frac{5}{6} + 12\frac{7}{9}$

Solution

$$5\frac{2}{3} = 5\frac{12}{18} \quad \bullet \text{ LCD} = 18$$

$$11\frac{5}{6} = 11\frac{15}{18}$$

$$+ 12\frac{7}{9} = 12\frac{14}{18}$$

$$\overline{28\frac{41}{18} = 30\frac{5}{18}}$$

YOU TRY IT 7

Add: $7\frac{4}{5} + 6\frac{7}{10} + 13\frac{11}{15}$

Your solution

Solutions on p. S5

OBJECTIVE D *To solve application problems*

EXAMPLE 8

The lengths of the luff, leech, and foot of the jib for a sailboat are shown at the right. Find the perimeter of the sail. (Perimeter is the distance around an object.)

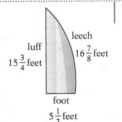

luff 15$\frac{3}{4}$ feet

leech 16$\frac{7}{8}$ feet

foot 5$\frac{1}{2}$ feet

Strategy

To find the perimeter, add the lengths of the luff, leech, and foot ($15\frac{3}{4}$, $16\frac{7}{8}$, and $5\frac{1}{2}$).

Solution

$$15\frac{3}{4} + 16\frac{7}{8} + 5\frac{1}{2} = 15\frac{6}{8} + 16\frac{7}{8} + 5\frac{4}{8}$$

$$= 36\frac{17}{8} = 38\frac{1}{8}$$

The perimeter of the sail is $38\frac{1}{8}$ feet.

YOU TRY IT 8

On Monday, you spent $4\frac{1}{2}$ hours in class, $3\frac{3}{4}$ hours studying, and $1\frac{1}{3}$ hours driving. Find the total number of hours spent on these three activities.

Your strategy

Your solution

EXAMPLE 9

This week, Barbara Walsh worked 4 hours on Tuesday, $2\frac{1}{3}$ hours on Wednesday, and $5\frac{2}{3}$ hours on Friday at a part-time job. Barbara is paid $9 an hour. How much did she earn this week?

Strategy

To find how much Barbara earned:
- Find the total number of hours worked.
- Multiply the total number of hours worked by the hourly wage (9).

Solution

$$\begin{array}{c} 4 \\ 2\frac{1}{3} \\ +5\frac{2}{3} \\ \hline 11\frac{3}{3} = 12 \text{ hours worked} \end{array} \qquad \begin{array}{r} 12 \\ \times\ 9 \\ \hline 108 \end{array}$$

Barbara earned $108 this week.

YOU TRY IT 9

Jeff Sapone, a carpenter, worked $1\frac{2}{3}$ hours of overtime on Monday, $3\frac{1}{3}$ hours of overtime on Tuesday, and 2 hours of overtime on Wednesday. At an overtime hourly rate of $36, find Jeff's overtime pay for the 3 days.

Your strategy

Your solution

Solutions on pp. S5–S6

2.4 EXERCISES

✔ Concept Check

For Exercises 1 and 2, replace the question marks to make a true statement.

1. $\dfrac{2}{9} + \dfrac{5}{9} = \dfrac{?+?}{9} = \dfrac{?}{9}$

2. $\dfrac{1}{8} + \dfrac{3}{8} = \dfrac{?+?}{8} = \dfrac{?}{8} = ?$

For Exercises 3 to 6, find the LCD of the fractions.

3. $\dfrac{1}{4}, \dfrac{3}{8}$

4. $\dfrac{2}{3}, \dfrac{3}{4}$

5. $\dfrac{5}{6}, \dfrac{4}{9}$

6. $\dfrac{1}{2}, \dfrac{3}{5}, \dfrac{3}{14}$

OBJECTIVE A   *To add fractions with the same denominator*

For Exercises 7 to 22, add.

7. $\dfrac{2}{7} + \dfrac{1}{7}$

8. $\dfrac{3}{11} + \dfrac{5}{11}$

9. $\dfrac{2}{9} + \dfrac{4}{9}$

10. $\dfrac{5}{8} + \dfrac{1}{8}$

11. $\dfrac{3}{14} + \dfrac{5}{14}$

12. $\dfrac{3}{20} + \dfrac{9}{20}$

13. $\dfrac{1}{2} + \dfrac{1}{2}$

14. $\dfrac{1}{3} + \dfrac{2}{3}$

15. $\dfrac{8}{11} + \dfrac{7}{11}$

16. $\dfrac{9}{13} + \dfrac{7}{13}$

17. $\dfrac{8}{5} + \dfrac{9}{5}$

18. $\dfrac{5}{3} + \dfrac{7}{3}$

19. $\dfrac{3}{8} + \dfrac{7}{8} + \dfrac{1}{8}$

20. $\dfrac{5}{12} + \dfrac{7}{12} + \dfrac{1}{12}$

21. $\dfrac{4}{15} + \dfrac{7}{15} + \dfrac{11}{15}$

22. $\dfrac{5}{7} + \dfrac{4}{7} + \dfrac{5}{7}$

23. Find the sum of $\frac{5}{12}$, $\frac{1}{12}$, and $\frac{11}{12}$.

24. Find the total of $\frac{5}{8}$, $\frac{3}{8}$, and $\frac{7}{8}$.

For Exercises 25 to 28, each statement concerns a pair of fractions that have the same denominator. State whether the sum of the fractions is a proper fraction, the number 1, a mixed number, or a whole number other than 1.

25. The sum of the numerators is a multiple of the denominator.

26. The sum of the numerators is one more than the denominator.

27. The sum of the numerators is the denominator.

28. The sum of the numerators is smaller than the denominator.

> **OBJECTIVE B** *To add fractions with different denominators*

For Exercises 29 to 48, add.

29. $\dfrac{1}{2} + \dfrac{2}{3}$

30. $\dfrac{2}{3} + \dfrac{1}{4}$

31. $\dfrac{3}{14} + \dfrac{5}{7}$

32. $\dfrac{3}{5} + \dfrac{7}{10}$

33. $\dfrac{8}{15} + \dfrac{7}{20}$

34. $\dfrac{1}{6} + \dfrac{7}{9}$

35. $\dfrac{3}{8} + \dfrac{9}{14}$

36. $\dfrac{5}{12} + \dfrac{5}{16}$

37. $\dfrac{3}{20} + \dfrac{7}{30}$

38. $\dfrac{5}{12} + \dfrac{7}{30}$

39. $\dfrac{1}{3} + \dfrac{5}{6} + \dfrac{7}{9}$

40. $\dfrac{2}{3} + \dfrac{5}{6} + \dfrac{7}{12}$

41. $\dfrac{5}{6} + \dfrac{1}{12} + \dfrac{5}{16}$

42. $\dfrac{2}{9} + \dfrac{7}{15} + \dfrac{4}{21}$

43. $\dfrac{2}{3} + \dfrac{1}{5} + \dfrac{7}{12}$

44. $\dfrac{3}{4} + \dfrac{4}{5} + \dfrac{7}{12}$

45. $\dfrac{2}{3} + \dfrac{3}{5} + \dfrac{7}{8}$

46. $\dfrac{3}{10} + \dfrac{14}{15} + \dfrac{9}{25}$

47. $\dfrac{2}{3} + \dfrac{5}{8} + \dfrac{7}{9}$

48. $\dfrac{1}{3} + \dfrac{2}{9} + \dfrac{7}{8}$

49. What is $\dfrac{3}{8}$ added to $\dfrac{3}{5}$?

50. What is $\dfrac{5}{9}$ added to $\dfrac{7}{12}$?

51. Find the sum of $\dfrac{3}{8}$, $\dfrac{5}{6}$, and $\dfrac{7}{12}$.

52. Find the total of $\dfrac{1}{2}$, $\dfrac{5}{8}$, and $\dfrac{7}{9}$.

53. Which statement describes a pair of fractions for which the least common denominator is the product of the denominators?
  (i) The denominator of one fraction is a multiple of the denominator of the second fraction.
  (ii) The denominators of the two fractions have no common factors.

OBJECTIVE C *To add whole numbers, mixed numbers, and fractions*

For Exercises 54 to 75, add.

54. $2\dfrac{2}{5}$
$+\ 3\dfrac{3}{10}$

55. $4\dfrac{1}{2}$
$+\ 5\dfrac{7}{12}$

56. $3\dfrac{3}{8}$
$+\ 2\dfrac{5}{16}$

57. 4
$+\ 5\dfrac{2}{7}$

58. $6\dfrac{8}{9}$
$+\ 12$

59. $7\dfrac{5}{12} + 2\dfrac{9}{16}$

60. $9\dfrac{1}{2} + 3\dfrac{3}{11}$

61. $6 + 2\dfrac{3}{13}$

62. $8\dfrac{21}{40} + 6$

63. $8\dfrac{29}{30} + 7\dfrac{11}{40}$

64. $17\dfrac{5}{16} + 3\dfrac{11}{24}$

65. $17\dfrac{3}{8} + 7\dfrac{7}{20}$

66. $14\dfrac{7}{12} + 29\dfrac{13}{21}$

67. $5\dfrac{7}{8} + 27\dfrac{5}{12}$

68. $7\dfrac{5}{6} + 3\dfrac{5}{9}$

69. $7\dfrac{5}{9} + 2\dfrac{7}{12}$

70. $3\dfrac{1}{2} + 2\dfrac{3}{4} + 1\dfrac{5}{6}$

71. $2\dfrac{1}{2} + 3\dfrac{2}{3} + 4\dfrac{1}{4}$

72. $3\dfrac{1}{3} + 7\dfrac{1}{5} + 2\dfrac{1}{7}$

73. $3\dfrac{1}{2} + 3\dfrac{1}{5} + 8\dfrac{1}{9}$

74. $6\dfrac{5}{9} + 6\dfrac{5}{12} + 2\dfrac{5}{18}$

75. $2\dfrac{3}{8} + 4\dfrac{7}{12} + 3\dfrac{5}{16}$

76. Carpentry For the bookcase shown at the right, what is the distance from the top of the bottom shelf to the top of the next shelf?

77. Building Maintenance A pole $6\dfrac{3}{8}$ feet long is used to change light bulbs in ceiling fixtures. The pole comes with an extension that is $3\dfrac{1}{2}$ feet long. What is the length of the pole with the extension in place?

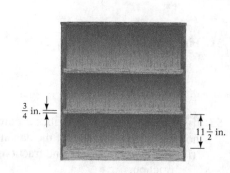

78. Find the sum of $2\frac{4}{9}$ and $5\frac{7}{12}$.

79. Find $5\frac{5}{6}$ more than $3\frac{3}{8}$.

80. What is $4\frac{3}{4}$ added to $9\frac{1}{3}$?

81. What is $4\frac{8}{9}$ added to $9\frac{1}{6}$?

82. Find the total of 2, $4\frac{5}{8}$, and $2\frac{2}{9}$.

83. Find the total of $1\frac{5}{8}$, 3, and $7\frac{7}{24}$.

For Exercises 84 and 85, state whether the given sum can be a whole number. Answer *yes* or *no*.

84. The sum of two mixed numbers

85. The sum of a mixed number and a whole number

OBJECTIVE D   *To solve application problems*

86. Mechanics   Find the length of the shaft.

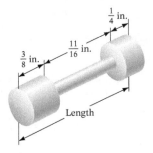

87. Mechanics   Find the length of the shaft.

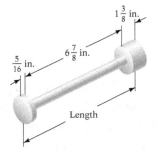

88. Carpentry   A table 30 inches high has a top that is $1\frac{1}{8}$ inches thick. Find the total thickness of the table top after a $\frac{3}{16}$-inch veneer is applied.

89.   For the table pictured at the right, what does the sum $30 + 1\frac{1}{8} + \frac{3}{16}$ represent?

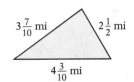

90. Wages   You are working a part-time job that pays \$11 an hour. You worked 5, $3\frac{3}{4}$, $2\frac{1}{3}$, $1\frac{1}{4}$, and $7\frac{2}{3}$ hours during the last five days.

   a. Find the total number of hours you worked during the last five days.
   b. Find your total wages for the five days.

91. Sports   The course of a yachting race is in the shape of a triangle with sides that measure $4\frac{3}{10}$ miles, $3\frac{7}{10}$ miles, and $2\frac{1}{2}$ miles. Find the total length of the course.

Construction   The size of an interior door frame is determined by the width of the wall into which it is installed. The width of the wall is determined by the width of the stud in the wall and the thickness of the sheets of drywall installed on each side of the wall. A 2×4 stud is $3\frac{5}{8}$ inches thick. A 2×6 stud is $5\frac{5}{8}$ inches thick. Use this information for Exercises 92 to 94.

92. Find the thickness of a wall constructed with 2×4 studs and drywall that is $\frac{1}{2}$ inch thick.

93. Find the thickness of a wall constructed with 2×6 studs and drywall that is $\frac{1}{2}$ inch thick.

94. A fire wall is a physical barrier in a building designed to limit the spread of fire. Suppose a fire wall is built between the garage and the kitchen of a house. Find the width of the fire wall if it is constructed using 2×4 studs and drywall that is $\frac{5}{8}$ inch thick.

95. **Construction**   Two pieces of wood must be bolted together. One piece of wood is $\frac{1}{2}$ inch thick. The second piece is $\frac{5}{8}$ inch thick. A washer will be placed on each of the outer side of the top piece of wood. The washer is $\frac{1}{16}$ inch thick. The nut is $\frac{3}{16}$ inch thick. Find the minimum length of bolt needed to bolt the two pieces of wood together.

Critical Thinking

96. A survey was conducted to determine people's favorite color from among blue, green, red, purple, and other. The surveyor claims that $\frac{1}{3}$ of the people responded blue, $\frac{1}{6}$ responded green, $\frac{1}{8}$ responded red, $\frac{1}{12}$ responded purple, and $\frac{2}{5}$ responded some other color. Is this possible? Explain your answer.

Projects or Group Activities

A **unit fraction** is a fraction with numerator 1 and denominator greater than 1. For instance, $\frac{1}{5}$ and $\frac{1}{12}$ are unit fractions.

97. List the three largest unit fractions.

98. Is there a smallest unit fraction? Explain.

Early Egyptians expressed nonunit fractions as the sums of unit fractions. For instance, $\frac{3}{10}$ would be represented as $\frac{1}{5} + \frac{1}{10}$ because $\frac{3}{10} = \frac{1}{5} + \frac{1}{10}$. For Exercises 99 to 101, represent the given fraction as the sum of two unit fractions.

99. $\dfrac{7}{12}$ 　　　　　　 100. $\dfrac{11}{24}$ 　　　　　　 101. $\dfrac{5}{12}$

2.5 | Subtraction of Fractions and Mixed Numbers

OBJECTIVE A   *To subtract fractions with the same denominator*

Subtraction of Fractions with the Same Denominator

To subtract fractions with the same denominator, subtract the numerators and place the difference over the common denominator.

EXAMPLE

$$\frac{6}{7} - \frac{2}{7} = \frac{6-2}{7} = \frac{4}{7}$$

EXAMPLE 1

Subtract: $\dfrac{11}{18} - \dfrac{7}{18}$

Solution

$\dfrac{11}{18} - \dfrac{7}{18} = \dfrac{11-7}{18}$ • The denominators are the same. Subtract the numerators.

$= \dfrac{4}{18}$ • Place the difference over the common denominator.

$= \dfrac{2}{9}$ • Write the answer in simplest form.

YOU TRY IT 1

Find the difference between $\dfrac{16}{27}$ and $\dfrac{7}{27}$.

Your solution

Solution on p. S6

OBJECTIVE B   *To subtract fractions with different denominators*

Subtraction of Fractions with Different Denominators

To subtract fractions with different denominators, first rewrite the fractions as equivalent fractions with a common denominator. Then subtract the numerators and place the difference over the common denominator.

EXAMPLE

Subtract: $\dfrac{5}{6} - \dfrac{1}{4}$

The LCD of the denominators 6 and 4 is 12.

$\dfrac{5}{6} - \dfrac{1}{4} = \dfrac{10}{12} - \dfrac{3}{12}$ • Rewrite each fraction as an equivalent fraction with 12 as the denominator.

$= \dfrac{10-3}{12} = \dfrac{7}{12}$ • Subtract the numerators and place the difference over the common denominator.

EXAMPLE 2

Subtract: $\dfrac{11}{16} - \dfrac{5}{12}$

Solution

The LCD of the denominators 16 and 12 is 48. Write equivalent fractions using 48 as the common denominator. Then subtract the fractions.

$$\frac{11}{16} - \frac{5}{12} = \frac{33}{48} - \frac{20}{48} = \frac{33 - 20}{48} = \frac{13}{48}$$

YOU TRY IT 2

Subtract: $\dfrac{13}{18} - \dfrac{7}{24}$

Your solution

EXAMPLE 3

Find the difference between $\dfrac{7}{8}$ and $\dfrac{5}{12}$.

Solution

The LCD of the denominators 8 and 12 is 24. Write equivalent fractions using 24 as the common denominator. Then subtract the fractions.

$$\frac{7}{8} - \frac{5}{12} = \frac{21}{24} - \frac{10}{24} = \frac{21 - 10}{24} = \frac{11}{24}$$

YOU TRY IT 3

Find $\dfrac{5}{6}$ less than $\dfrac{8}{9}$.

Your solution

Solutions on p. S6

OBJECTIVE C *To subtract whole numbers, mixed numbers, and fractions*

To subtract mixed numbers without borrowing, subtract the fractional parts and then subtract the whole numbers.

HOW TO 1 Subtract: $5\dfrac{5}{6} - 2\dfrac{3}{4}$

Subtract the fractional parts.

$$5\frac{5}{6} = 5\frac{10}{12}$$
$$-\,2\frac{3}{4} = 2\frac{9}{12}$$
$$\overline{\frac{1}{12}}$$

• The LCD of the denominators 6 and 4 is 12.

Subtract the whole numbers.

$$5\frac{5}{6} = 5\frac{10}{12}$$
$$-\,2\frac{3}{4} = 2\frac{9}{12}$$
$$\overline{3\frac{1}{12}}$$

The difference is $3\dfrac{1}{12}$.

Subtraction of mixed numbers sometimes involves borrowing.

HOW TO 2   Subtract: $7\dfrac{1}{6} - 2\dfrac{5}{8}$

Write equivalent fractions using the LCD.	Borrow 1 from 7. Add the 1 to $\frac{4}{24}$. Write $1\frac{4}{24}$ as $\frac{28}{24}$.	Subtract the mixed numbers.

$$7\dfrac{1}{6} = 7\dfrac{4}{24}$$
$$-2\dfrac{5}{8} = 2\dfrac{15}{24}$$

$$7\dfrac{1}{6} = \overset{6}{7}1\dfrac{4}{24} = 6\dfrac{28}{24}$$
$$-2\dfrac{5}{8} = \quad 2\dfrac{15}{24} = 2\dfrac{15}{24}$$

$$7\dfrac{1}{6} = 6\dfrac{28}{24}$$
$$-2\dfrac{5}{8} = 2\dfrac{15}{24}$$
$$\overline{4\dfrac{13}{24}}$$

The difference is $4\dfrac{13}{24}$.

HOW TO 3   Subtract: $5 - 2\dfrac{5}{8}$

Borrow 1 from 5.	Write 1 as a fraction so that the fractions have the same denominators.	Subtract the mixed numbers.

$$5 = \overset{4}{\cancel{5}}\,1$$
$$-2\dfrac{5}{8} = 2\dfrac{5}{8}$$

$$5 = 4\dfrac{8}{8}$$
$$-2\dfrac{5}{8} = 2\dfrac{5}{8}$$

$$5 = 4\dfrac{8}{8}$$
$$-2\dfrac{5}{8} = 2\dfrac{5}{8}$$
$$\overline{2\dfrac{3}{8}}$$

The difference is $2\dfrac{3}{8}$.

APPLY THE CONCEPT ···

The inseam of a pant leg is $30\dfrac{1}{2}$ inches long. What is the length of the inseam after a tailor cuts $\dfrac{3}{4}$ inch from the pant leg?

To find the length of the inseam, subtract $\dfrac{3}{4}$ from $30\dfrac{1}{2}$.

$$30\dfrac{1}{2} - \dfrac{3}{4} = 30\dfrac{2}{4} - \dfrac{3}{4} = 29\dfrac{6}{4} - \dfrac{3}{4} = 29\dfrac{3}{4}$$

The length of the inseam is $29\dfrac{3}{4}$ inches.

EXAMPLE 4

Find $11\frac{5}{12}$ decreased by $2\frac{11}{16}$.

Solution

$$11\frac{5}{12} = 11\frac{20}{48} = 10\frac{68}{48}$$ • LCD = 48

$$-2\frac{11}{16} = 2\frac{33}{48} = 2\frac{33}{48}$$
_____
$$8\frac{35}{48}$$

YOU TRY IT 4

What is $21\frac{7}{9}$ minus $7\frac{11}{12}$?

Your solution

EXAMPLE 5

Subtract: $9 - 4\frac{3}{11}$

Solution

$$9 \quad = 8\frac{11}{11}$$ • LCD = 11

$$-4\frac{3}{11} = 4\frac{3}{11}$$
_____
$$4\frac{8}{11}$$

YOU TRY IT 5

Subtract: $8 - 2\frac{4}{13}$

Your solution

Solutions on p. S6

OBJECTIVE D   *To solve application problems*

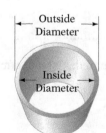

Outside Diameter

Inside Diameter

HOW TO 4   The outside diameter of a bushing is $3\frac{3}{8}$ inches, and the wall thickness is $\frac{1}{4}$ inch. Find the inside diameter of the bushing.

$$\frac{1}{4} + \frac{1}{4} = \frac{2}{4} = \frac{1}{2}$$ • Add $\frac{1}{4}$ and $\frac{1}{4}$ to find the total thickness of the two walls.

$$3\frac{3}{8} = 3\frac{3}{8} = 2\frac{11}{8}$$ • Subtract the total thickness of the two walls from the outside diameter to find the inside diameter.

$$-\frac{1}{2} = \frac{4}{8} = \frac{4}{8}$$
_____
$$2\frac{7}{8}$$

The inside diameter of the bushing is $2\frac{7}{8}$ inches.

EXAMPLE 6

A $2\frac{2}{3}$-inch piece is cut from a $6\frac{5}{8}$-inch board. How much of the board is left?

Strategy

To find the length remaining, subtract the length of the piece cut from the total length of the board.

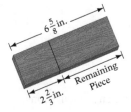

Solution

$$6\frac{5}{8} = 6\frac{15}{24} = 5\frac{39}{24}$$
$$-2\frac{2}{3} = 2\frac{16}{24} = 2\frac{16}{24}$$
$$\overline{3\frac{23}{24}}$$

$3\frac{23}{24}$ inches of the board are left.

YOU TRY IT 6

A flight from New York to Los Angeles takes $5\frac{1}{2}$ hours. After the plane has been in the air for $2\frac{3}{4}$ hours, how much flight time remains?

Your strategy

Your solution

EXAMPLE 7

Two painters are staining a house. In one day, one painter stained $\frac{1}{3}$ of the house and the other stained $\frac{1}{4}$ of the house. How much of the job remains to be done?

Strategy

To find how much of the job remains:
• Find the total amount of the house already stained $\left(\frac{1}{3} + \frac{1}{4}\right)$.
• Subtract the amount already stained from 1, which represents the complete job.

Solution

$$\frac{1}{3} = \frac{4}{12} \qquad\qquad 1 = \frac{12}{12}$$
$$+\frac{1}{4} = \frac{3}{12} \qquad -\frac{7}{12} = \frac{7}{12}$$
$$\overline{\qquad\frac{7}{12}} \qquad\qquad \overline{\qquad\frac{5}{12}}$$

$\frac{5}{12}$ of the house remains to be stained.

YOU TRY IT 7

A patient is put on a diet to lose 24 pounds in 3 months. The patient lost $7\frac{1}{2}$ pounds the first month and $5\frac{3}{4}$ pounds the second month. How much weight must be lost during the third month to achieve the goal?

Your strategy

Your solution

Solutions on p. S6

2.5 EXERCISES

✔ Concept Check

For Exercises 1 and 2, replace each question mark to make a true statement.

1. $\dfrac{5}{11} - \dfrac{3}{11} = \dfrac{? - ?}{11} = \dfrac{?}{11}$

2. $\dfrac{7}{9} - \dfrac{4}{9} = \dfrac{? - ?}{9} = \dfrac{?}{9} = ?$

For Exercises 3 and 4, answer the question without doing any calculations.

3. If $\dfrac{11}{18} - \dfrac{7}{12} = \dfrac{1}{36}$, what is the sum of $\dfrac{1}{36}$ and $\dfrac{7}{12}$?

4. If $\dfrac{9}{16} + \dfrac{1}{3} = \dfrac{43}{48}$, what is the difference between $\dfrac{43}{48}$ and $\dfrac{9}{16}$?

OBJECTIVE A *To subtract fractions with the same denominator*

For Exercises 5 to 14, subtract.

5. $\dfrac{9}{17} - \dfrac{7}{17}$

6. $\dfrac{11}{15} - \dfrac{3}{15}$

7. $\dfrac{11}{12} - \dfrac{7}{12}$

8. $\dfrac{13}{15} - \dfrac{4}{15}$

9. $\dfrac{9}{20} - \dfrac{7}{20}$

10. $\dfrac{48}{55} - \dfrac{13}{55}$

11. $\dfrac{42}{65} - \dfrac{17}{65}$

12. $\dfrac{11}{24} - \dfrac{5}{24}$

13. $\dfrac{23}{30} - \dfrac{13}{30}$

14. $\dfrac{17}{42} - \dfrac{5}{42}$

15. What is $\dfrac{5}{14}$ less than $\dfrac{13}{14}$?

16. Find the difference between $\dfrac{7}{8}$ and $\dfrac{5}{8}$.

17. Find $\dfrac{17}{24}$ decreased by $\dfrac{11}{24}$.

18. What is $\dfrac{19}{30}$ minus $\dfrac{11}{30}$?

For Exercises 19 and 20, each statement describes the difference between a pair of fractions that have the same denominator. State whether the difference of the fractions will need to be rewritten in order to be in simplest form. Answer *yes* or *no*.

19. The difference between the numerators is a factor of the denominator.

20. The difference between the numerators is 1.

OBJECTIVE B *To subtract fractions with different denominators*

For Exercises 21 to 30, subtract.

21. $\dfrac{2}{3} - \dfrac{1}{6}$

22. $\dfrac{7}{8} - \dfrac{5}{16}$

23. $\dfrac{5}{8} - \dfrac{2}{7}$

24. $\dfrac{5}{6} - \dfrac{3}{7}$

25. $\dfrac{5}{7} - \dfrac{3}{14}$

26. $\dfrac{5}{9} - \dfrac{7}{15}$

27. $\dfrac{8}{15} - \dfrac{7}{20}$

28. $\dfrac{7}{9} - \dfrac{1}{6}$

29. $\dfrac{9}{16} - \dfrac{17}{32}$

30. $\dfrac{29}{60} - \dfrac{3}{40}$

31. What is $\frac{3}{5}$ less than $\frac{11}{12}$?

32. What is $\frac{5}{9}$ less than $\frac{11}{15}$?

33. Find the difference between $\frac{11}{24}$ and $\frac{7}{18}$.

34. Find the difference between $\frac{9}{14}$ and $\frac{5}{42}$.

35. Find $\frac{11}{12}$ decreased by $\frac{11}{15}$.

36. Find $\frac{17}{20}$ decreased by $\frac{7}{15}$.

37. What is $\frac{13}{20}$ minus $\frac{1}{6}$?

38. What is $\frac{5}{6}$ minus $\frac{7}{9}$?

39. Which statement describes a pair of fractions for which the least common denominator is one of the denominators?
  (i) The denominator of one fraction is a factor of the denominator of the second fraction.
  (ii) The denominators of the two fractions have no common factors.

OBJECTIVE C   *To subtract whole numbers, mixed numbers, and fractions*

For Exercises 40 to 54, subtract.

40. $5\frac{7}{12}$
$-2\frac{5}{12}$

41. $16\frac{11}{15}$
$-11\frac{8}{15}$

42. $6\frac{1}{3}$
-2

43. $5\frac{7}{8}$
-1

44. 10
$-6\frac{1}{3}$

45. 3
$-2\frac{5}{21}$

46. $6\frac{2}{5}$
$-4\frac{4}{5}$

47. $16\frac{3}{8}$
$-10\frac{7}{8}$

48. $16\frac{2}{5}$
$-8\frac{4}{9}$

49. $23\frac{7}{8}$
$-16\frac{2}{3}$

50. 17
$-7\frac{8}{13}$

51. 6
$-4\frac{3}{5}$

52. $23\frac{1}{6}$
$-15\frac{3}{8}$

53. $40\frac{4}{9}$
$-24\frac{5}{6}$

54. $12\frac{5}{18}$
$-11\frac{11}{27}$

55. Interior Design   An interior decorator places a picture hook on a wall $29\frac{1}{2}$ inches down from the ceiling. If the support wire for the picture is $7\frac{3}{4}$ inches from the top of the picture as shown at the right, what is the distance from the ceiling to the top of the picture?

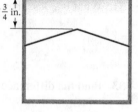

56. Storage Space   A laser printer $19\frac{3}{8}$ inches tall is placed on a shelf that is $23\frac{1}{4}$ inches below another shelf. Find the distance between the top of the printer and the bottom of the higher shelf.

57. What is $7\frac{3}{5}$ less than $23\frac{3}{20}$?

58. Find the difference between $12\frac{3}{8}$ and $7\frac{5}{12}$.

59. What is $10\frac{5}{9}$ minus $5\frac{11}{15}$?

60. Find $6\frac{1}{3}$ decreased by $3\frac{3}{5}$.

61. Can the difference between a whole number and a mixed number ever be a whole number?

OBJECTIVE D   *To solve application problems*

62. Mechanics   Find the missing dimension.

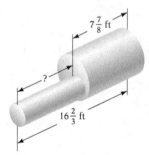

63. Mechanics   Find the missing dimension.

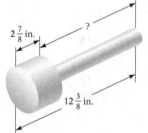

64. 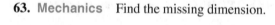 **Sports**   In the Kentucky Derby the horses run $1\frac{1}{4}$ miles. In the Belmont Stakes they run $1\frac{1}{2}$ miles, and in the Preakness Stakes they run $1\frac{3}{16}$ miles. How much farther do the horses run in the Kentucky Derby than in the Preakness Stakes? How much farther do they run in the Belmont Stakes than in the Preakness Stakes?

Cheryl Ann Quigley/Shutterstock.com

65. Carpentry   The standard height of a desk is $29\frac{1}{2}$ inches. A writer is building a desk that is $28\frac{3}{4}$ inches high. How much shorter is this desk than a desk of standard height?

66. Fundraising A 12-mile walkathon has three checkpoints. The first checkpoint is $3\frac{3}{8}$ miles from the starting point. The second checkpoint is $4\frac{1}{3}$ miles from the first.
a. How many miles is it from the starting point to the second checkpoint?
b. How many miles is it from the second checkpoint to the finish line?

67. Hiking Two hikers plan a 3-day, $27\frac{1}{2}$-mile backpack trip carrying a total of 80 pounds. The hikers plan to travel $7\frac{3}{8}$ miles the first day and $10\frac{1}{3}$ miles the second day.
a. How many total miles do the hikers plan to travel the first two days?
b. How many miles will be left to travel on the third day?

For Exercises 68 and 69, refer to Exercise 67. Describe what each difference represents.

68. $27\frac{1}{2} - 7\frac{3}{8}$ **69.** $10\frac{1}{3} - 7\frac{3}{8}$

70. Health A patient with high blood pressure who weighs 225 pounds is put on a diet to lose 25 pounds in 3 months. The patient loses $8\frac{3}{4}$ pounds the first month and $11\frac{5}{8}$ pounds the second month. How much weight must be lost during the third month for the goal to be achieved?

71. Sports A wrestler is entered in the 172-pound weight class in the conference finals coming up in 3 weeks. The wrestler needs to lose $12\frac{3}{4}$ pounds. The wrestler loses $5\frac{1}{4}$ pounds the first week and $4\frac{1}{4}$ pounds the second week.
a. Without doing the calculations, determine whether the wrestler can reach his weight class by losing less in the third week than in the second week.
b. How many pounds must be lost in the third week to reach the desired weight?

Istvan Csak/Shutterstock.com

72. Construction Find the difference in thickness between a fire wall constructed with 2 × 6 studs and drywall that is $\frac{1}{2}$ inch thick and a fire wall constructed with 2 × 4 studs and drywall that is $\frac{5}{8}$ inch thick. See Exercises 92 to 94 on page 86.

73. Finances If $\frac{4}{15}$ of an electrician's income is spent on housing, what fraction of the electrician's income is not spent on housing?

Critical Thinking

74. Fill in the square to produce a true statement: $5\frac{1}{3} - \boxed{} = 2\frac{1}{2}$

75. Fill in the square to produce a true statement: $\boxed{} - 4\frac{1}{2} = 1\frac{5}{8}$

Projects or Group Activities

76. Fill in the blank squares at the right so that the sum of the numbers is the same along any row, column, or diagonal. The resulting square is called a magic square.

		$\dfrac{3}{4}$
1	$\dfrac{5}{8}$	
$\dfrac{1}{2}$		$\dfrac{7}{8}$

✔ CHECK YOUR PROGRESS: CHAPTER 2

For Exercises 1 to 4, find the LCM of the numbers.

1. 12, 18

2. 6, 9, 18

3. 2, 5, 7

4. 28, 36

For Exercises 5 to 8, find the GCF of the numbers.

5. 18, 24

6. 27, 54

7. 3, 6, 14

8. 30, 70, 105

For Exercises 9 to 12, write the fraction in simplest form.

9. $\dfrac{36}{45}$

10. $\dfrac{17}{51}$

11. $\dfrac{25}{36}$

12. $\dfrac{36}{4}$

For Exercises 13 to 28, add or subtract.

13. $\dfrac{2}{9} + \dfrac{4}{9}$

14. $\dfrac{17}{24} - \dfrac{5}{24}$

15. $\dfrac{7}{9} - \dfrac{7}{18}$

16. $\dfrac{7}{20} + \dfrac{1}{4}$

17. $\dfrac{5}{6} + \dfrac{11}{16}$

18. $\dfrac{3}{4} - \dfrac{9}{26}$

19. $\dfrac{2}{3} - \dfrac{3}{16}$

20. $\dfrac{3}{5} + \dfrac{1}{4}$

21. $2\dfrac{1}{10} + 7\dfrac{1}{15}$

22. $11\dfrac{4}{9} + 7\dfrac{1}{6}$

23. $7\dfrac{6}{7} - 1\dfrac{1}{2}$

24. $3\dfrac{13}{28} - 1\dfrac{1}{8}$

25. $5\dfrac{8}{9} + 7\dfrac{5}{6}$

26. $9\dfrac{3}{4} + 7\dfrac{3}{10}$

27. $9 - 5\dfrac{3}{4}$

28. $8\dfrac{1}{4} - 5\dfrac{5}{6}$

2   Review Exercises

1. Write $\frac{30}{45}$ in simplest form.

2. Simplify: $\left(\frac{3}{4}\right)^3 \cdot \frac{20}{27} - \frac{1}{8}$

3. Express the shaded portion of the circles as an improper fraction.

4. Write an equivalent fraction with the given denominator.

$$\frac{8}{11} = \frac{}{44}$$

5. Place the correct symbol, $<$ or $>$, between the two numbers.

$\frac{11}{18} \quad \frac{17}{24}$

6. Subtract: $18\frac{1}{6}$

$-3\frac{5}{7}$

7. Simplify: $\frac{2}{7}\left(\frac{5}{8} - \frac{1}{3}\right) \div \frac{3}{5}$

8. Multiply: $2\frac{1}{3} \times 3\frac{7}{8}$

9. Divide: $1\frac{1}{3} \div \frac{2}{3}$

10. Find $\frac{17}{24}$ decreased by $\frac{3}{16}$.

11. Divide: $8\frac{2}{3} \div 2\frac{3}{5}$

12. Find the GCF of 20 and 48.

13. Write an equivalent fraction with the given denominator.

$$\frac{2}{3} = \frac{}{36}$$

14. What is $\frac{15}{28}$ divided by $\frac{5}{7}$?

15. Find the total of $\frac{2}{3}$, $\frac{5}{6}$, and $\frac{2}{9}$.

16. Multiply: $2\frac{1}{4} \times 7\frac{1}{3}$

17. Find the LCM of 18 and 12.

18. Write $\frac{16}{44}$ in simplest form.

19. Add: $\dfrac{3}{8} + \dfrac{5}{8} + \dfrac{1}{8}$

20. What is $\dfrac{11}{50}$ multiplied by $\dfrac{25}{44}$?

21. Add: $4\dfrac{4}{9} + 2\dfrac{1}{6} + 11\dfrac{17}{27}$

22. Find the GCF of 15 and 25.

23. Write $\dfrac{17}{5}$ as a mixed number.

24. Simplify: $\left(\dfrac{4}{5} - \dfrac{2}{3}\right)^2 \div \dfrac{4}{15}$

25. Add: $\dfrac{3}{8} + 1\dfrac{2}{3} + 3\dfrac{5}{6}$

26. Find the LCM of 18 and 27.

27. Subtract: $\dfrac{11}{18} - \dfrac{5}{18}$

28. Write $2\dfrac{5}{7}$ as an improper fraction.

29. Divide: $\dfrac{5}{6} \div \dfrac{5}{12}$

30. Multiply: $\dfrac{5}{12} \times \dfrac{4}{25}$

31. Subtract:
$$\begin{array}{r} 16 \\ -\ 5\dfrac{7}{8} \\ \hline \end{array}$$

32. Express the shaded portion of the circles as a mixed number.

33. **Meteorology** During 3 months of the rainy season, $5\dfrac{7}{8}$, $6\dfrac{2}{3}$, and $8\dfrac{3}{4}$ inches of rain fell. Find the total rainfall for the 3 months.

34. **Real Estate** A home building contractor bought $4\dfrac{2}{3}$ acres of land for \$168,000. What was the cost of each acre?

35. **Sports** A 15-mile race has three checkpoints. The first checkpoint is $4\dfrac{1}{2}$ miles from the starting point. The second checkpoint is $5\dfrac{3}{4}$ miles from the first checkpoint. How many miles is the second checkpoint from the finish line?

36. **Fuel Efficiency** A compact car gets 36 miles on each gallon of gasoline. How many miles can the car travel on $6\dfrac{3}{4}$ gallons of gasoline?

CHAPTER

2 | TEST

1. Multiply: $\dfrac{9}{11} \times \dfrac{44}{81}$

2. Find the GCF of 24 and 80.

3. Divide: $\dfrac{5}{9} \div \dfrac{7}{18}$

4. Simplify: $\left(\dfrac{3}{4}\right)^2 \div \left(\dfrac{2}{3} + \dfrac{5}{6}\right) - \dfrac{1}{12}$

5. Write $9\dfrac{4}{5}$ as an improper fraction.

6. What is $5\dfrac{2}{3}$ multiplied by $1\dfrac{7}{17}$?

7. Write $\dfrac{40}{64}$ in simplest form.

8. Place the correct symbol, $<$ or $>$, between the two numbers.
$\dfrac{3}{8} \qquad \dfrac{5}{12}$

9. Simplify: $\left(\dfrac{1}{4}\right)^3 \div \left(\dfrac{1}{8}\right)^2 - \dfrac{1}{6}$

10. Find the LCM of 24 and 40.

11. Subtract: $\dfrac{17}{24} - \dfrac{11}{24}$

12. Write $\dfrac{18}{5}$ as a mixed number.

13. Find the quotient of $6\dfrac{2}{3}$ and $3\dfrac{1}{6}$.

14. Write an equivalent fraction with the given denominator.

$\dfrac{5}{8} = \dfrac{}{72}$

15. Add:

$$\begin{array}{r} \dfrac{5}{6} \\[6pt] \dfrac{7}{9} \\[6pt] +\dfrac{1}{15} \\ \hline \end{array}$$

16. Subtract:

$$\begin{array}{r} 23\dfrac{1}{8} \\[6pt] -\;9\dfrac{9}{44} \\ \hline \end{array}$$

17. What is $\dfrac{9}{16}$ minus $\dfrac{5}{12}$?

18. Simplify: $\left(\dfrac{2}{3}\right)^{4} \cdot \dfrac{27}{32} + \dfrac{1}{32}$

19. Add: $\dfrac{7}{12} + \dfrac{11}{12} + \dfrac{5}{12}$

20. What is $12\dfrac{5}{12}$ more than $9\dfrac{17}{20}$?

21. Express the shaded portion of the circles as an improper fraction.

22. Compensation   An electrician earns \$240 for each day worked. What is the total of the electrician's earnings for working $3\dfrac{1}{2}$ days?

23. Real Estate   Grant Miura bought $7\dfrac{1}{4}$ acres of land for a housing project. One and three-fourths acres were set aside for a park, and the remaining land was developed into $\dfrac{1}{2}$-acre lots. How many lots were available for sale?

24. Architecture   A scale of $\dfrac{1}{2}$ inch to 1 foot is used to draw the plans for a house. The scale measurements for three walls are given in the table at the right. Complete the table to determine the actual wall lengths for the three walls A, B, and C.

Wall	Scale	Actual Wall Length
A	$6\dfrac{1}{4}$ in.	?
B	9 in.	?
C	$7\dfrac{7}{8}$ in.	?

25. Meteorology   In 3 successive months, the rainfall measured $11\dfrac{1}{2}$ inches, $7\dfrac{5}{8}$ inches, and $2\dfrac{1}{3}$ inches. Find the total rainfall for the 3 months.

Cumulative Review Exercises

1. Round 290,496 to the nearest thousand.

2. Subtract: $\begin{array}{r} 390{,}047 \\ -\ \ 98{,}769 \\ \hline \end{array}$

3. Find the product of 926 and 79.

4. Divide: $57\overline{)30{,}792}$

5. Simplify: $4 \cdot (6 - 3) \div 6 - 1$

6. Find the prime factorization of 44.

7. Find the LCM of 30 and 42.

8. Find the GCF of 60 and 80.

9. Write $7\frac{2}{3}$ as an improper fraction.

10. Write $\frac{25}{4}$ as a mixed number.

11. Write an equivalent fraction with the given denominator.

$$\frac{5}{16} = \frac{}{48}$$

12. Write $\frac{24}{60}$ in simplest form.

13. What is $\frac{9}{16}$ more than $\frac{7}{12}$?

14. Add: $\begin{array}{r} 3\frac{7}{8} \\ 7\frac{5}{12} \\ +\ 2\frac{15}{16} \\ \hline \end{array}$

15. Find $\frac{3}{8}$ less than $\frac{11}{12}$.

16. Subtract: $\begin{array}{r} 5\frac{1}{6} \\ -3\frac{7}{18} \\ \hline \end{array}$

17. Multiply: $\dfrac{3}{8} \times \dfrac{14}{15}$

18. Multiply: $3\dfrac{1}{8} \times 2\dfrac{2}{5}$

19. Divide: $\dfrac{7}{16} \div \dfrac{5}{12}$

20. Find the quotient of $6\dfrac{1}{8}$ and $2\dfrac{1}{3}$.

21. Simplify: $\left(\dfrac{1}{2}\right)^3 \cdot \dfrac{8}{9}$

22. Simplify: $\left(\dfrac{1}{2} + \dfrac{1}{3}\right) \div \left(\dfrac{2}{5}\right)^2$

23. Banking Molly O'Brien had $1359 in a checking account. During the week, Molly wrote checks for $128, $54, and $315. Find the amount in the checking account at the end of the week.

24. Entertainment The tickets for a movie were $10 for an adult and $4 for a student. Find the total income from the sale of 87 adult tickets and 135 student tickets.

25. Measurement Find the total weight of three packages that weigh $1\dfrac{1}{2}$ pounds, $7\dfrac{7}{8}$ pounds, and $2\dfrac{2}{3}$ pounds.

26. Carpentry A board $2\dfrac{5}{8}$ feet long is cut from a board $7\dfrac{1}{3}$ feet long. What is the length of the remaining piece?

27. Fuel Efficiency A car travels 27 miles on each gallon of gasoline. How many miles can the car travel on $8\dfrac{1}{3}$ gallons of gasoline?

28. Real Estate Jimmy Santos purchased $10\dfrac{1}{3}$ acres of land to build a housing development. Jimmy donated 2 acres for a park. How many $\dfrac{1}{3}$-acre parcels can be sold from the remaining land?

Integers and Signed Fractions

OBJECTIVES

SECTION 3.1
A To identify the order relation between two integers
B To evaluate expressions that contain the absolute value symbol

SECTION 3.2
A To add integers
B To subtract integers
C To solve application problems

SECTION 3.3
A To multiply integers
B To divide integers
C To solve application problems

SECTION 3.4
A To evaluate exponential expressions
B To use the Order of Operations Agreement to simplify expressions

SECTION 3.5
A To evaluate a variable expression

SECTION 3.6
A To multiply fractions
B To divide fractions
C To solve application problems and use formulas

SECTION 3.7
A To add fractions
B To subtract fractions
C To solve application problems

SECTION 3.8
A To simplify exponential expressions
B To simplify complex fractions
C To use the Order of Operations Agreement to simplify expressions

Focus on Success

What resources do you use when you need help in this course? You know to read and reread the text when you are having difficulty understanding a concept. Instructors are available to help you during their office hours. Most schools have a math center where students can get help. Some schools have a tutoring program. You might also ask a student who has been successful in this class for assistance. (See Habits of Successful Students, page AIM-6.)

Monkey Business Images/Shutterstock.com

Prep Test

Are you ready to succeed in this chapter? Take the Prep Test below to find out if you are ready to learn the new material.

1. Place the correct symbol, $<$ or $>$, between the two numbers.
   54   45

2. What is the distance from 4 to 8 on the number line?

For Exercises 3 to 14, add, subtract, multiply, or divide.

3. $7654 + 8193$

4. $6097 - 2318$

5. 472×56

6. $\dfrac{144}{24}$

7. $\dfrac{2}{3} + \dfrac{3}{5}$

8. $\dfrac{3}{4} - \dfrac{5}{16}$

9. $0.75 + 3.9 + 6.408$

10. $5.4 - 1.619$

11. $\dfrac{3}{4} \times \dfrac{8}{15}$

12. $\dfrac{5}{12} \div \dfrac{3}{4}$

13. 23.5×0.4

14. $0.96 \div 2.4$

15. Simplify: $(8 - 6)^2 + 12 \div 4 \cdot 3^2$

3.1 Introduction to Integers

OBJECTIVE A *To identify the order relation between two integers*

Thus far in the text, we have encountered only zero and the numbers greater than zero. The numbers greater than zero are called **positive numbers.** However, the phrases "12 degrees below zero," "$25 in debt," and "15 feet below sea level" refer to numbers less than zero. These numbers are called **negative numbers.**

The **integers** are . . . , -4, -3, -2, -1, 0, 1, 2, 3, 4, ...

Point of Interest
Among the slang words for zero are *zilch, zip,* and *goose egg.* The word *love* for zero in scoring a tennis game comes from the French word *l'oeuf,* which means "the egg."

Each integer can be shown on a number line. The integers to the left of zero on the number line are called **negative integers** and are represented by a negative sign ($-$) placed in front of the number. The integers to the right of zero are called **positive integers.** The positive integers are also called **natural numbers.** Zero is neither a positive nor a negative integer.

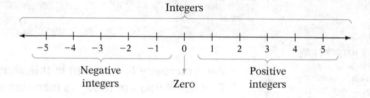

A number line can be used to visualize the order relation between two integers. A number that appears to the left of a given number is less than ($<$) the given number. A number that appears to the right of a given number is greater than ($>$) the given number.

2 is to the right of -4, so 2 is greater than -4.

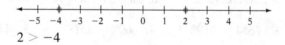

$2 > -4$

-5 is to the left of -3, so -5 is less than -3.

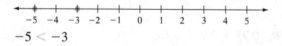

$-5 < -3$

APPLY THE CONCEPT ··

In golf, *par* is the number of strokes in which a golfer should complete the course. A player's score is given as a value relative to par, such as -4 ("4 under par") or $+2$ ("2 over par"). The person with the lowest score wins. If Paula Creamer has a score of -4 and Christie Kerr has a score of -6, which woman wins?

Because $-6 < -4$, Christie Kerr wins.

Place the correct symbol, $<$ or $>$, between the numbers -5 and -7.

Solution $-5 > -7$ • -5 is to the right of -7
on the number line.

Place the correct symbol, $<$ or $>$, between the numbers -12 and -8.

Your solution

Name the number 3 units to the left of -1 on the number line.

Solution   Using a number line, count 3 units to the left of -1.

The number is -4.

Name the number 5 units to the right of -5 on the number line.

Your solution

Solutions on p. S23

To evaluate expressions that contain the absolute value symbol

Two numbers that are the same distance from zero on the number line but on opposite sides of zero are called **opposites.**

-4 is the opposite of 4
and
4 is the opposite of -4.

Note that a negative sign can be read as "the opposite of."

$-(4) = -4$ The opposite of positive 4 is negative 4.

$-(-4) = 4$ The opposite of negative 4 is positive 4.

The **absolute value of a number** is the distance between zero and the number on the number line. Therefore, the absolute value of a number is a positive number or zero. The symbol for absolute value is $|\ \ |$.

The distance from 0 to 4 is 4. **Thus** $|4| = 4$ (the absolute value of 4 is 4).

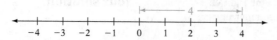

The distance from 0 to -4 is 4. **Thus** $|-4| = 4$ (the absolute value of -4 is 4).

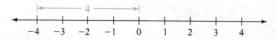

The absolute value of a positive number is the number itself. The absolute value of a negative number is the opposite of the negative number. The absolute value of zero is zero.

EXAMPLE 3

Find the absolute value of 2 and -3.

Solution

$|2| = 2$ • The absolute value of a positive number is the number itself.

$|-3| = 3$ • The absolute value of a negative number is the opposite of the number.

YOU TRY IT 3

Find the absolute value of -7 and 21.

Your solution

EXAMPLE 4

Evaluate $|-34|$ and $|0|$.

Solution

$|-34| = 34$

$|0| = 0$ • The absolute value of zero is zero.

YOU TRY IT 4

Evaluate $|13|$ and $|-9|$.

Your solution

EXAMPLE 5

Evaluate $-|-4|$.

Solution

The minus sign *in front of* the absolute value sign is not affected by the absolute value sign.

$-|-4| = -4$

YOU TRY IT 5

Evaluate $-|-12|$.

Your solution

Solutions on p. S23

3.1 EXERCISES

✔ Concept Check

For Exercises 1 and 2, represent the quantity as an integer.

1. A lake 120 ft below sea level

2. A temperature that is 15° below zero

3. Is any negative number less than any positive number?

4. Is zero less than or greater than any negative number?

OBJECTIVE A   *To identify the order relation between two integers*

For Exercises 5 to 8, graph the numbers on the number line.

5. 3 and −3

6. −2 and 0

7. −4 and 1

8. 4 and −1

For Exercises 9 to 24, place the correct symbol, < or >, between the two numbers.

9. −2   −5

10. −6   −1

11. −16   1

12. −2   13

13. −11   −8

14. −4   −10

15. −42   0

16. −36   49

17. 21   −34

18. 53   −46

19. 0   −39

20. −51   −20

21. −87   63

22. −75   92

23. −62   −84

24. −91   −70

For Exercises 25 to 30, state which number on the number line is in the given location.

25. 3 units to the right of −2

26. 5 units to the right of −3

27. 4 units to the left of 3

28. 2 units to the left of −1

29. 6 units to the right of −3

30. 4 units to the right of −4

For Exercises 31 to 34, use the following number line.

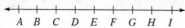

31. a. If *F* is 1 and *G* is 2, what number is *A?*   **32. a.** If *G* is 1 and *H* is 2, what number is *B?*

b. If *F* is 1 and *G* is 2, what number is *C?*   **b.** If *G* is 1 and *H* is 2, what number is *D?*

33. a. If *H* is 0 and *I* is 1, what number is *A?*   **34. a.** If *G* is 2 and *I* is 4, what number is *B?*

b. If *H* is 0 and *I* is 1, what number is *D?*   **b.** If *G* is 2 and *I* is 4, what number is *E?*

35. Which is the lower temperature, $-12°F$ or $-5°F$?

36. An ion is an atom that can have a positive or negative charge. Which has the lesser charge, an ion with a charge of -3 or an ion with a charge of $+2$?

37. Which is the higher elevation measured from sea level, -125 ft or -42 ft?

For Exercises 38 to 43, write the given numbers in order from smallest to largest.

38. $-6, 2, -8, 7$ **39.** $9, -4, 5, 0$ **40.** $6, -9, -12, 8$

41. $-10, 4, 12, -5, -7$ **42.** $11, -8, -1, 7, -6$ **43.** $10, -11, -2, 5, -7$

For Exercises 44 to 47, determine whether the statement is always true, never true, or sometimes true.

44. A number that is to the right of -6 on the number line is a negative number.   **45.** A number that is to the left of -2 on the number line is a negative number.

46. A number that is to the right of 7 on the number line is a negative number.   **47.** A number that is to the left of 4 on the number line is a negative number.

OBJECTIVE B   *To evaluate expressions that contain the absolute value symbol*

For Exercises 48 to 57, find the opposite number.

48. 4   **49.** 16   **50.** −2   **51.** −3   **52.** 22

53. 0   **54.** −31   **55.** −59   **56.** 70   **57.** −88

For Exercises 58 to 65, find the absolute value of the number.

58. 4   **59.** −4   **60.** −7   **61.** 9

62. −1   **63.** −11   **64.** 10   **65.** −12

For Exercises 66 to 89, evaluate.

66. $|9|$ **67.** $|-2|$ **68.** $|-6|$ **69.** $|6|$

70. $-|0|$ **71.** $|16|$ **72.** $|19|$ **73.** $|-12|$

74. $|-22|$ **75.** $-|29|$ **76.** $-|20|$ **77.** $-|-14|$

78. $-|-18|$ **79.** $|-15|$ **80.** $|-23|$ **81.** $-|33|$

82. $-|27|$ **83.** $|32|$ **84.** $|25|$ **85.** $-|-42|$

86. $|-74|$ **87.** $|-61|$ **88.** $-|88|$ **89.** $-|52|$

For Exercises 90 to 97, place the correct symbol, $<$, $=$, or $>$, between the two numbers.

90. $|7|$ $|-9|$ **91.** $|-12|$ $|8|$ **92.** $|-5|$ $|-2|$ **93.** $|6|$ $|13|$

94. $|-8|$ $|3|$ **95.** $|-1|$ $|-17|$ **96.** $|-14|$ $|14|$ **97.** $|17|$ $|-17|$

For Exercises 98 to 103, write the given numbers in order from smallest absolute value to largest absolute value.

98. −6, −17, 8, 7   **99.** 37, −25, 22, −3   **100.** −2, −29, −41, −14

101. 10, −23, −49, 42   **102.** 34, −25, 23, −26   **103.** −40, 23, −28, 9

For Exercises 104 to 107, determine whether the statement is true for positive integers, negative integers, or all integers.

104. The absolute value of an integer is the opposite of the integer.

105. The opposite of an integer is less than the integer.

106. The opposite of an integer is negative.

107. The absolute value of an integer is greater than the integer.

Critical Thinking

108. 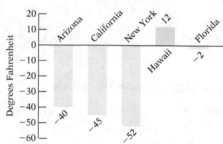 **Meteorology**   The graph at the right shows the lowest recorded temperatures, in degrees Fahrenheit, for selected states in the United States. Which state has the lowest recorded temperature?

Lowest Recorded Temperatures
Sources: National Climatic Data Center; NESDIS; NOAA; U.S. Dept. of Commerce

109. a. Name two numbers that are 5 units from 3 on the number line.

b. Name two numbers that are 3 units from -1 on the number line.

110. a. Find a number that is halfway between -7 and -5.
b. Find a number that is halfway between -10 and -6.
c. Find a number that is one-third of the way between -12 and -3.

111. Rocketry   Which is closer to blastoff, -12 min and counting or -17 min and counting?

112. Investments   In the stock market, the net change in the price of a share of stock is recorded as a positive or a negative number. If the price rises, the net change is positive. If the price falls, the net change is negative. If the net change for a share of Stock A is -2 and the net change for a share of Stock B is -1, which stock showed the least net change?

113. Business   Some businesses show a profit as a positive number and a loss as a negative number. During the first quarter of this year, the loss experienced by a company was recorded as $-12,575$. During the second quarter of this year, the loss experienced by the company was $-11,350$. During which quarter was the loss greater?

114. a. Find the values of a for which $|a| = 7$.
b. Find the values of y for which $|y| = 11$.

Projects or Group Activities

115. Accounting software programs such as Quick Books or Sage Peachtree do not use a negative sign to record negative numbers. Research some ways in which negative numbers are represented in accounting, and write a short paragraph about your findings.

3.2 Addition and Subtraction of Integers

OBJECTIVE A   *To add integers*

An integer can be graphed as a dot on a number line, as shown in the last section. An integer also can be represented anywhere along a number line by an arrow. A positive number is represented by an arrow pointing to the right. A negative number is represented by an arrow pointing to the left. The absolute value of the number is represented by the length of the arrow. The integers 5 and −4 are shown on the number lines below.

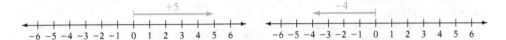

The sum of two integers can be shown on a number line. To add two integers, use arrows to represent the addends, with the first arrow starting at zero and the second arrow starting at the tip of the first. The sum is the number directly below the tip of the arrow that represents the second addend.

$4 + 2 = 6$

$-4 + (-2) = -6$

$-4 + 2 = -2$

$4 + (-2) = 2$

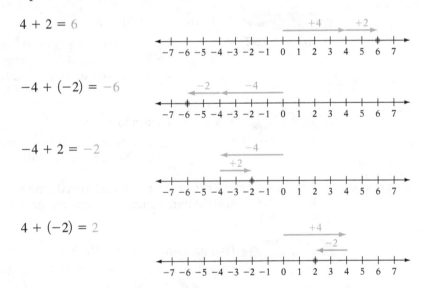

The sums of the integers shown above can be categorized by the signs of the addends.

Here the addends have the same sign:

$4 + 2$ *positive* 4 plus *positive* 2
$-4 + (-2)$ *negative* 4 plus *negative* 2

Here the addends have different signs:

$-4 + 2$ *negative* 4 plus *positive* 2
$4 + (-2)$ *positive* 4 plus *negative* 2

The rule for adding two integers depends on whether the signs of the addends are the same or different.

> ### Rules for Adding Two Numbers
>
> To add numbers with the same sign, add the absolute values of the numbers. Then attach the sign of the addends.
>
> To add numbers with different signs, find the difference between the absolute values of the numbers. Then attach the sign of the addend with the greater absolute value.

Point of Interest

Although today mathematical symbols are fairly standard in every country, that has not always been the case. Italian mathematicians in the 15th century used a "p" to indicate "plus." The "p" was from the Italian word *piu*, meaning "more" or "plus."

HOW TO 1 Add: $(-4) + (-9)$

$|-4| = 4, |-9| = 9$ • Because the signs of the addends are the same, add the
$4 + 9 = 13$ absolute values of the numbers.
$(-4) + (-9) = -13$ • Then attach the sign of the addends.

HOW TO 2 Add: $6 + (-13)$

$|6| = 6, |-13| = 13$ • Because the signs of the addends are different, subtract
$13 - 6 = 7$ the smaller absolute value from the larger absolute value.
$6 + (-13) = -7$ • Then attach the sign of the number with the larger absolute
                        value. Because $|-13| > |6|$, attach the negative sign.

HOW TO 3 Add: $162 + (-247)$

$162 + (-247) = -85$ • Because the signs are different, find the difference between
                        the absolute values of the numbers and attach the sign of
                        the number with the greater absolute value.

Integrating Technology

To add $-14 + (-47)$ on your calculator, enter the following:

14 +/- + 47 +/- =

HOW TO 4 What is -14 added to -47?

$-14 + (-47) = -61$ • Because the signs are the same, add the absolute values of
                        the numbers and attach the sign of the addends.

When adding more than two integers, start from the left and add the first two numbers. Then add the sum to the third number. Continue this process until all the numbers have been added.

HOW TO 5 Find the sum: $(-4) + (-6) + (-8) + 9$

$(-4) + (-6) + (-8) + 9 = (-10) + (-8) + 9$ • Add the first two numbers.
$= (-18) + 9$ • Add the sum to the next number.
$= -9$ • Continue adding until all numbers have been added.

EXAMPLE 1

What is the total of -162 and 98?

Solution

$-162 + 98 = -64$ • The signs of the addends
are different.

YOU TRY IT 1

What is -154 more than -37?

Your solution

Solution on p. S23

EXAMPLE 2

Add: $-2 + (-7) + 4 + (-6)$

Solution

$$\begin{aligned}
-2 + (-7) + 4 + (-6) &= -9 + 4 + (-6) \\
&= -5 + (-6) \\
&= -11
\end{aligned}$$

YOU TRY IT 2

Find the sum: $-5 + (-2) + 9 + (-3)$

Your solution

Solution on p. S23

OBJECTIVE B *To subtract integers*

Before the rules for subtracting two integers are explained, look at the verbal translations of expressions that represent the difference of two integers:

$9 - 3$	positive 9 minus positive 3
$(-9) - 3$	negative 9 minus positive 3
$9 - (-3)$	positive 9 minus negative 3
$(-9) - (-3)$	negative 9 minus negative 3

Note that the sign $-$ is used in two different ways. One way is as a negative sign, as in (-9), *negative* 9. The second way is to indicate the operation of subtraction, as in $9 - 3$, 9 *minus* 3.

Look at the next four subtraction expressions and decide whether the second number in each expression is a positive number or a negative number.

1. $(-10) - 8$ **2.** $(-10) - (-8)$ **3.** $10 - (-8)$ **4.** $10 - 8$

In expressions 1 and 4, the second number is positive 8. In expressions 2 and 3, the second number is negative 8.

> **Rule for Subtracting Two Numbers**
>
> To subtract two numbers, add the opposite of the second number to the first number.

This rule states that to subtract two integers, we rewrite the subtraction expression as the sum of the first number and the opposite of the second number.

Here are some examples:

First number	$-$	second number	$=$	first number	$+$	the opposite of the second number	
8	$-$	15	$=$	8	$+$	(-15)	$= -7$
8	$-$	(-15)	$=$	8	$+$	15	$= 23$
(-8)	$-$	15	$=$	(-8)	$+$	(-15)	$= -23$
(-8)	$-$	(-15)	$=$	(-8)	$+$	15	$= 7$

HOW TO 6 Subtract: $(-15) - 75$

$$\begin{aligned}
(-15) - 75 &= (-15) + (-75) \\
&= -90
\end{aligned}$$

• To subtract, add the opposite of the second number to the first number.

HOW TO 7 What is -32 less than 27?

$$27 - (-32) = 27 + 32$$
$$= 59$$

• To subtract, add the opposite of the second number to the first number.

When subtraction occurs several times in an expression, rewrite each subtraction as addition of the opposite, and then add.

HOW TO 8 Subtract: $-13 - 5 - (-8)$

$$-13 - 5 - (-8) = -13 + (-5) + 8$$
$$= -18 + 8 = -10$$

• Rewrite each subtraction as addition of the opposite, and then add.

EXAMPLE 3

Find 8 less than -12.

Solution

$$-12 - 8 = -12 + (-8)$$
$$= -20$$

• Rewrite "$-$" as "$+$" the opposite of 8, -8.

YOU TRY IT 3

Find the difference between -8 and 14.

Your solution

EXAMPLE 4

Subtract: $6 - (-20)$

Solution

$$6 - (-20) = 6 + 20$$
$$= 26$$

• Rewrite "$-$" as "$+$" the opposite of -20, 20.

YOU TRY IT 4

Subtract: $3 - (-15)$

Your solution

EXAMPLE 5

Subtract: $-8 - 30 - (-12) - 7$

Solution

$$-8 - 30 - (-12) - 7$$
$$= -8 + (-30) + 12 + (-7)$$
$$= -38 + 12 + (-7)$$
$$= -26 + (-7) = -33$$

YOU TRY IT 5

Subtract: $4 - (-3) - 12 - (-7) - 20$

Your solution

Solutions on p. S23

OBJECTIVE C *To solve application problems*

EXAMPLE 6

Find the temperature after an increase of 9°C from -6°C.

Strategy

To find the temperature, add the increase (9°C) to the previous temperature (-6°C).

Solution

$$-6 + 9 = 3$$

The temperature is 3°C.

YOU TRY IT 6

Find the temperature after an increase of 12°C from -10°C.

Your strategy

Your solution

Solution on p. S23

3.2 EXERCISES

✔ Concept Check

1. Name the negative integers in the list of numbers. $-14, 28, 0, -\frac{5}{7}, -364, -9.5$

2. For each pair of numbers, state which number has the larger absolute value.
a. $-41, 39$ **b.** $-10, -15$ **c.** $-13, 23$ **d.** $-32, 27$

For Exercises 3 to 6, translate the expression into words. Represent each number as positive or negative.

3. $-6 - 4$ **4.** $-6 - (-4)$ **5.** $6 - (-4)$ **6.** $6 - 4$

OBJECTIVE A *To add integers*

For Exercises 7 to 34, add.

7. $3 + (-5)$ **8.** $-4 + 2$ **9.** $8 + 12$ **10.** $16 + 23$

11. $-3 + (-8)$ **12.** $-12 + (-1)$ **13.** $-4 + (-5)$ **14.** $-12 + (-12)$

15. $6 + (-9)$ **16.** $4 + (-9)$ **17.** $-6 + 7$ **18.** $-12 + 6$

19. $2 + (-3) + (-4)$ **20.** $7 + (-2) + (-8)$

21. $-3 + (-12) + (-15)$ **22.** $9 + (-6) + (-16)$

23. $-17 + (-3) + 29$ **24.** $13 + 62 + (-38)$

25. $-3 + (-8) + 12$ **26.** $-27 + (-42) + (-18)$

27. $13 + (-22) + 4 + (-5)$ **28.** $-14 + (-3) + 7 + (-6)$

29. $-22 + 10 + 2 + (-18)$ **30.** $-6 + (-8) + 13 + (-4)$

31. $-16 + (-17) + (-18) + 10$ **32.** $-25 + (-31) + 24 + 19$

33. $-126 + (-247) + (-358) + 339$

34. $-651 + (-239) + 524 + 487$

35. What is -8 more than -12?

36. What is -5 more than 3?

37. What is -7 added to -16?

38. What is 7 added to -25?

39. What is -4 plus 2?

40. What is -22 plus -17?

41. Find the sum of -2, 8, and -12.

42. Find the sum of 4, -4, and -6.

43. What is the total of 2, -3, 8, and -13?

44. What is the total of -6, -8, 13, and -2?

For Exercises 45 to 48, determine whether the statement is always true, never true, or sometimes true.

45. The sum of an integer and its opposite is zero.

46. The sum of two negative integers is a positive integer.

47. The sum of two negative integers and one positive integer is a negative integer.

48. If the absolute value of a negative integer is greater than the absolute value of a positive integer, then the sum of the integers is negative.

OBJECTIVE B   *To subtract integers*

For Exercises 49 to 76, subtract.

49. $16 - 8$

50. $12 - 3$

51. $7 - 14$

52. $6 - 9$

53. $-7 - 2$

54. $-9 - 4$

55. $7 - (-29)$

56. $3 - (-4)$

57. $-6 - (-3)$

58. $-4 - (-2)$

59. $6 - (-12)$

60. $-12 - 16$

61. $-4 - 3 - 2$

62. $4 - 5 - 12$

63. $12 - (-7) - 8$

64. $-12 - (-3) - (-15)$

65. $4 - 12 - (-8)$

66. $13 - 7 - 15$

67. $-6 - (-8) - (-9)$

68. $7 - 8 - (-1)$

69. $-30 - (-65) - 29 - 4$

70. $42 - (-82) - 65 - 7$

71. $-16 - 47 - 63 - 12$

72. $42 - (-30) - 65 - (-11)$

73. $47 - (-67) - 13 - 15$

74. $-18 - 49 - (-84) - 27$

75. $167 - 432 - (-287) - 359$

76. $-521 - (-350) - 164 - (-299)$

77. Subtract -8 from -4.

78. Subtract -12 from 3.

79. What is the difference between -8 and 4?

80. What is the difference between 8 and -3?

81. What is -4 decreased by 8?

82. What is -13 decreased by 9?

83. Find -2 less than 1.

84. Find -3 less than -5.

For Exercises 85 to 88, determine whether the statement is always true, never true, or sometimes true.

85. The difference between a positive integer and a negative integer is zero.

86. A negative integer subtracted from a positive integer is a positive integer.

87. The difference between two negative integers is a positive integer.

88. The difference between an integer and its absolute value is zero.

OBJECTIVE C   *To solve application problems*

89. ● Temperature   The news clipping at the right was written on September 15, 2011. The record low temperature for Minnesota is −51°C. Find the difference between the low temperature in International Falls on September 15, 2011, and the record low temperature for Minnesota.

90. ● Temperature   The record high temperature in Illinois is 117°F. The record low temperature is −36°F. Find the difference between the record high and record low temperatures in Illinois.

91. Temperature   Find the temperature after a rise of 7°C from −8°C.

92. Temperature   Find the temperature after a rise of 5°C from −19°C.

93. 🔲 If the temperature begins at −54°C and rises more than 60°C, is the new temperature above or below 0°C?

94. 🔲 If the temperature begins at −37°C and falls more than 40°C, is the new temperature above or below 0°C?

95. Games   During a card game of Hearts, Nick had a score of 11 points before his opponent "shot the moon," subtracting a score of 26 from Nick's total. What was Nick's score after his opponent shot the moon?

96. Games   In a card game of Hearts, Monique had a score of −19 before she "shot the moon," entitling her to add 26 points to her score. What was Monique's score after she shot the moon?

97. Investments   The price of Byplex Corporation's stock fell each trading day of the first week of June. Use the figure at the right to find the change in the price of Byplex stock over the week's time.

98. ● Astronomy   The daytime temperature on the moon can reach 266°F, and the nighttime temperature can go as low as −292°F. Find the difference between daytime and nighttime temperatures.

99. ● Earth Science   The average temperature throughout Earth's stratosphere is −70°F. The average temperature on Earth's surface is 45°F. Find the difference between the average temperature on Earth's surface and the average temperature in the stratosphere.

In the NEWS!

Nation's Icebox Sets Another Record Low

Eight cities in the Upper Midwest set record low temperatures today, with International Falls, Minnesota, leading the way. The low of −7°C in the city officially known as the "Icebox of the Nation" is the city's coldest temperature on record for the month of September.

Source: www.mycastwx.com

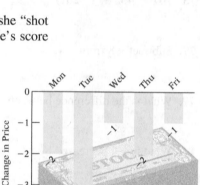

Change in Price of Byplex Corporation Stock (in dollars)

● Geography   The elevation, or height, of places on Earth is measured in relation to sea level, or the average level of the ocean's surface. The table below shows height above sea level as a positive number and depth below sea level as a negative number. Use the table for Exercises 100 to 102.

Continent	Highest Elevation (in meters)		Lowest Elevation (in meters)	
Africa	Mt. Kilimanjaro	5895	Lake Assal	−156
Asia	Mt. Everest	8850	Dead Sea	−411
North America	Mt. McKinley	5642	Death Valley	−28
South America	Mt. Aconcagua	6960	Valdes Peninsula	−86

Mt. Everest

100. What is the difference in elevation between Mt. Aconcagua and Death Valley?

101. What is the difference in elevation between Mt. Kilimanjaro and Lake Assal?

102. For which continent shown is the difference between the highest and lowest elevations greatest?

Critical Thinking

103. **Number Problem** Consider the numbers 4, −7, −5, 13, and −9. What is the largest difference that can be obtained by subtracting one number in the list from another number in the list? Find the smallest positive difference.

104. **Number Problem** Fill in the blank squares at the right with integers so that the sum of the integers along any row, column, or diagonal is zero.

−3		1
		3

105. **Number Problem** The sum of two negative integers is −8. Find the integers.

106. Explain the difference between the words *negative* and *minus*.

Projects or Group Activities

One model of addition of integers uses chips: blue chips for positive numbers and red chips for negative numbers. One positive chip added to one negative chip gives zero. To add −8 and 5, place 8 red chips and 5 blue chips in a region. Pair as many red and blue chips as possible and remove the pairs from the region. Remember that a pair of red and blue chips is zero. The remaining chips give the answer—in this case, 3 red chips, or −3.

Blue and red chips can also be used to model subtraction. To model 5 − (−3), place 5 blue chips in a region. Subtracting −3 requires removing 3 red chips, but because there are no red chips in the region, add 3 pairs of a red and a blue chip (you are adding three zeros). Now the 3 red chips can be removed. The result is 8 blue chips.

For Exercises 107 to 112, explain how you would use the chip model to find the value of the expression.

107. $8 + (-10)$

108. $-7 + (-6)$

109. $-5 + 5$

110. $6 - (-4)$

111. $-4 - 5$

112. $-5 - (-7)$

3.3 Multiplication and Division of Integers

OBJECTIVE A *To multiply integers*

Multiplication is the repeated addition of the same number.

Several different symbols are used to indicate multiplication:

$$3 \times 2 = 6 \qquad 3 \cdot 2 = 6 \qquad (3)(2) = 6$$

When 5 is multiplied by a sequence of decreasing integers, the products decrease by 5.

$$5 \times 3 = 15$$
$$5 \times 2 = 10$$
$$5 \times 1 = 5$$
$$5 \times 0 = 0$$

The pattern can be continued so that 5 is multiplied by a sequence of negative numbers. The resulting products must be negative in order to maintain the pattern of decreasing by 5.

$$5 \times (-1) = -5$$
$$5 \times (-2) = -10$$
$$5 \times (-3) = -15$$
$$5 \times (-4) = -20$$

This example illustrates that the product of a positive number and a negative number is negative.

When -5 is multiplied by a sequence of decreasing integers, the products increase by 5.

$$-5 \times 3 = -15$$
$$-5 \times 2 = -10$$
$$-5 \times 1 = -5$$
$$-5 \times 0 = 0$$

The pattern can be continued so that -5 is multiplied by a sequence of negative numbers. The resulting products must be positive in order to maintain the pattern of increasing by 5.

$$-5 \times (-1) = 5$$
$$-5 \times (-2) = 10$$
$$-5 \times (-3) = 15$$
$$-5 \times (-4) = 20$$

This example illustrates that the product of two negative numbers is positive.

The pattern for multiplication shown above is summarized in the following rules for multiplying integers.

Rules for Multiplying Two Numbers

For two numbers that have the same sign:
Multiply the absolute values of the factors. The product is positive.

EXAMPLES

1. $4 \cdot 9 = 36$ **2.** $(-12)(-8) = 96$

For two numbers that have different signs:
Multiply the absolute values of the factors. The product is negative.

EXAMPLES

3. $-7(6) = -42$ **4.** $9(-7) = -63$

Integrating Technology

To multiply $(-12)(-8)$ on your calculator, enter the following:

12 **+/−** **×** 8 **+/−** **=**

HOW TO 1 Multiply: $2(-3)(-5)(-7)$

$$2(-3)(-5)(-7) = -6(-5)(-7)$$
$$= 30(-7)$$
$$= -210$$

• To multiply more than two numbers, first multiply the first two numbers.
• Then multiply the product by the third number.
• Continue until all the numbers have been multiplied.

Exponents may cause confusion when evaluating expressions with signed numbers.

$$(-3)^2 = (-3) \times (-3) = 9$$
$$-3^2 = -(3)^2 = -(3 \times 3) = -9$$

Note that -3 is squared only when the negative sign is *inside* the parentheses.

 Take Note

In $(-3)^2$, we are squaring -3; we multiply -3 times -3. In -3^2, we are finding the opposite of 3^2.

HOW TO 2 Evaluate. **A.** $(-4)^3$ **B.** -2^4

A. $(-4)^3 = (-4)(-4)(-4)$
$$= 16(-4) = -64$$

B. $-2^4 = -(2^4)$
$$= -(2 \cdot 2 \cdot 2 \cdot 2)$$
$$= -(4 \cdot 2 \cdot 2)$$
$$= -(8 \cdot 2) = -16$$

 Take Note

Note the difference between $(-4)^3$ and -2^4. In part A, -4 is the base. In part B, 2 is the base. Here are two more examples.

$(-3)^4 = (-3)(-3)(-3)(-3)$
$$= 9(-3)(-3)$$
$$= -27(-3) = 81$$

$-5^3 = -(5^3) = -(5 \cdot 5 \cdot 5)$
$$= -(25 \cdot 5) = -125$$

EXAMPLE 1

Multiply: $(-2)(6)$

Solution

$(-2)(6) = -12$ • The signs are different. The product is negative.

YOU TRY IT 1

Multiply: $(-3)(-5)$

Your solution

EXAMPLE 2

Find the product of -42 and 62.

Solution

$-42 \cdot 62 = -2604$ • The signs are different. The product is negative.

YOU TRY IT 2

Find -38 multiplied by 51.

Your solution

EXAMPLE 3

Multiply: $-5(-4)(6)(-3)$

Solution

$-5(-4)(6)(-3) = 20(6)(-3)$
$$= 120(-3)$$
$$= -360$$

YOU TRY IT 3

Multiply: $-7(-8)(9)(-2)$

Your solution

Solutions on p. S24

OBJECTIVE B   *To divide integers*

For every division problem, there is a related multiplication problem.

Division: $\dfrac{8}{2} = 4$ Related multiplication: $4 \cdot 2 = 8$

This fact can be used to illustrate the rules for dividing signed numbers.

Rules for Dividing Two Numbers

For two numbers that have the same sign:
Divide the absolute values of the factors. The quotient is positive.

EXAMPLES

1. $\dfrac{56}{7} = 8$ because $8 \cdot 7 = 56$.   2. $\dfrac{-72}{-8} = 9$ because $9 \cdot (-8) = -72$.

For two numbers that have different signs:
Divide the absolute values of the factors. The quotient is negative.

EXAMPLES

3. $(-54) \div 6 = -9$ because $-9 \cdot 6 = -54$.
4. $36 \div (-9) = -4$ because $-4 \cdot (-9) = 36$.

Properties of One and Zero in Division

Any number divided by 1 is the number.

EXAMPLES

1. $\dfrac{-26}{1} = -26$ 2. $(-14) \div 1 = -14$

Any number *other than zero* divided by itself is 1.

EXAMPLES

3. $(-27) \div (-27) = 1$ 4. $\dfrac{-15}{-15} = 1$

EXAMPLES

Zero divided by any number *other than zero* is zero.

5. $\dfrac{0}{-16} = 0$ 5. $0 \div (-42) = 0$

Be very careful when using zero in division. Note the phrase *other than zero* in the properties shown above. Study the explanation below to see why the phrase *other than zero* is included in these properties.

Recall that every division problem has a related multiplication problem. An example is shown at the right.

$\dfrac{-12}{3} = -4$ because $-4(3) = -12$.

Now suppose we try to divide *by* zero. Look at the related multiplication problem. Because any number times 0 is 0, there is no way to replace the question mark and form a true statement. Division by zero is undefined.

If $\dfrac{-3}{0} = ?$, then $?(0) = -3$.

EXAMPLE 4

Divide: $(-120) \div (-8)$

Solution

$(-120) \div (-8) = 15$ • The signs are the same.
The quotient is positive.

YOU TRY IT 4

Divide: $(-135) \div (-9)$

Your solution

EXAMPLE 5

Divide: $\dfrac{-95}{5}$

Solution

$\dfrac{-95}{5} = -19$ • The signs are different.
The quotient is negative.

YOU TRY IT 5

Divide: $\dfrac{84}{-6}$

Your solution

EXAMPLE 6

Find the quotient of -81 and 3.

Solution

$-81 \div 3 = -27$

YOU TRY IT 6

What is -72 divided by 4?

Your solution

EXAMPLE 7

Divide: $0 \div (-24)$

Solution

$0 \div (-24) = 0$ • Zero divided by a nonzero
number is zero.

YOU TRY IT 7

Divide: $-39 \div 0$

Your solution

Solutions on p. S24

OBJECTIVE C *To solve application problems*

EXAMPLE 8

The combined scores of the top five golfers in a tournament equaled −10 (10 under par). What was the average score of the five golfers?

Strategy

To find the average score, divide the combined scores (−10) by the number of golfers (5).

Solution

$-10 \div 5 = -2$

The average score was 2.

YOU TRY IT 8

The melting point of mercury is −38°C. The melting point of argon is five times the melting point of mercury. Find the melting point of argon.

Your strategy

Your solution

EXAMPLE 9

The daily high temperatures during one week were recorded as follows: −9°F, 3°F, 0°F, −8°F, 2°F, 1°F, 4°F. Find the average daily high temperature for the week.

Strategy

To find the average daily high temperature:

- Add the seven temperature readings.
- Divide by 7.

Solution

$-9 + 3 + 0 + (-8) + 2 + 1 + 4 = -7$

$-7 \div 7 = -1$

The average daily high temperature was −1°F.

YOU TRY IT 9

The daily low temperatures during one week were recorded as follows: −6°F, −7°F, 1°F, 0°F, −5°F, −10°F, −1°F. Find the average daily low temperature for the week.

Your strategy

Your solution

3.3 EXERCISES

✔ Concept Check

1. Use the rules for multiplying and dividing integers to determine whether the given product or quotient is positive, negative, zero, or undefined.

   a. $-4(-5)$ **b.** $\dfrac{-21}{0}$ **c.** $9(-9)$ **d.** $0 \div (-2)$

2. Fill in the blank with $<$ or $>$ to make a true statement. Do not actually perform the operation; instead use your understanding of the rules for multiplying and dividing integers.

   a. $-46(58)$ _____ $\dfrac{-115}{-5}$ **b.** $0(-15)$ _____ $(-12)17$ **c.** $-25(-31)$ _____ $5(-42)$ **d.** $7(-14)$ _____ $2(3)$

OBJECTIVE A   *To multiply integers*

For Exercises 3 to 44, multiply.

3. 14×3

4. 62×9

5. $-4 \cdot 6$

6. $-7 \cdot 3$

7. $-2 \cdot (-3)$

8. $-5 \cdot (-1)$

9. $(9)(2)$

10. $(3)(8)$

11. $5(-4)$

12. $4(-7)$

13. $-8(2)$

14. $-9(3)$

15. $(-5)(-5)$

16. $(-3)(-6)$

17. $(-7)(0)$

18. $(-4)^2$

19. $(-6)^2$

20. -4^4

21. -2^3

22. -6^3

23. $(-5)^4$

24. $-5 \cdot 23$

25. $-6 \cdot 38$

26. $9(-27)$

27. $8(-40)$

28. $-7(-34)$

29. $-4(39)$

30. $4 \cdot (-8) \cdot 3$

31. $5 \cdot 7 \cdot (-2)$

32. $8(-6)(-1)$

33. $-9(-9)(2)$

34. $-8(-7)(-4)$

35. $-5(8)(-3)$

36. $-6(5)(7)$

37. $-1(4)(-9)$

38. $6(-3)(-2)$

39. $4(-4)(6)(-2)$

40. $-5(9)(-7)(3)$

41. $-9(4)(3)(1)$

42. $8(8)(-5)(-4)$

43. $(-6)(7)(-10)(-5)$

44. $-9(-6)(11)(-2)$

45. What is -5 multiplied by -4?

46. What is 6 multiplied by -5?

47. What is -8 times 6?

48. What is -8 times -7?

49. Find the product of -4, 7, and -5.

50. Find the product of -2, -4, and -7.

For Exercises 51 to 54, state whether the given product will be positive, negative, or zero.

51. The product of three negative integers

52. The product of two negative integers and one positive integer

53. The product of one negative integer, one positive integer, and zero

54. The product of five positive integers and one negative integer

---

OBJECTIVE B   *To divide integers*

For Exercises 55 to 58, write the related multiplication problem.

55. $\dfrac{-36}{-12} = 3$

56. $\dfrac{28}{-7} = -4$

57. $\dfrac{-55}{11} = -5$

58. $\dfrac{-20}{-10} = 2$

For Exercises 59 to 109, divide.

59. $12 \div (-6)$

60. $18 \div (-3)$

61. $(-72) \div (-9)$

62. $(-64) \div (-8)$

63. $0 \div (-6)$

64. $-49 \div 7$

65. $45 \div (-5)$

66. $-24 \div 4$

67. $-36 \div 4$

68. $-56 \div 7$

69. $-81 \div (-9)$

70. $-40 \div (-5)$

71. $\dfrac{72}{-3}$

72. $\dfrac{44}{-4}$

73. $\dfrac{-60}{5}$

74. $\dfrac{-66}{6}$

75. $\dfrac{-93}{-3}$

76. $\dfrac{-98}{-7}$

77. $\dfrac{-85}{-5}$

78. $\dfrac{-60}{-4}$

79. $\dfrac{120}{8}$

80. $\dfrac{144}{9}$

81. $\dfrac{78}{-6}$

82. $\dfrac{84}{-7}$

83. $-72 \div 4$

84. $-80 \div 5$

85. $-114 \div (-6)$

86. $-91 \div (-7)$

87. $-104 \div (-8)$

88. $-126 \div (-9)$

89. $57 \div (-3)$

90. $162 \div (-9)$

91. $-136 \div (-8)$

92. $-128 \div 4$

93. $-130 \div (-5)$

94. $-280 \div 8$

95. $-92 \div (-4)$

96. $-196 \div (-7)$

97. $-150 \div (-6)$

98. $\dfrac{-261}{9}$

99. $\dfrac{204}{-6}$

100. $\dfrac{165}{-5}$

101. $\dfrac{-132}{-12}$

102. $\dfrac{-156}{-13}$

103. $\dfrac{-182}{14}$

104. $-144 \div 12$

105. $143 \div 11$

106. $168 \div 14$

107. $-180 \div (-15)$

108. $-169 \div (-13)$

109. $154 \div (-11)$

110. Find the quotient of -132 and -11.

111. Find the quotient of 182 and -13.

112. What is -60 divided by -15?

113. What is 144 divided by -24?

114. Find the quotient of -135 and 15.

115. Find the quotient of -88 and 22.

For Exercises 116 to 119, determine whether the statement is always true, never true, or sometimes true.

116. The quotient of a negative integer and its absolute value is –1.

117. The quotient of zero and a positive integer is a positive integer.

118. A negative integer divided by zero is zero.

119. The quotient of two negative numbers is the same as the quotient of the absolute values of the two numbers.

OBJECTIVE C   *To solve application problems*

120. Meteorology   The daily low temperatures during one week were recorded as follows: 4°F, −5°F, 8°F, −1°F, −12°F, −14°F, −8°F. Find the average daily low temperature for the week.

121. Meteorology   The daily high temperatures during one week were recorded as follows: −6°F, −11°F, 1°F, 5°F, −3°F, −9°F, −5°F. Find the average daily high temperature for the week.

122. True or false? If five temperatures are all below 0°C, then the average of the five temperatures is also below 0°C.

123. True or false? If the average of 10 temperatures is below 0°C, then all 10 temperatures are below 0°C.

124. Chemistry   The graph at the right shows the boiling points of three chemical elements. The boiling point of neon is seven times the highest boiling point shown in the graph.
a. Without calculating the boiling point, determine whether the boiling point of neon is above 0°C or below 0°C.
b. What is the boiling point of neon?

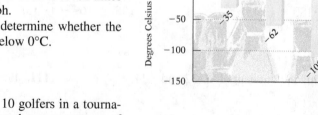

125. Sports   The combined scores of the top 10 golfers in a tournament equaled −20 (20 under par). What was the average score of the 10 golfers?

126. Sports   The combined scores of the top four golfers in a tournament equaled −12 (12 under par). What was the average score of the four golfers?

127. ● Meteorology   The wind chill factor when the temperature is $-20°F$ and the wind is blowing at 15 mph is five times the wind chill factor when the temperature is $10°F$ and the wind is blowing at 20 mph. If the wind chill factor at $10°F$ with a 20-mile-per-hour wind is $-9°F$, what is the wind chill factor at $-20°F$ with a 15-mile-per-hour wind?

128. ● Economics   A nation's balance of trade is the difference between the value of its exports and that of its imports. If the value of the exports is greater than that of the imports, the result is a positive number and a *favorable balance of trade*. If the value of the exports is less than that of the imports, the result is a negative number and an *unfavorable balance of trade*. The table at the right shows the U.S. unfavorable balance of trade, in billions of dollars, for each of the first six months of 2011. Find the average monthly balance of trade for January through June. Round to the nearest billion dollars.

U.S. Balance of Trade in 2011 (in billions of dollar)	
January	-61
February	-59
March	-60
April	-57
May	-64
June	-66

Source: U.S. Census Bureau

129. Education   To discourage guessing on a multiple-choice exam, an instructor graded the test by giving 5 points for a correct answer, -2 points for an answer left blank, and -5 points for an incorrect answer. How many points did a student score who answered 20 questions correctly, answered 5 questions incorrectly, and left 2 questions blank?

Critical Thinking

130. Use repeated addition to show that the product of two integers with different signs is a negative number.

131. Determine whether the statement is true or false.
   a. The product of a nonzero number and its opposite is negative.
   b. The square of a negative number is a positive number.

132. a. Number Problem   Find the greatest possible product of two negative integers whose sum is -10.
   b. Number Problem   Find the least possible sum of two negative integers whose product is 16.

Projects or Group Activities

133. ◣ Write a short lesson that you could use to teach multiplication and division of integers.

✔ CHECK YOUR PROGRESS: CHAPTER 3

For Exercises 1 to 3, place the correct symbol, $<$ or $>$, between the two numbers.

1. $-12 \quad -15$

2. $0 \quad -11$

3. $-49 \quad 4$

For Exercises 4 to 6, evaluate the expression.

4. $|-7|$

5. $-|21|$

6. $|0|$

For Exercises 7 to 18, perform the indicated operation.

7. $-15 + 27$

8. $-25 + (-20)$

9. $-17 - (-23)$

10. $-5 - 11$

11. $0 - (-13)$

12. $-48 + 0$

13. $-12(-7)$

14. $5(-15)$

15. $-23(0)$

16. $-50 \div 10$

17. $0 \div (-7)$

18. $-84 \div (-7)$

19. Find the sum of -9 and 12.

20. What is the quotient of -54 and -6?

21. Find 7 less than -9.

22. Find the total of 17 and -23.

23. What is the product of -8 and -9?

24. Find -13 more than 13.

25. Chemistry Liquid oxygen has a freezing point of $-223°C$ and a boiling point of $-183°C$. What is the difference between the boiling point temperature and the freezing point temperature?

3.4 Exponents and the Order of Operations Agreement

OBJECTIVE A   *To evaluate exponential expressions*

Repeated multiplication of the same factor can be written using an exponent.

$$2 \cdot 2 \cdot 2 \cdot 2 \cdot 2 = 2^5 \leftarrow \text{Exponent} \qquad a \cdot a \cdot a \cdot a = a^4 \leftarrow \text{Exponent}$$
$$\uparrow \text{—— Base} \qquad\qquad\qquad \uparrow \text{—— Base}$$

Point of Interest
René Descartes (1596–1650) was the first mathematician to use exponential notation extensively as it is used today. However, for some unknown reason, he always used *xx* for x^2.

The **exponent** indicates how many times the factor, which is called the **base,** occurs in the multiplication. The multiplication $2 \cdot 2 \cdot 2 \cdot 2 \cdot 2$ is in **factored form.** The expression 2^5 is in **exponential form.**

2^1 is read "2 to the first power" or just "2." Usually the exponent 1 is not written.

2^2 is read "2 to the second power" or "2 squared."

2^3 is read "2 to the third power" or "2 cubed."

2^4 is read "2 to the fourth power."

a^4 is read "*a* to the fourth power."

The first three natural-number powers can be interpreted geometrically as length, area, and volume, respectively.

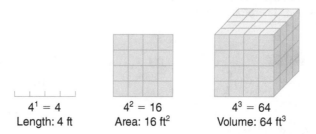

| $4^1 = 4$ | $4^2 = 16$ | $4^3 = 64$ |
| Length: 4 ft | Area: 16 ft² | Volume: 64 ft³ |

To evaluate an exponential expression, write each factor as many times as indicated by the exponent. Then multiply.

Take Note
Note the difference between $(-2)^4$ and -2^4. $(-2)^4$ is the fourth power of -2:
$$(-2)^4 = 16$$
-2^4 is the opposite of the fourth power of 2:
$$-2^4 = -16.$$

HOW TO 1   Evaluate $(-2)^4$.

$$(-2)^4 = (-2)(-2)(-2)(-2)$$ • Write -2 as a factor 4 times.
$$= 16$$ • Multiply.

HOW TO 2   Evaluate -2^4.

$$-2^4 = -(2 \cdot 2 \cdot 2 \cdot 2)$$ • Write 2 as a factor 4 times.
$$= -16$$ • Multiply.

EXAMPLE 1

Evaluate -5^3.

Solution

$-5^3 = -(5 \cdot 5 \cdot 5) = -125$

YOU TRY IT 1

Evaluate -6^3.

Your solution

EXAMPLE 2

Evaluate $(-4)^4$.

Solution

$(-4)^4 = (-4)(-4)(-4)(-4)$
$= 256$

YOU TRY IT 2

Evaluate $(-3)^4$.

Your solution

EXAMPLE 3

Evaluate $(-3)^2 \cdot 2^3$.

Solution

$(-3)^2 \cdot 2^3 = (-3)(-3) \cdot (2)(2)(2)$
$= 9 \cdot 8 = 72$

YOU TRY IT 3

Evaluate $(3^3)(-2)^3$.

Your solution

EXAMPLE 4

Evaluate $(-1)^6$.

Solution

The product of an even number of negative factors is positive. Therefore, $(-1)^6 = 1$.

YOU TRY IT 4

Evaluate $(-1)^7$.

Your solution

EXAMPLE 5

Evaluate $-2 \cdot (-3)^2 \cdot (-1)^9$.

Solution

$-2 \cdot (-3)^2 \cdot (-1)^9$
$= -2 \cdot 9 \cdot (-1)$ • $(-3)^2 = 9; (-1)^9 = -1$
$= 18$

YOU TRY IT 5

Evaluate $-2^2 \cdot (-1)^{12} \cdot (-3)^2$.

Your solution

Solutions on p. S1

OBJECTIVE B *To use the Order of Operations Agreement to simplify expressions*

Let's evaluate $2 + 3 \cdot 5$.

There are two arithmetic operations, addition and multiplication, in this expression. The operations could be performed in different orders. We could multiply first and then add, or we could add first and then multiply. To prevent there being more than one answer when simplifying a numerical expression, an Order of Operations Agreement has been established.

The Order of Operations Agreement

Step 1. Perform operations inside grouping symbols. Grouping symbols include parentheses ( ), brackets [ ], braces { }, the absolute value symbol ||, and the fraction bar.

Step 2. Simplify exponential expressions.

Step 3. Do multiplication and division as they occur from left to right.

Step 4. Do addition and subtraction as they occur from left to right.

EXAMPLE

Simplify: $(-4)^2 - 2(3 - 8)$

$(-4)^2 - 2(3 - 8)$

$= (-4)^2 - 2(-5)$ • Perform operations inside parentheses.

$= 16 - 2(-5)$ • Simplify exponential expressions.

$= 16 + 10$ • Do multiplication and division from left to right.

$= 26$ • Do addition and subtraction from left to right.

Integrating Technology

See the Keystroke Guide: *Basic Operations* for instruction on using a calculator to evaluate a numerical expression.

One or more of the steps listed above may not be needed to evaluate an expression. In that case, proceed to the next step in the Order of Operations Agreement.

HOW TO 3 Evaluate $\dfrac{4 + 8}{2 + 1} - (3 - 1) + 2$.

$\dfrac{4 + 8}{2 + 1} - (3 - 1) + 2 = \dfrac{12}{3} - 2 + 2$ • Perform operations above and below the fraction bar and inside parentheses.

$= 4 - 2 + 2$ • Do multiplication and division as they occur from left to right.

$= 2 + 2$ • Do addition and subtraction as they occur from left to right.

$= 4$

EXAMPLE 6

Evaluate $6 \div [4 - (6 - 8)] - 2^3$.

Solution

$6 \div [4 - (6 - 8)] - 2^3$

$= 6 \div [4 - (-2)] - 2^3$ • Perform operations inside grouping symbols.

$= 6 \div 6 - 2^3$

$= 6 \div 6 - 8$ • Simplify exponential expressions.

$= 1 - 8$ • Do multiplication and division from left to right.

$= -7$ • Do addition and subtraction from left to right.

YOU TRY IT 6

Evaluate $7 - 2[2 \cdot 3 - 7 \cdot 2]^2$.

Your solution

Solution on p. S2

EXAMPLE 7

Evaluate $4 - 3[4 - 2(6 - 3)] \div 2$.

Solution

$4 - 3[4 - 2(6 - 3)] \div 2$

$= 4 - 3[4 - 2 \cdot 3] \div 2$ • Perform operations
                                    inside grouping
$= 4 - 3[4 - 6] \div 2$ symbols.

$= 4 - 3[-2] \div 2$

$= 4 + 6 \div 2$ • Do multiplication
                                    and division from
$= 4 + 3$ left to right.

$= 7$ • Do addition and
                                    subtraction from
                                    left to right.

YOU TRY IT 7

Evaluate $18 - 5[8 - 2(2 - 5)] \div 10$.

Your solution

EXAMPLE 8

Evaluate $27 \div (5 - 2)^2 + (-3)^2 \cdot 4$.

Solution

$27 \div (5 - 2)^2 + (-3)^2 \cdot 4$

$= 27 \div 3^2 + (-3)^2 \cdot 4$ • Perform
                                    operations inside
                                    grouping symbols.
$= 27 \div 9 + 9 \cdot 4$ • Simplify
                                    exponential
                                    expressions.
$= 3 + 9 \cdot 4$ • Do multiplication
                                    and division from
$= 3 + 36$ left to right.
$= 39$ • Do addition and
                                    subtraction from
                                    left to right.

YOU TRY IT 8

Evaluate $36 \div (8 - 5)^2 - (-3)^2 \cdot 2$.

Your solution

Solutions on p. S2

3.4 EXERCISES

✓ Concept Check

For Exercises 1 to 3, write the expression as an exponential expression.

1. Nine to the fifth power

2. y to the fourth power

3. Seven to the nth power

4. True or false? To evaluate the expression $6 + 7 \cdot 10$ means to determine the one number it is equal to.

OBJECTIVE A   *To evaluate exponential expressions*

For Exercises 5 to 27, evaluate.

5. 6^2

6. 7^4

7. -7^2

8. -4^3

9. $(-3)^2$

10. $(-2)^3$

11. $(-3)^4$

12. $(-5)^3$

13. -4^4

14. $(-4)^4$

15. $2 \cdot (-3)^2$

16. $-2 \cdot (-4)^2$

17. $(-1)^9 \cdot 3^3$

18. $(-1)^8(-8)^2$

19. $(3)^3 \cdot 2^3$

20. $(5)^2 \cdot 3^3$

21. $(-3) \cdot 2^2$

22. $(-5) \cdot 3^4$

23. $2^3 \cdot 3^3 \cdot (-4)$

24. $(-3)^3 \cdot 5^2 \cdot 10$

25. $(-7) \cdot 4^2 \cdot 3^2$

26. $(-2) \cdot 2^3 \cdot (-3)^2$

27. $(-2)^3(-3)^2(-1)^7$

For Exercises 28 to 31, without finding the product, determine whether the product is positive or negative.

28. The fifth power of -18

29. The opposite of $(-7)^8$

30. $-(9^2)(-6^3)$

31. $(-9)^2(-6)^3$

OBJECTIVE B   *To use the Order of Operations Agreement to simplify expressions*

For Exercises 32 to 58, evaluate by using the Order of Operations Agreement.

32. $4 - 8 \div 2$

33. $2^2 \cdot 3 - 3$

34. $2(3 - 4) - (-3)^2$

35. $16 - 32 \div 2^3$

36. $24 - 18 \div 3 + 2$

37. $8 - (-3)^2 - (-2)$

38. $8 - 2(3)^2$

39. $16 - 16 \cdot 2 \div 4$

40. $12 + 16 \div 4 \cdot 2$

41. $16 - 2 \cdot 4^2$

42. $27 - 18 \div (-3^2)$

43. $4 + 12 \div 3 \cdot 2$

44. $16 + 15 \div (-5) - 2$

45. $14 - 2^2 - (4 - 7)$

46. $3 - 2[8 - (3 - 2)]$

47. $-2^2 + 4[16 \div (3 - 5)]$

48. $6 + \dfrac{16 - 4}{2^2 + 2} - 2$

49. $24 \div \dfrac{3^2}{8 - 5} - (-5)$

50. $96 \div 2[12 + (6 - 2)] - 3^2$

51. $4[16 - (7 - 1)] \div 10$

52. $18 \div 2 - 4^2 - (-3)^2$

53. $18 \div (9 - 2^3) + (-3)$

54. $16 - 3(8 - 3)^2 \div 5$

55. $4(-8) \div [2(7 - 3)^2]$

56. $\dfrac{(-19) + (-2)}{6^2 - 29} \div (2 - 5)$

57. $16 - 4 \cdot \dfrac{3^3 - 7}{2^3 + 2} - (-2)^2$

58. $7 - 3[1 - (2 - (-3))^2]$

59. Which expression is equivalent to $15 + 15 \div 3 - 4^2$?

   (i) $30 \div 3 - 16$ (ii) $15 + 5 - 16$ (iii) $15 + 5 + 16$ (iv) $15 + 15 \div (-1)^2$

Critical Thinking

60. The following was offered as the simplification of $6 + 2(4 - 9)$.

$$6 + 2(4 - 9) = 6 + 2(-5)$$
$$= 8(-5)$$
$$= -40$$

If this is a correct simplification, write *yes* for the answer. If it is incorrect, write *no* and explain the incorrect step.

Projects or Group Activities

61. In which column is the number 1 million, column A, B, or C?

A	B	C
1	8	27
64	125	216
.	.	.
.	.	.
.	.	.

✔ CHECK YOUR PROGRESS: CHAPTER 3 ....

1. Use the roster method to write the set of positive integers less than 9.

2. Given $A = \{-7, 0, 2, 5\}$, which elements of A are less than 1?

3. Find the additive inverse of -13.

4. Evaluate $|-44|$ and $-|-18|$.

5. Place the correct symbol, $<$ or $>$, between the two expressions.

$|31| \qquad |-13|$

6. Add: $-47 + 23$

7. Subtract: $-11 - (-27)$

8. Add: $-32 + 40 + (-9)$

9. Subtract: $42 - (-82) - 65 - 7$

10. Multiply: $16(-2)$

11. Multiply: $-9(7)(-5)$

12. Divide: $250 \div (-25)$

13. Divide: $-\dfrac{-80}{-5}$

14. Divide: $\dfrac{-58}{0}$

15. Evaluate: $-3^2 \cdot (-2)^4$

16. Evaluate: $5 - 4[3 - 2(7 - 1)] \div 9$

17. Evaluate: $-4 \cdot 2^3 - \dfrac{1 - 13}{2^2 \cdot 3}$

18. Evaluate: $(8 - 3^2)^6 + (2 \cdot 3 - 7)^9$

19. Temperature Find the temperature after a rise of 8°C from -3°C.

20. Temperature The daily low temperatures (in degrees Celsius) during one week were recorded as $-8°$, $-12°$, $0°$, $-4°$, $5°$, $-7°$, and $-9°$. Find the average daily low temperature for the week.

3.5 Evaluating Variable Expressions

OBJECTIVE A *To evaluate a variable expression*

Often we discuss a quantity without knowing its exact value—for example, the price of gold next month, the cost of a new automobile next year, or the tuition cost for next semester. Recall that a letter of the alphabet, called a **variable,** is used to stand for a quantity that is unknown or that can change, or *vary.* An expression that contains one or more variables is called a **variable expression.**

A variable expression is shown at the right. The expression can be rewritten by writing subtraction as the addition of the opposite.

$$3x^2 - 5y + 2xy - x - 7$$
$$3x^2 + (-5y) + 2xy + (-x) + (-7)$$

Note that the expression has five addends. The **terms** of a variable expression are the addends of the expression. The expression has five terms.

Five terms

$$\overbrace{3x^2 \quad - \quad 5y \quad + \quad 2xy \quad - \quad x}^{\text{Variable terms}} \quad \underbrace{- \quad 7}_{\substack{\text{Constant} \\ \text{term}}}$$

The terms $3x^2$, $-5y$, $2xy$, and $-x$ are **variable terms.**

The term -7 is a **constant term,** or simply a **constant.**

Each variable term is composed of a **numerical coefficient** and a **variable part** (the variable or variables and their exponents).

When the numerical coefficient is 1 or -1, the 1 is usually not written $(x = 1x \text{ and } -x = -1x)$.

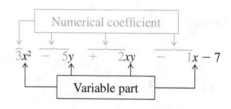

Variable expressions can be used to model scientific phenomena. In a physics lab, a student may discover that a weight of 1 pound will stretch a spring $\frac{1}{2}$ inch. Two pounds will stretch the spring 1 inch. By experimenting, the student can discover that the distance the spring will stretch is found by multiplying the weight by $\frac{1}{2}$. By letting W represent the weight attached to the spring, the student can represent the distance the spring stretches by the variable expression $\frac{1}{2}W$.

With a weight of W pounds attached, the spring will stretch $\frac{1}{2} \cdot W = \frac{1}{2}W$ inches.

With a weight of 10 pounds attached, the spring will stretch $\frac{1}{2} \cdot 10 = 5$ inches. The number 10 is called the **value of the variable** W.

With a weight of 3 pounds attached, the spring will stretch $\frac{1}{2} \cdot 3 = 1\frac{1}{2}$ inches.

Integrating Technology

See the Keystroke Guide: *Evaluating Variable Expressions* for instructions on using a graphing calculator to evaluate variable expressions.

Replacing each variable by its value and then simplifying the resulting numerical expression is called **evaluating a variable expression.**

HOW TO 1   Evaluate $ab - b^2$ when $a = 2$ and $b = -3$.

Replace each variable in the expression by its value. Then use the Order of Operations Agreement to simplify the resulting numerical expression.

$$ab - b^2$$
$$2(-3) - (-3)^2 = -6 - 9 = -15$$

EXAMPLE 1

Name the variable terms of the expression $2a^2 - 5a + 7$.

Solution

$2a^2$ and $-5a$

YOU TRY IT 1

Name the constant term of the expression $6n^2 + 3n - 4$.

Your solution

EXAMPLE 2

Evaluate $x^2 - 3xy$ when $x = 3$ and $y = -4$.

Solution

$x^2 - 3xy$
$3^2 - 3(3)(-4) = 9 - 3(3)(-4)$ • $x = 3, y = -4$
$= 9 - 9(-4)$
$= 9 - (-36)$
$= 9 + 36 = 45$

YOU TRY IT 2

Evaluate $2xy + y^2$ when $x = -4$ and $y = 2$.

Your solution

EXAMPLE 3

Evaluate $\dfrac{a^2 - b^2}{a - b}$ when $a = 3$ and $b = -4$.

Solution

$$\dfrac{a^2 - b^2}{a - b}$$

$$\dfrac{3^2 - (-4)^2}{3 - (-4)} = \dfrac{9 - 16}{3 - (-4)}$$ • $a = 3, b = -4$

$$= \dfrac{-7}{7} = -1$$

YOU TRY IT 3

Evaluate $\dfrac{a^2 + b^2}{a + b}$ when $a = 5$ and $b = -3$.

Your solution

EXAMPLE 4

Evaluate $x^2 - 3(x - y) - z^2$ when $x = 2$, $y = -1$, and $z = 3$.

Solution

$x^2 - 3(x - y) - z^2$
$2^2 - 3[2 - (-1)] - 3^2$ • $x = 2, y = -1, z = 3$
$= 2^2 - 3(3) - 3^2$
$= 4 - 3(3) - 9$
$= 4 - 9 - 9$
$= -5 - 9 = -14$

YOU TRY IT 4

Evaluate $x^3 - 2(x + y) + z^2$ when $x = 2$, $y = -4$, and $z = -3$.

Your solution

Solutions on p. S4

3.5 EXERCISES

✔ Concept Check

For Exercises 1 to 3, name the terms of the variable expression. Then underline the constant term.

1. $2x^2 + 5x - 8$

2. $-3n^2 - 4n + 7$

3. $6 - a^4$

For Exercises 4 to 6, name the variable terms of the expression. Then underline the variable part of each term.

4. $9b^2 - 4ab + a^2$

5. $7x^2y + 6xy^2 + 10$

6. $5 - 8n - 3n^2$

For Exercises 7 to 9, name the coefficients of the variable terms.

7. $x^2 - 9x + 2$

8. $12a^2 - 8ab - b^2$

9. $n^3 - 4n^2 - n + 9$

10. ◤ What is the numerical coefficient of a variable term?

11. ◤ Explain the meaning of the phrase "evaluate a variable expression."

OBJECTIVE A   *To evaluate a variable expression*

For Exercises 12 to 32, evaluate the variable expression when $a = 2$, $b = 3$, and $c = -4$.

12. $3a + 2b$

13. $a - 2c$

14. $-a^2$

15. $2c^2$

16. $-3a + 4b$

17. $3b - 3c$

18. $b^2 - 3$

19. $-3c + 4$

20. $16 \div (2c)$

21. $6b \div (-a)$

22. $bc \div (2a)$

23. $b^2 - 4ac$

24. $a^2 - b^2$

25. $b^2 - c^2$

26. $(a + b)^2$

27. $a^2 + b^2$

28. $2a - (c + a)^2$

29. $(b - a)^2 + 4c$

30. $b^2 - \dfrac{ac}{8}$

31. $\dfrac{5ab}{6} - 3cb$

32. $(b - 2a)^2 + bc$

For Exercises 33 to 50, evaluate the variable expression when $a = -2$, $b = 4$, $c = -1$, and $d = 3$.

33. $\dfrac{b + c}{d}$

34. $\dfrac{d - b}{c}$

35. $\dfrac{2d + b}{-a}$

36. $\dfrac{b + 2d}{b}$

37. $\dfrac{b - d}{c - a}$

38. $\dfrac{2c - d}{-ad}$

39. $(b + d)^2 - 4a$

40. $(d - a)^2 - 3c$

41. $(d - a)^2 \div 5$

42. $3(b - a) - bc$

43. $\dfrac{b - 2a}{bc^2 - d}$

44. $\dfrac{b^2 - a}{ad + 3c}$

45. $\dfrac{1}{3}d^2 - \dfrac{3}{8}b^2$

46. $\dfrac{5}{8}a^4 - c^2$

47. $\dfrac{-4bc}{2a - b}$

48. $-\dfrac{3}{4}b + \dfrac{1}{2}(ac + bd)$

49. $-\dfrac{2}{3}d - \dfrac{1}{5}(bd - ac)$

50. $(b - a)^2 - (d - c)^2$

For Exercises 51 to 54, without evaluating the expression, determine whether the expression is positive or negative when $a = -25$, $b = 67$, and $c = -82$.

51. $(c - a)(-b)$

52. $(a - c) + 3b$

53. $\dfrac{b + c}{abc}$

54. $\dfrac{ac}{-b^2}$

Critical Thinking

55. The value of a is the value of $3x^2 - 4x - 5$ when $x = -2$. Find the value of $3a - 4$.

56. The value of c is the value of $a^2 + b^2$ when $a = 2$ and $b = -2$. Find the value of $c^2 - 4$.

For Exercises 57 to 60, evaluate the expression for $x = 2$, $y = 3$, and $z = -2$.

57. $3^x - x^3$

58. z^x

59. $x^x - y^y$

60. $y^{(x^2)}$

Projects or Group Activities

61. For each of the following, determine the first natural number x, greater than 2, for which the second expression is larger than the first. On the basis of your answers, make a conjecture that appears to be true about the expressions x^n and n^x, where $n = 3, 4, 5, 6, 7, \ldots$ and x is a natural number greater than 2.

 a. $x^3, 3^x$

 b. $x^4, 4^x$

 c. $x^5, 5^x$

 d. $x^6, 6^x$

3.6 | Multiplication and Division of Fractions

OBJECTIVE A *To multiply fractions*

To multiply two fractions, multiply the numerators and multiply the denominators.

Multiplication of Fractions

The product of two fractions is the product of the numerators over the product of the denominators.

$$\frac{a}{b} \cdot \frac{c}{d} = \frac{ac}{bd}, \quad \text{where} \quad b \neq 0 \quad \text{and} \quad d \neq 0$$

EXAMPLES

1. $\dfrac{2}{5} \cdot \dfrac{1}{3} = \dfrac{2 \cdot 1}{5 \cdot 3} = \dfrac{2}{15}$ 2. $\dfrac{3}{4} \cdot \dfrac{5}{8} = \dfrac{3 \cdot 5}{4 \cdot 8} = \dfrac{15}{32}$

> **Take Note**
>
> Note that fractions do not need to have the same denominator in order to be multiplied.

The product $\frac{2}{5} \cdot \frac{1}{3}$ shown in the example (1) above can be read "$\frac{2}{5}$ times $\frac{1}{3}$" or "$\frac{2}{5}$ of $\frac{1}{3}$." Reading the times sign as "of" is useful in diagramming the product of two fractions.

$\frac{1}{3}$ of the bar at the right is shaded.

We want to shade $\frac{2}{5}$ of the $\frac{1}{3}$ already shaded.

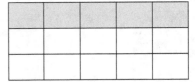

$\frac{2}{15}$ of the bar is now shaded.

$$\frac{2}{5} \text{ of } \frac{1}{3} = \frac{2}{5} \cdot \frac{1}{3} = \frac{2}{15}$$

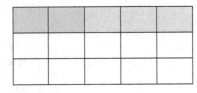

After multiplying two fractions, write the product in simplest form.

HOW TO 1 Multiply: $\dfrac{3}{8} \cdot \dfrac{4}{9}$

Multiply the numerators.
Multiply the denominators.

$$\frac{3}{8} \cdot \frac{4}{9} = \frac{3 \cdot 4}{8 \cdot 9}$$

Express the fraction in simplest form by first writing the prime factorization of each number.

$$= \frac{3 \cdot 2 \cdot 2}{2 \cdot 2 \cdot 2 \cdot 3 \cdot 3}$$

Divide by the common factors and write the product in simplest form.

$$= \frac{1}{6}$$

If a is a natural number, then $\frac{1}{a}$ is called the **reciprocal** or **multiplicative inverse** of a. Note that $a \cdot \frac{1}{a} = \frac{a}{1} \cdot \frac{1}{a} = \frac{a}{a} = 1$.

The product of a number and its multiplicative inverse is 1. $\frac{1}{8} \cdot 8 = 8 \cdot \frac{1}{8} = 1$

The sign rules for multiplying positive and negative fractions are the same rules used to multiply integers.

> **The product of two numbers with the same sign is positive.**
> **The product of two numbers with different signs is negative.**

HOW TO 2   Multiply: $-\dfrac{3}{4} \cdot \dfrac{8}{15}$

The signs are different.
The product is negative.

$$-\frac{3}{4} \cdot \frac{8}{15} = -\left(\frac{3}{4} \cdot \frac{8}{15}\right)$$

Multiply the numerators.
Multiply the denominators.

$$= -\frac{3 \cdot 8}{4 \cdot 15}$$

Write the product in simplest form.

$$= -\frac{3 \cdot 2 \cdot 2 \cdot 2}{2 \cdot 2 \cdot 3 \cdot 5}$$

$$= -\frac{2}{5}$$

HOW TO 3   Multiply: $-\dfrac{3}{8}\left(-\dfrac{2}{5}\right)\left(-\dfrac{10}{21}\right)$

$$-\frac{3}{8}\left(-\frac{2}{5}\right)\left(-\frac{10}{21}\right)$$

Multiply the first two fractions. The product is positive.

$$= \left(\frac{3}{8} \cdot \frac{2}{5}\right)\left(-\frac{10}{21}\right)$$

The product of the first two fractions and the third fraction is negative.

$$= -\left(\frac{3}{8} \cdot \frac{2}{5} \cdot \frac{10}{21}\right)$$

Multiply the numerators.
Multiply the denominators.

$$= -\frac{3 \cdot 2 \cdot 10}{8 \cdot 5 \cdot 21}$$

Write the product in simplest form.

$$= -\frac{3 \cdot 2 \cdot 2 \cdot 5}{2 \cdot 2 \cdot 2 \cdot 5 \cdot 3 \cdot 7}$$

$$= -\frac{1}{14}$$

Thus, the product of three negative fractions is negative. We can modify the rule for multiplying positive and negative fractions to say that the product of an odd number of negative fractions is negative, and the product of an even number of negative fractions is positive.

To multiply a whole number by a fraction or a mixed number, first write the whole number as a fraction with a denominator of 1.

Point of Interest

Try this: What is the result if you take one-third of a half-dozen and add to it one-fourth of the product of the result and 8?

HOW TO 4 Multiply: $3 \cdot \dfrac{5}{8}$

Write the whole number 3 as the fraction $\frac{3}{1}$.

$$3 \cdot \frac{5}{8} = \frac{3}{1} \cdot \frac{5}{8}$$

Multiply the fractions.
There are no common factors in the numerator and denominator.

$$= \frac{3 \cdot 5}{1 \cdot 8}$$

Write the improper fraction as a mixed number.

$$= \frac{15}{8} = 1\frac{7}{8}$$

APPLY THE CONCEPT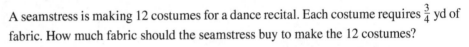

A seamstress is making 12 costumes for a dance recital. Each costume requires $\frac{3}{4}$ yd of fabric. How much fabric should the seamstress buy to make the 12 costumes?

To find the amount of fabric the seamstress should buy, multiply the amount of fabric needed for each costume $\left(\frac{3}{4}\right)$ by the number of costumes (12).

$$12 \cdot \frac{3}{4} = \frac{12}{1} \cdot \frac{3}{4} = \frac{12 \cdot 3}{1 \cdot 4} = \frac{36}{4} = 9$$

The seamstress should buy 9 yd of fabric.

Sergemi/Shutterstock.com

HOW TO 5 Multiply: $\dfrac{x}{7} \cdot \dfrac{y}{5}$

Multiply the numerators.
Multiply the denominators.

$$\frac{x}{7} \cdot \frac{y}{5} = \frac{x \cdot y}{7 \cdot 5}$$

Write the product in simplest form.

$$= \frac{xy}{35}$$

When a factor is a mixed number, first write the mixed number as an improper fraction. Then multiply.

HOW TO 6 Find the product of $-4\frac{1}{6}$ and $2\frac{7}{10}$.

The signs are different.
The product is negative.

$$-4\frac{1}{6} \cdot 2\frac{7}{10} = -\left(4\frac{1}{6} \cdot 2\frac{7}{10}\right)$$

Write each mixed number as an improper fraction.

$$= -\left(\frac{25}{6} \cdot \frac{27}{10}\right)$$

Multiply the fractions.

$$= -\frac{25 \cdot 27}{6 \cdot 10}$$

Write the product in simplest form.

$$= -\frac{5 \cdot 5 \cdot 3 \cdot 3 \cdot 3}{2 \cdot 3 \cdot 2 \cdot 5}$$

$$= -\frac{45}{4} = -11\frac{1}{4}$$

HOW TO 7 Is $-\frac{2}{3}$ a solution of the equation $\frac{3}{4}x = -\frac{1}{2}$?

Replace x by $-\frac{2}{3}$ and then simplify.

$$
\begin{array}{c|c}
\dfrac{3}{4}x = -\dfrac{1}{2} & \\
\hline
\dfrac{3}{4}\left(-\dfrac{2}{3}\right) & -\dfrac{1}{2} \\
-\dfrac{3 \cdot 2}{4 \cdot 3} & -\dfrac{1}{2} \\
-\dfrac{3 \cdot 2}{2 \cdot 2 \cdot 3} & -\dfrac{1}{2} \\
-\dfrac{1}{2} = -\dfrac{1}{2}
\end{array}
$$

The results are equal.

Yes, $-\frac{2}{3}$ is a solution of the equation.

EXAMPLE 1

Multiply: $\dfrac{7}{9} \cdot \dfrac{3}{14} \cdot \dfrac{2}{5}$

Solution

$$\dfrac{7}{9} \cdot \dfrac{3}{14} \cdot \dfrac{2}{5} = \dfrac{7 \cdot 3 \cdot 2}{9 \cdot 14 \cdot 5}$$

$$= \dfrac{7 \cdot 3 \cdot 2}{3 \cdot 3 \cdot 2 \cdot 7 \cdot 5} = \dfrac{1}{15}$$

YOU TRY IT 1

Multiply: $\dfrac{5}{12} \cdot \dfrac{9}{35} \cdot \dfrac{7}{8}$

Your solution

EXAMPLE 2

Multiply: $\dfrac{6}{x} \cdot \dfrac{8}{y}$

Solution

$$\dfrac{6}{x} \cdot \dfrac{8}{y} = \dfrac{6 \cdot 8}{x \cdot y}$$

$$= \dfrac{48}{xy}$$

YOU TRY IT 2

Multiply: $\dfrac{y}{10} \cdot \dfrac{z}{7}$

Your solution

EXAMPLE 3

Multiply: $-\dfrac{3}{4}\left(\dfrac{1}{2}\right)\left(-\dfrac{8}{9}\right)$

Solution

$$-\dfrac{3}{4}\left(\dfrac{1}{2}\right)\left(-\dfrac{8}{9}\right)$$

$$= \dfrac{3}{4} \cdot \dfrac{1}{2} \cdot \dfrac{8}{9}$$ • The product of two negative fractions is positive.

$$= \dfrac{3 \cdot 1 \cdot 8}{4 \cdot 2 \cdot 9}$$

$$= \dfrac{3 \cdot 1 \cdot 2 \cdot 2 \cdot 2}{2 \cdot 2 \cdot 2 \cdot 3 \cdot 3} = \dfrac{1}{3}$$

YOU TRY IT 3

Multiply: $-\dfrac{1}{3}\left(-\dfrac{5}{12}\right)\left(\dfrac{8}{15}\right)$

Your solution

Solutions on p. S8

EXAMPLE 4

What is the product of $\frac{7}{12}$ and 4?

Solution $\frac{7}{12} \cdot 4 = \frac{7}{12} \cdot \frac{4}{1}$ • Write 4 as $\frac{4}{1}$.

$$= \frac{7 \cdot 4}{12 \cdot 1}$$

$$= \frac{7 \cdot 2 \cdot 2}{2 \cdot 2 \cdot 3 \cdot 1}$$

$$= \frac{7}{3}$$

$$= 2\frac{1}{3}$$

YOU TRY IT 4

Find the product of $\frac{8}{9}$ and 6.

Your solution

EXAMPLE 5

Multiply: $-7\frac{1}{2} \cdot 4\frac{2}{5}$

Solution $-7\frac{1}{2} \cdot 4\frac{2}{5} = -\left(\frac{15}{2} \cdot \frac{22}{5} \right)$

$$= -\frac{15 \cdot 22}{2 \cdot 5}$$

$$= -\frac{3 \cdot 5 \cdot 2 \cdot 11}{2 \cdot 5}$$

$$= -\frac{33}{1} = -33$$

YOU TRY IT 5

Multiply: $3\frac{6}{7} \cdot 2\frac{4}{9}$

Your solution

EXAMPLE 6

Evaluate the variable expression xy for $x = 1\frac{4}{5}$ and $y = -\frac{5}{6}$.

Solution xy

$$1\frac{4}{5}\left(-\frac{5}{6}\right) = -\left(\frac{9}{5} \cdot \frac{5}{6} \right)$$

$$= -\frac{9 \cdot 5}{5 \cdot 6}$$

$$= -\frac{3 \cdot 3 \cdot 5}{5 \cdot 2 \cdot 3}$$

$$= -\frac{3}{2} = -1\frac{1}{2}$$

YOU TRY IT 6

Evaluate the variable expression xy for $x = 5\frac{1}{8}$ and $y = \frac{2}{3}$.

Your solution

Solutions on pp. S8–S9

OBJECTIVE B *To divide fractions*

The **reciprocal** of a fraction is that fraction with the numerator and denominator interchanged.

The reciprocal of $\frac{3}{4}$ is $\frac{4}{3}$.   The reciprocal of $\frac{a}{b}$ is $\frac{b}{a}$.

The process of interchanging the numerator and denominator of a fraction is called **inverting** the fraction.

To find the reciprocal of a whole number, $6 = \frac{6}{1}$
first rewrite the whole number as a fraction
with a denominator of 1. Then invert the fraction.   The reciprocal of 6 is $\frac{1}{6}$.

Reciprocals are used to rewrite division problems as related multiplication problems. Look at the following two problems:

$$6 \div 2 = 3 \qquad\qquad 6 \cdot \frac{1}{2} = 3$$

6 divided by 2 equals 3.   6 times the reciprocal of 2 equals 3.

Division is defined as multiplication by the reciprocal. Therefore, "divided by 2" is the same as "times $\frac{1}{2}$." Fractions are divided by making this substitution.

Division of Fractions

To divide two fractions, multiply by the reciprocal of the divisor.

$$\frac{a}{b} \div \frac{c}{d} = \frac{a}{b} \cdot \frac{d}{c}, \qquad \text{where} \quad b \neq 0,\ c \neq 0, \quad \text{and} \quad d \neq 0$$

EXAMPLE

Divide: $\dfrac{2}{5} \div \dfrac{3}{4}$

$\dfrac{2}{5} \div \dfrac{3}{4} = \dfrac{2}{5} \cdot \dfrac{4}{3}$ • Rewrite the division as multiplication by the reciprocal.

$= \dfrac{2 \cdot 4}{5 \cdot 3} = \dfrac{8}{15}$ • Multiply the fractions.

The sign rules for dividing positive and negative fractions are the same rules used to divide integers.

The quotient of two numbers with the same sign is positive.
The quotient of two numbers with different signs is negative.

Point of Interest

Try this: What number when multiplied by its reciprocal is equal to 1?

HOW TO 8   Simplify: $-\dfrac{7}{10} \div \left(-\dfrac{14}{15}\right)$

The signs are the same.
The quotient is positive.

$$-\dfrac{7}{10} \div \left(-\dfrac{14}{15}\right) = \dfrac{7}{10} \div \dfrac{14}{15}$$

Rewrite the division as multiplication by the reciprocal.

$$= \dfrac{7}{10} \cdot \dfrac{15}{14}$$

Multiply the fractions.

$$= \dfrac{7 \cdot 15}{10 \cdot 14}$$

$$= \dfrac{7 \cdot 3 \cdot 5}{2 \cdot 5 \cdot 2 \cdot 7}$$

$$= \dfrac{3}{4}$$

Note in the next example that when we divide a fraction and a whole number, we first write the whole number as a fraction with a denominator of 1.

Take Note

$\dfrac{3}{4} \div 6 = \dfrac{1}{8}$ means that if $\dfrac{3}{4}$ is divided into 6 equal parts, each equal part is $\dfrac{1}{8}$.
Therefore, if 6 people share $\dfrac{3}{4}$ of a pizza, each person eats $\dfrac{1}{8}$ of the pizza.

APPLY THE CONCEPT

If 6 people share $\dfrac{3}{4}$ of a pizza, what fraction of the pizza does each person eat?

To find the fraction, find the quotient of $\dfrac{3}{4}$ and 6.

$$\dfrac{3}{4} \div 6 = \dfrac{3}{4} \div \dfrac{6}{1}$$ • Write 6 as $\dfrac{6}{1}$.

$$= \dfrac{3}{4} \cdot \dfrac{1}{6}$$ • Rewrite the division as multiplication by the reciprocal.

$$= \dfrac{3 \cdot 1}{4 \cdot 6}$$ • Multiply the fractions.

$$= \dfrac{3 \cdot 1}{2 \cdot 2 \cdot 2 \cdot 3} = \dfrac{1}{8}$$

Each person eats $\dfrac{1}{8}$ of the pizza.

When a number in a quotient is a mixed number, first write the mixed number as an improper fraction. Then divide the fractions.

HOW TO 9   Divide: $\dfrac{2}{3} \div 1\dfrac{1}{4}$

Write the mixed number $1\dfrac{1}{4}$ as an improper fraction.

$$\dfrac{2}{3} \div 1\dfrac{1}{4} = \dfrac{2}{3} \div \dfrac{5}{4}$$

Rewrite the division as multiplication by the reciprocal.

$$= \dfrac{2}{3} \cdot \dfrac{4}{5}$$

Multiply the fractions.

$$= \dfrac{2 \cdot 4}{3 \cdot 5} = \dfrac{8}{15}$$

EXAMPLE 7

Divide: $\dfrac{4}{5} \div \dfrac{8}{15}$

Solution $\dfrac{4}{5} \div \dfrac{8}{15} = \dfrac{4}{5} \cdot \dfrac{15}{8}$ • Multiply by the reciprocal.

$$= \dfrac{4 \cdot 15}{5 \cdot 8}$$

$$= \dfrac{2 \cdot 2 \cdot 3 \cdot 5}{5 \cdot 2 \cdot 2 \cdot 2}$$

$$= \dfrac{3}{2} = 1\dfrac{1}{2}$$

YOU TRY IT 7

Divide: $\dfrac{5}{6} \div \dfrac{10}{27}$

Your solution

EXAMPLE 8

Divide: $3\dfrac{4}{15} \div 2\dfrac{1}{10}$

Solution $3\dfrac{4}{15} \div 2\dfrac{1}{10} = \dfrac{49}{15} \div \dfrac{21}{10}$

$$= \dfrac{49}{15} \cdot \dfrac{10}{21}$$

$$= \dfrac{49 \cdot 10}{15 \cdot 21}$$

$$= \dfrac{7 \cdot 7 \cdot 2 \cdot 5}{3 \cdot 5 \cdot 3 \cdot 7}$$

$$= \dfrac{14}{9} = 1\dfrac{5}{9}$$

YOU TRY IT 8

Divide: $4\dfrac{3}{8} \div 3\dfrac{1}{2}$

Your solution

EXAMPLE 9

What is the quotient of 6 and $-\dfrac{3}{5}$?

Solution $6 \div \left(-\dfrac{3}{5}\right) = -\left(\dfrac{6}{1} \div \dfrac{3}{5}\right)$

$$= -\left(\dfrac{6}{1} \cdot \dfrac{5}{3}\right)$$

$$= -\dfrac{6 \cdot 5}{1 \cdot 3}$$

$$= -\dfrac{2 \cdot 3 \cdot 5}{1 \cdot 3}$$

$$= -\dfrac{10}{1} = -10$$

YOU TRY IT 9

Find the quotient of 4 and $-\dfrac{6}{7}$.

Your solution

Solutions on p. S9

EXAMPLE 10

Divide: $\dfrac{x}{2} \div \dfrac{y}{4}$

Solution

$$\dfrac{x}{2} \div \dfrac{y}{4} = \dfrac{x}{2} \cdot \dfrac{4}{y}$$

$$= \dfrac{x \cdot 4}{2 \cdot y}$$

$$= \dfrac{x \cdot 2 \cdot 2}{2 \cdot y} = \dfrac{2x}{y}$$

YOU TRY IT 10

Divide: $\dfrac{x}{8} \div \dfrac{y}{6}$

Your solution

EXAMPLE 11

Evaluate $x \div y$ for $x = 3\frac{1}{8}$ and $y = 5$.

Solution $x \div y$

$$3\frac{1}{8} \div 5 = \dfrac{25}{8} \div \dfrac{5}{1}$$

$$= \dfrac{25}{8} \cdot \dfrac{1}{5}$$

$$= \dfrac{25 \cdot 1}{8 \cdot 5}$$

$$= \dfrac{5 \cdot 5 \cdot 1}{2 \cdot 2 \cdot 2 \cdot 5} = \dfrac{5}{8}$$

YOU TRY IT 11

Evaluate $x \div y$ for $x = 2\frac{1}{4}$ and $y = 9$.

Your solution

Solutions on p. S9

OBJECTIVE C   *To solve application problems and use formulas*

Figure ABC is a triangle. AB is the **base,** b, of the triangle. The line segment from C that forms a right angle with the base is the **height,** h, of the triangle. The formula for the area of a triangle is given below.

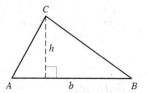

Area of a Triangle

The formula for the area of a triangle is $A = \frac{1}{2}bh$, where A is the area of the triangle, b is the base, and h is the height.

EXAMPLE

$$A = \frac{1}{2}bh = \frac{1}{2}(6)(2) = 3(2) = 6$$

The area of the triangle at the right is 6 m².

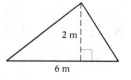

EXAMPLE 12

A riveter uses metal plates that are in the shape of a triangle and have a base of 12 cm and a height of 6 cm. Find the area of one metal plate.

Strategy

To find the area, use the formula for the area of a triangle, $A = \frac{1}{2}bh$. $b = 12$ and $h = 6$.

Solution

$A = \dfrac{1}{2}bh$

$A = \dfrac{1}{2}(12)(6)$

$A = 36$

The area is 36 cm².

YOU TRY IT 12

Find the amount of felt needed to make a banner that is in the shape of a triangle with a base of 18 in. and a height of 9 in.

Your strategy

Your solution

EXAMPLE 13

A 12-foot board is cut into pieces $2\frac{1}{2}$ ft long for use as bookshelves. What is the length of the remaining piece after as many shelves as possible are cut?

Strategy

To find the length of the remaining piece:

• Divide the total length (12) by the length of each shelf $\left(2\frac{1}{2}\right)$. The quotient is the number of shelves cut, with a certain fraction of a shelf left over.
• Multiply the fraction left over by the length of a shelf.

Solution

$12 \div 2\dfrac{1}{2} = \dfrac{12}{1} \div \dfrac{5}{2} = \dfrac{12}{1} \cdot \dfrac{2}{5} = \dfrac{12 \cdot 2}{1 \cdot 5} = \dfrac{24}{5} = 4\dfrac{4}{5}$

4 shelves, each $2\frac{1}{2}$ ft long, can be cut from the board. The piece remaining is $\frac{4}{5}$ of $2\frac{1}{2}$ ft long.

$\dfrac{4}{5} \cdot 2\dfrac{1}{2} = \dfrac{4}{5} \cdot \dfrac{5}{2} = \dfrac{4 \cdot 5}{5 \cdot 2} = 2$

The length of the remaining piece is 2 ft.

YOU TRY IT 13

The Booster Club is making 22 sashes for the high school band members. Each sash requires $1\frac{3}{8}$ yd of material at a cost of $12 per yard. Find the total cost of the material.

Your strategy

Your solution

Solutions on p. S9

3.6 EXERCISES

✔ Concept Check

1. Circle the correct word to complete the sentence.

   a. Fractions <u>can/cannot</u> be multiplied when their denominators are not the same.

   b. To multiply two fractions, write the <u>sum/product</u> of the numerators over the <u>sum/product</u> of the denominators.

2. The reciprocal of $\frac{7}{3}$ is _____.

3. The reciprocal of $-\frac{5}{6}$ is _____.

4. Fill in the blank with the correct operation: A gardener wants to space his rows of vegetables $1\frac{1}{4}$ ft apart. His garden is 12 ft long. To find how many rows he can fit in the garden, use _____.

5. A car used $10\frac{1}{4}$ gal of gas to travel 246 mi. To find the number of miles the car travels on 1 gal of gas, divide _____ by _____.

6. ◤ The product of 1 and a number is $\frac{3}{8}$. Find the number. Explain how you arrived at your answer.

OBJECTIVE A   *To multiply fractions*

Multiply.

7. $\frac{2}{3} \cdot \frac{9}{10}$

8. $\frac{3}{8} \cdot \frac{4}{5}$

9. $-\frac{6}{7} \cdot \frac{11}{12}$

10. $\frac{5}{6} \cdot \left(-\frac{2}{5}\right)$

11. $\frac{14}{15} \cdot \frac{6}{7}$

12. $\frac{15}{16} \cdot \frac{4}{9}$

13. $-\frac{6}{7} \cdot \frac{0}{10}$

14. $\frac{5}{12} \cdot \frac{3}{0}$

15. $\left(-\frac{4}{15}\right) \cdot \left(-\frac{3}{8}\right)$

16. $\left(-\frac{3}{4}\right) \cdot \left(-\frac{2}{9}\right)$

17. $-\frac{3}{4} \cdot \frac{1}{2}$

18. $-\frac{8}{15} \cdot \frac{5}{12}$

19. $\frac{9}{x} \cdot \frac{7}{y}$

20. $\frac{4}{c} \cdot \frac{8}{d}$

21. $-\frac{y}{5} \cdot \frac{z}{6}$

22. $-\frac{a}{10} \cdot \left(-\frac{b}{6}\right)$

23. $\dfrac{2}{3} \cdot \dfrac{3}{8} \cdot \dfrac{4}{9}$

24. $\dfrac{5}{7} \cdot \dfrac{1}{6} \cdot \dfrac{14}{15}$

25. $-\dfrac{7}{12} \cdot \dfrac{5}{8} \cdot \dfrac{16}{25}$

26. $\dfrac{5}{12} \cdot \left(-\dfrac{1}{3}\right) \cdot \left(-\dfrac{8}{15}\right)$

27. $\left(-\dfrac{3}{5}\right) \cdot \dfrac{1}{2} \cdot \left(-\dfrac{5}{8}\right)$

28. $\dfrac{5}{6} \cdot \left(-\dfrac{2}{3}\right) \cdot \dfrac{3}{25}$

29. $6 \cdot \dfrac{1}{6}$

30. $\dfrac{1}{10} \cdot 10$

31. $\dfrac{3}{4} \cdot 8$

32. $\dfrac{5}{7} \cdot 14$

33. $12 \cdot \left(-\dfrac{5}{8}\right)$

34. $24 \cdot \left(-\dfrac{3}{8}\right)$

35. $-16 \cdot \dfrac{7}{30}$

36. $-9 \cdot \dfrac{7}{15}$

37. $\dfrac{6}{7} \cdot 0$

38. $0 \cdot \dfrac{9}{11}$

39. $\dfrac{5}{22} \cdot 2\dfrac{1}{5}$

40. $\dfrac{4}{15} \cdot 1\dfrac{7}{8}$

41. $3\dfrac{1}{2} \cdot 5\dfrac{3}{7}$

42. $2\dfrac{1}{4} \cdot 1\dfrac{1}{3}$

43. $3\dfrac{1}{3} \cdot \left(-\dfrac{7}{10}\right)$

44. $2\dfrac{1}{4} \cdot \left(-\dfrac{7}{9}\right)$

45. $-1\dfrac{2}{3} \cdot \left(-\dfrac{3}{5}\right)$

46. $-2\dfrac{1}{8} \cdot \left(-\dfrac{4}{17}\right)$

47. $3\dfrac{1}{3} \cdot 2\dfrac{1}{3}$

48. $3\dfrac{1}{4} \cdot 2\dfrac{2}{3}$

49. $3\dfrac{1}{3} \cdot (-9)$

50. $-2\dfrac{1}{2} \cdot 4$

51. $8 \cdot 5\dfrac{1}{4}$

52. $3 \cdot 2\dfrac{1}{9}$

53. $3\dfrac{1}{2} \cdot 1\dfrac{5}{7} \cdot \dfrac{11}{12}$

54. $2\dfrac{2}{3} \cdot \dfrac{8}{9} \cdot 1\dfrac{5}{16}$

55. Find the product of $\frac{3}{4}$ and $\frac{14}{15}$.

56. Find the product of $\frac{12}{25}$ and $\frac{5}{16}$.

57. Find $-\frac{9}{16}$ multiplied by $\frac{4}{27}$.

58. Find $\frac{3}{7}$ multiplied by $-\frac{14}{15}$.

59. What is the product of $-\frac{7}{24}$, $\frac{8}{21}$, and $\frac{3}{7}$?

60. What is the product of $-\frac{5}{13}$, $-\frac{26}{75}$, and $\frac{5}{8}$?

61. What is $4\frac{4}{5}$ times $\frac{3}{8}$?

62. What is $5\frac{1}{3}$ times $\frac{3}{16}$?

63. Find the product of $-2\frac{2}{3}$ and $-1\frac{11}{16}$.

64. Find the product of $1\frac{3}{11}$ and $5\frac{1}{2}$.

● **Cost of Living** A typical household in the United States has an average after-tax income of $45,000. The graph at the right represents how this annual income is spent. Use this graph for Exercises 65 and 66.

65. Find the amount of money a typical household in the United States spends on housing per year.

66. How much money does a typical household in the United States spend annually on food?

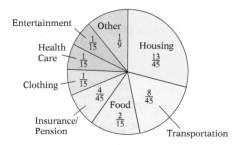

How a Typical U.S. Household Spends Its Annual Income

Source: Based on data from American Demographics

Evaluate the variable expression xy for the given values of x and y.

67. $x = -\frac{5}{16}$, $y = \frac{7}{15}$

68. $x = -\frac{2}{5}$, $y = -\frac{5}{6}$

69. $x = \frac{4}{7}$, $y = 6\frac{1}{8}$

70. $x = 6\frac{3}{5}$, $y = 3\frac{1}{3}$

71. $x = -49$, $y = \frac{5}{14}$

72. $x = -\frac{3}{10}$, $y = -35$

73. $x = 1\frac{3}{13}$, $y = -6\frac{1}{2}$

74. $x = -3\frac{1}{2}$, $y = -2\frac{2}{7}$

Evaluate the variable expression xyz for the given values of x, y, and z.

75. $x = \frac{3}{8}$, $y = \frac{2}{3}$, $z = \frac{4}{5}$

76. $x = 4$, $y = \frac{0}{8}$, $z = 1\frac{5}{9}$

77. $x = 2\frac{3}{8}$, $y = -\frac{3}{19}$, $z = -\frac{4}{9}$

78. $x = \frac{4}{5}$, $y = -15$, $z = \frac{7}{8}$

79. $x = \frac{5}{6}$, $y = -3$, $z = 1\frac{7}{15}$

80. $x = 4\frac{1}{2}$, $y = 3\frac{5}{9}$, $z = 1\frac{7}{8}$

81. Is $-\frac{1}{3}$ a solution of the equation $\frac{3}{4}y = -\frac{1}{4}$?

82. Is $\frac{2}{5}$ a solution of the equation $-\frac{5}{6}z = \frac{1}{3}$?

83. Is $\frac{3}{4}$ a solution of the equation $\frac{4}{5}x = \frac{5}{3}$?

84. Is $\frac{1}{2}$ a solution of the equation $\frac{3}{4}p = \frac{3}{2}$?

85. Is $-\frac{1}{6}$ a solution of the equation $6x = 1$?

86. Is $-\frac{4}{5}$ a solution of the equation $\frac{5}{4}n = -1$?

87. Is the product $\frac{2}{3} \cdot n$ greater than n or less than n when n is a proper fraction?

88. Give an example of a proper fraction and an improper fraction whose product is -1.

OBJECTIVE B *To divide fractions*

Divide.

89. $\dfrac{5}{7} \div \dfrac{2}{5}$

90. $\dfrac{3}{8} \div \dfrac{2}{3}$

91. $\dfrac{4}{7} \div \left(-\dfrac{4}{7}\right)$

92. $-\dfrac{5}{7} \div \left(-\dfrac{5}{6}\right)$

93. $0 \div \dfrac{7}{9}$

94. $0 \div \dfrac{4}{5}$

95. $\left(-\dfrac{1}{3}\right) \div \dfrac{1}{2}$

96. $\left(-\dfrac{3}{8}\right) \div \dfrac{7}{8}$

97. $-\dfrac{5}{16} \div \left(-\dfrac{3}{8}\right)$

98. $\left(-\dfrac{3}{4}\right) \div \left(-\dfrac{5}{6}\right)$

99. $\dfrac{0}{1} \div \dfrac{1}{9}$

100. $\dfrac{1}{2} \div \left(-\dfrac{8}{0}\right)$

101. $6 \div \dfrac{3}{4}$

102. $8 \div \dfrac{2}{3}$

103. $\dfrac{3}{4} \div (-6)$

104. $-\dfrac{2}{3} \div 8$

105. $\dfrac{9}{10} \div 0$

106. $\dfrac{2}{11} \div 0$

107. $\dfrac{5}{12} \div \left(-\dfrac{15}{32}\right)$

108. $\dfrac{3}{8} \div \left(-\dfrac{5}{12}\right)$

109. $\left(-\dfrac{2}{3}\right) \div (-4)$ **110.** $\left(-\dfrac{4}{9}\right) \div (-6)$ **111.** $\dfrac{8}{x} \div \left(-\dfrac{y}{4}\right)$ **112.** $-\dfrac{9}{m} \div \dfrac{n}{7}$

113. $\dfrac{b}{6} \div \dfrac{5}{d}$ **114.** $\dfrac{y}{10} \div \dfrac{4}{z}$ **115.** $3\dfrac{1}{3} \div \dfrac{5}{8}$ **116.** $5\dfrac{1}{2} \div \dfrac{1}{4}$

117. $5\dfrac{3}{5} \div \left(-\dfrac{7}{10}\right)$ **118.** $6\dfrac{8}{9} \div \left(-\dfrac{31}{36}\right)$ **119.** $-1\dfrac{1}{2} \div 1\dfrac{3}{4}$ **120.** $-1\dfrac{3}{5} \div 3\dfrac{1}{10}$

121. $5\dfrac{1}{2} \div 11$ **122.** $4\dfrac{2}{3} \div 7$ **123.** $5\dfrac{2}{7} \div 1$ **124.** $9\dfrac{5}{6} \div 1$

125. $-16 \div 1\dfrac{1}{3}$ **126.** $-9 \div \left(-3\dfrac{3}{5}\right)$ **127.** $2\dfrac{4}{13} \div 1\dfrac{5}{26}$ **128.** $3\dfrac{3}{8} \div 2\dfrac{7}{16}$

● **The Food Industry**   The table at the right shows the net weights of four different boxes of cereal. Use this table for Exercises 129 and 130.

129. Find the number of $\dfrac{3}{4}$-ounce servings in a box of Kellogg Honey Crunch Corn Flakes.

130. Find the number of $1\dfrac{1}{4}$-ounce servings in a box of Post Shredded Wheat.

Cereal	Net Weight
Kellogg Honey Crunch Corn Flakes	24 oz
Nabisco Instant Cream of Wheat	28 oz
Post Shredded Wheat	18 oz
Quaker Oats	41 oz

131. Find the quotient of $\dfrac{9}{10}$ and $\dfrac{3}{4}$.   **132.** Find the quotient of $\dfrac{3}{5}$ and $\dfrac{12}{25}$.

133. What is $-\dfrac{15}{24}$ divided by $\dfrac{3}{5}$?   **134.** What is $\dfrac{5}{6}$ divided by $-\dfrac{10}{21}$?

135. Find $\frac{7}{8}$ divided by $3\frac{1}{4}$.

136. Find $-\frac{3}{8}$ divided by $2\frac{1}{4}$.

137. What is the quotient of $-3\frac{5}{11}$ and $3\frac{4}{5}$?

138. What is the quotient of $-10\frac{1}{5}$ and $-1\frac{7}{10}$?

Evaluate the variable expression $x \div y$ for the given values of x and y.

139. $x = -\frac{5}{8}, y = -\frac{15}{2}$

140. $x = -\frac{14}{3}, y = -\frac{7}{9}$

141. $x = \frac{1}{7}, y = 0$

142. $x = \frac{4}{0}, y = 12$

143. $x = -18, y = \frac{3}{8}$

144. $x = 20, y = -\frac{5}{6}$

145. $x = -\frac{1}{2}, y = -3\frac{5}{8}$

146. $x = 4\frac{3}{8}, y = 7$

147. $x = 6\frac{2}{5}, y = -4$

148. $x = -2\frac{5}{8}, y = 1\frac{3}{4}$

149. $x = -3\frac{2}{5}, y = -1\frac{7}{10}$

150. $x = -5\frac{2}{5}, y = -9$

151. Is the quotient $n \div \frac{1}{2}$ greater than n or less than n when n is a proper fraction?

152. Give an example of two fractions whose quotient is -1.

OBJECTIVE C *To solve application problems and use formulas*

153. Polo A chukker is one period of play in a polo match. A chukker lasts $7\frac{1}{2}$ min. Find the length of time in four chukkers.

154. History The Assyrian calendar was based on the phases of the moon. One lunation was $29\frac{1}{2}$ days long. There were 12 lunations in one year. Find the number of days in one year in the Assyrian calendar.

Dennis Donohue/Shutterstock.com

155. Measurement   One rod is equal to $5\frac{1}{2}$ yd. How many feet are in one rod? How many inches are in one rod?

156. Travel   A car used $12\frac{1}{2}$ gal of gasoline on a 275-mile trip. How many miles can this car travel on 1 gal of gasoline?

157. Housework   According to a national survey, the average couple spends $4\frac{1}{2}$ h cleaning house each week. How many hours does the average couple spend cleaning house each year?

158. Assembly Work   A factory worker can assemble a product in $7\frac{1}{2}$ min. How many products can the worker assemble in 1 h?

159. Real Estate   A developer purchases $25\frac{1}{2}$ acres of land and plans to set aside 3 acres for an entranceway to a housing development to be built on the property. Each house will be built on a $\frac{3}{4}$-acre plot of land. How many houses does the developer plan to build on the property?

160. Party Planning   You are planning a barbecue for 25 people. You want to serve $\frac{1}{4}$-pound hamburger patties to your guests, and you estimate that each person will eat two hamburgers. How much hamburger meat should you buy for the barbecue?

161. Asteroids   Read the news clipping at the right. The distance between Earth and the moon is approximately 250,000 mi. At its closest point, asteroid GA6 was $\frac{9}{10}$ of that distance from Earth. Approximate the asteroid's distance from Earth at its closest point.

162. Wages   Find the total wages of an employee who worked $26\frac{1}{2}$ h this week and who earns an hourly wage of $12.

163. Gardens   A vegetable garden is in the shape of a triangle with a base of 21 ft and a height of 13 ft. Find the area of the vegetable garden.

In the NEWS!

Asteroid to Fly Within Orbit of the Moon

Asteroid GA6 will zip past Earth on Thursday at 7:06 P.M. EDT. The asteroid, a space rock about 71 ft wide, will fly within the orbit of the moon while it passes Earth.

Source: news.yahoo.com

164. Sailing A sail is in the shape of a triangle with a base of 12 m and a height of 16 m. How much canvas was needed to make the body of the sail?

165. Parks and Recreation A city plans to plant grass seed in a public playground that has the shape of a triangle with a height of 24 m and a base of 20 m. Each bag of grass seed will seed 120 m². How many bags of seed should be purchased?

166. Hiking Find the rate of a hiker who walked $4\frac{2}{3}$ mi in $1\frac{1}{3}$ h. Use the equation $r = \frac{d}{t}$, where r is the rate in miles per hour, d is the distance, and t is the time.

167. Deep Sea Diving The pressure on a submerged object is given by $P = 15 + \frac{1}{2}D$, where D is the depth in feet and P is the pressure measured in pounds per square inch. Find the pressure on a diver who is at a depth of $12\frac{1}{2}$ ft.

168. Physics Find the amount of force necessary to push a 75-pound crate across a floor for which the coefficient of friction is $\frac{3}{8}$. Use the equation $F = \mu N$, where F is the force, μ is the coefficient of friction, and N is the weight of the crate. Force is measured in pounds.

Critical Thinking

169. Cartography On a map, two cities are $3\frac{1}{8}$ in. apart. If $\frac{1}{8}$ in. on the map represents 50 mi, what is the number of miles between the two cities?

170. Determine whether the statement is always true, sometimes true, or never true.

a. Let n be an even number. Then $\frac{1}{2}n$ is a whole number.

b. Let n be an odd number. Then $\frac{1}{2}n$ is an improper fraction.

Projects or Group Activities

171. On page 182, Exercise 154 describes the Assyrian calendar. Our calendar is based on the solar year. One solar year is $365\frac{1}{4}$ days. Use this fact to explain leap years.

✔ CHECK YOUR PROGRESS: CHAPTER 3

1. Find the LCM of 10 and 25.

2. Find the LCM of 5, 12, and 15.

3. Find the GCF of 26 and 52.

4. Find the GCF of 41 and 67.

5. Write $\frac{10}{3}$ as a mixed number.

6. Write $\frac{81}{9}$ as a whole number.

7. Write $3\frac{1}{4}$ as an improper fraction.

8. Write 17 as an improper fraction.

9. Write $\frac{2}{3}$ as an equivalent fraction with a denominator of 12.

10. Write $\frac{24}{64}$ in simplest form.

11. Place the correct symbol, $<$ or $>$, between the two numbers. $\frac{2}{3}$ $\frac{5}{8}$

12. Multiply: $-\frac{4}{15} \cdot \frac{5}{12}$

13. Multiply: $2\frac{1}{4} \cdot 1\frac{2}{9}$

14. Multiply: $\frac{3}{4}\left(-\frac{2}{9}\right)\left(\frac{2}{5}\right)$

15. Divide: $-\frac{1}{4} \div \frac{1}{3}$

16. Divide: $\left(-\frac{6}{m}\right) \div \frac{n}{5}$

17. Divide: $8\frac{1}{3} \div 25$

18. Find the product of $-\frac{6}{7}$ and $\frac{14}{15}$.

19. Evaluate the variable expression xy when $x = -\frac{2}{3}$ and $y = -\frac{5}{6}$.

20. Is $\frac{1}{3}$ a solution of the equation $-\frac{3}{5}x = \frac{1}{5}$?

21. Find the quotient of $-2\frac{5}{8}$ and $5\frac{1}{4}$.

22. Evaluate the variable expression $x \div y$ when $x = \frac{2}{3}$ and $y = -\frac{7}{9}$.

23. **Hospital Supplies**   An online website advertises pairs of hospital booties. A hospital representative must order 200, 250, or 300 pairs of booties. How many pairs of booties should be packaged together so that no package needs to be opened when an order is being filled?

24. **Measurement**   A pound is equal to 16 oz. What fractional part of a pound is 12 oz?

25. **Board Games**   A wooden travel game board has hinges that allow the board to be folded in half. If the dimensions of the open board are 14 in. by 14 in. by $\frac{7}{8}$ in., what are the dimensions of the board when it is closed?

3.7   Addition and Subtraction of Fractions

OBJECTIVE A   *To add fractions*

Tips for Success

Before the class meeting in which your professor begins a new section, you should read each objective statement for that section. Next, browse through the material in that objective. The purpose of browsing through the material is to prepare your brain to accept and organize the new information when it is presented to you. See *AIM for Success* at the front of the book.

Suppose you and a friend order a pizza. The pizza has been cut into 8 equal pieces. If you eat 3 pieces of the pizza and your friend eats 2 pieces, then together you have eaten $\frac{5}{8}$ of the pizza.

Note that in adding the fractions $\frac{3}{8}$ and $\frac{2}{8}$, the numerators are added and the denominator remains the same.

$$\frac{3}{8} + \frac{2}{8} = \frac{3+2}{8}$$

$$= \frac{5}{8}$$

Addition of Fractions

To add fractions with the same denominator, add the numerators and place the sum over the common denominator.

$$\frac{a}{b} + \frac{c}{b} = \frac{a+c}{b}, \quad \text{where } b \neq 0$$

EXAMPLE

Add: $\dfrac{5}{16} + \dfrac{7}{16}$

$$\frac{5}{16} + \frac{7}{16} = \frac{5+7}{16}$$

- The denominators are the same. Add the numerators and place the sum over the common denominator.

$$= \frac{12}{16} = \frac{3}{4}$$

- Write the answer in simplest form.

HOW TO 1   Add: $\dfrac{4}{x} + \dfrac{8}{x}$

The denominators are the same. Add the numerators and place the sum over the common denominator.

$$\frac{4}{x} + \frac{8}{x} = \frac{4+8}{x}$$

$$= \frac{12}{x}$$

Before two fractions can be added, the fractions must have the same denominator. To add fractions with different denominators, first rewrite the fractions as equivalent fractions with a common denominator. The common denominator is the least common multiple (LCM) of the denominators of the fractions. The LCM of denominators is sometimes called the least common denominator (LCD).

HOW TO 2   Find the sum of $\frac{5}{6}$ and $\frac{3}{8}$.

The common denominator is the LCM of 6 and 8.

The LCM of 6 and 8 is 24.

Write the fractions as equivalent fractions with the common denominator.

$$\frac{5}{6} + \frac{3}{8} = \frac{20}{24} + \frac{9}{24}$$

Add the fractions.

$$= \frac{20 + 9}{24}$$

$$= \frac{29}{24} = 1\frac{5}{24}$$

APPLY THE CONCEPT

During a recent year, over 42 million Americans changed homes. Figure 3.1 shows what fractions of the people moved within the same county, moved to a different county in the same state, and moved to a different state. What fractional part of those who changed homes moved outside the county they had been living in?

Add the fraction of the people who moved to a different county in the same state and the fraction who moved to a different state.

$$\frac{4}{21} + \frac{1}{7} = \frac{4}{21} + \frac{3}{21} = \frac{7}{21} = \frac{1}{3}$$

$\frac{1}{3}$ of the Americans who changed homes moved outside of the county they had been living in.

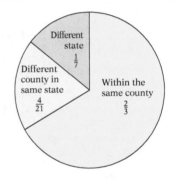

Figure 3.1   Where Americans Moved
Source: Census Bureau; *Geographical Mobility*

To add a fraction with a negative sign, rewrite the fraction with the negative sign in the numerator. Then add the numerators and place the sum over the common denominator.

HOW TO 3   Add: $-\frac{5}{6} + \frac{3}{4}$

The common denominator is the LCM of 4 and 6.

The LCM of 4 and 6 is 12.

Rewrite the first fraction with the negative sign in the numerator.

$$-\frac{5}{6} + \frac{3}{4} = \frac{-5}{6} + \frac{3}{4}$$

Rewrite each fraction in terms of the common denominator.

$$= \frac{-10}{12} + \frac{9}{12}$$

Add the fractions.

$$= \frac{-10 + 9}{12}$$

Simplify the numerator and write the negative sign in front of the fraction.

$$= \frac{-1}{12} = -\frac{1}{12}$$

HOW TO 4 Add: $-\dfrac{2}{3} + \left(-\dfrac{4}{5}\right)$

Rewrite each negative fraction with the negative sign in the numerator.

$$-\dfrac{2}{3} + \left(-\dfrac{4}{5}\right) = \dfrac{-2}{3} + \dfrac{-4}{5}$$

Rewrite each fraction as an equivalent fraction using the LCM as the denominator.

$$= \dfrac{-10}{15} + \dfrac{-12}{15}$$

Add the fractions.

$$= \dfrac{-10 + (-12)}{15}$$

$$= \dfrac{-22}{15} = -1\dfrac{7}{15}$$

HOW TO 5 Is $-\dfrac{2}{3}$ a solution of the equation $\dfrac{3}{4} + y = -\dfrac{1}{12}$?

$$\dfrac{3}{4} + y = -\dfrac{1}{12}$$

Replace y by $-\dfrac{2}{3}$. Then simplify.

$$\dfrac{3}{4} + \left(-\dfrac{2}{3}\right) \quad \bigg| \quad -\dfrac{1}{12}$$

The common denominator is 12.

$$\dfrac{9}{12} + \left(\dfrac{-8}{12}\right) \quad \bigg| \quad -\dfrac{1}{12}$$

$$\dfrac{9 + (-8)}{12} \quad \bigg| \quad -\dfrac{1}{12}$$

The results are not equal.

$$\dfrac{1}{12} \neq -\dfrac{1}{12}$$

No, $-\dfrac{2}{3}$ is not a solution of the equation.

The mixed number $2\dfrac{1}{2}$ is the sum of 2 and $\dfrac{1}{2}$.

$$2\dfrac{1}{2} = 2 + \dfrac{1}{2}$$

Therefore, the sum of a whole number and a fraction is a mixed number.

$$2 + \dfrac{1}{2} = 2\dfrac{1}{2}$$

$$3 + \dfrac{4}{5} = 3\dfrac{4}{5}$$

$$8 + \dfrac{7}{9} = 8\dfrac{7}{9}$$

The sum of a whole number and a mixed number is a mixed number.

Take Note

$$5 + 4\dfrac{2}{7} = 5 + \left(4 + \dfrac{2}{7}\right)$$

$$= (5 + 4) + \dfrac{2}{7}$$

$$= 9 + \dfrac{2}{7} = 9\dfrac{2}{7}$$

HOW TO 6 Add: $5 + 4\dfrac{2}{7}$

Add the whole numbers (5 and 4).

$$5 + 4\dfrac{2}{7} = 9\dfrac{2}{7}$$

Write the fraction.

To add two mixed numbers, first write the fractional parts as equivalent fractions with a common denominator. Then add the fractional parts and add the whole numbers.

HOW TO 7   Add: $3\frac{5}{8} + 4\frac{7}{12}$

Write the fractions as equivalent fractions with a common denominator. The common denominator is the LCM of 8 and 12. The LCM is 24.

$$3\frac{5}{8} + 4\frac{7}{12} = 3\frac{15}{24} + 4\frac{14}{24}$$

Add the fractional parts and add the whole numbers.

$$= 7\frac{29}{24}$$

Write the sum in simplest form.

$$= 7 + \frac{29}{24}$$

$$= 7 + 1\frac{5}{24}$$

$$= 8\frac{5}{24}$$

EXAMPLE 1

Add: $\frac{9}{16} + \frac{5}{12}$

Solution $\frac{9}{16} + \frac{5}{12} = \frac{27}{48} + \frac{20}{48}$

$$= \frac{27 + 20}{48} = \frac{47}{48}$$

YOU TRY IT 1

Add: $\frac{7}{12} + \frac{3}{8}$

Your solution

EXAMPLE 2

Add: $\frac{4}{5} + \frac{3}{4} + \frac{5}{8}$

Solution

$\frac{4}{5} + \frac{3}{4} + \frac{5}{8} = \frac{32}{40} + \frac{30}{40} + \frac{25}{40} = \frac{87}{40} = 2\frac{7}{40}$

YOU TRY IT 2

Add: $\frac{3}{5} + \frac{2}{3} + \frac{5}{6}$

Your solution

EXAMPLE 3

Find the sum of $12\frac{4}{7}$ and 19.

Solution

$12\frac{4}{7} + 19 = 31\frac{4}{7}$ • Add the whole numbers. Write the fraction.

YOU TRY IT 3

What is the sum of 16 and $8\frac{5}{9}$?

Your solution

Solutions on p. S9

EXAMPLE 4

Add: $-\dfrac{3}{8} + \dfrac{3}{4} + \left(-\dfrac{5}{6}\right)$

Solution

$$-\dfrac{3}{8} + \dfrac{3}{4} + \left(-\dfrac{5}{6}\right) = \dfrac{-3}{8} + \dfrac{3}{4} + \dfrac{-5}{6}$$

$$= \dfrac{-9}{24} + \dfrac{18}{24} + \dfrac{-20}{24}$$

$$= \dfrac{-9 + 18 + (-20)}{24}$$

$$= \dfrac{-11}{24} = -\dfrac{11}{24}$$

Add: $-\dfrac{5}{12} + \dfrac{5}{8} + \left(-\dfrac{1}{6}\right)$

Your solution

EXAMPLE 5

Evaluate $x + y + z$ for $x = 2\dfrac{1}{6}$, $y = 4\dfrac{3}{8}$, and $z = 7\dfrac{5}{9}$.

Solution

$x + y + z$

$$2\dfrac{1}{6} + 4\dfrac{3}{8} + 7\dfrac{5}{9} = 2\dfrac{12}{72} + 4\dfrac{27}{72} + 7\dfrac{40}{72}$$

$$= 13\dfrac{79}{72}$$

$$= 14\dfrac{7}{72}$$

Evaluate $x + y + z$ for $x = 3\dfrac{5}{6}$, $y = 2\dfrac{1}{9}$, and $z = 5\dfrac{5}{12}$.

Your solution

Solutions on pp. S9–S10

OBJECTIVE B *To subtract fractions*

Point of Interest

The first woman mathematician for whom documented evidence exists is Hypatia (370–415). She lived in Alexandria, Egypt, and lectured at the Museum, the forerunner of our modern university. She made important contributions in mathematics, astronomy, and philosophy.

In the last objective, it was stated that in order for fractions to be added, the fractions must have the same denominator. The same is true for subtracting fractions: The two fractions must have the same denominator.

Subtraction of Fractions

To subtract fractions with the same denominator, subtract the numerators and place the difference over the common denominator.

$$\dfrac{a}{b} - \dfrac{c}{b} = \dfrac{a - c}{b}, \qquad \text{where} \quad b \neq 0$$

EXAMPLE

Subtract: $\dfrac{5}{8} - \dfrac{3}{8}$

$\dfrac{5}{8} - \dfrac{3}{8} = \dfrac{5-3}{8}$ • The denominators are the same. Subtract the numerators and place the difference over the common denominator.

$= \dfrac{2}{8} = \dfrac{1}{4}$ • Write the answer in simplest form.

To subtract fractions with different denominators, first rewrite the fractions as equivalent fractions with a common denominator. The common denominator is the least common multiple (LCM) of the denominators of the fractions.

HOW TO 8 Subtract: $\dfrac{5}{12} - \dfrac{3}{8}$

The common denominator is the LCM of 12 and 8.   The LCM of 12 and 8 is 24.

Write the fractions as equivalent fractions with the common denominator.

$\dfrac{5}{12} - \dfrac{3}{8} = \dfrac{10}{24} - \dfrac{9}{24}$

Subtract the fractions.

$= \dfrac{10-9}{24} = \dfrac{1}{24}$

To subtract fractions with negative signs, first rewrite the fractions with the negative signs in the numerators.

HOW TO 9 Simplify: $-\dfrac{2}{9} - \dfrac{5}{12}$

Rewrite the negative fraction with the negative sign in the numerator.

$-\dfrac{2}{9} - \dfrac{5}{12} = \dfrac{-2}{9} - \dfrac{5}{12}$

Write the fractions as equivalent fractions with a common denominator.

$= \dfrac{-8}{36} - \dfrac{15}{36}$

Subtract the numerators and place the difference over the common denominator.

$= \dfrac{-8-15}{36} = \dfrac{-23}{36}$

Write the negative sign in front of the fraction.

$= -\dfrac{23}{36}$

HOW TO 10 Subtract: $\dfrac{2}{3} - \left(-\dfrac{4}{5}\right)$

Rewrite subtraction as addition of the opposite.

$\dfrac{2}{3} - \left(-\dfrac{4}{5}\right) = \dfrac{2}{3} + \dfrac{4}{5}$

Write the fractions as equivalent fractions with a common denominator.

$= \dfrac{10}{15} + \dfrac{12}{15}$

Add the fractions.

$= \dfrac{10+12}{15}$

$= \dfrac{22}{15} = 1\dfrac{7}{15}$

To subtract mixed numbers when borrowing is not necessary, subtract the fractional parts and then subtract the whole numbers.

> **HOW TO 11**   Find the difference between $5\frac{8}{9}$ and $2\frac{5}{6}$.
>
> Write the fractions as equivalent fractions with the LCM as the common denominator.
>
> Subtract the fractional parts and subtract the whole numbers.

The LCM of 9 and 6 is 18.

$$5\frac{8}{9} - 2\frac{5}{6} = 5\frac{16}{18} - 2\frac{15}{18}$$
$$= 3\frac{1}{18}$$

As in subtraction with whole numbers, subtraction of mixed numbers may involve borrowing.

> **HOW TO 12**   Subtract: $7 - 4\frac{2}{3}$
>
> Borrow 1 from 7. Write the 1 as a fraction with the same denominator as the fractional part of the mixed number (3).
>
> *Note:* $7 = 6 + 1 = 6 + \frac{3}{3} = 6\frac{3}{3}$
>
> Subtract the fractional parts and subtract the whole numbers.

$$7 - 4\frac{2}{3} = 6\frac{3}{3} - 4\frac{2}{3}$$

$$= 2\frac{1}{3}$$

> **HOW TO 13**   Subtract: $9\frac{1}{8} - 2\frac{5}{6}$
>
> Write the fractions as equivalent fractions with a common denominator.
>
> $3 < 20$. Borrow 1 from 9. Add the 1 to $\frac{3}{24}$.
>
> *Note:* $9\frac{3}{24} = 9 + \frac{3}{24} = 8 + 1 + \frac{3}{24}$
>
> $= 8 + \frac{24}{24} + \frac{3}{24} = 8 + \frac{27}{24} = 8\frac{27}{24}$
>
> Subtract.

$$9\frac{1}{8} - 2\frac{5}{6} = 9\frac{3}{24} - 2\frac{20}{24}$$

$$= 8\frac{27}{24} - 2\frac{20}{24}$$

$$= 6\frac{7}{24}$$

APPLY THE CONCEPT

The inseam of a pant leg is $30\frac{1}{2}$ in. long. What is the length of the inseam after a tailor cuts $\frac{3}{4}$ in. from the pant leg?

To find the length of the inseam, subtract $\frac{3}{4}$ from $30\frac{1}{2}$.

$$30\frac{1}{2} - \frac{3}{4} = 30\frac{2}{4} - \frac{3}{4} = 29\frac{6}{4} - \frac{3}{4} = 29\frac{3}{4}$$

After the tailor cuts $\frac{3}{4}$ in. from the pant leg, the length of the inseam is $29\frac{3}{4}$ in.

HOW TO 14 Evaluate $x - y$ for $x = 7\frac{2}{9}$ and $y = 3\frac{5}{12}$.

$x - y$

Replace x with $7\frac{2}{9}$ and y with $3\frac{5}{12}$.

$7\frac{2}{9} - 3\frac{5}{12}$

Write the fractions as equivalent fractions with a common denominator.

$= 7\frac{8}{36} - 3\frac{15}{36}$

$8 < 15$. Borrow 1 from 7. Add the 1 to $\frac{8}{36}$.

Note: $7\frac{8}{36} = 6 + \frac{36}{36} + \frac{8}{36} = 6\frac{44}{36}$

$= 6\frac{44}{36} - 3\frac{15}{36}$

Subtract.

$= 3\frac{29}{36}$

EXAMPLE 6

Subtract: $-\frac{5}{6} - \left(-\frac{3}{8}\right)$

Solution

$-\frac{5}{6} - \left(-\frac{3}{8}\right) = -\frac{5}{6} + \frac{3}{8} = \frac{-20}{24} + \frac{9}{24}$

$= \frac{-20 + 9}{24}$

$= \frac{-11}{24} = -\frac{11}{24}$

YOU TRY IT 6

Subtract: $-\frac{5}{6} - \frac{7}{9}$

Your solution

EXAMPLE 7

Find the difference between $8\frac{5}{6}$ and $2\frac{3}{4}$.

Solution

$8\frac{5}{6} - 2\frac{3}{4} = 8\frac{10}{12} - 2\frac{9}{12} = 6\frac{1}{12}$

YOU TRY IT 7

Find the difference between $9\frac{7}{8}$ and $5\frac{2}{3}$.

Your solution

EXAMPLE 8

Subtract: $7 - 3\frac{5}{13}$

Solution

$7 - 3\frac{5}{13} = 6\frac{13}{13} - 3\frac{5}{13} = 3\frac{8}{13}$ • Write 7 as $6\frac{13}{13}$.

YOU TRY IT 8

Subtract: $6 - 4\frac{2}{11}$

Your solution

Solutions on p. S10

EXAMPLE 9

Is $\frac{3}{8}$ a solution of the equation $\frac{2}{3} = w - \frac{5}{6}$?

Solution

$$\frac{2}{3} = w - \frac{5}{6}$$

$$
\begin{array}{c|c}
\dfrac{2}{3} & \dfrac{3}{8} - \dfrac{5}{6} \\[2ex]
\dfrac{2}{3} & \dfrac{9}{24} - \dfrac{20}{24} \\[2ex]
\dfrac{2}{3} & \dfrac{-11}{24}
\end{array}
$$

- Replace w with $\frac{3}{8}$.

- Write equivalent fractions with a common denominator.

- Subtract the fractions.

$$\frac{2}{3} \neq -\frac{11}{24}$$

No, $\frac{3}{8}$ is not a solution of the equation.

Is $-\frac{1}{4}$ a solution of the equation $\frac{2}{3} - v = \frac{11}{12}$?

Your solution

Solution on p. S10

OBJECTIVE C   *To solve application problems*

EXAMPLE 10

⬤ The length of a regulation NCAA football must be no less than $10\frac{7}{8}$ in. and no more than $11\frac{7}{16}$ in. What is the difference between the minimum and maximum lengths of an NCAA regulation football?

Strategy

To find the difference, subtract the minimum length $\left(10\frac{7}{8}\right)$ from the maximum length $\left(11\frac{7}{16}\right)$.

Solution

$$11\frac{7}{16} - 10\frac{7}{8} = 11\frac{7}{16} - 10\frac{14}{16} = 10\frac{23}{16} - 10\frac{14}{16} = \frac{9}{16}$$

The difference is $\frac{9}{16}$ in.

⬤ The Heller Research Group conducted a survey to determine favorite doughnut flavors. $\frac{2}{5}$ of the respondents named glazed doughnuts, $\frac{8}{25}$ named filled doughnuts, and $\frac{3}{20}$ named frosted doughnuts. What fraction of the respondents did not name glazed, filled, or frosted as their favorite type of doughnut?

Your strategy

Your solution

Solution on p. S10

3.7 EXERCISES

✔ Concept Check

For Exercises 1 and 2, circle the correct phrase to complete the sentence.

1. Fractions cannot be added unless their <u>numerators/denominators</u> are the same.

2. To add two fractions with the same denominator, place the sum of the numerators over the <u>sum of the denominators/common denominator.</u>

3. a. Write "the difference of $\frac{1}{2}$ and $-\frac{3}{7}$" as a subtraction problem:

$$\underline{\hspace{1.5cm}} \;-\; \underline{\hspace{1.5cm}}.$$

    b. Rewrite the subtraction problem in part (a) as an addition problem:

$$\underline{\hspace{1.5cm}} \;+\; \underline{\hspace{1.5cm}}$$

4. Complete the subtraction: $8 - 3\dfrac{4}{5} = 7\dfrac{\boxed{}}{5} - 3\dfrac{4}{5} = 4\dfrac{\boxed{}}{5}$

For Exercises 5 and 6, state whether you would use addition or subtraction to find the specified amount.

5. You have $3\frac{1}{2}$ h available to do an English assignment and to study for a math test. You spend $1\frac{2}{3}$ h on the English assignment. To find the amount of time you have left to study for the math test, use _____.

Diego Cervo/Shutterstock.com

6. This morning you studied for $1\frac{1}{4}$ h, and this afternoon you studied for $1\frac{1}{2}$ h. To find the total amount of time you spent studying today, use _____.

OBJECTIVE A   *To add fractions*

Add.

7. $\dfrac{4}{11} + \dfrac{5}{11}$ **8.** $\dfrac{3}{7} + \dfrac{2}{7}$ **9.** $\dfrac{2}{3} + \dfrac{1}{3}$ **10.** $\dfrac{1}{2} + \dfrac{1}{2}$

11. $\dfrac{5}{6} + \dfrac{5}{6}$

12. $\dfrac{3}{8} + \dfrac{7}{8}$

13. $\dfrac{7}{18} + \dfrac{13}{18} + \dfrac{1}{18}$

14. $\dfrac{8}{15} + \dfrac{2}{15} + \dfrac{11}{15}$

15. $\dfrac{7}{b} + \dfrac{9}{b}$

16. $\dfrac{3}{y} + \dfrac{6}{y}$

17. $\dfrac{5}{c} + \dfrac{4}{c}$

18. $\dfrac{2}{a} + \dfrac{8}{a}$

19. $\dfrac{1}{x} + \dfrac{4}{x} + \dfrac{6}{x}$

20. $\dfrac{8}{n} + \dfrac{5}{n} + \dfrac{3}{n}$

21. $\dfrac{1}{4} + \dfrac{2}{3}$

22. $\dfrac{2}{3} + \dfrac{1}{2}$

23. $\dfrac{7}{15} + \dfrac{9}{20}$

24. $\dfrac{4}{9} + \dfrac{1}{6}$

25. $\dfrac{2}{3} + \dfrac{1}{12} + \dfrac{5}{6}$

26. $\dfrac{3}{8} + \dfrac{1}{2} + \dfrac{5}{12}$

27. $\dfrac{7}{12} + \dfrac{3}{4} + \dfrac{4}{5}$

28. $\dfrac{7}{11} + \dfrac{1}{2} + \dfrac{5}{6}$

29. $-\dfrac{3}{4} + \dfrac{2}{3}$

30. $-\dfrac{7}{12} + \dfrac{5}{8}$

31. $\dfrac{2}{5} + \left(-\dfrac{11}{15}\right)$

32. $\dfrac{1}{4} + \left(-\dfrac{1}{7}\right)$

33. $\dfrac{3}{8} + \left(-\dfrac{1}{2}\right) + \dfrac{7}{12}$

34. $-\dfrac{7}{12} + \dfrac{2}{3} + \left(-\dfrac{4}{5}\right)$

35. $\dfrac{2}{3} + \left(-\dfrac{5}{6}\right) + \dfrac{1}{4}$

36. $-\dfrac{5}{8} + \dfrac{3}{4} + \dfrac{1}{2}$

37. $8 + 7\dfrac{2}{3}$

38. $6 + 9\dfrac{3}{5}$

39. $2\dfrac{1}{6} + 3\dfrac{1}{2}$

40. $1\dfrac{3}{10} + 4\dfrac{3}{5}$

41. $8\dfrac{3}{5} + 6\dfrac{9}{20}$

42. $7\dfrac{5}{12} + 3\dfrac{7}{9}$

43. $5\dfrac{5}{12} + 4\dfrac{7}{9}$

44. $2\dfrac{11}{12} + 3\dfrac{7}{15}$

45. $2\dfrac{1}{4} + 3\dfrac{1}{2} + 1\dfrac{2}{3}$

46. $1\dfrac{2}{3} + 2\dfrac{5}{6} + 4\dfrac{7}{9}$

47. What is $-\dfrac{5}{6}$ added to $\dfrac{4}{9}$?

48. What is $\dfrac{7}{12}$ added to $-\dfrac{11}{16}$?

49. Find the total of $\frac{2}{7}$, $\frac{3}{14}$, and $\frac{1}{4}$.

50. Find the total of $\frac{1}{3}$, $\frac{5}{18}$, and $\frac{2}{9}$.

51. What is $-\frac{2}{3}$ more than $-\frac{5}{6}$?

52. What is $-\frac{7}{12}$ more than $-\frac{5}{9}$?

53. Find $3\frac{7}{12}$ plus $2\frac{5}{8}$.

54. Find the sum of $7\frac{11}{15}$, $2\frac{7}{10}$, and $5\frac{2}{5}$.

Evaluate the variable expression $x + y$ for the given values of x and y.

55. $x = \frac{3}{5}, y = \frac{4}{5}$

56. $x = \frac{5}{8}, y = \frac{3}{8}$

57. $x = \frac{2}{3}, y = -\frac{3}{4}$

58. $x = -\frac{3}{8}, y = \frac{2}{9}$

59. $x = \frac{5}{6}, y = \frac{8}{9}$

60. $x = \frac{3}{10}, y = -\frac{7}{15}$

61. $x = -\frac{5}{8}, y = -\frac{1}{6}$

62. $x = -\frac{3}{8}, y = -\frac{5}{6}$

Evaluate the variable expression $x + y + z$ for the given values of x, y, and z.

63. $x = \frac{3}{8}, y = \frac{1}{4}, z = \frac{7}{12}$

64. $x = \frac{5}{6}, y = \frac{2}{3}, z = \frac{7}{24}$

65. $x = 1\frac{1}{2}, y = 3\frac{3}{4}, z = 6\frac{5}{12}$

66. $x = 7\frac{2}{3}, y = 2\frac{5}{6}, z = 5\frac{4}{9}$

67. $x = 4\frac{3}{5}, y = 8\frac{7}{10}, z = 1\frac{9}{20}$

68. $x = 2\frac{3}{14}, y = 5\frac{5}{7}, z = 3\frac{1}{2}$

69. Is $-\frac{3}{5}$ a solution of the equation $z + \frac{1}{4} = -\frac{7}{20}$?

70. Is $\frac{3}{8}$ a solution of the equation $\frac{3}{4} = t + \frac{3}{8}$?

71. Is $-\frac{5}{6}$ a solution of the equation $\frac{1}{4} + x = -\frac{7}{12}$?

72. Is $-\frac{4}{5}$ a solution of the equation $0 = q + \frac{4}{5}$?

● **Loans** The figure at the right shows how the money borrowed on home equity loans is spent. Use this graph for Exercises 73 and 74.

73. What fractional part of the money borrowed on home equity loans is spent on debt consolidation and home improvement?

74. What fractional part of the money borrowed on home equity loans is spent on home improvement, cars, and tuition?

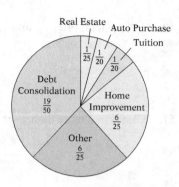

How Money Borrowed on Home Equity Loans Is Spent
Source: Consumer Bankers Association

75. 📝 Which expression is equivalent to $\frac{3}{4} + \frac{1}{5}$?

(i) $\dfrac{3 + 1}{4 + 5}$ (ii) $\dfrac{(3 + 5) + (1 + 4)}{4 + 5}$ (iii) $\dfrac{(3 \cdot 5) + (1 \cdot 4)}{4 \cdot 5}$ (iv) $\dfrac{3 + 1}{4 \cdot 5}$

76. 📝 Estimate the sum to the nearest integer.

a. $\dfrac{7}{8} + \dfrac{4}{5}$ b. $\dfrac{1}{3} + \left(-\dfrac{1}{2}\right)$ c. $-\dfrac{1}{8} + 1\dfrac{1}{4}$ d. $-1\dfrac{1}{3} + \dfrac{1}{5}$

OBJECTIVE B *To subtract fractions*

Subtract.

77. $\dfrac{7}{12} - \dfrac{5}{12}$ 　　 78. $\dfrac{17}{20} - \dfrac{9}{20}$ 　　 79. $\dfrac{11}{24} - \dfrac{7}{24}$ 　　 80. $\dfrac{39}{48} - \dfrac{23}{48}$

81. $\dfrac{8}{d} - \dfrac{3}{d}$ 　　 82. $\dfrac{12}{y} - \dfrac{7}{y}$ 　　 83. $\dfrac{5}{n} - \dfrac{10}{n}$ 　　 84. $\dfrac{6}{c} - \dfrac{13}{c}$

85. $\dfrac{3}{7} - \dfrac{5}{14}$ 　　 86. $\dfrac{7}{8} - \dfrac{5}{16}$ 　　 87. $\dfrac{2}{3} - \dfrac{1}{6}$ 　　 88. $\dfrac{5}{21} - \dfrac{1}{6}$

89. $\dfrac{11}{12} - \dfrac{2}{3}$ 　　 90. $\dfrac{9}{20} - \dfrac{1}{30}$ 　　 91. $-\dfrac{1}{2} - \dfrac{3}{8}$ 　　 92. $-\dfrac{5}{6} - \dfrac{1}{9}$

93. $-\dfrac{3}{10} - \dfrac{4}{5}$ **94.** $-\dfrac{7}{15} - \dfrac{3}{10}$ **95.** $-\dfrac{5}{12} - \left(-\dfrac{2}{3}\right)$ **96.** $-\dfrac{3}{10} - \left(-\dfrac{5}{6}\right)$

97. $-\dfrac{5}{9} - \left(-\dfrac{11}{12}\right)$ **98.** $-\dfrac{5}{8} - \left(-\dfrac{7}{12}\right)$ **99.** $4\dfrac{11}{18} - 2\dfrac{5}{18}$ **100.** $3\dfrac{7}{12} - 1\dfrac{1}{12}$

101. $8\dfrac{3}{4} - 2$ **102.** $6\dfrac{5}{9} - 4$ **103.** $8\dfrac{5}{6} - 7\dfrac{3}{4}$ **104.** $5\dfrac{7}{8} - 3\dfrac{2}{3}$

105. $7 - 3\dfrac{5}{8}$ **106.** $6 - 2\dfrac{4}{5}$ **107.** $10 - 4\dfrac{8}{9}$ **108.** $5 - 2\dfrac{7}{18}$

109. $7\dfrac{3}{8} - 4\dfrac{5}{8}$ **110.** $11\dfrac{1}{6} - 8\dfrac{5}{6}$ **111.** $12\dfrac{5}{12} - 10\dfrac{17}{24}$ **112.** $16\dfrac{1}{3} - 11\dfrac{5}{12}$

113. $6\dfrac{2}{3} - 1\dfrac{7}{8}$ **114.** $7\dfrac{7}{12} - 2\dfrac{5}{6}$ **115.** $10\dfrac{2}{5} - 8\dfrac{7}{10}$ **116.** $5\dfrac{5}{6} - 4\dfrac{7}{8}$

117. What is $-\dfrac{7}{12}$ minus $\dfrac{7}{9}$?   **118.** What is $\dfrac{3}{5}$ decreased by $-\dfrac{7}{10}$?

119. What is $-\dfrac{2}{3}$ less than $-\dfrac{7}{8}$?   **120.** Find the difference between $-\dfrac{1}{6}$ and $-\dfrac{8}{9}$.

121. Find 8 less $1\dfrac{7}{12}$.   **122.** Find 9 minus $5\dfrac{3}{20}$.

Evaluate the variable expression $x - y$ for the given values of x and y.

123. $x = \dfrac{8}{9}, y = \dfrac{5}{9}$ **124.** $x = \dfrac{5}{6}, y = \dfrac{1}{6}$ **125.** $x = -\dfrac{11}{12}, y = \dfrac{5}{12}$ **126.** $x = -\dfrac{15}{16}, y = \dfrac{5}{16}$

127. $x = -\dfrac{2}{3}, y = -\dfrac{3}{4}$ **128.** $x = -\dfrac{5}{12}, y = -\dfrac{5}{9}$ **129.** $x = -\dfrac{3}{10}, y = -\dfrac{7}{15}$ **130.** $x = -\dfrac{5}{6}, y = -\dfrac{2}{15}$

131. $x = 5\dfrac{7}{9}, y = 4\dfrac{2}{3}$ **132.** $x = 9\dfrac{5}{8}, y = 2\dfrac{3}{16}$ **133.** $x = 7\dfrac{9}{10}, y = 3\dfrac{1}{2}$ **134.** $x = 6\dfrac{4}{9}, y = 1\dfrac{1}{6}$

135. $x = 5, y = 2\dfrac{7}{9}$ **136.** $x = 8, y = 4\dfrac{5}{6}$ **137.** $x = 10\dfrac{1}{2}, y = 5\dfrac{7}{12}$ **138.** $x = 9\dfrac{2}{15}, y = 6\dfrac{11}{15}$

139. Is $-\dfrac{3}{4}$ a solution of the equation $\dfrac{4}{5} = \dfrac{31}{20} - y$?   **140.** Is $\dfrac{5}{8}$ a solution of the equation $-\dfrac{1}{4} = x - \dfrac{7}{8}$?

141. Is $-\dfrac{3}{5}$ a solution of the equation $x - \dfrac{1}{4} = -\dfrac{17}{20}$?   **142.** Is $-\dfrac{2}{3}$ a solution of the equation $\dfrac{2}{3} - x = 0$?

143. Which statement describes a pair of fractions for which the least common denominator is one of the denominators?
  (i) The denominator of one fraction is a factor of the denominator of the second fraction.
  (ii) The denominators of the two fractions have no common factors.

OBJECTIVE C   *To solve application problems*

144. ◗ **Demographics**   Three-twentieths of the men in the United States are left-handed. (*Source*: Scripps Survey Research Center Poll) What fraction of the men in the United States are not left-handed?

145. **Real Estate**   You purchased $3\dfrac{1}{4}$ acres of land and then sold $1\dfrac{1}{2}$ acres of the property. How many acres of the property do you own now?

146. **Carpentry**   A $2\dfrac{3}{4}$-foot piece is cut from a 6-foot board. Find the length of the remaining piece of board.

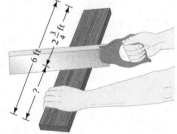

147. **Community Service**   You are required to contribute 20 h of community service to the town in which your college is located. After you have contributed $12\dfrac{1}{4}$ h, how many more hours of community service are still required of you?

148. ◔ Student Debt   Read the news clipping at the right.
   a. What fraction of undergraduate students do not go into debt to go to college?
   b. What fraction of student debt is owed to the federal government?

149. Construction   A roofer and an apprentice are roofing a newly constructed house. In one day, the roofer completes $\frac{1}{3}$ of the job and the apprentice completes $\frac{1}{4}$ of the job. How much of the job remains to be done? Working at the same rate, can the roofer and the apprentice complete the job in one more day?

150. ◔ Sociology   The table at the right below shows the results of a survey in which adults in the United States were asked how many evening meals they cook at home during an average week. **a.** Which response was given most frequently? **b.** What fraction of the adult population cooks two or fewer dinners at home per week? **c.** What fraction of the adult population cooks five or more dinners at home per week? Is this less than half or more than half of the people?

151. Wages   A student worked $4\frac{1}{3}$ h, 5 h, and $3\frac{2}{3}$ h this week at a part-time job. The student is paid $9 an hour. How much did the student earn this week?

152. Geometry   The course of a yachting race is in the shape of a triangle with sides that measure $4\frac{3}{10}$ mi, $3\frac{7}{10}$ mi, and $2\frac{1}{2}$ mi. Find the total length of the course. Use the formula $P = a + b + c$.

153. Geometry   You want to fence in the triangular plot of land shown at the right. How many feet of fencing do you need? Use the formula $P = a + b + c$.

◔ Golf   During the second half of the 1900s, greenskeepers mowed the grass on golf putting surfaces progressively lower. The table at the right shows the average grass height by decade. Use this table for Exercises 154 and 155.

154. What was the difference between the average height of the grass in the 1980s and in the 1950s?

155. Calculate the difference between the average grass height in the 1970s and in the 1960s.

In the NEWS!

Average Student Debt for College is $19,202

Approximately $\frac{2}{3}$ of undergraduate students go into debt to go to college. The average debt is $19,202. Most often the student debt is owed to the federal government.

Source: www.msnbc.msn.com

Responses to the question, "How many evening meals do you cook at home each week?"	
0	$\frac{2}{25}$
1	$\frac{1}{20}$
2	$\frac{1}{10}$
3	$\frac{13}{100}$
4	$\frac{3}{20}$
5	$\frac{21}{100}$
6	$\frac{9}{100}$
7	$\frac{19}{100}$

Source: Millward Brown for Whirlpool

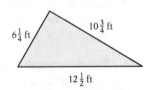

Average Height of Grass on Golf Putting Surfaces	
Decade	Height (in inches)
1950s	$\frac{1}{4}$
1960s	$\frac{7}{32}$
1970s	$\frac{3}{16}$
1980s	$\frac{5}{32}$
1990s	$\frac{1}{8}$

Source: Golf Course Superintendents Association of America

156. **Horse Racing**   The 3-year-olds in the Kentucky Derby run $1\frac{1}{4}$ mi. The horses in the Belmont Stakes run $1\frac{1}{2}$ mi, and the horses in the Preakness Stakes run $1\frac{3}{16}$ mi. How much farther do the horses run in the Kentucky Derby than in the Preakness Stakes? How much farther do they run in the Belmont Stakes than in the Preakness Stakes?

157. Boxing   A boxer is put on a diet to gain 15 lb in 4 weeks. The boxer gains $4\frac{1}{2}$ lb the first week and $3\frac{3}{4}$ lb the second week. How much weight must the boxer gain during the third and fourth weeks in order to gain a total of 15 lb?

Critical Thinking

158. The figure at the right is divided into 5 parts. Is each part of the figure $\frac{1}{5}$ of the figure? Why or why not?

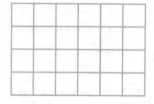

159. Draw a diagram that illustrates the addition of two fractions with the same denominator.

160. Use the diagram at the right to illustrate the sum of $\frac{1}{8}$ and $\frac{5}{6}$. Why does the figure contain 24 squares? Would it be possible to illustrate the sum of $\frac{1}{8}$ and $\frac{5}{6}$ if there were 48 squares in the figure? What if there were 16 squares? Make a list of the possible numbers of squares that could be used to illustrate the sum of $\frac{1}{8}$ and $\frac{5}{6}$.

Projects or Group Activities

For Exercises 161 to 168, give an example of a problem that meets the described condition. The fractions in your examples must be proper fractions with different denominators. If it is not possible to write a problem that meets the given condition, write "not possible."

161. A positive fraction is added to a positive fraction and the result is a negative fraction.

162. A positive fraction is added to a negative fraction and the result is a negative fraction.

163. A negative fraction is added to a positive fraction and the result is a positive fraction.

164. A negative fraction is added to a negative fraction and the result is a positive fraction.

165. A positive fraction is subtracted from a positive fraction and the result is a negative fraction.

166. A negative fraction is subtracted from a positive fraction and the result is a negative fraction.

167. A positive fraction is subtracted from a negative fraction and the result is a positive fraction.

168. A negative fraction is subtracted from a negative fraction and the result is a positive fraction.

3.8

Exponents, Complex Fractions, and the Order of Operations Agreement

OBJECTIVE A   *To simplify exponential expressions*

 Point of Interest

René Descartes (1596–1650) was the first mathematician to extensively use exponential notation as it is used today. However, for some unknown reason, he always used *xx* for *x*².

Recall that an exponent indicates the repeated multiplication of the same factor. For example,

$$3^5 = 3 \cdot 3 \cdot 3 \cdot 3 \cdot 3$$

The exponent, 5, indicates how many times the base, 3, occurs as a factor in the multiplication.

The base of an exponential expression can be a fraction; for example, $\left(\frac{2}{3}\right)^4$. To evaluate this expression, write the factor as many times as indicated by the exponent and then multiply.

$$\left(\frac{2}{3}\right)^4 = \frac{2}{3} \cdot \frac{2}{3} \cdot \frac{2}{3} \cdot \frac{2}{3} = \frac{2 \cdot 2 \cdot 2 \cdot 2}{3 \cdot 3 \cdot 3 \cdot 3} = \frac{16}{81}$$

HOW TO 1   Evaluate $\left(-\frac{3}{5}\right)^2 \cdot \left(\frac{5}{6}\right)^3$.

$$\left(-\frac{3}{5}\right)^2 \cdot \left(\frac{5}{6}\right)^3$$

Write each factor as many times as indicated by the exponent.

$$= \left(-\frac{3}{5}\right) \cdot \left(-\frac{3}{5}\right) \cdot \frac{5}{6} \cdot \frac{5}{6} \cdot \frac{5}{6}$$

Multiply. The product of two negative numbers is positive.

$$= \frac{3}{5} \cdot \frac{3}{5} \cdot \frac{5}{6} \cdot \frac{5}{6} \cdot \frac{5}{6}$$

$$= \frac{3 \cdot 3 \cdot 5 \cdot 5 \cdot 5}{5 \cdot 5 \cdot 6 \cdot 6 \cdot 6}$$

Write the product in simplest form.

$$= \frac{5}{24}$$

HOW TO 2   Evaluate x^3 for $x = 2\frac{1}{2}$.

$$x^3$$

Replace x with $2\frac{1}{2}$.

$$\left(2\frac{1}{2}\right)^3$$

Write the mixed number as an improper fraction.

$$= \left(\frac{5}{2}\right)^3$$

Write the base as many times as indicated by the exponent.

$$= \frac{5}{2} \cdot \frac{5}{2} \cdot \frac{5}{2}$$

Multiply.

$$= \frac{125}{8}$$

Write the improper fraction as a mixed number.

$$= 15\frac{5}{8}$$

EXAMPLE 1

Evaluate $\left(-\dfrac{3}{4}\right)^3 \cdot 8^2$.

Solution $\left(-\dfrac{3}{4}\right)^3 \cdot 8^2$

$$= \left(-\dfrac{3}{4}\right)\left(-\dfrac{3}{4}\right)\left(-\dfrac{3}{4}\right) \cdot 8 \cdot 8$$

$$= -\left(\dfrac{3}{4} \cdot \dfrac{3}{4} \cdot \dfrac{3}{4} \cdot \dfrac{8}{1} \cdot \dfrac{8}{1}\right)$$

$$= -\dfrac{3 \cdot 3 \cdot 3 \cdot 8 \cdot 8}{4 \cdot 4 \cdot 4 \cdot 1 \cdot 1} = -27$$

YOU TRY IT 1

Evaluate $\left(\dfrac{2}{9}\right)^2 \cdot (-3)^4$.

Your solution

EXAMPLE 2

Evaluate $x^2 y^2$ for $x = 1\dfrac{1}{2}$ and $y = \dfrac{2}{3}$.

Solution

$x^2 y^2$

$$\left(1\dfrac{1}{2}\right)^2 \cdot \left(\dfrac{2}{3}\right)^2 = \left(\dfrac{3}{2}\right)^2 \cdot \left(\dfrac{2}{3}\right)^2$$

$$= \dfrac{3}{2} \cdot \dfrac{3}{2} \cdot \dfrac{2}{3} \cdot \dfrac{2}{3}$$

$$= \dfrac{3 \cdot 3 \cdot 2 \cdot 2}{2 \cdot 2 \cdot 3 \cdot 3} = 1$$

YOU TRY IT 2

Evaluate $x^4 y^3$ for $x = 2\dfrac{1}{3}$ and $y = \dfrac{3}{7}$.

Your solution

Solutions on p. S11

OBJECTIVE B *To simplify complex fractions*

A **complex fraction** is a fraction whose numerator or denominator contains one or more fractions. Examples of complex fractions are shown below.

Main fraction bar $\longrightarrow$
$$\dfrac{\dfrac{3}{4}}{\dfrac{7}{8}} \qquad \dfrac{4}{3 - \dfrac{1}{2}} \qquad \dfrac{\dfrac{9}{10} + \dfrac{3}{5}}{\dfrac{5}{6}} \qquad \dfrac{3\dfrac{1}{2} \cdot 2\dfrac{5}{8}}{\left(4\dfrac{2}{3}\right) \div \left(3\dfrac{1}{5}\right)}$$

Look at the first example given above and recall that the fraction bar can be read "divided by."

Therefore, $\dfrac{\dfrac{3}{4}}{\dfrac{7}{8}}$ can be read "$\dfrac{3}{4}$ divided by $\dfrac{7}{8}$" and can be written $\dfrac{3}{4} \div \dfrac{7}{8}$. This is the division

of two fractions, which can be simplified by multiplying by the reciprocal, as shown at the top of the next page.

$$\frac{\dfrac{3}{4}}{\dfrac{7}{8}} = \frac{3}{4} \div \frac{7}{8} = \frac{3}{4} \cdot \frac{8}{7} = \frac{3 \cdot 8}{4 \cdot 7} = \frac{6}{7}$$

To simplify a complex fraction, first simplify the expression above the main fraction bar and the expression below the main fraction bar; the result is one number in the numerator and one number in the denominator. Then rewrite the complex fraction as a division problem by reading the main fraction bar as "divided by."

HOW TO 3 Simplify: $\dfrac{4}{3 - \dfrac{1}{2}}$

The numerator (4) is already simplified. Simplify the expression in the denominator.

Note: $3 - \frac{1}{2} = \frac{6}{2} - \frac{1}{2} = \frac{5}{2}$

$$\frac{4}{3 - \dfrac{1}{2}} = \frac{4}{\dfrac{5}{2}}$$

Rewrite the complex fraction as division.

$$= 4 \div \frac{5}{2}$$

Divide.

$$= \frac{4}{1} \div \frac{5}{2}$$

$$= \frac{4}{1} \cdot \frac{2}{5}$$

Write the answer in simplest form.

$$= \frac{8}{5} = 1\frac{3}{5}$$

HOW TO 4 Simplify: $\dfrac{-\dfrac{9}{10} + \dfrac{3}{5}}{1\dfrac{1}{4}}$

Simplify the expression in the numerator.

Note: $-\frac{9}{10} + \frac{3}{5} = \frac{-9}{10} + \frac{6}{10} = \frac{-3}{10} = -\frac{3}{10}$

Write the mixed number in the denominator as an improper fraction.

$$\frac{-\dfrac{9}{10} + \dfrac{3}{5}}{1\dfrac{1}{4}} = \frac{-\dfrac{3}{10}}{\dfrac{5}{4}}$$

Rewrite the complex fraction as division. The quotient will be negative.

$$= -\left(\frac{3}{10} \div \frac{5}{4}\right)$$

Divide by multiplying by the reciprocal.

$$= -\left(\frac{3}{10} \cdot \frac{4}{5}\right)$$

Write the answer in simplest form.

$$= -\frac{6}{25}$$

HOW TO 5 Evaluate $\frac{wx}{yz}$ for $w = 1\frac{1}{3}$, $x = 2\frac{5}{8}$, $y = 4\frac{1}{2}$, and $z = 3\frac{1}{3}$.

$$\frac{wx}{yz}$$

Replace each variable with its given value.

$$\frac{1\frac{1}{3} \cdot 2\frac{5}{8}}{4\frac{1}{2} \cdot 3\frac{1}{3}}$$

Simplify the numerator.

Note: $1\frac{1}{3} \cdot 2\frac{5}{8} = \frac{4}{3} \cdot \frac{21}{8} = \frac{7}{2}$

Simplify the denominator.

Note: $4\frac{1}{2} \cdot 3\frac{1}{3} = \frac{9}{2} \cdot \frac{10}{3} = 15$

$$= \frac{\frac{7}{2}}{15}$$

Rewrite the complex fraction as division.

$$= \frac{7}{2} \div 15$$

Divide by multiplying by the reciprocal.

Note: $15 = \frac{15}{1}$; the reciprocal of $\frac{15}{1}$ is $\frac{1}{15}$.

$$= \frac{7}{2} \cdot \frac{1}{15} = \frac{7}{30}$$

EXAMPLE 3

Is $\frac{2}{3}$ a solution of $\dfrac{x + \frac{1}{2}}{x} = \frac{7}{4}$?

Solution

$$\frac{x + \frac{1}{2}}{x} = \frac{7}{4}$$

$$\dfrac{\frac{2}{3} + \frac{1}{2}}{\frac{2}{3}} \,\Big|\, \frac{7}{4} \qquad \bullet \text{ Replace } x \text{ with } \frac{2}{3}.$$

$$\dfrac{\frac{7}{6}}{\frac{2}{3}} \,\Big|\, \frac{7}{4} \qquad \bullet \text{ Simplify the complex fraction.}$$

$$\frac{7}{6} \div \frac{2}{3} \,\Big|\, \frac{7}{4} \qquad \bullet \text{ The main fraction bar is read "divided by."}$$

$$\frac{7}{6} \cdot \frac{3}{2} \,\Big|\, \frac{7}{4}$$

$$\frac{7}{4} = \frac{7}{4}$$

Yes, $\frac{2}{3}$ is a solution of the equation.

YOU TRY IT 3

Is $-\frac{1}{2}$ a solution of $\dfrac{2y - 3}{y} = -2$?

Your solution

Solution on p. S11

EXAMPLE 4

Evaluate the variable expression $\frac{x-y}{z}$ for $x = 4\frac{1}{8}$, $y = 2\frac{5}{8}$, and $z = \frac{3}{4}$.

Solution

$\frac{x-y}{z}$

$$\frac{4\frac{1}{8} - 2\frac{5}{8}}{\frac{3}{4}} = \frac{\frac{3}{2}}{\frac{3}{4}} = \frac{3}{2} \div \frac{3}{4} = \frac{3}{2} \cdot \frac{4}{3} = 2$$

YOU TRY IT 4

Evaluate the variable expression $\frac{x}{y-z}$ for $x = 2\frac{4}{9}$, $y = 3$, and $z = 1\frac{1}{3}$.

Your solution

Solution on p. S11

OBJECTIVE C   *To use the Order of Operations Agreement to simplify expressions*

The Order of Operations Agreement applies in simplifying expressions containing fractions.

The Order of Operations Agreement
Step 1   Do all operations inside parentheses.
Step 2   Simplify any numerical expressions containing exponents.
Step 3   Do multiplication and division as they occur from left to right.
Step 4   Do addition and subtraction as they occur from left to right.

HOW TO 6   Simplify: $\left(\frac{1}{2}\right)^2 + \left(\frac{2}{3} \div \frac{5}{9}\right) \cdot \frac{5}{6}$

$$\left(\frac{1}{2}\right)^2 + \left(\frac{2}{3} \div \frac{5}{9}\right) \cdot \frac{5}{6}$$

Do the operation inside the parentheses (Step 1).

$$= \left(\frac{1}{2}\right)^2 + \left(\frac{6}{5}\right) \cdot \frac{5}{6}$$

Simplify the exponential expression (Step 2).

$$= \frac{1}{4} + \left(\frac{6}{5}\right) \cdot \frac{5}{6}$$

Do the multiplication (Step 3).

$$= \frac{1}{4} + 1$$

Do the addition (Step 4).

$$= 1\frac{1}{4}$$

A fraction bar acts like parentheses. Therefore, simplify the numerator and denominator of a fraction as part of Step 1 in the Order of Operations Agreement.

HOW TO 7   Simplify: $6 - \dfrac{2+1}{15-8} \div \dfrac{3}{14}$

$$6 - \frac{2+1}{15-8} \div \frac{3}{14}$$

Perform operations above and below the fraction bar.

$$= 6 - \frac{3}{7} \div \frac{3}{14}$$

Do the division.

$$= 6 - \left(\frac{3}{7} \cdot \frac{14}{3}\right)$$

$$= 6 - 2$$

Do the subtraction.

$$= 4$$

HOW TO 8   Evaluate $\dfrac{w+x}{y} - z$ for $w = \frac{3}{4}$, $x = \frac{1}{4}$, $y = 2$, and $z = \frac{1}{3}$.

$$\frac{w+x}{y} - z$$

Replace each variable with its given value.

$$\frac{\frac{3}{4} + \frac{1}{4}}{2} - \frac{1}{3}$$

Simplify the numerator of the complex fraction.

$$= \frac{1}{2} - \frac{1}{3}$$

Do the subtraction.

$$= \frac{1}{6}$$

EXAMPLE 5

Simplify: $\left(-\dfrac{2}{3}\right)^2 \div \dfrac{7-2}{13-4} - \dfrac{1}{3}$

Solution $\left(-\dfrac{2}{3}\right)^2 \div \dfrac{7-2}{13-4} - \dfrac{1}{3}$

$$= \left(-\frac{2}{3}\right)^2 \div \frac{5}{9} - \frac{1}{3} \qquad \bullet \text{ Simplify } \frac{7-2}{13-4}.$$

$$= \frac{4}{9} \div \frac{5}{9} - \frac{1}{3} \qquad \bullet \text{ Simplify } \left(-\frac{2}{3}\right)^2.$$

$$= \frac{4}{9} \cdot \frac{9}{5} - \frac{1}{3} \qquad \bullet \text{ Rewrite division as}$$
$$\text{multiplication by the}$$
$$= \frac{4}{5} - \frac{1}{3} = \frac{7}{15} \qquad \text{reciprocal.}$$

YOU TRY IT 5

Simplify: $\left(-\dfrac{1}{2}\right)^3 \cdot \dfrac{7-3}{4-9} + \dfrac{4}{5}$

Your solution

Solution on p. S11

3.8 EXERCISES

✔ Concept Check

1. To evaluate $\left(-\frac{1}{5}\right)^4$, write $-\frac{1}{5}$ as a factor _____ times and then multiply.

2. To evaluate $\left(-\frac{4}{5}\right)^3$, write $-\frac{4}{5}$ as a factor _____ times and then multiply.

3. To simplify the complex fraction $\dfrac{\frac{1}{3}}{\frac{5}{6}}$, first write it as the division problem

_____ $\div$ _____.

4. To simplify the complex fraction $\dfrac{5}{3 - \frac{1}{2}}$, first simplify the denominator of the com-

plex fraction: $3 - \frac{1}{2} = \frac{\blacksquare}{2} - \frac{1}{2} = \frac{\blacksquare}{2}$.

OBJECTIVE A   *To simplify exponential expressions*

Evaluate.

5. $\left(\frac{3}{4}\right)^2$

6. $\left(\frac{5}{8}\right)^2$

7. $\left(-\frac{1}{6}\right)^3$

8. $\left(-\frac{2}{7}\right)^3$

9. $\left(\frac{5}{8}\right)^3 \cdot \left(\frac{2}{5}\right)^2$

10. $\left(\frac{3}{5}\right)^3 \cdot \left(\frac{1}{3}\right)^2$

11. $\left(\frac{4}{5}\right)^4 \cdot \left(-\frac{5}{8}\right)^3$

12. $\left(-\frac{9}{11}\right)^2 \cdot \left(\frac{1}{3}\right)^4$

13. $7^2 \cdot \left(\frac{2}{7}\right)^3$

14. $4^3 \cdot \left(\frac{5}{12}\right)^2$

15. $4 \cdot \left(\frac{4}{7}\right)^2 \cdot \left(-\frac{3}{4}\right)^3$

16. $3 \cdot \left(\frac{2}{5}\right)^2 \cdot \left(-\frac{1}{6}\right)^2$

Evaluate the variable expression for the given values of x and y.

17. x^4, for $x = \frac{2}{3}$

18. y^3, for $y = -\frac{3}{4}$

19. $x^4 y^2$, for $x = \frac{5}{6}$ and $y = -\frac{3}{5}$

20. $x^5 y^3$, for $x = -\frac{5}{8}$ and $y = \frac{4}{5}$

21. x^3y^2, for $x = \frac{2}{3}$ and $y = 1\frac{1}{2}$

22. x^2y^4, for $x = 2\frac{1}{3}$ and $y = \frac{3}{7}$

23. True or false? If a is positive and b is negative, then $\left(-\frac{a}{b}\right)^5$ is a positive number.

24. True or false? If a is negative and b is negative, then $\left(-\frac{a}{b}\right)^4$ is a positive number.

OBJECTIVE B   *To simplify complex fractions*

Simplify.

25. $\dfrac{\frac{9}{16}}{\frac{3}{4}}$

26. $\dfrac{\frac{7}{24}}{\frac{3}{8}}$

27. $\dfrac{-\frac{5}{6}}{\frac{15}{16}}$

28. $\dfrac{\frac{7}{12}}{-\frac{5}{18}}$

29. $\dfrac{\frac{2}{3} + \frac{1}{2}}{7}$

30. $\dfrac{-5}{\frac{3}{8} - \frac{1}{4}}$

31. $\dfrac{2 + \frac{1}{4}}{\frac{3}{8}}$

32. $\dfrac{1 - \frac{3}{4}}{\frac{5}{12}}$

33. $\dfrac{\frac{9}{25}}{\frac{4}{5} - \frac{1}{10}}$

34. $\dfrac{-\frac{5}{7}}{\frac{4}{7} - \frac{3}{14}}$

35. $\dfrac{\frac{1}{3} - \frac{3}{4}}{\frac{1}{6} + \frac{2}{3}}$

36. $\dfrac{\frac{9}{14} - \frac{1}{7}}{\frac{9}{14} + \frac{1}{7}}$

37. $\dfrac{3 + 2\frac{1}{3}}{5\frac{1}{6} - 1}$

38. $\dfrac{4 - 3\frac{5}{8}}{2\frac{1}{2} - \frac{3}{4}}$

39. $\dfrac{5\frac{2}{3} - 1\frac{1}{6}}{3\frac{5}{8} - 2\frac{1}{4}}$

40. $\dfrac{3\frac{1}{4} - 2\frac{1}{2}}{4\frac{3}{4} + 1\frac{1}{2}}$

Evaluate the expression for the given values of the variables.

41. $\frac{x + y}{z}$, for $x = \frac{2}{3}$, $y = \frac{3}{4}$, and $z = \frac{1}{12}$

42. $\frac{x}{y + z}$, for $x = \frac{8}{15}$, $y = \frac{3}{5}$, and $z = \frac{2}{3}$

43. $\frac{xy}{z}$, for $x = \frac{3}{4}$, $y = -\frac{2}{3}$, and $z = \frac{5}{8}$

44. $\frac{x}{yz}$, for $x = -\frac{5}{12}$, $y = \frac{8}{9}$, and $z = -\frac{3}{4}$

45. $\frac{x - y}{z}$, for $x = 2\frac{5}{8}$, $y = 1\frac{1}{4}$, and $z = 1\frac{3}{8}$

46. $\frac{x}{y - z}$, for $x = 2\frac{3}{10}$, $y = 3\frac{2}{5}$, and $z = 1\frac{4}{5}$

State whether the given expression is equivalent to 0, equivalent to 1, equivalent to $\left(\frac{a}{b}\right)^2$, or undefined.

47. $\dfrac{\dfrac{a}{b}}{\dfrac{a}{b}}$

48. $\dfrac{\dfrac{a}{b}}{\dfrac{0}{b}}$

49. $\dfrac{\dfrac{0}{b}}{\dfrac{a}{b}}$

50. $\dfrac{\dfrac{a}{b}}{\dfrac{b}{a}}$

OBJECTIVE C *To use the Order of Operations Agreement to simplify expressions*

51. Simplifying the expression $\dfrac{2}{3} - \dfrac{4}{3 + \dfrac{3}{8}}$ involves performing three operations: subtraction, division, and addition. List these three operations in the order in which they must be performed.

52. Simplifying the expression $\dfrac{2}{9} \cdot \left(\dfrac{3}{4}\right)^2 + \dfrac{5}{6}$ involves performing three operations: multiplication, squaring, and addition. List these three operations in the order in which they must be performed.

Simplify.

53. $-\dfrac{3}{7} \cdot \dfrac{14}{15} + \dfrac{4}{5}$

54. $\dfrac{3}{5} \div \dfrac{6}{7} + \dfrac{4}{5}$

55. $\left(\dfrac{5}{6}\right)^2 - \dfrac{5}{9}$

56. $\left(\dfrac{3}{5}\right)^2 - \dfrac{3}{10}$

57. $\dfrac{3}{4} \cdot \left(\dfrac{11}{12} - \dfrac{7}{8}\right) + \dfrac{5}{16}$

58. $-\dfrac{7}{18} + \dfrac{5}{6} \cdot \left(\dfrac{2}{3} - \dfrac{1}{6}\right)$

59. $\dfrac{11}{16} - \left(\dfrac{3}{4}\right)^2 + \dfrac{7}{8}$

60. $\left(-\dfrac{2}{3}\right)^2 - \dfrac{7}{18} + \dfrac{5}{6}$

61. $\left(1\dfrac{1}{3} - \dfrac{5}{6}\right) + \dfrac{7}{8} \div \left(-\dfrac{1}{2}\right)^2$

62. $\left(\dfrac{1}{4}\right)^2 \div \left(2\dfrac{1}{2} - \dfrac{3}{4}\right) + \dfrac{5}{7}$

63. $\left(\dfrac{2}{3}\right)^2 + \dfrac{8-7}{3-9} \div \dfrac{3}{8}$

64. $\left(\dfrac{1}{3}\right)^2 \cdot \dfrac{14-5}{6-10} + \dfrac{3}{4}$

65. $-\dfrac{1}{2} + \dfrac{\frac{13}{25}}{4 - \frac{3}{4}} \div \dfrac{1}{5}$

66. $\dfrac{4}{5} - \dfrac{3 - \frac{7}{9}}{\frac{5}{6}} \cdot \dfrac{3}{8}$

67. $\left(\dfrac{2}{3}\right)^2 + \dfrac{\frac{5}{8} - \frac{1}{4}}{\frac{2}{3} - \frac{1}{6}} \cdot \dfrac{8}{9}$

Evaluate the expression for the given values of the variables.

68. $x^2 + \dfrac{y}{z}$, for $x = -\dfrac{2}{3}$, $y = \dfrac{5}{8}$, and $z = \dfrac{3}{4}$

69. $\dfrac{x}{y} - z^2$, for $x = \dfrac{5}{6}$, $y = \dfrac{1}{3}$, and $z = -\dfrac{3}{4}$

70. $x - y^3 z$, for $x = \dfrac{5}{6}$, $y = \dfrac{1}{2}$, and $z = \dfrac{8}{9}$

71. $xy^3 + z$, for $x = \dfrac{9}{10}$, $y = \dfrac{1}{3}$, and $z = \dfrac{7}{15}$

72. $\dfrac{wx}{y} + z$, for $w = \dfrac{4}{5}$, $x = \dfrac{5}{8}$, $y = \dfrac{3}{4}$, and $z = \dfrac{2}{3}$

73. $\dfrac{w}{xy} - z$, for $w = 2\dfrac{1}{2}$, $x = 4$, $y = \dfrac{3}{8}$, and $z = \dfrac{2}{3}$

Critical Thinking

74. Computers A computer can perform 600,000 operations in 1 s. To the nearest minute, how many minutes will it take for the computer to perform 10^8 operations?

75. Find the product $\left(1 - \dfrac{1}{2^2}\right)\left(1 - \dfrac{1}{3^2}\right)\left(1 - \dfrac{1}{4^2}\right) \cdots \left(1 - \dfrac{1}{9^2}\right)\left(1 - \dfrac{1}{10^2}\right)$.

Projects or Group Activities

76. Given that x is a whole number, for what value of x will the expression $\left(\dfrac{3}{4}\right)^2 + x^5 \div \dfrac{7}{8}$ have a minimum value? What is the minimum value?

77. Fill in the blank squares at the right so that the sum of the numbers is the same along any row, column, or diagonal. The resulting square is called a magic square.

		$\dfrac{3}{4}$
1	$\dfrac{5}{8}$	
$\dfrac{1}{2}$		$\dfrac{7}{8}$

Decimals

4

OBJECTIVES

SECTION 4.1
A To write decimals in standard form and in words
B To identify the order relation between two decimals
C To round a decimal to a given place value
D To solve application problems

SECTION 4.2
A To add and subtract decimals
B To solve application problems and use formulas

SECTION 4.3
A To multiply decimals
B To divide decimals
C To convert between decimals and fractions and to identify the order relation between a decimal and a fraction
D To solve application problems and use formulas

SECTION 4.4
A To simplify a variable expression using the Properties of Addition
B To simplify a variable expression using the Properties of Multiplication
C To simplify a variable expression using the Distributive Property
D To simplify general variable expressions

Focus on Success

Do you have trouble with word problems? Word problems show the variety of ways in which math can be used. The solution of every word problem can be broken down into two steps: Strategy and Solution. The Strategy consists of reading the problem, writing down what is known and unknown, and devising a plan to find the unknown. The Solution often consists of solving an equation and then checking the solution. (See Use a Strategy to Solve Word Problems, page AIM-10.)

© iStockphoto.com/RidofranzRidofranz

Prep Test

Are you ready to succeed in this chapter? Take the Prep Test below to find out if you are ready to learn the new material.

1. Express the shaded portion of the rectangle as a fraction.

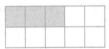

2. Round 36,852 to the nearest hundred.

3. Write 4791 in words.

4. Write six thousand eight hundred forty-two in standard form.

5. Graph -3 on the number line.

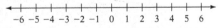

For Exercises 6 to 9, add, subtract, multiply, or divide.

6. $-37 + 8892 + 456$

7. $2403 - (-765)$

8. $-844(-91)$

9. $23\overline{)6412}$

10. Evaluate 8^2.

SECTION

4.1

Introduction to Decimals

OBJECTIVE A *To write decimals in standard form and in words*

The price tag on a sweater reads $61.88. The number 61.88 is in **decimal notation.** A number written in decimal notation is often called simply a **decimal.**

A number written in decimal notation has three parts.

61   .   88

Whole number part   **Decimal point**   **Decimal part**

The decimal part of the number represents a number less than 1. For example, $.88 is less than one dollar. The decimal point (.) separates the whole number part from the decimal part.

The position of a digit in a decimal determines the digit's **place value.** The place-value chart is extended to the right to show the place values of digits to the right of a decimal point.

In the decimal 458.302719, the position of the digit 7 determines that its place value is ten-thousandths.

Note the relationship between fractions and numbers written in decimal notation.

seven tenths	seven hundredths	seven thousandths
$\dfrac{7}{10} = 0.7$	$\dfrac{7}{100} = 0.07$	$\dfrac{7}{1000} = 0.007$
1 zero in 10	2 zeros in 100	3 zeros in 1000
1 decimal place in 0.7	2 decimal places in 0.07	3 decimal places in 0.007

To write a decimal in words, write the decimal part of the number as though it were a whole number, and then name the place value of the last digit.

0.9684   nine thousand six hundred eighty-four ten-thousandths

The decimal point in a decimal is read as "and."

372.516   three hundred seventy-two and five hundred sixteen thousandths

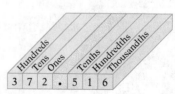

 Point of Interest

The idea that all fractions should be represented in tenths, hundredths, and thousandths was presented in 1585 in Simon Stevin's publication *De Thiende.* Its French translation, *La Disme,* was widely read and accepted by the French. This may help to explain why the French accepted the metric system so easily 200 years later.

In *De Thiende,* Stevin argued in favor of his notation by including examples for astronomers, tapestry makers, surveyors, tailors, and the like. He stated that using decimals would enable calculations to be "performed . . . with as much ease as counter-reckoning."

To write a decimal in standard form when it is written in words, write the whole number part, replace the word *and* with a decimal point, and write the decimal part so that the last digit is in the given place-value position.

four and twenty-three <u>hundredths</u>

3 is in the hundredths place.   4.2<u>3</u>

When writing a decimal in standard form, you may need to insert zeros after the decimal point so that the last digit is in the given place-value position.

ninety-one and eight <u>thousandths</u>

8 is in the thousandths place.
Insert two zeros so that the 8 is in
the thousandths place.   91.00<u>8</u>

sixty-five <u>ten-thousandths</u>

5 is in the ten-thousandths place.
Insert two zeros so that the 5 is in
the ten-thousandths place.   0.006<u>5</u>

EXAMPLE 1

Name the place value of the digit 8 in the number 45.687.

Solution   The digit 8 is in the hundredths place.

YOU TRY IT 1

Name the place value of the digit 4 in the number 907.1342.

Your solution

EXAMPLE 2

Write $\frac{43}{100}$ as a decimal.

Solution $\frac{43}{100} = 0.43$ • 43 hundredths

YOU TRY IT 2

Write $\frac{501}{1000}$ as a decimal.

Your solution

EXAMPLE 3

Write 0.289 as a fraction.

Solution $0.289 = \frac{289}{1000}$ • 289 thousandths

YOU TRY IT 3

Write 0.67 as a fraction.

Your solution

EXAMPLE 4

Write 293.50816 in words.

Solution   two hundred ninety-three and fifty thousand eight hundred sixteen hundred-thousandths

YOU TRY IT 4

Write 55.6083 in words.

Your solution

Solutions on p. S12

EXAMPLE 5

Write twenty-three and two hundred forty-seven millionths in standard form.

Solution   23.000247
                    ↑
                    └── millionths place

YOU TRY IT 5

Write eight hundred six and four hundred ninety-one hundred-thousandths in standard form.

Your solution

Solution on p. S12

OBJECTIVE B   *To identify the order relation between two decimals*

A whole number can be written as a decimal by writing a decimal point to the right of the last digit. For example,

$$62 = 62. \qquad\qquad 497 = 497.$$

You know that $62 and $62.00 both represent sixty-two dollars. Any number of zeros may be written to the right of the decimal point in a whole number without changing the value of the number.

$$62 = 62.00 = 62.0000 \qquad 497 = 497.0 = 497.000$$

Also, any number of zeros may be written to the right of the last digit in a decimal without changing the value of the number.

$$0.8 = 0.80 = 0.800 \qquad 1.35 = 1.350 = 1.3500 = 1.35000 = 1.350000$$

This fact is used to find the order relation between two decimals.

To compare two decimals, write the decimal part of each number so that each has the same number of decimal places. Then compare the two numbers.

HOW TO 1   Place the correct symbol, $<$ or $>$, between the two numbers 0.693 and 0.71.

0.693 has 3 decimal places.
0.71 has 2 decimal places.
Write 0.71 with 3 decimal places. $0.71 = 0.710$

Compare 0.693 and 0.710.
693 thousandths $<$ 710 thousandths $0.693 < 0.710$

Remove the zero written in 0.710. $0.693 < 0.71$

HOW TO 2   Place the correct symbol, $<$ or $>$, between the two numbers 5.8 and 5.493.

Write 5.8 with 3 decimal places. $5.8 = 5.800$

Compare 5.800 and 5.493.
The whole number part (5) is the same.
800 thousandths $>$ 493 thousandths $5.800 > 5.493$

Remove the extra zeros written in 5.800. $5.8 > 5.493$

Point of Interest

The decimal point did not make its appearance until the early 1600s. Stevin's notation used subscripts with circles around them after each digit: 0 for ones, 1 for tenths (which he called "primes"), 2 for hundredths (called "seconds"), 3 for thousandths ("thirds"), and so on. For example, 1.375 would have been written

1 ⓪ 3 ① 7 ② 5 ③

EXAMPLE 6

Place the correct symbol, $<$ or $>$, between the two numbers.

0.039   0.1001

Solution $0.039 = 0.0390$

$0.0390 < 0.1001$

$0.039 < 0.1001$

YOU TRY IT 6

Place the correct symbol, $<$ or $>$, between the two numbers.

0.065   0.0802

Your solution

EXAMPLE 7

Write the given numbers in order from smallest to largest.

1.01, 1.2, 1.002, 1.1, 1.12

Solution   Write each number with 3 decimal places. Then write the numbers in order.

1.010, 1.200, 1.002, 1.100, 1.120
1.002, 1.010, 1.100, 1.120, 1.200

1.002, 1.01, 1.1, 1.12, 1.2

YOU TRY IT 7

Write the given numbers in order from smallest to largest.

3.03, 0.33, 0.3, 3.3, 0.03

Your solution

Solutions on p. S12

OBJECTIVE C   *To round a decimal to a given place value*

In general, rounding decimals is similar to rounding whole numbers except that the digits to the right of the given place value are dropped instead of being replaced by zeros.

If the digit to the right of the given place value is less than 5, that digit and all digits to the right are dropped.

Round 6.9237 to the nearest hundredth.

┌──── Given place value (hundredths)

6.9237

└──── 3 < 5   Drop the digits 3 and 7.

6.9237 rounded to the nearest hundredth is 6.92.

If the digit to the right of the given place value is greater than or equal to 5, increase the digit in the given place value by 1, and drop all digits to its right.

Round 12.385 to the nearest tenth.

┌──── Given place value (tenths)

12.385

└──── 8 > 5   Increase 3 by 1 and drop all digits to the right of 3.

12.385 rounded to the nearest tenth is 12.4.

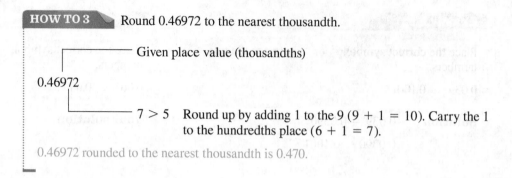

HOW TO 3   Round 0.46972 to the nearest thousandth.

Given place value (thousandths)

0.46972

7 > 5   Round up by adding 1 to the 9 (9 + 1 = 10). Carry the 1 to the hundredths place (6 + 1 = 7).

0.46972 rounded to the nearest thousandth is 0.470.

Note that in HOW TO 3, the zero in the given place value is not dropped. This indicates that the number is rounded to the nearest thousandth. If we dropped the zero and wrote 0.47, it would indicate that the number was rounded to the nearest hundredth.

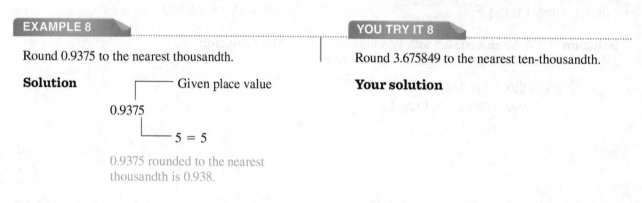

EXAMPLE 8

Round 0.9375 to the nearest thousandth.

Solution

Given place value

0.9375

5 = 5

0.9375 rounded to the nearest thousandth is 0.938.

YOU TRY IT 8

Round 3.675849 to the nearest ten-thousandth.

Your solution

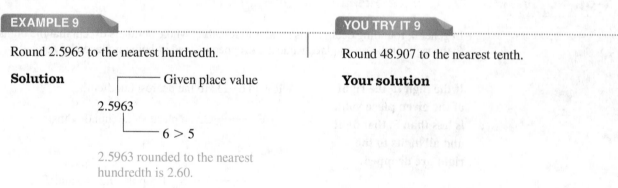

EXAMPLE 9

Round 2.5963 to the nearest hundredth.

Solution

Given place value

2.5963

6 > 5

2.5963 rounded to the nearest hundredth is 2.60.

YOU TRY IT 9

Round 48.907 to the nearest tenth.

Your solution

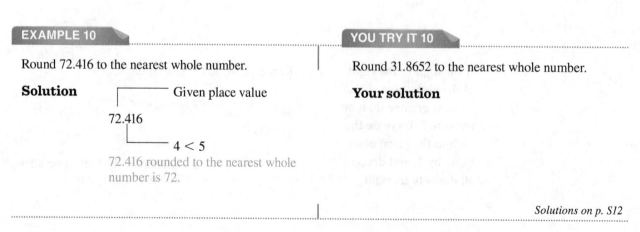

EXAMPLE 10

Round 72.416 to the nearest whole number.

Solution

Given place value

72.416

4 < 5

72.416 rounded to the nearest whole number is 72.

YOU TRY IT 10

Round 31.8652 to the nearest whole number.

Your solution

Solutions on p. S12

OBJECTIVE D   *To solve application problems*

NY Daily News Archive via Getty Images

Babe Ruth

The table below shows the number of home runs hit, for every 100 times at bat, by four Major League baseball players. Use this table for Example 11 and You Try It 11.

Home Runs Hit for Every 100 At-Bats	
Harmon Killebrew	7.03
Ralph Kiner	7.09
Babe Ruth	8.05
Ted Williams	6.76

Source: Major League Baseball

EXAMPLE 11

According to the table above, who had more home runs for every 100 times at bat, Ted Williams or Babe Ruth?

Strategy

To determine who had more home runs for every 100 times at bat, compare the numbers 6.76 and 8.05.

Solution

8.05 > 6.76

Babe Ruth had more home runs for every 100 at-bats.

YOU TRY IT 11

According to the table above, who had more home runs for every 100 times at bat, Harmon Killebrew or Ralph Kiner?

Your strategy

Your solution

EXAMPLE 12

On average, an American goes to the movies 4.56 times per year. To the nearest whole number, how many times per year does an American go to the movies?

Strategy

To find the number, round 4.56 to the nearest whole number.

Solution

4.56 rounded to the nearest whole number is 5.

An American goes to the movies about 5 times per year.

YOU TRY IT 12

One of the driest cities in the Southwest is Yuma, Arizona, with an average annual precipitation of 2.65 in. To the nearest inch, what is the average annual precipitation in Yuma?

Your strategy

Your solution

Solutions on p. S12

4.1 EXERCISES

✔ Concept Check

1. In a decimal, the place values of the first six digits to the right of the decimal point are tenths, _____, _____, ten-thousandths, _____, and _____.

2. The place value of the digit 3 in 0.53 is _____, so when 0.53 is written as a fraction, the denominator is _____. The numerator is _____.

3. To write 85.102 in words, first write *eighty-five*. Replace the decimal point with the word _____ and then write *one hundred two* _____.

4. To write seventy-three millionths in standard form, insert _____ zeros between the decimal point and 73 so that the digit 3 is in the millionths place.

For Exercises 5 and 6, fill in each blank with < or >.

5. To decide on the order relation between 0.017 and 0.107, compare 17 thousandths and 107 thousandths. Because 17 thousandths _____ 107 thousandths, 0.017 _____ 0.107.

6. To decide on the order relation between 3.4 and 3.05, write 3.4 as 3.40. The numbers have the same whole number parts, so compare 40 hundredths and 5 hundredths. Because 40 hundredths _____ 5 hundredths, 3.4 _____ 3.05.

OBJECTIVE A   *To write decimals in standard form and in words*

Name the place value of the digit 5.

7. 76.31587

8. 291.508

9. 432.09157

10. 0.0006512

11. 38.2591

12. 0.0000853

Write the fraction as a decimal.

13. $\dfrac{3}{10}$

14. $\dfrac{9}{10}$

15. $\dfrac{21}{100}$

16. $\dfrac{87}{100}$

17. $\dfrac{461}{1000}$

18. $\dfrac{853}{1000}$

19. $\dfrac{93}{1000}$

20. $\dfrac{61}{1000}$

Write the decimal as a fraction.

21. 0.1   **22.** 0.3   **23.** 0.47   **24.** 0.59

25. 0.289   **26.** 0.601   **27.** 0.09   **28.** 0.013

Write the number in words.

29. 0.37   **30.** 25.6   **31.** 9.4

32. 1.004   **33.** 0.0053   **34.** 41.108

35. 0.045   **36.** 3.157   **37.** 26.04

Write the number in standard form.

38. six hundred seventy-two thousandths

39. three and eight hundred six ten-thousandths

40. nine and four hundred seven ten-thousandths

41. four hundred seven and three hundredths

42. six hundred twelve and seven hundred four thousandths

43. two hundred forty-six and twenty-four thousandths

44. two thousand sixty-seven and nine thousand two ten-thousandths

45. seventy-three and two thousand six hundred eighty-four hundred-thousandths

OBJECTIVE B   *To identify the order relation between two decimals*

Place the correct symbol, < or >, between the two numbers.

46. 0.16   0.6   **47.** 0.7   0.56   **48.** 5.54   5.45   **49.** 3.605   3.065

50. 0.047   0.407   **51.** 9.004   9.04   **52.** 1.0008   1.008   **53.** 9.31   9.031

54. 7.6005   7.605   **55.** 4.6   40.6   **56.** 0.31502   0.3152   **57.** 0.07046   0.07036

Write the given numbers in order from smallest to largest.

58. 0.39, 0.309, 0.399

59. 0.66, 0.699, 0.696, 0.609

60. 0.24, 0.024, 0.204, 0.0024

61. 1.327, 1.237, 1.732, 1.372

62. 0.06, 0.059, 0.061, 0.0061

63. 21.87, 21.875, 21.805, 21.78

64. Use the inequality symbol < to rewrite the order relation expressed by the inequality 9.4 > 0.94.

65. Use the inequality symbol > to rewrite the order relation expressed by the inequality 0.062 < 0.62.

OBJECTIVE C *To round a decimal to a given place value*

Round the number to the given place value.

66. 6.249; tenths

67. 5.398; tenths

68. 21.007; tenths

69. 30.0092; tenths

70. 18.40937; hundredths

71. 413.5972; hundredths

72. 72.4983; hundredths

73. 6.061745; thousandths

74. 936.2905; thousandths

75. 96.8027; whole number

76. 47.3192; whole number

77. 5439.83; whole number

78. 7014.96; whole number

79. 0.023591; ten-thousandths

80. 2.975268; hundred-thousandths

OBJECTIVE D *To solve application problems*

81. **Coins** Read the news clipping at the right. The cost to mint a nickel is 7.7¢, and it costs 10¢ to mint a quarter. **a.** Is the cost to mint a penny greater than or less than the face value of a penny? **b.** To the nearest cent, what is the cost to mint a penny? **c.** Is the cost to mint a nickel greater than or less than the face value of a nickel? **d.** To the nearest cent, what is the cost to mint a nickel?

82. **Coins** A nickel weighs about 0.1763668 oz. Find the weight of a nickel to the nearest hundredth of an ounce.

In the NEWS!

Rising Costs to Mint Coins

A U.S. penny contains zinc and copper. The prices of these metals have risen, which is why it now costs 1.67¢ to mint a penny. Some people suggest changing the content of the penny. Others advocate eliminating the penny from our currency. Both suggestions meet opposition from the public.
Source: answers.yahoo.com

83. ● **Boston Marathon**   Runners in the Boston Marathon run a distance of 26.21875 mi. To the nearest tenth of a mile, find the distance run by an entrant who completes the Boston Marathon.

84. **Minimum Payments**   Charge accounts generally require a minimum payment on the balance in the account each month. Use the minimum payment schedule shown below to determine the minimum payment due on the given account balances.

	Account Balance	Minimum Payment
a.	$187.93	
b.	$342.55	
c.	$261.48	
d.	$16.99	
e.	$310.00	
f.	$158.32	
g.	$200.10	

If the New Balance is:	The Minimum Required Payment Is:
Up to $20.00	The new balance
$20.01 to $200.00	$20.00
$200.01 to $250.00	$25.00
$250.01 to $300.00	$30.00
$300.01 to $350.00	$35.00
$350.01 to $400.00	$40.00

85. **Shipping and Handling Charges**   Shipping and handling charges when ordering online generally are based on the dollar amount of the order. Use the table shown below to determine the cost of shipping each order.

	Amount of Order	Shipping Cost
a.	$12.42	
b.	$23.56	
c.	$47.80	
d.	$66.91	
e.	$35.75	
f.	$20.00	
g.	$18.25	

If the Amount Ordered is:	The Shipping and Handling Charge Is:
$10.00 and under	$1.60
$10.01 to $20.00	$2.40
$20.01 to $30.00	$3.60
$30.01 to $40.00	$4.70
$40.01 to $50.00	$6.00
$50.01 and up	$7.00

Critical Thinking

86. ▦ Indicate which digits of the number, if any, need not be entered on a calculator.
    a. 1.500   **b.** 0.908   **c.** 60.07   **d.** 0.0032

87. Find a number between **a.** 0.1 and 0.2, **b.** 1 and 1.1, and **c.** 0 and 0.005.

Projects or Group Activities

88. ◣ Use newspapers or the Internet to find and list situations in which decimals are used. Determine whether the decimals you find are exact values or approximations. [*Note:* Large numbers (such as 3.2 billion) used to describe values such as the balance of trade or the national debt are approximations. Smaller numbers (such as 1.5866) used to describe business transactions such as an exchange rate or a stock price are exact values.]

4.2 Addition and Subtraction of Decimals

OBJECTIVE A   *To add and subtract decimals*

To add decimals, write the numbers so that the decimal points are on a vertical line. Add as you would with whole numbers. Then write the decimal point in the sum directly below the decimal points in the addends.

HOW TO 1   Add: $0.326 + 4.8 + 57.23$

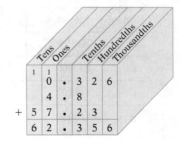

Note that placing the decimal points on a vertical line ensures that digits of the same place value are added.

HOW TO 2   Find the sum of 0.64, 8.731, 12, and 5.9.

Arrange the numbers vertically, placing the decimal points on a vertical line.

Add the numbers in each column.

Write the decimal point in the sum directly below the decimal points in the addends.

$$\begin{array}{r} {}^{1\ 2} \\ 0.64 \\ 8.731 \\ 12. \\ +\ \ 5.9 \\ \hline 27.271 \end{array}$$

To subtract decimals, write the numbers so that the decimal points are on a vertical line. Subtract as you would with whole numbers. Then write the decimal point in the difference directly below the decimal point in the subtrahend.

HOW TO 3   Subtract and check: $31.642 - 8.759$

Note that placing the decimal points on a vertical line ensures that digits of the same place value are subtracted.

Check:

$$\begin{array}{lr} \text{Subtrahend} & 8.759 \\ +\ \text{Difference} & +\ 22.883 \\ \hline =\ \text{Minuend} & 31.642 \end{array}$$

HOW TO 4   Subtract and check: 5.4 − 1.6832

Insert zeros in the minuend so that it has the
same number of decimal places as the subtrahend.

$$\begin{array}{r} 5.4000 \\ -\ 1.6832 \end{array}$$

Subtract and then check.

$$\begin{array}{r} {\scriptstyle 4\ \ 13\,9\ \ 9\,10} \\ \cancel{5.4000} \\ -\ 1.6832 \\ \hline 3.7168 \end{array} \qquad Check: \begin{array}{r} 1.6832 \\ +\ 3.7168 \\ \hline 5.4000 \end{array}$$

Stephen Coburn/Shutterstock.com

APPLY THE CONCEPT

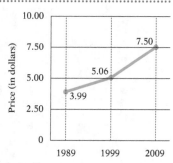

Figure 4.1 shows the average price of a movie
theater ticket in 1989, 1999, and 2009. Find the
increase in price from 1989 to 2009.

To find the increase in price, subtract the price in
1989 ($3.99) from the price in 2009 ($7.50).

$$\begin{array}{r} 7.50 \\ -\ 3.99 \\ \hline 3.51 \end{array}$$

From 1989 to 2009, the average price of a movie
theater ticket increased by $3.51.

Figure 4.1   Average Price of a
Movie Theater Ticket
Source: www.natoonline.org

The sign rules for adding and subtracting decimals are the same rules used to add and
subtract integers.

Take Note

Recall that the absolute value
of a number is the distance
from zero to the number on
the number line. The absolute
value of a number is a
positive number or zero.

|54.29| = 54.29

|−36.087| = 36.087

HOW TO 5   Simplify: −36.087 + 54.29

The signs of the addends are different.
Subtract the smaller absolute value from
the larger absolute value.

54.29 − 36.087 = 18.203

Attach the sign of the number with
the larger absolute value.

|54.29| > |−36.087|

The sum is positive.   −36.087 + 54.29 = 18.203

Recall that the opposite or additive inverse of *n* is −*n*, and the opposite of −*n* is *n*. To find
the opposite of a number, change the sign of the number.

HOW TO 6   Simplify: −2.86 − 10.3

Rewrite subtraction as addition of
the opposite. The opposite of 10.3
is −10.3.

$$-2.86 - 10.3$$

$$= -2.86 + (-10.3)$$

The signs of the addends are the same.
Add the absolute values of the numbers.
Attach the sign of the addends.

$$= -13.16$$

Point of Interest

Try this brain teaser. You have two U.S. coins that add up to $.55. One is not a nickel. What are the two coins?

HOW TO 7 Evaluate $c - d$ when $c = 6.731$ and $d = -2.48$.

	$c - d$
Replace c with 6.731 and d with -2.48.	$6.731 - (-2.48)$
Rewrite subtraction as addition of the opposite.	$= 6.731 + 2.48$
Add.	$= 9.211$

Recall that to estimate the answer to a calculation, round each number to the highest place value of the number; the first digit of each number will be nonzero and all other digits will be zero. Perform the calculation using the rounded numbers.

HOW TO 8 Estimate the sum of 23.037 and 16.7892.

Round each number to the nearest ten.

Add the rounded numbers.

$$23.037 \longrightarrow 20$$
$$16.7892 \longrightarrow + 20$$
$$\overline{40}$$

40 is an estimate of the sum of 23.037 and 16.7892. Note that 40 is very close to the actual sum of 39.8262.

$$23.037$$
$$+ 16.7892$$
$$\overline{39.8262}$$

When a number in an estimation is a decimal less than 1, round the decimal so that there is one nonzero digit.

HOW TO 9 Estimate the difference between 4.895 and 0.6193.

Round 4.895 to the nearest one.
Round 0.6193 to the nearest tenth.
Subtract the rounded numbers.

$$4.895 \longrightarrow 5.0$$
$$0.6193 \longrightarrow - 0.6$$
$$\overline{4.4}$$

4.4 is an estimate of the difference between 4.895 and 0.6193.
It is close to the actual difference of 4.2757.

$$4.8950$$
$$- 0.6193$$
$$\overline{4.2757}$$

EXAMPLE 1

Add: $35.8 + 182.406 + 71.0934$

Solution

$$
\begin{array}{r}
{\scriptstyle 1 \quad 1} \\
35.8 \\
182.406 \\
+ \quad 71.0934 \\
\hline
289.2994
\end{array}
$$

YOU TRY IT 1

Add: $8.64 + 52.7 + 0.39105$

Your solution

EXAMPLE 2

What is -251.49 more than -638.7?

Solution $-638.7 + (-251.49) = -890.19$

YOU TRY IT 2

What is 4.002 minus 9.378?

Your solution

Solutions on p. S12

EXAMPLE 3	YOU TRY IT 3

Subtract and check: $73 - 8.16$

Solution

$$\begin{array}{r} {\scriptstyle 6\;\;12\;\;9\;\;10} \\ 7\cancel{3}.\cancel{0}\cancel{0} \\ -\;\;8.16 \\ \hline 64.84 \end{array}$$

Check:

$$\begin{array}{r} 8.16 \\ +\;64.84 \\ \hline 73.00 \end{array}$$

Subtract and check: $25 - 4.91$

Your solution

EXAMPLE 4	YOU TRY IT 4

Estimate the sum of 0.3927, 0.4856, and 0.2104.

Solution

$$\begin{array}{rcl} 0.3927 &\longrightarrow& 0.4 \\ 0.4856 &\longrightarrow& 0.5 \\ 0.2104 &\longrightarrow& +0.2 \\ && \hline \\ && 1.1 \end{array}$$

Estimate the sum of 6.514, 8.903, and 2.275.

Your solution

EXAMPLE 5	YOU TRY IT 5

Evaluate $x + y + z$ for $x = -1.6$, $y = 7.9$, and $z = -4.8$.

Solution $x + y + z$

$$-1.6 + 7.9 + (-4.8) = 6.3 + (-4.8)$$
$$= 1.5$$

Evaluate $x + y + z$ for $x = -7.84$, $y = -3.05$, and $z = 2.19$.

Your solution

EXAMPLE 6	YOU TRY IT 6

Is -4.3 a solution of the equation $9.7 - b = 5.4$?

Solution

$$\begin{array}{c|c} 9.7 - b = 5.4 & \\ \hline 9.7 - (-4.3) & 5.4 \\ 9.7 + 4.3 & 5.4 \\ 14.0 & \neq 5.4 \end{array}$$

• Replace b with -4.3.

No, -4.3 is not a solution of the equation.

Is -23.8 a solution of the equation $-m + 16.9 = 40.7$?

Your solution

Solutions on p. S12

OBJECTIVE B *To solve application problems and use formulas*

Figure 4.2 shows the breakdown by age group of Americans who are hearing impaired. Use this graph for Example 7 and You Try It 7.

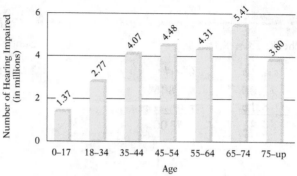

Figure 4.2 Breakdown by Age Group of Hearing-Impaired Americans

Source: American Speech-Language-Hearing Association

EXAMPLE 7

Use Figure 4.2 to determine whether the number of hearing-impaired individuals under the age of 45 is more or less than the number of hearing impaired who are over the age of 64.

Strategy

To make the comparison:

- Find the number of hearing-impaired individuals under the age of 45 by adding the numbers who are aged 0–17 (1.37 million), aged 18–34 (2.77 million), and aged 35–44 (4.07 million).
- Find the number of hearing-impaired individuals over the age of 64 by adding the numbers who are aged 65–74 (5.41 million) and aged 75 or older (3.80 million).
- Compare the two sums.

Solution

$1.37 + 2.77 + 4.07 = 8.21$ • Under age 45

$5.41 + 3.80 = 9.21$ • Over age 64

$8.21 < 9.21$

The number of hearing-impaired individuals under the age of 45 is less than the number of hearing impaired who are over the age of 64.

YOU TRY IT 7

Use Figure 4.2 to determine whether the number of hearing-impaired individuals under the age of 55 is more or less than the number of hearing impaired who are 55 or older.

Your strategy

Your solution

Solution on pp. S12–S13

4.2 EXERCISES

✔ Concept Check

1. Set up the addition problem 2.391 + 45 + 13.0784 in a vertical format, as shown at the right. One addend is already placed. Fill in the first two shaded areas with the other addends lined up correctly. In the third shaded region, show the placement of the decimal point in the sum. Then add.

+ 13.0784

2. Set up the subtraction problem 34 − 18.21 in a vertical format, as shown at the right. Fill in the first two shaded regions with the minuend and subtrahend lined up correctly and zeros inserted as needed. In the third shaded region, show the placement of the decimal point in the difference. Then subtract.

OBJECTIVE A   *To add and subtract decimals*

Add or subtract.

3. 1.864 + 39 + 25.0781

4. 2.04 + 35.6 + 4.918

5. 35.9 + 8.217 + 146.74

6. 12 + 73.59 + 6.482

7. 36.47 − 15.21

8. 85.69 − 2.13

9. 28 − 6.74

10. 5 − 1.386

11. 6.02 − 3.252

12. 0.92 − 0.0037

13. −42.1 − 8.6

14. −6.57 − 8.933

15. 5.73 − 9.042

16. −31.894 + 7.5

17. −9.37 + 3.465

18. 1.09 − (−8.3)

19. −19 − (−2.65)

20. 3.18 − 5.72 − 6.4

21. −12.3 − 4.07 + 6.82

22. −8.9 + 7.36 − 14.2

23. −5.6 − (−3.82) − 17.409

24. Find the sum of 2.536, 14.97, 8.014, and 21.67.

25. Find the total of 6.24, 8.573, 19.06, and 22.488.

26. What is 6.9217 decreased by 3.4501?

27. What is 8.9 less than 62.57?

28. How much greater is 5 than 1.63?

29. What is the sum of −65.47 and −32.91?

30. Find 382.9 more than −430.6.

31. Find −138.72 minus 510.64.

32. What is 4.793 less than −6.82?

33. How much greater is −31 than −62.09?

Add or subtract. Then check by estimating the sum or difference.

34. 45.06 + 80.71

35. 6.408 + 5.917

36. 0.24 + 0.38 + 0.96

37. 56.87 − 23.24

38. 6.272 − 1.848

39. 0.931 − 0.628

40. 5.37 + 26.49

41. 87.65 − 49.032

42. 387.6 − 54.92

43. ⬤ Education The graph at the right shows where U.S. children in grades K–12 are being educated. Figures are in millions of children.
 a. Find the total number of children in grades K–12.
 b. How many more children are being educated in public school than in private school?

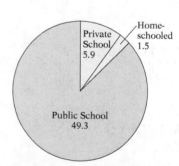

Where Children in Grades K–12 are Being Educated in the United States
Source: National Center for Education Statistics

Evaluate the variable expression $x + y$ for the given values of x and y.

44. $x = 62.97; y = -43.85$

45. $x = 5.904; y = -7.063$

46. $x = -125.41; y = 361.55$

47. $x = -6.175; y = -19.49$

Evaluate the variable expression $x + y + z$ for the given values of x, y, and z.

48. $x = 41.33; y = -26.095; z = 70.08$

49. $x = -6.059; y = 3.884; z = 15.71$

50. $x = 81.72; y = 36.067; z = -48.93$

51. $x = -16.219; y = 47; z = -2.3885$

Evaluate the variable expression $x - y$ for the given values of x and y.

52. $x = 43.29; y = 18.76$

53. $x = 6.029; y = -4.708$

54. $x = -16.329; y = 4.54$

55. $x = -21.073; y = 6.48$

56. $x = -3.69; y = -1.527$

57. $x = -8.21; y = -6.798$

58. Is -1.2 a solution of the equation $6.4 = 5.2 + a$?

59. Is -2.8 a solution of the equation $0.8 - p = 3.6$?

60. Is -0.5 a solution of the equation $x - 0.5 = 1$?

61. Is 36.8 a solution of the equation $27.4 = y - 9.4$?

62. Suppose n is a decimal number for which the difference $4.83 - n$ is a negative number. Which statement *must* be true about n?

   (i) $n < 4.83$ **(ii)** $n > 4.83$ **(iii)** $n < -4.83$ **(iv)** $n > -4.83$

63. Suppose n is a decimal number for which the sum $6.875 + n$ is a negative number. Which statement *must* be true about n?

   (i) $n < 6.875$ **(ii)** $n > 6.875$ **(iii)** $n < -6.875$ **(iv)** $n > -6.875$

OBJECTIVE B *To solve application problems and use formulas*

64. You have $20 to spend, and you make purchases for the following amounts: $4.24, $8.66, and $.54. Which of the following expressions correctly represent the amount of money you have left?

(i) 20 − 4.24 + 8.66 + 0.54   **(ii)** (4.24 + 8.66 + 0.54) − 20
(iii) 20 − (4.24 + 8.66 + 0.54)   **(iv)** 20 − 4.24 − 8.66 − 0.54

65. You had $859.12 in your bank account at the beginning of the month. During the month, you made deposits of $25 and $180.50 and withdrawals of $20, $75, and $10.78. Write a verbal description of what each expression below represents.

a. 25 + 180.50
b. 20 + 75 + 10.78
c. 859.12 + (25 + 180.50) − (20 + 75 + 10.78)

66. **Temperature** On January 22, 1943, in Spearfish, South Dakota, the temperature fell from 12.22°C at 9:00 A.M. to −20°C at 9:27 A.M. How many degrees did the temperature fall during the 27-minute period?

67. **Temperature** On January 10, 1911, in Rapid City, South Dakota, the temperature fell from 12.78°C at 7:00 A.M. to −13.33°C at 7:15 A.M. How many degrees did the temperature fall during the 15-minute period?

Spearfish, South Dakota

Net Income The graph at the right shows the net income, in billions of dollars, of Ford Motor Company for December of the years 2006 through 2010. Use this graph for Exercises 68 and 69.

68. What was the increase in net income from December 2008 to December 2010?

69. Between which two years shown in the graph was the difference in net income the greatest?

70. **Budgets** You have a monthly budget of $2620. This month you have already spent $82.78 for the telephone bill, $264.93 for food, $95.50 for gasoline, $860 for your share of the rent, and $391.62 for a loan repayment. How much money do you have left in the budget for the remainder of the month?

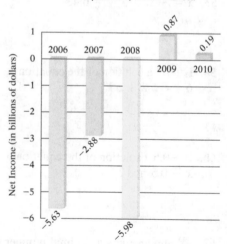

Net Income of Ford Motor Company
Source: ycharts.com

71. **Banking** You had a balance of $347.08 in your checking account. You then made a deposit of $189.53 and wrote a check for $62.89. Find the new balance in your checking account.

72. **Geometry** The lengths of three sides of a triangle are 7.5 m, 6.1 m, and 4.9 m. Find the perimeter of the triangle. Use the formula $P = a + b + c$.

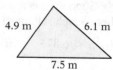

4.9 m   6.1 m
7.5 m

73. Consumerism   Using the menu shown below, estimate the bill for the following order: 1 soup, 1 cheese sticks, 1 blackened swordfish, 1 chicken divan, and 1 carrot cake.

Appetizers
Soup of the Day $5.75
Cheese Sticks $8.25
Potato Skins $8.50

Entrees
Roast Prime Rib $28.95
Blackened Swordfish $26.95
Chicken Divan $24.95

Desserts
Carrot Cake $7.25
Ice Cream Pie $8.50
Cheese Cake $9.75

74. Consumerism   Using the menu shown above, estimate the bill for the following order: 1 potato skins, 1 cheese sticks, 1 roast prime rib, 1 chicken divan, 1 ice cream pie, and 1 cheese cake.

75. ● **Life Expectancy**   The graph below shows the life expectancy at birth for males and females in the United States for each decade from 1900 to 2000.
   a. Has life expectancy increased for both males and females with every 10-year period shown in the graph?
   b. Did males or females have a longer life expectancy in 2000? How much longer?
   c. During which year shown in the graph was the difference between male life expectancy and female life expectancy greatest?

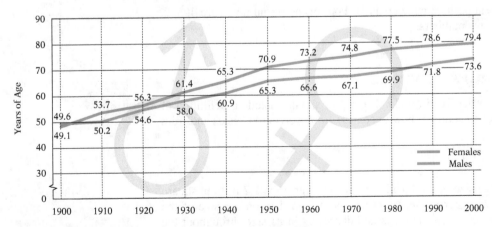

Life Expectancies of Males and Females in the United States

76. ● Marriage   Read the news clipping at the right. Find the difference in average age at first marriage from 1970 to 2010 for **a.** women and **b.** men.

77. Markup   Use the formula $M = S - C$, where M is the markup on a consumer product, S is the selling price, and C is the cost of the product to the business, to find the markup on a product that cost a business $1653.19 and has a selling price of $2231.81.

78. Federal Earnings   The amount of an employee's earnings that is subject to federal withholding is called federal earnings. Find the federal earnings for an employee who earns $694.89 and has a withholding allowance of $132.69. Use the formula $F = E - W$, where F is the federal earnings, E is the employee's earnings, and W is the withholding allowance.

79. Home Equity   Find the equity on a home that is valued at $225,000 when the homeowner has $167,853.25 in loans on the property. Use the formula $E = V - L$, where E is the equity, V is the value of the home, and L is the loan amount on the property.

Critical Thinking

80. Using the method presented in this section for estimating the sum of two decimals, what is the largest amount by which the estimate of the sum of two decimals with tenths, hundredths, and thousandths places could differ from the exact sum? Assume that the number in the thousandths place is not zero.

81. Choose three of the numbers below such that the sum of the numbers is 19.24.

    0.12   3.45   6.78   9.01   2.34

82. The sum of six different positive numbers is 11. Four of the six numbers are 4, 3, 2, and 1. Find the other two numbers.

Projects or Group Activities

83. ◥ Prepare a report on the Kelvin scale. The report should include a definition of absolute zero and an explanation of how to convert from Kelvin to Celsius and from Celsius to Kelvin.

84. ◥ In 2010, the average size of the hole in the ozone layer was 22.2 million square kilometers. (*Source:* www.earthobservatory.nasa.gov) Find data on the size of the ozone hole. Prepare a report on increases and decreases in its size throughout the years.

In the NEWS!

Average Age at First Marriage Increasing

Men and women are marrying later in life. In 1970, the average age at first marriage was 20.8 years for women and 23.2 years for men. In 2010, the average age was 26.1 years for women and 28.2 years for men.

Source: Time, March 21, 2011

SECTION

4.3

Multiplication and Division of Decimals

OBJECTIVE A   *To multiply decimals*

Decimals are multiplied as though they were whole numbers; then the decimal point is placed in the product. Writing the decimals as fractions shows where to write the decimal point in the product.

$$0.4 \cdot 2 = \frac{4}{10} \cdot \frac{2}{1} = \frac{8}{10} = 0.8$$

1 decimal place in 0.4   1 decimal place in 0.8

$$0.4 \cdot 0.2 = \frac{4}{10} \cdot \frac{2}{10} = \frac{8}{100} = 0.08$$

1 decimal place in 0.4   2 decimal places in 0.08
1 decimal place in 0.2

$$0.4 \cdot 0.02 = \frac{4}{10} \cdot \frac{2}{100} = \frac{8}{1000} = 0.008$$

1 decimal place in 0.4   3 decimal places in 0.008
2 decimal places in 0.02

To multiply decimals, multiply the numbers as you would whole numbers. Then write the decimal point in the product so that the number of decimal places in the product is the sum of the numbers of decimal places in the factors.

APPLY THE CONCEPT ···

The cost, including tax, of one adult admission ticket to a theme park is $53.46. What is the total cost of 4 adult tickets to this theme park?

To find the total cost, multiply the cost per ticket ($53.46) by the number of tickets (4).

$$
\begin{array}{r}
53.46 \\
\times \quad 4 \\
\hline
213.84
\end{array}
$$

• 2 **decimal places**
• 0 **decimal places**
• 2 **decimal places**

The total cost of 4 adult tickets is $213.84.

HOW TO 1   Multiply: $(32.41)(7.6)$

$$
\begin{array}{r}
32.41 \\
\times \quad 7.6 \\
\hline
19446 \\
22687 \quad \\
\hline
246.316
\end{array}
$$

2 decimal places
1 decimal place

3 decimal places

HOW TO 2 Multiply: 0.061(0.08)

0.061	3 decimal places
✕ 0.08	2 decimal places
0.00488	5 decimal places

Insert two zeros between the 4 and the decimal point so that there are 5 decimal places in the product.

To multiply a decimal by a power of 10 (10, 100, 1000, . . .), move the decimal point to the right the same number of places as there are zeros in the power of 10.

$$2.7935 \cdot 10 \qquad = 27.935$$

1 zero   1 decimal place

$$2.7935 \cdot 100 \qquad = 279.35$$

2 zeros   2 decimal places

$$2.7935 \cdot 1000 \qquad = 2793.5$$

3 zeros   3 decimal places

$$2.7935 \cdot 10,000 \qquad = 27,935.$$

4 zeros   4 decimal places

$$2.7935 \cdot 100,000 \qquad = 279,350.$$

A zero must be inserted before the decimal point.

5 zeros   5 decimal places

Note that if the power of 10 is written in exponential notation, the exponent indicates how many places to move the decimal point.

$$2.7935 \cdot 10^1 = 27.935$$

1 decimal place

$$2.7935 \cdot 10^2 = 279.35$$

2 decimal places

$$2.7935 \cdot 10^3 = 2793.5$$

3 decimal places

$$2.7935 \cdot 10^4 = 27,935.$$

4 decimal places

$$2.7935 \cdot 10^5 = 279,350.$$

5 decimal places

HOW TO 3 Find the product of 64.18 and 10^3.

The exponent on 10 is 3. Move the decimal point in 64.18 three places to the right.

$$64.18 \cdot 10^3 = 64,180$$

HOW TO 4 Evaluate $100x$ with $x = 5.714$.

$$100x$$

Replace x with 5.714.

$$100(5.714)$$

Multiply. There are two zeros in 100. Move the decimal point in 5.714 two places to the right.

$$= 571.4$$

The sign rules for multiplying decimals are the same rules used to multiply integers.

The product of two numbers with the same sign is positive.

The product of two numbers with different signs is negative.

HOW TO 5 Multiply: $(-3.2)(-0.008)$

The signs are the same.
The product is positive.
Multiply the absolute values of
the numbers.

$$(-3.2)(-0.008) = 0.0256$$

HOW TO 6 Is -0.6 a solution of the equation $4.3a = -2.58$?

$$4.3a = -2.58$$

Replace a by -0.6 and then simplify.
The results are equal.

$$4.3(-0.6) \mid -2.58$$
$$-2.58 = -2.58$$

Yes, -0.6 is a solution of the equation.

EXAMPLE 1

Multiply: $0.00073(0.052)$

Solution

$$
\begin{array}{r}
0.00073 \longleftarrow \text{5 decimal places} \\
\times \quad 0.052 \longleftarrow \text{3 decimal places} \\
\hline
146 \\
365 \\
\hline
0.00003796 \longleftarrow \text{8 decimal places}
\end{array}
$$

YOU TRY IT 1

Multiply: $0.000081(0.025)$

Your solution

EXAMPLE 2

Estimate the product of 0.7639 and 0.2188.

Solution

$$
\begin{array}{r}
0.7639 \longrightarrow \quad 0.8 \\
0.2188 \longrightarrow \times \ 0.2 \\
\hline
0.16
\end{array}
$$

YOU TRY IT 2

Estimate the product of 6.407 and 0.959.

Your solution

Solutions on p. S13

EXAMPLE 3	YOU TRY IT 3

EXAMPLE 3

What is 835.294 multiplied by 1000?

Solution   Move the decimal point 3 places to the right.

$$835.294 \cdot 1000 = 835,294$$

YOU TRY IT 3

Find the product of 1.756 and 10^4.

Your solution

EXAMPLE 4

Multiply: $-3.42(6.1)$

Solution $-3.42(6.1) = -20.862$

YOU TRY IT 4

Multiply: $(-0.7)(-5.8)$

Your solution

EXAMPLE 5

Evaluate $50ab$ for $a = -0.9$ and $b = -0.2$.

Solution $50ab$

$$50(-0.9)(-0.2) = -45(-0.2)$$
$$= 9$$

YOU TRY IT 5

Evaluate $25xy$ for $x = -0.8$ and $y = 0.6$.

Your solution

Solutions on p. S13

OBJECTIVE B   *To divide decimals*

 Point of Interest

Benjamin Banneker (1731–1806) was the first African American to earn distinction as a mathematician and a scientist. He was on the survey team that determined the boundaries of Washington, D.C. The mathematics of surveying requires extensive use of decimals.

To divide decimals, move the decimal point in the divisor to the right so that the divisor is a whole number. Move the decimal point in the dividend the same number of places to the right. Place the decimal point in the quotient directly above the decimal point in the dividend. Then divide as you would with whole numbers.

HOW TO 7   Divide: $29.585 \div 4.85$

$$4.85.\overline{)29.58.5}$$

Move the decimal point 2 places to the right in the divisor. Move the decimal point 2 places to the right in the dividend. Place the decimal point in the quotient. Then divide as shown at the right.

$$
\begin{array}{r}
6.1 \\
485.\overline{)\,2958.5} \\
-2910 \\
\hline
48\ 5 \\
-48\ 5 \\
\hline
0
\end{array}
$$

Moving the decimal point the same number of places in the divisor and the dividend does not change the quotient because the process is the same as multiplying the numerator and denominator of a fraction by the same number. For HOW TO 7 above,

$$4.85\overline{)29.585} = \frac{29.585}{4.85} = \frac{29.585 \cdot 100}{4.85 \cdot 100} = \frac{2958.5}{485} = 485\overline{)2958.5}$$

In division of decimals, rather than writing the quotient with a remainder, we usually round the quotient to a specified place value. The symbol ≈ is read "is approximately equal to"; it is used to indicate that the quotient is an approximate value after being rounded.

HOW TO 8   Divide and round to the nearest tenth: 0.86 ÷ 0.7

$$
\begin{array}{r}
1.22 \approx 1.2 \\
0.7.\overline{)0.8.60} \\
-7 \\
\hline
1\,6 \\
-1\,4 \\
\hline
2\,0 \\
-1\,4 \\
\hline
6
\end{array}
$$

To round the quotient to the nearest tenth, the division must be carried to the hundredths place. Therefore, zeros must be inserted in the dividend so that the quotient has a digit in the hundredths place.

APPLY THE CONCEPT

Figure 4.3 shows average hourly earnings in the United States. How many times greater were the average hourly earnings in 2010 than in 1995? Round to the nearest whole number.

Divide the 2010 average hourly earnings ($22.61) by the average hourly earnings in 1995 ($11.71).

22.61 ÷ 11.71 ≈ 2

The average hourly earnings in 2010 were about 2 times the average hourly earnings in 1995.

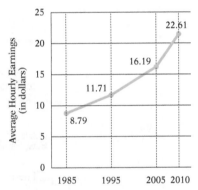

Figure 4.3 Average Hourly Earnings
Source: Bureau of Labor Statistics

To divide a decimal by a power of 10 (10, 100, 1000, 10,000, . . .), move the decimal point to the left the same number of places as there are zeros in the power of 10.

462.81 ÷ 1<u>0</u>   = 46.281

        1 zero   1 decimal place

462.81 ÷ <u>100</u>   = 4.6281

        2 zeros   2 decimal places

462.81 ÷ <u>1000</u>   = 0.46281

        3 zeros   3 decimal places

462.81 ÷ <u>10,000</u>   = 0.046281

        4 zeros   4 decimal places

A zero must be inserted between the decimal point and the 4.

462.81 ÷ <u>100,000</u> = 0.0046281

        5 zeros   5 decimal places

Two zeros must be inserted between the decimal point and the 4.

If the power of 10 is written in exponential notation, the exponent indicates how many places to move the decimal point.

$$462.81 \div 10^1 = 46.281$$

1 decimal place

$$462.81 \div 10^2 = 4.6281$$

2 decimal places

$$462.81 \div 10^3 = 0.46281$$

3 decimal places

$$462.81 \div 10^4 = 0.046281$$

4 decimal places

$$462.81 \div 10^5 = 0.0046281$$

5 decimal places

HOW TO 9 Find the quotient of 3.59 and 100.

There are two zeros in 100. Move the
decimal point in 3.59 two places to the left. $3.59 \div 100 = 0.0359$

HOW TO 10 What is the quotient of 64.79 and 10^4?

The exponent on 10 is 4. Move the decimal
point in 64.79 four places to the left. $64.79 \div 10^4 = 0.006479$

The sign rules for dividing decimals are the same rules used to divide integers.

The quotient of two numbers with the same sign is positive.

The quotient of two numbers with different signs is negative.

HOW TO 11 Divide: $-1.16 \div 2.9$

The signs are different.
The quotient is negative.
Divide the absolute values of the numbers. $-1.16 \div 2.9 = -0.4$

HOW TO 12 Evaluate $c \div d$ for $c = -8.64$ and $d = -0.4$.

$$c \div d$$

Replace c with -8.64 and d with -0.4. $(-8.64) \div (-0.4)$

The signs are the same. The quotient is positive.
Divide the absolute values of the numbers. $= 21.6$

EXAMPLE 6

Divide: $431.97 \div 7.26$

Solution

$$
\begin{array}{r}
5\,9.5 \\
7.26\overline{)\,4\,3\,1.9\,7.0} \\
-3\,6\,3\,0 \\
\hline
6\,8\,9\,7 \\
-6\,5\,3\,4 \\
\hline
3\,6\,3\,0 \\
-3\,6\,3\,0 \\
\hline
0
\end{array}
$$

• Move the decimal point 2 places to the right.

YOU TRY IT 6

Divide: $314.746 \div 6.53$

Your solution

EXAMPLE 7

Estimate the quotient of 8.37 and 0.219.

Solution
$$8.37 \longrightarrow 8$$
$$0.219 \longrightarrow 0.2$$

$$8 \div 0.2 = 40$$

YOU TRY IT 7

Estimate the quotient of 62.7 and 3.45.

Your solution

EXAMPLE 8

Divide and round to the nearest hundredth:
$448.2 \div 53$

Solution

$$
\begin{array}{r}
8.4\,5\,6 \approx 8.46 \\
53\overline{)\,4\,4\,8.2\,0\,0} \\
-4\,2\,4 \\
\hline
2\,4\,2 \\
-2\,1\,2 \\
\hline
3\,0\,0 \\
-2\,6\,5 \\
\hline
3\,5\,0 \\
-3\,1\,8 \\
\hline
3\,2
\end{array}
$$

YOU TRY IT 8

Divide and round to the nearest thousandth:
$519.37 \div 86$

Your solution

EXAMPLE 9

Find the quotient of 592.4 and 10^4.

Solution Move the decimal point 4 places to the left.

$$592.4 \div 10^4 = 0.05924$$

YOU TRY IT 9

What is 63.7 divided by 100?

Your solution

EXAMPLE 10

Divide and round to the nearest tenth: $-6.94 \div (-1.5)$

Solution The quotient is positive.

$$-6.94 \div (-1.5) \approx 4.6$$

YOU TRY IT 10

Divide and round to the nearest tenth: $-25.7 \div 0.31$

Your solution

Solutions on p. S13

EXAMPLE 11

Evaluate $\frac{x}{y}$ for $x = -76.8$ and $y = 0.8$.

Solution $\quad \dfrac{x}{y}$

$$\frac{-76.8}{0.8} = -96$$

YOU TRY IT 11

Evaluate $\frac{x}{y}$ for $x = -40.6$ and $y = -0.7$.

Your solution

EXAMPLE 12

Is -0.4 a solution of the equation $\frac{8}{x} = -20$?

Solution $\qquad \dfrac{8}{x} = -20$

$$\dfrac{8}{-0.4} \;\Big|\; -20 \qquad \bullet \ \text{Replace } x \text{ by} \\ \qquad\qquad\qquad -0.4.$$

$$-20 = -20$$

Yes, -0.4 is a solution of the equation.

YOU TRY IT 12

Is -1.2 a solution of the equation $-2 = \frac{d}{-0.6}$?

Your solution

Solutions on p. S13

OBJECTIVE C   *To convert between decimals and fractions and to identify the order relation between a decimal and a fraction*

Because the fraction bar can be read "divided by," any fraction can be written as a decimal. To write a fraction as a decimal, divide the numerator of the fraction by the denominator.

HOW TO 13   Convert $\frac{3}{4}$ to a decimal.

$$\begin{array}{r} 0.75 \\ 4{\overline{\smash{\big)}\,3.00}} \\ \underline{-2\,8} \\ 20 \\ \underline{-20} \\ 0 \end{array}$$

$\quad \longleftarrow$ This is a **terminating decimal.**

$\quad \longleftarrow$ The remainder is zero.

$$\frac{3}{4} = 0.75$$

Take Note

The fraction bar can be read "divided by."

$$\frac{3}{4} = 3 \div 4$$

Dividing the numerator by the denominator results in a remainder of zero. The decimal 0.75 is a terminating decimal.

HOW TO 14   Convert $\frac{5}{11}$ to a decimal.

$$
\begin{array}{r}
0.4545 \longleftarrow \text{This is a \textbf{repeating decimal.}} \\
11)\overline{5.0000} \\
-4\,4 \\
\hline
60 \\
-55 \\
\hline
50 \\
-44 \\
\hline
60 \\
-55 \\
\hline
5 \longleftarrow \text{The remainder is never zero.}
\end{array}
$$

Take Note

No matter how far we carry out the division, the remainder is never zero. The decimal $0.\overline{45}$ is a repeating decimal.

$\frac{5}{11} = 0.\overline{45}$ The bar over the digits 45 is used to show that these digits repeat.

HOW TO 15   Convert $2\frac{4}{9}$ to a decimal.

Write the fractional part of the mixed number as a decimal. Divide the numerator by the denominator.

$$\begin{array}{r} 0.444 = 0.\overline{4} \\ 9)\overline{4.000} \end{array}$$

The whole number part of the mixed number is the whole number part of the decimal.

$$2\frac{4}{9} = 2.\overline{4}$$

To convert a decimal to a fraction, remove the decimal point and place the decimal part over a denominator equal to the place value of the last digit in the decimal.

$$0.57 = \underset{\text{hundredths}}{\frac{57}{100}} \qquad 7.65 = 7\underset{\text{hundredths}}{\frac{65}{100}} = 7\frac{13}{20} \qquad 8.6 = 8\underset{\text{tenths}}{\frac{6}{10}} = 8\frac{3}{5}$$

HOW TO 16   Convert 4.375 to a fraction.

The 5 in 4.375 is in the thousandths place. Write 0.375 as a fraction with a denominator of 1000.

$$4.375 = 4\frac{375}{1000}$$

Simplify the fraction.

$$= 4\frac{3}{8}$$

Integrating Technology

Some calculators *truncate* a decimal number that exceeds the calculator display. This means that the digits beyond the calculator's display are not shown. For this type of calculator, $\frac{2}{3}$ would be shown as 0.66666666. Other calculators *round* a decimal number when the calculator display is exceeded. For this type of calculator, $\frac{2}{3}$ would be shown as 0.66666667.

To find the order relation between a fraction and a decimal, first rewrite the fraction as a decimal. Then compare the two decimals.

HOW TO 17   Find the order relation between $\frac{6}{7}$ and 0.855.

Write the fraction as a decimal. Round to one more place value than the given decimal. (0.855 has 3 decimal places; round to 4 decimal places.)

$$\frac{6}{7} \approx 0.8571$$

Compare the two decimals.

$$0.8571 > 0.8550$$

Replace the decimal approximation of $\frac{6}{7}$ with $\frac{6}{7}$.

$$\frac{6}{7} > 0.855$$

EXAMPLE 13

Convert $\frac{5}{8}$ to a decimal.

Solution

$$8\overline{)5.000} \quad \frac{0.625}{}$$

$$\frac{5}{8} = 0.625$$

YOU TRY IT 13

Convert $\frac{4}{5}$ to a decimal.

Your solution

EXAMPLE 14

Convert $3\frac{1}{3}$ to a decimal.

Solution   Write $\frac{1}{3}$ as a decimal.

$$3\overline{)1.000} \quad 0.333 = 0.\overline{3}$$

$$3\frac{1}{3} = 3.\overline{3}$$

YOU TRY IT 14

Convert $1\frac{5}{6}$ to a decimal.

Your solution

EXAMPLE 15

Convert 7.25 to a fraction.

Solution $7.25 = 7\frac{25}{100} = 7\frac{1}{4}$

YOU TRY IT 15

Convert 6.2 to a fraction.

Your solution

EXAMPLE 16

Place the correct symbol, $<$ or $>$, between the two numbers.

$$0.845 \qquad \frac{5}{6}$$

Solution $\frac{5}{6} \approx 0.8333$

$$0.8450 > 0.8333$$

$$0.845 > \frac{5}{6}$$

YOU TRY IT 16

Place the correct symbol, $<$ or $>$, between the two numbers.

$$0.588 \qquad \frac{7}{12}$$

Your solution

OBJECTIVE D   *To solve application problems and use formulas*

EXAMPLE 17

A one-year subscription to a monthly magazine costs $93. The price of each issue at the newsstand is $9.80. How much would you save per issue by buying a year's subscription rather than buying each issue at the newsstand?

Strategy

To find the amount saved:

• Find the subscription price per issue by dividing the cost of the subscription (93) by the number of issues (12).
• Subtract the subscription price per issue from the newsstand price (9.80).

Solution

```
        7.75      • Subscription price        9.80
  12) 93.00          per issue              −7.75
      −84                                    2.05
        9 0
       −8 4
         60
        −60
          0
```

The savings would be $2.05 per issue.

YOU TRY IT 17

You hand a postal clerk a ten-dollar bill to pay for the purchase of twelve 45¢ stamps. How much change do you receive?

Your strategy

Your solution

EXAMPLE 18

Use the formula $P = BF$, where P is the insurance premium, B is the base rate, and F is the rating factor, to find the insurance premium due on an insurance policy with a base rate of $342.50 and a rating factor of 2.2.

Strategy

To find the insurance premium due, replace B by 342.50 and F by 2.2 in the given formula, and solve for P.

Solution

$P = BF$
$P = 342.50(2.2)$
$P = 753.50$

The insurance premium due is $753.50.

YOU TRY IT 18

Use the formula $P = BF$, where P is the insurance premium, B is the base rate, and F is the rating factor, to find the insurance premium due on an insurance policy with a base rate of $276.25 and a rating factor of 1.8.

Your strategy

Your solution

Solutions on pp. S13–S14

4.3 EXERCISES

✔ Concept Check

1. The multiplication problem 5.3(0.21) is shown at the right. Fill in the blanks with the numbers of decimal places in the factors and in the product. Then calculate the product.

$$\begin{array}{r} 5.3 \\ \times\ 0.21 \\ \hline 53 \\ 106 \\ \hline \end{array}$$

_____ decimal places
_____ decimal places

_____ decimal places

2. When a decimal is multiplied by 100, the decimal point is moved _____ places to the_____.

3. The division problem 3.648 ÷ 3.04 is shown at the right. The decimal point of the divisor was moved _____ places to the right in order to make the divisor a _____ number. Show the correct placement of the decimal point in the dividend and in the quotient.

$$\begin{array}{r} 12 \\ 304.\overline{)\ 3648} \\ -304 \\ \hline 608 \\ -608 \\ \hline 0 \end{array}$$

4. To round the quotient of two decimals to the nearest hundredth, carry out the division to the _____ place.

5. To convert $\frac{5}{4}$ to a decimal, divide _____ by _____. The quotient is 1.25. This is called a _____ decimal.

For Exercises 6 and 7, state whether you would use multiplication or division to find the specified amount.

6. A 12-pack of bottled spring water sells for $3.49. To find the cost of one bottle of spring water, use _____.

7. A 12-pack of bottled spring water sells for $3.49. To find the cost of three 12-packs of spring water, use _____.

OBJECTIVE A   *To multiply decimals*

Multiply.

8. 0.9(0.3)

9. (3.4)(0.5)

10. (0.72)(3.7)

11. 8.29(0.004)

12. −5.2(0.8)

13. (−6.3)(−2.4)

14. (1.9)(−3.7)

15. −1.3(4.2)

16. −8.1(−7.5)

17. 1.31(−0.006)

18. −10(0.59)

19. (−100)(4.73)

20. What is the product of 5.92 and 100?

21. What is 1000 times 4.25?

22. Find 0.82 times 10^2.

23. Find the product of 6.71 and 10^4.

24. Find the product of 2.7, -16, and 3.04.

25. What is the product of 0.06, -0.4, and -1.5?

Multiply. Then check by estimating the product.

26. $86.4(4.2)$

27. $(9.81)(0.77)$

28. $0.238(8.2)$

29. $(6.88)(9.97)$

30. $(8.432)(0.043)$

31. $28.45(1.13)$

Exchange Rates   The table at the right shows currency exchange rates for several foreign countries. To determine how many Swiss francs would be exchanged for 1000 U.S. dollars, multiply the number of francs exchanged for one U.S. dollar (0.8804) by 1000: $1000(0.8804) = 880.4$. Use this table for Exercises 32 and 33.

32. How many Mexican pesos would be exchanged for 5000 U.S. dollars?

33. How many British pounds would be exchanged for 20,000 U.S. dollars?

Country and Monetary Unit	Number of Units Exchanged for 1 U.S. Dollar
Britain (Pound)	0.6267
Canada (Dollar)	0.9928
European Union (Euro)	0.7237
Japan (Yen)	77.7882
Mexico (Peso)	12.6009
Switzerland (Franc)	0.8804

Evaluate the expression for the given values of the variables.

34. xy, for $x = 5.68$ and $y = 0.2$

35. ab, for $a = 6.27$ and $b = 8$

36. $40c$, for $c = 2.5$

37. $10t$, for $t = -4.8$

38. xy, for $x = -3.71$ and $y = 2.9$

39. ab, for $a = 0.379$ and $b = -0.22$

40. ab, for $a = 452$ and $b = -0.86$

41. cd, for $c = -2.537$ and $d = -9.1$

42. cd, for $c = -4.259$ and $d = -6.3$

43. Is -8 a solution of the equation $1.6 = -0.2z$?

44. Is -1 a solution of the equation $-7.9c = -7.9$?

45. Is -10 a solution of the equation $-83.25r = 8.325$?

46. Is -3.6 a solution of the equation $32.4 = -9w$?

47. A number rounded to the nearest tenth is multiplied by 1000. How many zeros must be inserted to the right of the number when moving the decimal point to write the product?

48. A decimal whose value is between 0 and 1 is multiplied by 10, and the result is a positive integer less than 10. List all possible values of the decimal.

OBJECTIVE B *To divide decimals*

Divide.

49. $16.15 \div 0.5$

50. $7.02 \div 3.6$

51. $27.08 \div (-0.4)$

52. $-8.919 \div 0.9$

53. $(-3.312) \div (-0.8)$

54. $84.66 \div (-1.7)$

55. $-2.501 \div 0.41$

56. $1.003 \div (-0.59)$

Divide. Round to the nearest tenth.

57. $55.63 \div 8.8$

58. $1.873 \div 1.4$

59. $(-52.8) \div (-9.1)$

60. $-6.824 \div 0.053$

Divide. Round to the nearest hundredth.

61. $6.457 \div 8$

62. $19.07 \div 0.54$

63. $0.0416 \div (-0.53)$

64. $(-31.792) \div (-0.86)$

65. Find the quotient of 52.78 and 10.

66. What is 37,942 divided by 1000?

67. What is the quotient of 48.05 and 10^2?

68. Find 9.407 divided by 10^3.

In Exercises 69 to 72, round answers to the nearest tenth.

69. Find the quotient of −19.04 and 0.75.

70. What is the quotient of −21.892 and −0.96?

71. Find 27.735 divided by −60.3.

72. What is −13.97 divided by 28.4?

Divide and round to the nearest hundredth. Then check by estimating the quotient.

73. $42.43 \div 3.8$

74. $678 \div 0.71$

75. $6.398 \div 5.5$

76. $0.994 \div 0.456$

77. $1.237 \div 0.021$

78. $421.093 \div 4.087$

79. $33.14 \div 4.6$

80. $129.38 \div 4.47$

81. 🌐 **Organic Food** The graph at the right shows sales of organic food in the United States for 1997, 2005, and 2010. Figures are given in billions of dollars. How many times greater were sales in 2010 than sales in 1997? Round to the nearest whole number.

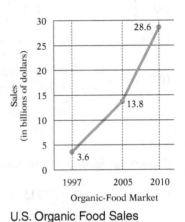

U.S. Organic Food Sales
Source: Organic Trade Association

Evaluate the variable expression $\frac{x}{y}$ for the given values of x and y.

82. $x = 52.8; y = 0.4$

83. $x = 3.542; y = 0.7$

84. $x = -2.436; y = 0.6$

85. $x = 0.648; y = -2.7$

86. $x = 26.22; y = -6.9$

87. $x = -8.034; y = -3.9$

88. $x = -64.05; y = -6.1$

89. $x = -2.501; y = 0.41$

90. $x = 1.003; y = -0.59$

91. Is 24.8 a solution of the equation $\frac{q}{-8} = -3.1$?

92. Is 0.48 a solution of the equation $\frac{-6}{z} = -12.5$?

93. Is -8.4 a solution of the equation $21 = \frac{t}{0.4}$?

94. Is -0.9 a solution of the equation $\frac{-2.7}{a} = \frac{a}{-0.3}$?

95. 🐦 A number greater than 1 but less than 10 is divided by 10,000. How many zeros must be inserted to the left of the number when moving the decimal point to write the quotient?

96. 🐦 A number n is rounded to the nearest hundredth. Which number can n be divided by to produce a quotient that is an integer?

(i) 1   **(ii)** 100   **(iii)** 0.1   **(iv)** 0.01

OBJECTIVE C   *To convert between decimals and fractions and to identify the order relation between a decimal and a fraction*

Convert the fraction to a decimal. Place a bar over repeating digits of a repeating decimal.

97. $\dfrac{3}{8}$ **98.** $\dfrac{7}{15}$ **99.** $\dfrac{8}{11}$ **100.** $\dfrac{9}{16}$ **101.** $\dfrac{7}{12}$

102. $\dfrac{5}{3}$ **103.** $\dfrac{7}{4}$ **104.** $2\dfrac{3}{4}$ **105.** $1\dfrac{1}{2}$ **106.** $3\dfrac{2}{9}$

107. $4\dfrac{1}{6}$ **108.** $\dfrac{3}{25}$ **109.** $2\dfrac{1}{4}$ **110.** $6\dfrac{3}{5}$ **111.** $3\dfrac{8}{9}$

Convert the decimal to a fraction.

112. 0.6   **113.** 0.2   **114.** 0.25   **115.** 0.75   **116.** 0.48

117. 0.125   **118.** 0.325   **119.** 2.5   **120.** 3.4   **121.** 4.55

122. 9.95   **123.** 1.72   **124.** 5.68   **125.** 0.045   **126.** 0.085

Place the correct symbol, $<$ or $>$, between the two numbers.

127. $\dfrac{9}{10}$ 0.89   **128.** $\dfrac{7}{20}$ 0.34   **129.** $\dfrac{4}{5}$ 0.803   **130.** $\dfrac{3}{4}$ 0.706

131. 0.444 $\dfrac{4}{9}$ **132.** 0.72 $\dfrac{5}{7}$ **133.** 0.13 $\dfrac{3}{25}$ **134.** 0.25 $\dfrac{13}{50}$

135. $\dfrac{5}{16}$ 0.312   **136.** $\dfrac{7}{18}$ 0.39   **137.** $\dfrac{10}{11}$ 0.909   **138.** $\dfrac{8}{15}$ 0.543

139. 🖋 What is the largest fraction with a denominator of 5 that is less than 0.78?

140. 🖋 What is the smallest fraction with a denominator of 4 that is greater than 2.5? Write your answer as an improper fraction.

OBJECTIVE D *To solve application problems and use formulas*

141. Three friends share two pizzas that cost $9.75 and $10.50. Each person has a soda that costs $1.70. The friends plan to split the cost of the meal equally. Write a verbal description of what each expression represents.

a. $3 \cdot 1.70$ **b.** $9.75 + 10.50 + 3 \cdot 1.70$ **c.** $\dfrac{9.75 + 10.50 + 3 \cdot 1.70}{3}$

142. Salaries If you earn an annual salary of $59,619, what is your monthly salary?

143. Car Purchases You bought a car for $5000 down and made payments of $499.50 each month for 36 months.
a. Find the amount of the payments over the 36 months.
b. Find the total cost of the car.

144. Compensation A nurse earns a salary of $1396 for a 40-hour work week. This week the nurse worked 15 h of overtime at a rate of $52.35 for each hour of overtime worked.
a. Find the nurse's overtime pay.
b. Find the nurse's total income for the week.

145. Football Ramon, a high school football player, gained 162 yards on 26 carries in a high school football game. Find the average number of yards gained per carry. Round to the nearest hundredth.

146. Tourism See the news clipping at the right. Find the average amount spent by each visitor to the United States. Round to the nearest cent.

147. Electricity In the United States, a homeowner's average monthly bill for electricity is $95.66. (*Source:* Department of Energy) What is a U.S. homeowner's average annual cost of electricity?

148. Transportation A long-haul truck driver earns $.43 for each mile driven. How much will a truck driver earn for driving 1507 mi from Boston to Miami?

149. Recycling Four hundred empty soft drink cans weigh 18.75 lb. A recycling center pays $.75 per pound for cans. Find the amount received for the 400 cans. Round to the nearest cent.

150. Recycling A recycling center pays $.045 per pound for newspapers.
a. Estimate the payment for recycling 520 lb of newspapers.
b. Find the actual amount received from recycling the newspapers.

In the NEWS!

Tourists Boost the Economy

This past summer, 14.3 million visitors came to the United States, spending a record $30.7 billion.
Source: Commerce Department

Huguette Roe/Shutterstock.com

151. ⬤ **Taxes**   The tax per gallon of gasoline in California is $.466 (*Source:* Tax Foundation) If you fill your gasoline tank with 12.5 gal of gasoline in California, how much will you pay in taxes?

152. Fuel Consumption   You travel 295 mi on 12.5 gal of gasoline. How many miles can you travel on 1 gal of gasoline?

153. ⬤ **Electronic Checks**   See the news clipping at the right. Find the added cost to the government for issuing paper checks to the 4 million Social Security recipients who request a paper check because they do not have a bank account.

In the NEWS!

Paper Checks Cost Government Millions

The federal government's cost to issue a paper check is $.89, while the cost for an electronic check is $.09.

Source: finance.yahoo.com

154. Fuel Efficiency   A car with an odometer reading of 17,814.2 mi is filled with 9.4 gal of gas. At an odometer reading of 18,130.4, the tank is empty and the car is filled with 12.4 gal of gas. How many miles does the car travel on 1 gal of gasoline?

155. Carbon Footprint   Depending on the efficiency of a power plant, 1 ton of coal can produce about 3000 kilowatt-hours of electricity. Suppose your family uses 25 kilowatt-hours of electricity per month. How many tons of coal will your family use in one year?

156. Carbon Footprint   One barrel of oil produces approximately 800 kilowatt-hours of electricity. Suppose you use 27 kilowatt-hours of electricity per month. How many barrels of oil will you use in one year?

In the NEWS!

"Green" Banking Has Far-Reaching Effects

Banking and paying bills online not only saves trees; it cuts down on the amount of fuel used by vehicles that transport paper checks. According to Javelin Strategy and Research, if every household in the United States paid its bills online, solid waste would be reduced by 1.6 billion tons a year and greenhouse-gas emissions would be cut by 2.1 million tons a year.

Source: Time, April 9, 2008

157. ⬤ **Going Green**   See the news clipping at the right. Write your answers in standard form, rounded to the nearest whole number.
   a. Find the reduction in solid waste per month if every U.S. household viewed and paid its bills online.
   b. Find the reduction in greenhouse gas emissions per month if every U.S. household viewed and paid its bills online.

158. ⬤ **Computer Use**   The table below shows the average numbers of hours per week that students use a computer. On average, how many more hours per year does a second-grade student use a computer than a fifth-grade student?

Grade Level	Average Number of Hours of Computer Use per Week
Pre Kindergarten–Kindergarten	3.9
1st–3rd	4.9
4th–6th	4.2
7th–8th	6.9
9th–12th	6.7

Source: Find/SVP American Learning Household Survey

159. Business   For $175, a druggist purchases 5 L of cough syrup and repackages it in 250-milliliter bottles. Each bottle costs the druggist $.75. Each bottle of cough syrup is sold for $15.89. Find the profit on the 5 L of cough syrup. (*Hint:* There are 1000 ml in 1 L.)

160. Geometry   The length of each side of a square is 3.5 ft. Find the perimeter of the square. Use the formula $P = 4s$.

3.5 ft

3.5 ft

161. Geometry   Find the perimeter of a rectangle that measures 4.5 in. by 3.25 in. Use the formula $P = 2L + 2W$.

162. Geometry   Find the perimeter of a rectangle that measures 2.8 m by 6.4 m. Use the formula $P = 2L + 2W$.

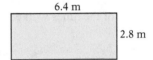

6.4 m

2.8 m

163. Geometry   Find the area of a rectangle that measures 4.5 in. by 3.25 in. Use the formula $A = LW$.

164. Geometry   Find the area of a rectangle that has a length of 7.8 cm and a width of 4.6 cm. Use the formula $A = LW$.

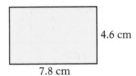

4.6 cm

7.8 cm

165. Geometry   Find the perimeter of a triangle with sides that measure 2.8 m, 4.75 m, and 6.4 m. Use the formula $P = a + b + c$.

166. Car Rentals   Use the formula $M = \frac{C}{N}$, where M is the cost per mile for a rental car, C is the total cost, and N is the number of miles driven, to find the cost per mile when the total cost of renting a car is $260.16 and you drive the car 542 mi.

167. Physics   Find the force exerted on a falling object that has a mass of 4.25 kg. Use the formula $F = ma$, where F is the force exerted by gravity on a falling object, m is the mass of the object, and a is the acceleration due to gravity. The acceleration due to gravity is -9.80 m/s^2 (meters per second squared). The force is measured in newtons.

168. Utilities   Find the cost of operating a 1800-watt TV set for 5 h at a cost of $.06 per kilowatt-hour. Use the formula $c = 0.001wtk$, where c is the cost of operating an appliance, w is the number of watts, t is the time in hours, and k is the cost per kilowatt-hour.

Critical Thinking

169. Show how the decimal is placed in the product of 1.3×2.31 by first writing each number as a fraction and then multiplying. Then change the product back to decimal notation.

For Exercises 170 to 175, insert $+$, $-$, $\times$, or $\div$ into the square so that the statement is true.

170. $3.45 \ \square \ 0.5 = 6.9$ **171.** $3.46 \ \square \ 0.24 = 0.8304$ **172.** $6.009 \ \square \ 4.68 = 1.329$

173. $0.064 \ \square \ 1.6 = 0.1024$ **174.** $9.876 \ \square \ 23.12 = 32.996$ **175.** $3.0381 \ \square \ 1.23 = 2.47$

Projects or Group Activities

176. Automotive Repair Chris works at B & W Garage as an auto mechanic and has just completed an engine overhaul for a customer. To determine the cost of the repair job, Chris keeps a list of times worked and parts used. A parts list and a list of the times worked are shown below.

Parts Used		Time Spent	
Item	Quantity	Day	Hours
Gasket set	1	Monday	7.0
Ring set	1	Tuesday	7.5
Valves	8	Wednesday	6.5
Wrist pins	8	Thursday	8.5
Valve springs	16	Friday	9.0
Rod bearings	8		
Main bearings	5		
Valve seals	16		
Timing chain	1		

Price List		
Item Number	Description	Unit Price
27345	Valve spring	$9.25
41257	Main bearing	$17.49
54678	Valve	$16.99
29753	Ring set	$169.99
45837	Gasket set	$174.90
23751	Timing chain	$50.49
23765	Fuel pump	$229.99
28632	Wrist pin	$23.55
34922	Rod bearing	$13.69
2871	Valve seal	$1.69

a. Organize a table of data showing the parts used, the unit price for each part, and the price of the quantity used. *Hint:* Use the following headings for the table.

    Quantity   Item Number   Description   Unit Price   Total

b. Add up the numbers in the "Total" column to find the total cost of the parts.

c. If the charge for labor is $66.75 per hour, compute the cost of labor.

d. What is the total cost for parts and labor?

177. ◣ Explain how baseball batting averages are determined.

4.4 Simplifying Variable Expressions

OBJECTIVE A *To simplify a variable expression using the Properties of Addition*

Like terms of a variable expression are terms with the same variable part. (Because $x^2 = x \cdot x$, x^2 and x are not like terms.)

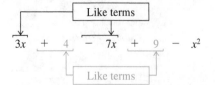

Constant terms are like terms. 4 and 9 are like terms.

To simplify a variable expression, we use the Distributive Property to add the numerical coefficients of like variable terms. The variable part remains unchanged. This is called **combining like terms.**

> **📝 Take Note**
>
> Here is an example of the Distributive Property using just numbers.
> $2(5 + 9) = 2(5) + 2(9)$
> $= 10 + 18 = 28$
> This is the same result we would obtain using the Order of Operations Agreement.
> $2(5 + 9) = 2(14) = 28$
> The usefulness of the Distributive Property will become more apparent as we explore variable expressions.

The Distributive Property

If a, b, and c are real numbers, then $a(b + c) = ab + ac$ or $(b + c)a = ba + ca$.

By the Distributive Property, the term outside the parentheses is multiplied by each term inside the parentheses.

EXAMPLES

1. $2(3 + 4) = 2 \cdot 3 + 2 \cdot 4$
　　　$2(7) = 6 + 8$
　　　$14 = 14$

2. $(4 + 5)2 = 4 \cdot 2 + 5 \cdot 2$
　　　$(9)2 = 8 + 10$
　　　$18 = 18$

The Distributive Property in the form $(b + c)a = ba + ca$ is used to simplify a variable expression.

To simplify $2x + 3x$, use the Distributive Property to add the numerical coefficients of the like variable terms.

$$2x + 3x = (2 + 3)x$$
$$= 5x$$

HOW TO 1 Simplify: $5y - 11y$

$5y - 11y = (5 - 11)y$ • **Use the Distributive Property.**
　　　　　$= -6y$

> **📝 Take Note**
>
> Simplifying an expression means combining like terms. The constant term 5 and the variable term $7p$ are not like terms and therefore cannot be combined.

HOW TO 2 Simplify: $5 + 7p$

The terms 5 and $7p$ are not like terms.

The expression $5 + 7p$ is in simplest form.

The following Properties of Addition are used to simplify variable expressions.

The Associative Property of Addition

If a, b, and c are real numbers, then $(a + b) + c = a + (b + c)$.

When three or more terms are added, the terms can be grouped (with parentheses, for example) in any order; the sum is the same.

EXAMPLES

1. $(5 + 7) + 15 = 5 + (7 + 15)$
$\qquad 12 + 15 = 5 + 22$
$\qquad\qquad 27 = 27$

2. $(3x + 5x) + 9x = 3x + (5x + 9x)$
$\qquad 8x + 9x = 3x + 14x$
$\qquad\quad 17x = 17x$

The Commutative Property of Addition

If a and b are real numbers, then $a + b = b + a$.

When two terms are added, the terms can be added in either order; the sum is the same.

EXAMPLES

1. $15 + (-28) = (-28) + 15$
$\qquad\quad -13 = -13$

2. $2x + (-4x) = -4x + 2x$
$\qquad\quad -2x = -2x$

The Addition Property of Zero

If a is a real number, then $a + 0 = a$ and $0 + a = a$.

The sum of a term and zero is the term.

EXAMPLES

1. $-9 + 0 = -9$ and $0 + (-9) = -9$

2. $0 + 5x = 5x$ and $5x + 0 = 5x$

The Inverse Property of Addition

If a is a real number, then $a + (-a) = 0$ and $(-a) + a = 0$.

The sum of a term and its additive inverse (or opposite) is zero.

EXAMPLES

1. $8 + (-8) = 0$ and $-8 + 8 = 0$

2. $-7x + 7x = 0$ and $7x + (-7x) = 0$

HOW TO 3   Simplify: $8x + 4y - 8x + y$

$8x + 4y - 8x + y$

$= (8x - 8x) + (4y + y)$ • Use the Commutative and Associative Properties of Addition to rearrange and group like terms.

$= 0 + 5y = 5y$ • Combine like terms.

HOW TO 4   Simplify: $4x^2 + 5x - 6x^2 - 2x + 1$

$$4x^2 + 5x - 6x^2 - 2x + 1$$
$$= (4x^2 - 6x^2) + (5x - 2x) + 1$$
$$= -2x^2 + 3x + 1$$

- Use the Commutative and Associative Properties of Addition to rearrange and group like terms.
- Combine like terms.

EXAMPLE 1

Simplify: $3x + 4y - 10x + 7y$

Solution

$$3x + 4y - 10x + 7y = (3x - 10x) + (4y + 7y)$$
$$= -7x + 11y$$

YOU TRY IT 1

Simplify: $3a - 2b - 5a + 6b$

Your solution

EXAMPLE 2

Simplify: $x^2 - 7 + 4x^2 - 16$

Solution

$$x^2 - 7 + 4x^2 - 16 = (x^2 + 4x^2) + (-7 - 16)$$
$$= 5x^2 - 23$$

YOU TRY IT 2

Simplify: $-3y^2 + 7 + 8y^2 - 14$

Your solution

Solutions on p. S4

OBJECTIVE B   *To simplify a variable expression using the Properties of Multiplication*

In simplifying variable expressions, the following Properties of Multiplication are used.

The Associative Property of Multiplication

If a, b, and c are real numbers, then $(ab)c = a(bc)$.

When three or more factors are multiplied, the factors can be grouped in any order; the product is the same.

EXAMPLES

1. $3(5 \cdot 6) = (3 \cdot 5)6$
$\ 3(30) = (15)6$
$\ \ \ 90 = 90$

2. $2(3x) = (2 \cdot 3)x$
$\ \ \ \ \ = 6x$

Take Note

The Associative Property of Multiplication allows us to multiply a coefficient by a number. Without this property, the expression $2(3x)$ could not be simplified.

The Commutative Property of Multiplication

If a and b are real numbers, then $ab = ba$.

Two factors can be multiplied in either order; the product is the same.

EXAMPLES

1. $5(-7) = -7(5)$
$\ -35 = -35$

2. $(5x) \cdot 3 = 3 \cdot (5x)$
$\ = (3 \cdot 5)x$
$\ = 15x$

- Commutative Property of Multiplication
- Associative Property of Multiplication

Take Note

The Commutative Property of Multiplication allows us to rearrange factors. This property, along with the Associative Property of Multiplication, enables us to simplify some variable expressions.

The Multiplication Property of One

If a is a real number, then $a \cdot 1 = a$ and $1 \cdot a = a$.

The product of a term and 1 is the term.

EXAMPLES

1. $9 \cdot 1 = 9$

2. $(8x) \cdot 1 = 8x$

The Inverse Property of Multiplication

If a is a real number and a is not equal to zero, then $a \cdot \dfrac{1}{a} = 1$ and $\dfrac{1}{a} \cdot a = 1$.

$\dfrac{1}{a}$ is called the **reciprocal** of a. $\dfrac{1}{a}$ is also called the **multiplicative inverse** of a.

The product of a number and its reciprocal is 1.

EXAMPLES

1. $7 \cdot \dfrac{1}{7} = 1$ and $\dfrac{1}{7} \cdot 7 = 1$

2. $x \cdot \dfrac{1}{x} = 1$ and $\dfrac{1}{x} \cdot x = 1, \quad x \neq 0$

> **Take Note**
> We must state that $x \neq 0$ because division by zero is undefined.

The multiplication properties are used to simplify variable expressions.

HOW TO 5   Simplify: $2(-x)$

$$2(-x) = 2(-1 \cdot x)$$
$$= [2(-1)]x$$
$$= -2x$$

- Use the Associative Property of Multiplication to group factors.

HOW TO 6   Simplify: $\dfrac{3}{2}\left(\dfrac{2x}{3}\right)$

$$\dfrac{3}{2}\left(\dfrac{2x}{3}\right) = \dfrac{3}{2}\left(\dfrac{2}{3}x\right)$$
$$= \left(\dfrac{3}{2} \cdot \dfrac{2}{3}\right)x$$
$$= 1 \cdot x$$
$$= x$$

- Note that $\dfrac{2x}{3} = \dfrac{2}{3}x$.

- Use the Associative Property of Multiplication to group factors.

HOW TO 7   Simplify: $(16x)2$

$$(16x)2 = 2(16x)$$
$$= (2 \cdot 16)x$$
$$= 32x$$

- Use the Commutative and Associative Properties of Multiplication to rearrange and group factors.

EXAMPLE 3	**YOU TRY IT 3**
Simplify: $-2(3x^2)$	Simplify: $-5(4y^2)$
Solution	**Your solution**
$-2(3x^2) = (-2 \cdot 3)x^2$ $= -6x^2$	

EXAMPLE 4	**YOU TRY IT 4**
Simplify: $-5(-10x)$	Simplify: $-7(-2a)$
Solution	**Your solution**
$-5(-10x) = [(-5)(-10)]x$ $= 50x$	

EXAMPLE 5	**YOU TRY IT 5**
Simplify: $-\dfrac{3}{4}\left(\dfrac{2}{3}x\right)$	Simplify: $-\dfrac{3}{5}\left(-\dfrac{7}{9}a\right)$
Solution	**Your solution**
$\left(-\dfrac{3}{4}\right)\left(\dfrac{2}{3}x\right) = \left(-\dfrac{3}{4}\cdot\dfrac{2}{3}\right)x$ $= -\dfrac{1}{2}x$	

Solutions on p. S4

> **OBJECTIVE C**   *To simplify a variable expression using the Distributive Property*

Recall that the Distributive Property states that if a, b, and c are real numbers, then

$$a(b + c) = ab + ac$$

The Distributive Property is used to remove parentheses from a variable expression.

HOW TO 8   Simplify: $3(2x + 7)$

$3(2x + 7) = 3(2x) + 3(7)$ • Use the **Distributive Property**. Multiply
$\quad\quad\quad\quad = 6x + 21$ each term inside the parentheses by 3.

HOW TO 9   Simplify: $-5(4x + 6)$

$-5(4x + 6) = -5(4x) + (-5)(6)$ • Use the **Distributive Property**.
$\quad\quad\quad\quad\quad = -20x - 30$

HOW TO 10   Simplify: $-(2x - 4)$

$-(2x - 4) = -1(2x - 4)$ • Use the **Distributive Property**.
$\quad\quad\quad\quad = -1(2x) - (-1)(4)$
$\quad\quad\quad\quad = -2x + 4$

From **HOW TO 10**, note that when a negative sign immediately precedes the parentheses, the sign of each term inside the parentheses is changed.

HOW TO 11   Simplify: $-\dfrac{1}{2}(8x - 12y)$

$$-\dfrac{1}{2}(8x - 12y) = -\dfrac{1}{2}(8x) - \left(-\dfrac{1}{2}\right)(12y)$$ • Use the Distributive Property.

$$= -4x + 6y$$

An extension of the Distributive Property is used when an expression contains more than two terms.

HOW TO 12   Simplify: $3(4x - 2y - z)$

$$3(4x - 2y - z) = 3(4x) - 3(2y) - 3(z)$$ • Use the Distributive Property.

$$= 12x - 6y - 3z$$

EXAMPLE 6

Simplify: $7(4 + 2x)$

Solution
Use the Distributive Property.

$$7(4 + 2x) = 28 + 14x$$

YOU TRY IT 6

Simplify: $5(3 + 7b)$

Your solution

EXAMPLE 7

Simplify: $(2x - 6)2$

Solution
Use the Distributive Property.

$$(2x - 6)2 = 4x - 12$$

YOU TRY IT 7

Simplify: $(3a - 1)5$

Your solution

EXAMPLE 8

Simplify: $-3(-5a + 7b)$

Solution
Use the Distributive Property.

$$-3(-5a + 7b) = 15a - 21b$$

YOU TRY IT 8

Simplify: $-8(-2a + 7b)$

Your solution

EXAMPLE 9

Simplify: $3(x^2 - x - 5)$

Solution
Use the Distributive Property.

$$3(x^2 - x - 5) = 3x^2 - 3x - 15$$

YOU TRY IT 9

Simplify: $3(12x^2 - x + 8)$

Your solution

Solutions on p. S4

EXAMPLE 10

Simplify: $-2(x^2 + 5x - 4)$

Solution
Use the Distributive Property.

$-2(x^2 + 5x - 4)$
$= -2x^2 - 10x + 8$

YOU TRY IT 10

Simplify: $3(-a^2 - 6a + 7)$

Your solution

Solution on p. S4

OBJECTIVE D *To simplify general variable expressions*

When simplifying variable expressions, use the Distributive Property to remove parentheses and brackets used as grouping symbols.

HOW TO 13 Simplify: $4(x - y) - 2(-3x + 6y)$

$4(x - y) - 2(-3x + 6y)$
$= 4x - 4y + 6x - 12y$ • Use the Distributive Property.
$= 10x - 16y$ • Combine like terms.

EXAMPLE 11

Simplify: $2x - 3(2x - 7y)$

Solution
$2x - 3(2x - 7y)$
$= 2x - 6x + 21y$ • Use the Distributive Property.
$= -4x + 21y$ • Combine like terms.

YOU TRY IT 11

Simplify: $3y - 2(y - 7x)$

Your solution

EXAMPLE 12

Simplify: $7(x - 2y) - (-x - 2y)$

Solution
$7(x - 2y) - (-x - 2y)$
$= 7x - 14y + x + 2y$ • Use the Distributive Property.
$= 8x - 12y$ • Combine like terms.

YOU TRY IT 12

Simplify: $-2(x - 2y) - (-x + 3y)$

Your solution

EXAMPLE 13

Simplify: $2x - 3[2x - 3(x + 7)]$

Solution
$2x - 3[2x - 3(x + 7)]$
$= 2x - 3[2x - 3x - 21]$ • Use the Distributive Property.
$= 2x - 3[-x - 21]$ • Combine like terms.
$= 2x + 3x + 63$ • Use the Distributive Property.
$= 5x + 63$ • Combine like terms.

YOU TRY IT 13

Simplify: $3y - 2[x - 4(2 - 3y)]$

Your solution

Solutions on p. S4

4.4 EXERCISES

✔ Concept Check

1. The fact that two terms can be added in either order is called the _____ Property of Addition.

2. The fact that three or more factors can be multiplied by grouping them in any order is called the _____ Property of Multiplication.

3. The Inverse Property of Multiplication tells us that the product of a number and its _____ is 1.

4. The Inverse Property of Addition tells us that the sum of a number and its _____ is 0.

5. ◣ What are *like terms*? Give an example of two like terms. Give an example of two terms that are not like terms.

6. ◣ Explain the meaning of the phrase "simplify a variable expression."

OBJECTIVE A   *To simplify a variable expression using the Properties of Addition*

For Exercises 7 to 42, simplify.

7. $6x + 8x$

8. $12x + 13x$

9. $9a - 4a$

10. $12a - 3a$

11. $4y - 10y$

12. $8y - 6y$

13. $7 - 3b$

14. $5 + 2a$

15. $-12a + 17a$

16. $-3a + 12a$

17. $5ab - 7ab$

18. $9ab - 3ab$

19. $-12xy + 17xy$

20. $-15xy + 3xy$

21. $-3ab + 3ab$

22. $-7ab + 7ab$

23. $-\dfrac{1}{2}x - \dfrac{1}{3}x$

24. $-\dfrac{2}{5}y + \dfrac{3}{10}y$

25. $2.3x + 4.2x$

26. $6.1y - 9.2y$

27. $x - 0.55x$

28. $0.65A - A$

29. $5a - 3a + 5a$

30. $10a - 17a + 3a$

31. $-5x^2 - 12x^2 + 3x^2$

32. $-y^2 - 8y^2 + 7y^2$

33. $\dfrac{3}{4}x - \dfrac{1}{3}x - \dfrac{7}{8}x$

34. $-\dfrac{2}{5}a - \left(-\dfrac{3}{10}a\right) - \dfrac{11}{15}a$

35. $7x - 3y + 10x$

36. $8y + 8x - 8y$

37. $3a + (-7b) - 5a + b$

38. $-5b + 7a - 7b + 12a$

39. $3x + (-8y) - 10x + 4x$

40. $3y + (-12x) - 7y + 2y$

41. $x^2 - 7x + (-5x^2) + 5x$

42. $3x^2 + 5x - 10x^2 - 10x$

43. Which of the following expressions are equivalent to $-10x - 10y - 10y - 10x$?

   (i) 0 **(ii)** $-20y$ **(iii)** $-20x$ **(iv)** $-20x - 20y$ **(v)** $-20y - 20x$

OBJECTIVE B   *To simplify a variable expression using the Properties of Multiplication*

For Exercises 44 to 83, simplify.

44. $4(3x)$

45. $12(5x)$

46. $-3(7a)$

47. $-2(5a)$

48. $-2(-3y)$

49. $-5(-6y)$

50. $(4x)2$

51. $(6x)12$

52. $(3a)(-2)$

53. $(7a)(-4)$

54. $(-3b)(-4)$

55. $(-12b)(-9)$

56. $-5(3x^2)$

57. $-8(7x^2)$

58. $\dfrac{1}{3}(3x^2)$

59. $\dfrac{1}{6}(6x^2)$

60. $\dfrac{1}{5}(5a)$

61. $\dfrac{1}{8}(8x)$

62. $-\dfrac{1}{2}(-2x)$

63. $-\dfrac{1}{4}(-4a)$

64. $-\dfrac{1}{7}(-7n)$

65. $-\dfrac{1}{9}(-9b)$

66. $(3x)\left(\dfrac{1}{3}\right)$

67. $(12x)\left(\dfrac{1}{12}\right)$

68. $(-6y)\left(-\dfrac{1}{6}\right)$

69. $(-10n)\left(-\dfrac{1}{10}\right)$

70. $\dfrac{1}{3}(9x)$

71. $\dfrac{1}{7}(14x)$

72. $-0.2(10x)$

73. $-0.25(8x)$

74. $-\dfrac{2}{3}(12a^2)$ **75.** $-\dfrac{5}{8}(24a^2)$ **76.** $-0.5(-16y)$ **77.** $-0.75(-8y)$ **78.** $(16y)\left(\dfrac{1}{4}\right)$

79. $(33y)\left(\dfrac{1}{11}\right)$ **80.** $(-6x)\left(\dfrac{1}{3}\right)$ **81.** $(-10x)\left(\dfrac{1}{5}\right)$ **82.** $(-8a)\left(-\dfrac{3}{4}\right)$ **83.** $(21y)\left(-\dfrac{3}{7}\right)$

84. After multiplying $\dfrac{2}{7}x^2$ by a proper fraction, is the coefficient of x^2 greater than 1 or less than 1?

OBJECTIVE C *To simplify a variable expression using the Distributive Property*

For Exercises 85 to 123, simplify.

85. $2(4x - 3)$ **86.** $5(2x - 7)$ **87.** $-2(a + 7)$ **88.** $-5(a + 16)$

89. $-3(2y - 8)$ **90.** $-5(3y - 7)$ **91.** $-(x + 2)$ **92.** $-(x + 7)$

93. $(5 - 3b)7$ **94.** $(10 - 7b)2$ **95.** $\dfrac{1}{3}(6 - 15y)$ **96.** $\dfrac{1}{2}(-8x + 4y)$

97. $3(5x^2 + 2x)$ **98.** $6(3x^2 + 2x)$ **99.** $-2(-y + 9)$ **100.** $-5(-2x + 7)$

101. $(-3x - 6)5$ **102.** $(-2x + 7)7$ **103.** $2(-3x^2 - 14)$ **104.** $5(-6x^2 - 3)$

105. $-3(2y^2 - 7)$ **106.** $-8(3y^2 - 12)$ **107.** $3(x^2 - y^2)$ **108.** $5(x^2 + y^2)$

109. $-\dfrac{2}{3}(6x - 18y)$ **110.** $-\dfrac{1}{2}(x - 4y)$ **111.** $-(6a^2 - 7b^2)$

112. $3(x^2 + 2x - 6)$ **113.** $4(x^2 - 3x + 5)$ **114.** $-2(y^2 - 2y + 4)$

115. $\dfrac{3}{4}(2x - 6y + 8)$

116. $-\dfrac{2}{3}(6x - 9y + 1)$

117. $4(-3a^2 - 5a + 7)$

118. $-5(-2x^2 - 3x + 7)$

119. $-3(-4x^2 + 3x - 4)$

120. $3(2x^2 + xy - 3y^2)$

121. $5(2x^2 - 4xy - y^2)$

122. $-(3a^2 + 5a - 4)$

123. $-(8b^2 - 6b + 9)$

124. After the expression $17x - 31$ is multiplied by a negative integer, is the constant term positive or negative?

OBJECTIVE D   *To simplify general variable expressions*

125. Which of the following expressions is equivalent to $12 - 7(y - 9)$?
   (i) $5(y - 9)$ **(ii)** $12 - 7y - 63$ **(iii)** $12 - 7y + 63$ **(iv)** $12 - 7y - 9$

For Exercises 126 to 149, simplify.

126. $4x - 2(3x + 8)$

127. $6a - (5a + 7)$

128. $9 - 3(4y + 6)$

129. $10 - (11x - 3)$

130. $5n - (7 - 2n)$

131. $8 - (12 + 4y)$

132. $3(x + 2) - 5(x - 7)$

133. $2(x - 4) - 4(x + 2)$

134. $12(y - 2) + 3(7 - 3y)$

135. $6(2y - 7) - (3 - 2y)$

136. $3(a - b) - (a + b)$

137. $2(a + 2b) - (a - 3b)$

138. $4[x - 2(x - 3)]$

139. $2[x + 2(x + 7)]$

140. $-2[3x + 2(4 - x)]$

141. $-5[2x + 3(5 - x)]$

142. $-3[2x - (x + 7)]$

143. $-2[3x - (5x - 2)]$

144. $2x - 3[x - (4 - x)]$

145. $-7x + 3[x - (3 - 2x)]$

146. $-5x - 2[2x - 4(x + 7)] - 6$

147. $0.12(2x + 3) + x$

148. $0.05x + 0.02(4 - x)$

149. $0.03x + 0.04(1000 - x)$

Critical Thinking

150. Determine whether the statement is true or false. If the statement is false, give an example that illustrates that it is false.
  a. Division is a commutative operation.
  b. Division is an associative operation.
  c. Subtraction is an associative operation.
  d. Subtraction is a commutative operation.

151. ▧ Give examples of two operations that occur in everyday experience that are not commutative (for example, putting on socks and then shoes).

152. Which of the following expressions are equivalent?
  (i) $2x + 4(2x + 1)$
  (ii) $x - (4 - 9x) + 8$
  (iii) $7(x - 4) - 3(2x + 6)$
  (iv) $3(2x + 8) + 4(x - 5)$
  (v) $6 - 2[x + (3x - 4)] + 2(9x - 5)$

Projects or Group Activities

153. Define an operation $\otimes$ as $a \otimes b = (a \cdot b) - (a + b)$.
  For example, $7 \otimes 5 = (7 \cdot 5) - (7 + 5) = 35 - 12 = 23$.
  a. Is $\otimes$ a commutative operation? Support your answer.
  b. Is $\otimes$ an associative operation? Support your answer.

✔ CHECK YOUR PROGRESS: CHAPTER 4

Evaluate the variable expression when $a = 3$, $b = -2$, and $c = 4$.

1. $-2a + 3b$ **2.** $c^2 - 5ab$ **3.** $2c - (a + b)^2$

Evaluate the variable expression when $x = 2$, $y = -3$, and $z = -1$.

4. $\dfrac{y + z}{x}$ **5.** $(y + x)^2 - 5z$ **6.** $\dfrac{-yz}{2x + z}$

Simplify.

7. $10y - 16y + 3y$ **8.** $-5a + 6b + 8a - 2b$ **9.** $(8a)(-5)$

10. $(-9z)\left(-\dfrac{1}{9}\right)$ **11.** $(12 - 8b)3$ **12.** $-2(-3x^2 + 4x - 5)$

13. $3x - 4(2x - 5)$ **14.** $6(3a - 7) - (4 + 9a)$ **15.** $5 - 3[2x - (6 - 4x)]$

Introduction to Linear Equations and Variables

5

OBJECTIVES

SECTION 5.1
A   To determine whether a given number is a solution of an equation
B   To solve an equation of the form $x + a = b$
C   To solve an equation of the form $ax = b$
D   To solve application problems using formulas

SECTION 5.2
A   To solve an equation of the form $ax + b = c$
B   To solve application problems using formulas

SECTION 5.3
A   To solve an equation of the form $ax + b = cx + d$
B   To solve an equation containing parentheses

SECTION 5.4
A   To solve equations of the form $ax + b = c$
B   To solve application problems using formulas

SECTION 5.5
A   To translate a verbal expression into a mathematical expression given the variable
B   To translate a verbal expression into a mathematical expression by assigning the variable

SECTION 5.6
A   To translate a sentence into an equation and solve
B   To solve application problems

Focus on Success

Remember to prepare your brain for the material you will learn in this chapter. Read the list of objectives on this page. Look through the entire chapter, noting words that are in bold type. Read the rules and definitions that appear in boxes. By getting an overview of the new material, you will be building a foundation for learning it. (See Understand the Organization, page AIM-8.)

Aron Hsiao/Shutterstock.com

Prep Test

Are you ready to succeed in this chapter? Take the Prep Test below to find out if you are ready to learn the new material.

For Exercises 1 to 9, simplify.

1. $2 - 9$

2. $-5(4)$

3. $-16 + 16$

4. $\dfrac{-7}{-7}$

5. $-\dfrac{3}{8}\left(-\dfrac{8}{3}\right)$

6. $\left(\dfrac{3}{5}\right)^3\left(\dfrac{5}{9}\right)^2$

7. $\dfrac{2}{3} + \left(\dfrac{3}{4}\right)^2 \cdot \dfrac{2}{9}$

8. $-8 \div (-2)^2 + 6$

9. $4 + 5(2 - 7)^2 \div (-8 + 3)$

5.1   Introduction to Equations

OBJECTIVE A   *To determine whether a given number is a solution of an equation*

 Point of Interest

Finding solutions of equations has been a principal aim of mathematics for thousands of years. However, the equals sign did not appear in any text until 1557.

An **equation** expresses the equality of two mathematical expressions. These expressions can be either numerical or variable expressions.

$$
\left.\begin{array}{l} 5 + 4 = 9 \\ 3x + 13 = x - 8 \\ y^2 + 4 = 6y + 1 \\ x = -3 \end{array}\right\} \text{Equations}
$$

In the equation at the right, if the variable is replaced by 4, the equation is true.

$x + 3 = 7$
$4 + 3 = 7$ A true equation

If the variable is replaced by 6, the equation is false.

$6 + 3 = 7$ A false equation

A **solution of an equation** is a number that, when substituted for the variable, results in a true equation. 4 is a solution of the equation $x + 3 = 7$. 6 is not a solution of the equation $x + 3 = 7$.

HOW TO 1   Is -2 a solution of the equation $-2x + 1 = 2x + 9$?

$$
-2x + 1 = 2x + 9
$$

$-2(-2) + 1$	$2(-2) + 9$
$4 + 1$	$-4 + 9$

$5 = 5$

- Replace the variable by the given number.
- Evaluate the numerical expressions.
- Compare the results. If the results are equal, the given number is a solution. If the results are not equal, the given number is not a solution.

Yes, -2 is a solution of the equation $-2x + 1 = 2x + 9$.

EXAMPLE 1

Is $\frac{1}{2}$ a solution of $2x(x + 2) = 3x + 1$?

Solution

$$
2x(x + 2) = 3x + 1
$$

$2\left(\dfrac{1}{2}\right)\left(\dfrac{1}{2} + 2\right)$	$3\left(\dfrac{1}{2}\right) + 1$
$2\left(\dfrac{1}{2}\right)\left(\dfrac{5}{2}\right)$	$\dfrac{3}{2} + 1$

$$
\frac{5}{2} = \frac{5}{2}
$$

Yes, $\frac{1}{2}$ is a solution.

YOU TRY IT 1

Is -2 a solution of $x(x + 3) = 4x + 6$?

Your solution

Solution on p. S26

EXAMPLE 2

Is 5 a solution of $(x - 2)^2 = x^2 - 4x + 2$?

Solution

$$\begin{array}{c|c} (x - 2)^2 = x^2 - 4x + 2 \\ \hline (5 - 2)^2 & 5^2 - 4(5) + 2 \\ 3^2 & 25 - 4(5) + 2 \\ 9 & 25 - 20 + 2 \\ & 25 + (-20) + 2 \\ 9 \ne 7 & (\ne \text{ means "is not equal to")} \end{array}$$

No, 5 is not a solution.

YOU TRY IT 2

Is -3 a solution of $x^2 - x = 3x + 7$?

Your solution

Solution on p. S26

OBJECTIVE B *To solve an equation of the form $x + a = b$*

Recall that a solution of an equation is a number that, when substituted for the variable, results in a true equation. The phrase **solving an equation** means finding a solution of the equation.

The simplest equation to solve is an equation of the form *variable = constant*. The constant is the solution of the equation.

If $x = 7$, then 7 is the solution of the equation because $7 = 7$ is a true equation.

In solving an equation of the form $x + a = b$, the goal is to simplify the given equation to one of the form *variable = constant*. The Addition Properties that follow are used to simplify equations to this form.

Additive Inverse Property

$a + (-a) = 0 \qquad -a + a = 0$

$-a$ is called the **additive inverse** or **opposite** of a. The Additive Inverse Property states that the sum of a number and its additive inverse (opposite) is zero.

EXAMPLES

1. $9 + (-9) = 0$ **2.** $-7 + 7 = 0$

Addition Property of Zero

$a + 0 = a \qquad 0 + a = a$

The Addition Property of Zero states that the sum of a number and zero is the number.

EXAMPLES

1. $-3 + 0 = -3$ **2.** $0 + 9 = 9$

> ## Addition Property of Equations
>
> If a, b, and c are algebraic expressions, then the equation $a = b$ and the equation $a + c = b + c$ have the same solutions.
>
> The Addition Property of Equations states that the same number can be added to each side of an equation without changing the solution of the equation.
>
> **EXAMPLE**
>
> The solution of the equation $x = 3$ is 3.
>
> | | |
> |---|---|
> | $x = 3$ | • The solution is 3. |
> | $x + 7 = 3 + 7$ | • Add 7 to each side of the equation. |
> | $x + 7 = 10$ | • The solution is still 3. $(3 + 7 = 10)$ |

The Addition Property of Equations is used to rewrite an equation in the form *variable* = *constant*. We remove a term from one side of the equation by adding the opposite of that term to each side of the equation.

HOW TO 2 Solve: $x - 7 = -2$

$$x - 7 = -2$$

• The goal is to simplify the equation to one of the form *variable* = *constant*.

$$x - 7 + 7 = -2 + 7$$
$$x + 0 = 5$$
$$x = 5$$

• Add the opposite of the constant term -7 to each side of the equation. After we simplify and use the Addition Property of Zero, the equation will be in the form *variable* = *constant*.

The solution is 5.

Take Note

Always check the solution to an equation.
Check: $\dfrac{x - 7 = -2}{5 - 7 \mid -2}$
$\qquad -2 = -2$ True

Because subtraction is defined in terms of addition, the Addition Property of Equations allows the same number to be subtracted from each side of an equation.

HOW TO 3 Solve: $x + 8 = 5$

$$x + 8 = 5$$

• The goal is to simplify the equation to one of the form *variable* = *constant*.

$$x + 8 - 8 = 5 - 8$$
$$x + 0 = -3$$
$$x = -3$$

• Add the opposite of the constant term 8 to each side of the equation. This procedure is equivalent to subtracting 8 from each side of the equation.

The solution is -3. **You should check this solution.**

Tips for Success

When we suggest that you check a solution, you should substitute the solution into the *original* equation. For instance,
$\dfrac{x + 8 = 5}{-3 + 8 \mid 5}$
$\qquad 5 = 5$
The solution checks.

EXAMPLE 3

Solve: $4 + m = -2$

Solution

$$4 + m = -2$$
$$4 - 4 + m = -2 - 4$$
$$0 + m = -6$$
$$m = -6$$

• Subtract 4 from each side.

The solution is -6.

YOU TRY IT 3

Solve: $-2 + y = -5$

Your solution

Solution on p. S26

EXAMPLE 4

Solve: $3 = y - 2$

Solution

$$3 = y - 2$$
$$3 + 2 = y - 2 + 2 \qquad \text{• Add 2 to}$$
$$5 = y + 0 \qquad \text{each side.}$$
$$5 = y$$

The solution is 5.

YOU TRY IT 4

Solve: $7 = y + 8$

Your solution

EXAMPLE 5

Solve: $\dfrac{2}{7} = \dfrac{5}{7} + t$

Solution

$$\dfrac{2}{7} = \dfrac{5}{7} + t$$

$$\dfrac{2}{7} - \dfrac{5}{7} = \dfrac{5}{7} - \dfrac{5}{7} + t \qquad \text{• Subtract } \tfrac{5}{7} \text{ from}$$
$$\text{each side.}$$

$$-\dfrac{3}{7} = 0 + t$$

$$-\dfrac{3}{7} = t$$

The solution is $-\dfrac{3}{7}$.

YOU TRY IT 5

Solve: $\dfrac{1}{5} = z + \dfrac{4}{5}$

Your solution

Solutions on p. S26

OBJECTIVE C *To solve an equation of the form $ax = b$*

In solving an equation of the form $ax = b$, the goal is to simplify the given equation to one of the form *variable = constant*. The Multiplication Properties that follow are used to simplify equations to this form.

Multiplication Property of Reciprocals

For $a \neq 0$,

$$a \cdot \dfrac{1}{a} = 1 \qquad \dfrac{1}{a} \cdot a = 1$$

$\dfrac{1}{a}$ is called the **multiplicative inverse** or **reciprocal** of a. The Multiplication Property of Reciprocals states that the product of a nonzero number and its reciprocal is 1.

EXAMPLES

1. $-3 \cdot \left(-\dfrac{1}{3}\right) = 1$ **2.** $\dfrac{2}{3} \cdot \dfrac{3}{2} = 1$

Multiplication Property of One

$$a \cdot 1 = a \qquad 1 \cdot a = a$$

The Multiplication Property of One states that the product of a number and 1 is the number.

EXAMPLES

1. $-5 \cdot 1 = -5$ **2.** $1 \cdot 13 = 13$

Multiplication Property of Equations

If a, b, and c are algebraic expressions and $c \neq 0$, then the equation $a = b$ and the equation $ac = bc$ have the same solutions.

The Multiplication Property of Equations states that each side of an equation can be multiplied by the same nonzero number without changing the solution of the equation.

EXAMPLE

The solution of the equation $z = 8$ is 8.

$z = 8$	• The solution is 8.
$3z = 3(8)$	• Multiply each side of the equation by 3.
$3z = 24$	• The solution is still 8. $(3 \cdot 8 = 24)$

Recall that the goal of solving an equation is to rewrite the equation in the form *variable = constant*. The Multiplication Property of Equations is used to rewrite an equation in this form by multiplying each side of the equation by the reciprocal of the coefficient.

HOW TO 4   Solve: $\dfrac{2}{3}x = 8$

$$\frac{2}{3}x = 8$$

$$\left(\frac{3}{2}\right)\left(\frac{2}{3}\right)x = \left(\frac{3}{2}\right)8$$

• Multiply each side of the equation by $\frac{3}{2}$, the reciprocal of $\frac{2}{3}$. After simplifying, the equation will be in the form *variable = constant*.

$$1 \cdot x = 12$$

$$x = 12$$

Check: $\dfrac{2}{3}x = 8$

$$\frac{\frac{2}{3}(12) \;\bigg|\; 8}{8 = 8}$$

The solution is 12.

Because division is defined in terms of multiplication, the Multiplication Property of Equations allows each side of an equation to be divided by the same nonzero quantity.

⭐ **Tips for Success**

When we suggest that you check a solution, you should substitute the solution into the *original* equation. For instance,
$$-4x = 24$$
$$\frac{-4(-6) \;\big|\; 24}{24 = 24}$$
The solution checks.

HOW TO 5   Solve: $-4x = 24$

$$-4x = 24$$

• The goal is to rewrite the equation in the form *variable = constant*.

$$\frac{-4x}{-4} = \frac{24}{-4}$$

• Multiply each side of the equation by the reciprocal of -4. This is equivalent to dividing each side of the equation by -4. Then simplify.

$$1x = -6$$

$$x = -6$$

The solution is -6. You should check this solution.

In using the Multiplication Property of Equations, it is usually easier to multiply each side of the equation by the reciprocal of the coefficient when the coefficient is a fraction. Divide each side of the equation by the coefficient when the coefficient is an integer or a decimal.

EXAMPLE 6

Solve: $-2x = 6$

Solution

$-2x = 6$

$\dfrac{-2x}{-2} = \dfrac{6}{-2}$ • **Divide each side by -2.**

$1x = -3$

$x = -3$

The solution is -3.

YOU TRY IT 6

Solve: $4z = -20$

Your solution

EXAMPLE 7

Solve: $-9 = \dfrac{3}{4}y$

Solution

$-9 = \dfrac{3}{4}y$

$\left(\dfrac{4}{3}\right)(-9) = \left(\dfrac{4}{3}\right)\left(\dfrac{3}{4}y\right)$ • **Multiply each side by $\dfrac{4}{3}$.**

$-12 = 1y$

$-12 = y$

The solution is -12.

YOU TRY IT 7

Solve: $8 = \dfrac{2}{5}n$

Your solution

EXAMPLE 8

Solve: $6z - 8z = -5$

Solution

$6z - 8z = -5$

$-2z = -5$ • **Combine like terms.**

$\dfrac{-2z}{-2} = \dfrac{-5}{-2}$ • **Divide each side by -2.**

$1z = \dfrac{5}{2}$

$z = \dfrac{5}{2}$

The solution is $\dfrac{5}{2}$.

YOU TRY IT 8

Solve: $\dfrac{2}{3}t - \dfrac{1}{3}t = -2$

Your solution

Solutions on p. S26

OBJECTIVE D   *To solve application problems using formulas*

A **formula** is an equation that expresses a relationship among variables. Formulas are used in the examples below.

EXAMPLE 9

An accountant for a greeting card store found that the weekly profit for the store was $1700 and the total amount spent during the week was $2400. Use the formula $P = R - C$, where P is the profit, R is the revenue, and C is the amount spent, to find the revenue for the week.

Strategy

To find the revenue for the week, replace the variables P and C in the formula by the given values, and solve for R.

Solution

$$P = R - C$$
$$1700 = R - 2400$$
$$1700 + 2400 = R - 2400 + 2400$$
$$4100 = R + 0$$
$$4100 = R$$

The revenue for the week was $4100.

EXAMPLE 10

A store manager uses the formula $S = R - dR$, where S is the sale price, R is the regular price, and d is the discount rate. During a clearance sale, all items are discounted 20%. Find the regular price of running shoes that are on sale for $120.

Strategy

To find the regular price of the running shoes, replace the variables S and d in the formula by the given values, and solve for R.

Solution

$$S = R - dR$$
$$120 = R - 0.20R$$
$$120 = 0.80R \qquad \bullet \; R - 0.20R = 1R - 0.20R$$
$$\frac{120}{0.80} = \frac{0.80R}{0.80}$$
$$150 = R$$

The regular price of the running shoes is $150.

YOU TRY IT 9

A clothing store's sale price for a college sweatshirt is $44. This is a discount of $16 off the regular price. Use the formula $S = R - D$, where S is the sale price, R is the regular price, and D is the discount, to find the regular price.

Your strategy

Your solution

YOU TRY IT 10

Find the monthly payment on a loan when the total amount of the loan is $6840 and the loan is paid off in 24 months. Use the formula $A = MN$, where A is the total amount of the loan, M is the monthly payment, and N is the number of monthly payments.

Your strategy

Your solution

Solutions on p. S26

5.1 EXERCISES

Concept Check

1. State whether each part shows an *equation* or an *expression*.
   a. $x^2 + 4x - 7$
   b. $-7 = x$
   c. $\dfrac{2x}{3} - 17 = y$

   d. $6 = 12$
   e. $\dfrac{x + 7}{2x - 3} + 4$
   f. $-1 + 3(2x - 7)$

2. Name the property of addition or multiplication illustrated by each equation.
   a. $-4 + 4 = 0$
   b. $7x - 7x = 0$
   c. $\dfrac{1}{2}(2x) = 1x$

   d. $2x + 0 = 2x$
   e. $1 \cdot 3x = 3x$
   f. $\left(-\dfrac{2}{5}\right)\left(-\dfrac{5}{2}\right) = 1$

OBJECTIVE A   *To determine whether a given number is a solution of an equation*

3. Is -3 a solution of
   $2x + 9 = 3$?

4. Is -2 a solution of
   $5x + 7 = 12$?

5. Is 2 a solution of
   $4 - 2x = 8$?

6. Is 4 a solution of
   $5 - 2x = 4x$?

7. Is 3 a solution of
   $3x - 2 = x + 4$?

8. Is 2 a solution of
   $4x + 8 = 4 - 2x$?

9. Is 3 a solution of
   $x^2 - 5x + 1 = 10 - 5x$?

10. Is -5 a solution of
    $x^2 - 3x - 1 = 9 - 6x$?

11. Is -1 a solution of
    $2x(x - 1) = 3 - x$?

12. Is 2 a solution of
    $3x(x - 3) = x - 8$?

13. Is 2 a solution of
    $x(x - 2) = x^2 - 4$?

14. Is -4 a solution of
    $x(x + 4) = x^2 + 16$?

15. Is $-\dfrac{2}{3}$ a solution of
    $3x + 6 = 4$?

16. Is $\dfrac{1}{2}$ a solution of
    $2x - 7 = -3$?

17. Is $\dfrac{1}{4}$ a solution of
    $2x - 3 = 1 - 14x$?

18. Is 1.32 a solution of
    $x^2 - 3x = -0.8776 - x$?

19. Is -1.9 a solution of
    $x^2 - 3x = x + 3.8$?

20. Is 1.05 a solution of
    $x^2 + 3x = x(x + 3)$?

For Exercises 21 and 22, determine whether the statement is true or false.

21. Any number that is a solution of the equation $5x + 1 = -9$ must be a negative number.

22. Any number that is a solution of the equation $3x + 6 = 3 - 4x$ must also be a solution of the equation $3(x + 2) = 3 + 4x - 8x$.

OBJECTIVE B *To solve an equation of the form $x + a = b$*

For Exercises 23 to 50, solve.

23. $y - 6 = 16$ **24.** $z - 4 = 10$ **25.** $3 + n = 4$ **26.** $6 + x = 8$

27. $z + 7 = 2$ **28.** $w + 9 = 5$ **29.** $x - 3 = -7$ **30.** $m - 4 = -9$

31. $y + 6 = 6$ **32.** $t - 3 = -3$ **33.** $-7 = -4 + v$ **34.** $5 = 6 + w$

35. $1 + x = 0$ **36.** $3 + y = 0$ **37.** $x - 10 = 5$ **38.** $y - 7 = 3$

39. $4 = -3 + x$ **40.** $-3 = 5 + t$ **41.** $7 = w + 8$ **42.** $12 = z - 1$

43. $x + \dfrac{1}{2} = -\dfrac{1}{2}$ **44.** $x - \dfrac{5}{6} = -\dfrac{1}{6}$ **45.** $\dfrac{2}{5} + x = -\dfrac{3}{5}$ **46.** $\dfrac{7}{8} + y = -\dfrac{1}{8}$

47. $x + \dfrac{1}{2} = -\dfrac{1}{3}$ **48.** $\dfrac{1}{4} = y + \dfrac{3}{8}$ **49.** $-\dfrac{1}{2} = t + \dfrac{1}{4}$ **50.** $x + \dfrac{1}{3} = \dfrac{5}{12}$

For Exercises 51 to 54, use the given conditions for a and b to determine whether the value of x in the equation $x + a = b$ *must be negative, must be positive,* or *could be either positive or negative.*

51. a is positive and b is negative. **52.** a is a positive proper fraction and b is greater than 1.

53. a is the opposite of b, and b is positive. **54.** a is negative and b is negative.

OBJECTIVE C   *To solve an equation of the form ax = b*

For Exercises 55 to 86, solve.

55. $3y = 12$

56. $5x = 30$

57. $5z = -20$

58. $3z = -27$

59. $-2x = 6$

60. $-4t = 20$

61. $-5x = -40$

62. $-2y = -28$

63. $40 = 8x$

64. $24 = 3y$

65. $-24 = 4x$

66. $-21 = 7y$

67. $\dfrac{x}{3} = 5$

68. $\dfrac{y}{2} = 10$

69. $\dfrac{n}{4} = -2$

70. $\dfrac{y}{7} = -3$

71. $-\dfrac{x}{4} = 1$

72. $-\dfrac{y}{3} = 5$

73. $\dfrac{2}{3}w = 4$

74. $\dfrac{5}{8}x = 10$

75. $\dfrac{3}{4}v = -3$

76. $\dfrac{2}{7}x = -12$

77. $-\dfrac{1}{3}x = -2$

78. $-\dfrac{1}{5}y = -3$

79. $-4 = -\dfrac{2}{3}z$

80. $-12 = -\dfrac{3}{8}y$

81. $\dfrac{2}{3}x = -\dfrac{2}{7}$

82. $\dfrac{3}{7}y = \dfrac{5}{6}$

83. $4x - 2x = 7$

84. $3a - 6a = 8$

85. $\dfrac{4}{5}m - \dfrac{1}{5}m = 9$

86. $\dfrac{1}{3}b - \dfrac{2}{3}b = -1$

For Exercises 87 to 89, determine whether the statement is *true* or *false*.

87. If a is positive and b is negative, then the value of x in the equation $ax = b$ must be negative.

88. If a is the opposite of b, then the value of x in the equation $ax = b$ must be -1.

89. If a is negative and b is negative, then the value of x in the equation $ax = b$ must be negative.

OBJECTIVE D   *To solve application problems using formulas*

90. A store's cost for a pair of jeans is $38. The store sells the jeans and makes a $14 profit. Which equations can you use to find the selling price of the jeans? In each equation, S represents the selling price of the item.
(i) $S - 14 = 38$ **(ii)** $14 = 38 - S$ **(iii)** $38 - 14 = S$ **(iv)** $S - 38 = 14$

Fuel Efficiency   In Exercises 91 to 94, use the formula $D = MG$, where D is the distance in miles, M is the number of miles per gallon, and G is the number of gallons. Round to the nearest tenth.

91. Julio, a sales executive, averaged 28 mi/gal on a 621-mile trip. Find the number of gallons of gasoline used on the trip.

92. Over a 3-day weekend, you take a 592-mile trip. If you average 32 mi/gal on the trip, how many gallons of gasoline did you use?

93. The manufacturer of a hatchback estimates that the car can travel 560 mi on a 15-gallon tank of gas. Find the number of miles per gallon.

94. You estimate that your car can travel 410 mi on 12 gal of gasoline. Find the number of miles per gallon.

Investments   For Exercises 95 to 98, use the formula $A = P + I$, where A is the value of the investment after one year, P is the original investment, and I is the increase in value of the investment.

95. The value of an investment in a high-tech company after one year was $17,700. The increase in value during the year was $2700. Find the amount of the original investment.

96. The value of an investment in a software company after one year was $26,440. The increase in value during the year was $2830. Find the amount of the original investment.

97. The original investment in a mutual fund was $8000. The value of the mutual fund after one year was $11,420. Find the increase in value of the investment.

98. The original investment in a money market fund was $7500. The value of the mutual fund after one year was $8690. Find the increase in value of the investment.

Markup   For Exercises 99 and 100, use the formula $S = C + M$, where S is the selling price, C is the cost, and M is the markup.

99. A store sells a tablet computer for \$499. The computer has a markup of \$175. Find the cost of the computer.

100. A toy store buys stuffed animals for \$23.50 each and sells them for \$39.80. Find the markup on each stuffed animal.

Markup   For Exercises 101 and 102, use the formula $S = C + RC$, where S is the selling price, C is the cost, and R is the markup rate.

101. A store manager uses a markup rate of 24% on all children's furniture. Find the cost of a crib that sells for \$232.50.

102. A music store uses a markup rate of 30%. Find the cost of a compact disc that sells for \$18.85.

Critical Thinking

For Exercises 103 to 108, let $a = 3$, $b = -5$, and $c = 8$. Solve each equation.

103. $x + a = b$

104. $ax = b$

105. $(a + b)x = c$

106. $x + (a + b) = a$

107. $c = (a - b)x$

108. $\dfrac{x}{b + c} = a$

Projects or Group Activities

109. Write out the steps for solving the equation $x - 3 = -5$. Identify the property of real numbers or property of equations that is used at each step.

110. Write out the steps for solving the equation $\frac{3}{4}x = 6$. Identify the property of real numbers or property of equations that is used at each step.

111. Write an equation of the form $x + a = b$ that has -4 as its solution.

5.2 General Equations: Part I

OBJECTIVE A   *To solve an equation of the form $ax + b = c$*

 Point of Interest
Evariste Galois, despite being killed in a duel at the age of 21, made significant contributions to the study of equations. In fact, there is a branch of mathematics called Galois theory that explores what kinds of equations can be solved and what kinds cannot.

To solve an equation of the form $ax + b = c$, it is necessary to use both the Addition and Multiplication Properties to simplify the equation to one of the form *variable = constant*.

HOW TO 1   Solve: $\dfrac{x}{4} - 1 = 3$

$$\frac{x}{4} - 1 = 3$$

- The goal is to simplify the equation to one of the form *variable = constant*.

$$\frac{x}{4} - 1 + 1 = 3 + 1$$

- Add the opposite of the constant term -1 to each side of the equation. Then simplify (Addition Properties).

$$\frac{x}{4} + 0 = 4$$

$$\frac{x}{4} = 4$$

$$4 \cdot \frac{x}{4} = 4 \cdot 4$$

- Multiply each side of the equation by the reciprocal of the numerical coefficient of the variable term. Then simplify (Multiplication Properties).

$$1x = 16$$

$$x = 16$$

The solution is 16.

- Write the solution.

 Take Note
Note that
$$\frac{x}{4} = \frac{1}{4}x$$
The reciprocal of $\frac{1}{4}$ is 4.

EXAMPLE 1

Solve: $3x + 7 = 2$

Solution

$$3x + 7 = 2$$
$$3x + 7 - 7 = 2 - 7$$
$$3x = -5$$
$$\frac{3x}{3} = \frac{-5}{3}$$
$$x = -\frac{5}{3}$$

- Subtract 7 from each side.

- Divide each side by 3.

The solution is $-\frac{5}{3}$.

YOU TRY IT 1

Solve: $5x + 8 = 6$

Your solution

EXAMPLE 2

Solve: $-1 = 5 - 6x$

Solution

$$-1 = 5 - 6x$$
$$-1 - 5 = 5 - 5 - 6x$$
$$-6 = -6x$$
$$\frac{-6}{-6} = \frac{-6x}{-6}$$
$$1 = x$$

- Subtract 5 from each side.

- Divide each side by -6.

The solution is 1.

YOU TRY IT 2

Solve: $9 = 3x + 15$

Your solution

Solutions on pp. S26–S27

OBJECTIVE B   *To solve application problems using formulas*

Anders Celsius

The Fahrenheit temperature scale was devised by Daniel Gabriel Fahrenheit (1686–1736), a German physicist and maker of scientific instruments. He invented the mercury thermometer in 1714. On the Fahrenheit scale, the temperature at which water freezes is 32°F, and the temperature at which water boils is 212°F. *Note:* The small raised circle is the symbol for "degrees," and the capital F is for "Fahrenheit." The Fahrenheit scale is used only in the United States.

In the metric system, temperature is measured on the Celsius scale. The Celsius temperature scale was devised by Anders Celsius (1701–1744), a Swedish astronomer. On the Celsius scale, the temperature at which water freezes is 0°C, and the temperature at which water boils is 100°C. *Note:* The small raised circle is the symbol for "degrees," and the capital C is for "Celsius."

On both the Celsius scale and the Fahrenheit scale, temperatures below 0° are represented by negative numbers.

The relationship between Celsius temperature and Fahrenheit temperature is given by the formula

$$F = \frac{9}{5}C + 32$$

where *F* represents degrees Fahrenheit and *C* represents degrees Celsius.

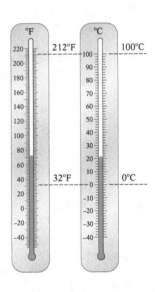

HOW TO 2   Normal body temperature is 98.6°F. Convert this temperature to degrees Celsius.

$$F = \frac{9}{5}C + 32$$

$$98.6 = \frac{9}{5}C + 32$$ • Substitute 98.6 for *F*.

$$98.6 - 32 = \frac{9}{5}C + 32 - 32$$ • Subtract 32 from each side.

$$66.6 = \frac{9}{5}C$$ • Combine like terms on each side.

$$\frac{5}{9}(66.6) = \frac{5}{9}\left(\frac{9}{5}C\right)$$ • Multiply each side by $\frac{5}{9}$.

$$37 = C$$

Normal body temperature is 37°C.

Integrating Technology

You can check the solution to this equation by using a calculator. Substitute 37 for *C* in the right side of the equation and evaluate. Enter

9 ÷ 5 × 37 + 32 =

The display reads 98.6, the given Fahrenheit temperature. The solution checks.

EXAMPLE 3

Find the Celsius temperature when the Fahrenheit temperature is 212°. Use the formula $F = \frac{9}{5}C + 32$, where F is the Fahrenheit temperature and C is the Celsius temperature.

Strategy

To find the Celsius temperature, replace the variable F in the formula by the given value, and solve for C.

Solution

$$F = \frac{9}{5}C + 32$$

$$212 = \frac{9}{5}C + 32 \qquad \bullet \text{ Substitute 212 for } F.$$

$$212 - 32 = \frac{9}{5}C + 32 - 32 \qquad \bullet \text{ Subtract 32 from each side.}$$

$$180 = \frac{9}{5}C \qquad \bullet \text{ Combine like terms.}$$

$$\frac{5}{9}(180) = \frac{5}{9}\left(\frac{9}{5}C\right) \qquad \bullet \text{ Multiply each side by } \frac{5}{9}.$$

$$100 = C$$

The Celsius temperature is 100°.

YOU TRY IT 3

Find the Celsius temperature when the Fahrenheit temperature is −22°. Use the formula $F = \frac{9}{5}C + 32$, where F is the Fahrenheit temperature and C is the Celsius temperature.

Your strategy

Your solution

EXAMPLE 4

To find the total cost of production, an economist uses the formula $T = UN + F$, where T is the total cost, U is the cost per unit, N is the number of units made, and F is the fixed cost. Find the number of units made during a week in which the total cost was $8000, the cost per unit was $16, and the fixed costs were $2000.

Strategy

To find the number of units made, replace the variables T, U, and F in the formula by the given values, and solve for N.

Solution

$$T = UN + F$$

$$8000 = 16N + 2000$$

$$8000 - 2000 = 16N + 2000 - 2000$$

$$6000 = 16N$$

$$\frac{6000}{16} = \frac{16N}{16}$$

$$375 = N$$

The number of units made was 375.

YOU TRY IT 4

Find the cost per unit during a week in which the total cost was $4500, the number of units produced was 250, and the fixed costs were $1500. Use the formula $T = UN + F$, where T is the total cost, U is the cost per unit, N is the number of units made, and F is the fixed cost.

Your strategy

Your solution

Solutions on p. S27

5.2 EXERCISES

✔ Concept Check

For Exercises 1 and 2, fill in the blank to make a true statement.

1. To solve the equation $2x - 3 = 17$, the first step is to add the _____ of the constant term -3 to each side of the equation. After simplifying, the resulting equation is $2x =$ _____.

2. At one point in solving an equation, you reach the equation $\frac{2}{3}x = 8$. The next step is to multiply each side of the equation by _____. After simplifying, the resulting equation is $x =$ _____.

OBJECTIVE A   *To solve an equation of the form $ax + b = c$*

For Exercises 3 to 70, solve.

3. $3x + 5 = 14$

4. $5z + 6 = 31$

5. $2n - 3 = 7$

6. $4y - 4 = 20$

7. $5w + 8 = 3$

8. $3x + 10 = 1$

9. $3z - 4 = -16$

10. $6x - 1 = -13$

11. $5 + 2x = 7$

12. $12 + 7x = 33$

13. $6 - x = 3$

14. $4 - x = -2$

15. $3 - 4x = 11$

16. $2 - 3x = 11$

17. $5 - 4x = 17$

18. $8 - 6x = 14$

19. $3x + 6 = 0$

20. $5x - 20 = 0$

21. $-3x - 4 = -1$

22. $-7x - 22 = -1$

23. $12y - 30 = 6$

24. $9b - 7 = 2$

25. $3c + 7 = 4$

26. $8t + 13 = 5$

27. $9x + 13 = 13$

28. $5z + 10 = 0$

29. $7d - 14 = 0$

30. $-13m - 1 = -1$

31. $3x + 5 = 7$

32. $4x + 6 = 9$

33. $6x - 1 = 16$

34. $12x - 3 = 7$

35. $-2x - 3 = -7$ **36.** $-5x - 7 = -4$ **37.** $3x + 8 = 2$ **38.** $2x - 9 = 8$

39. $3 = 4x - 5$ **40.** $5 = 3 + 4x$ **41.** $-3 = 2 - 5x$ **42.** $-4 = 7x + 10$

43. $\dfrac{1}{2}x - 2 = 3$ **44.** $\dfrac{1}{3}x + 1 = 4$ **45.** $\dfrac{3}{5}w - 1 = 2$ **46.** $\dfrac{2}{5}w + 5 = 6$

47. $3 - \dfrac{2}{9}t = 5$ **48.** $5 + \dfrac{3}{4}z = 8$ **49.** $-3 + \dfrac{5}{8}t = -13$ **50.** $5 - \dfrac{1}{2}v = 9$

51. $\dfrac{x}{3} - 2 = -5$ **52.** $\dfrac{x}{4} - 3 = 5$ **53.** $\dfrac{5}{8}v + 6 = 3$ **54.** $\dfrac{2}{3}v - 4 = 3$

55. $5 = \dfrac{4}{7}z + 10$ **56.** $4 = \dfrac{3}{8}v - 3$ **57.** $13 = 3 - \dfrac{5}{9}w$ **58.** $-5 = 3 + \dfrac{2}{3}x$

59. $1.5x - 0.5 = 2.5$ **60.** $2.5w - 1.3 = 3.7$ **61.** $0.8t + 1.1 = 4.3$

62. $0.3v + 2.4 = 1.5$ **63.** $0.4x - 2.3 = 1.3$ **64.** $1.2t + 6.5 = 2.9$

65. $3.5y - 3.5 = 10.5$ **66.** $1.9x - 1.9 = -1.9$ **67.** $6m + 2m - 3 = 5$

68. $4a - 7a - 8 = 4$ **69.** $-2y + y - 3 = 6$ **70.** $x - 4x + 5 = 11$

For Exercises 71 to 73, suppose that a is positive and b is negative. Determine whether the value of x in the given equation *must be negative*, *must be positive*, or *could be either positive or negative*.

71. $bx - a = 12$ **72.** $bx + 5 = a$ **73.** $a - x = b$

OBJECTIVE B   *To solve application problems using formulas*

74. In the formula $T = UN + F$, T is the total cost, U is the cost per unit, N is the number of units produced, and F is the fixed cost. When you know the number of units produced, the fixed cost, and the total cost for one week, which of the following is the first step in solving the formula for the cost per unit?
  (i) Subtract the fixed cost from each side of the equation.
  (ii) Divide each side of the equation by the number of units produced.
  (iii) Subtract the number of units produced from each side of the equation.

Temperature Conversion For Exercises 75 and 76, use the relationship between Fahrenheit temperature and Celsius temperature, which is given by the formula $F = \frac{9}{5}C + 32$, where F is the Fahrenheit temperature and C is the Celsius temperature.

75. Find the Celsius temperature when the Fahrenheit temperature is $-40°$.

76. Find the Celsius temperature when the Fahrenheit temperature is $72°$. Round to the nearest tenth of a degree.

Physics For Exercises 77 and 78, use the formula $V = V_0 + 32t$, where V is the final velocity of a falling object, V_0 is the starting velocity of the falling object, and t is the time for the object to fall.

77. Find the time required for an object to increase in velocity from 8 ft/s to 472 ft/s.

78. Find the time required for an object to increase in velocity from 16 ft/s to 128 ft/s.

Manufacturing For Exercises 79 and 80, use the formula $T = UN + F$, where T is the total cost, U is the cost per unit, N is the number of units made, and F is the fixed cost.

79. Find the number of units made during a week in which the total cost was $25,000, the cost per unit was $8, and the fixed costs were $5000.

80. Find the cost per unit during a week in which the total cost was $80,000, the total number of units produced was 500, and the fixed costs were $15,000.

Compensation For Exercises 81 to 84, use the formula $M = SR + B$, where M is the monthly earnings, S is the total sales, R is the commission rate, and B is the base monthly salary.

81. A sales representative for an advertising firm earns a base monthly salary of $600 plus a 9% commission on total sales. Find the total sales during a month in which the representative earned $3480.

82. A sales executive earns a base monthly salary of $1000 plus a 5% commission on total sales. Find the total sales during a month in which the executive earned $2800.

83. Miguel earns a base monthly salary of $750. Find his commission rate during a month in which total sales were $42,000 and he earned $2640.

84. Tina earns a base monthly salary of $500. Find her commission rate during a month in which total sales were $42,500 and her earnings were $3560.

Critical Thinking

85. Does the sentence "Solve $3x + 4(x - 3)$" make sense? Why or why not?

86. Make up an equation of the form $ax + b = c$ that has -3 as its solution.

Projects or Group Activities

87. Explain in your own words the steps you would take to solve the equation $\frac{2}{3}x - 4 = 10$. State the property of real numbers or the property of equations that is used at each step.

✔ CHECK YOUR PROGRESS: CHAPTER 5

For Exercises 1 and 2, evaluate the expression $a = -5$, $b = 2$, and $c = -3$.

1. $3ab - 2c^2$

2. $4a - 4(b + 2c)$

For Exercises 3 to 6, solve.

3. $4 + x = -3$

4. $8 = 2y$

5. $-3z + 12 = 0$

6. $5 - 8x = 7$

For Exercises 7 to 10, simplify the expression.

7. $-3(-2x)$

8. $5(2z - 3)$

9. $7ab - 5b - 9ab + 6b$

10. $-3(4x - 7) + 6(2x + 3)$

For Exercises 11 and 12, name the Property of Addition or Multiplication illustrated by the equation.

11. $a + 3 = 3 + a$

12. $-4\left(-\frac{1}{4}\right) = 1$

13. Investments The value of an investment after one year is given by $P + rP$, where P is the amount invested and r is the annual simple interest rate. Find the value of an investment of $2000 after one year if the interest rate is 5%.

5.3 General Equations: Part II

OBJECTIVE A *To solve an equation of the form ax + b = cx + d*

When a variable occurs on each side of an equation, the Addition Properties are used to rewrite the equation so that all variable terms are on one side of the equation and all constant terms are on the other side of the equation. The Multiplication Properties are then used to simplify the equation to one of the form *variable = constant*.

HOW TO 1 Solve: $4x - 6 = 8 - 3x$

$$4x - 6 = 8 - 3x$$

- The goal is to write the equation in the form *variable = constant*.

$$4x + 3x - 6 = 8 - 3x + 3x$$
$$7x - 6 = 8 + 0$$
$$7x - 6 = 8$$

- Add $3x$ to each side of the equation. Then simplify (Addition Properties). Now only one variable term occurs in the equation.

$$7x - 6 + 6 = 8 + 6$$
$$7x + 0 = 14$$
$$7x = 14$$

- Add 6 to each side of the equation. Then simplify (Addition Properties). Now only one constant term occurs in the equation.

$$\frac{7x}{7} = \frac{14}{7}$$
$$1x = 2$$
$$x = 2$$

- Divide each side of the equation by the numerical coefficient of the variable term. Then simplify (Multiplication Properties).

The solution is 2.

- Write the solution.

Tips for Success

Always check the solution of an equation. For the equation at the right:

$$\frac{4x - 6 = 8 - 3x}{\begin{array}{c|c} 4(2) - 6 & 8 - 3(2) \\ 8 - 6 & 8 - 6 \\ 2 = 2 \end{array}}$$

The solution checks.

EXAMPLE 1

Solve: $\dfrac{2}{9}x - 3 = \dfrac{7}{9}x + 2$

Solution

$$\frac{2}{9}x - 3 = \frac{7}{9}x + 2$$

$$\frac{2}{9}x - \frac{7}{9}x - 3 = \frac{7}{9}x - \frac{7}{9}x + 2$$

- Subtract $\frac{7}{9}x$ from each side.

$$-\frac{5}{9}x - 3 = 2$$

$$-\frac{5}{9}x - 3 + 3 = 2 + 3$$

- Add 3 to each side.

$$-\frac{5}{9}x = 5$$

$$\left(-\frac{9}{5}\right)\left(-\frac{5}{9}\right)x = \left(-\frac{9}{5}\right)5$$

- Multiply each side by $-\frac{9}{5}$.

$$x = -9$$

The solution is -9.

YOU TRY IT 1

Solve: $\dfrac{1}{5}x - 2 = \dfrac{2}{5}x + 4$

Your solution

Solution on p. S27

OBJECTIVE B   *To solve an equation containing parentheses*

When an equation contains parentheses, one of the steps involved in solving the equation makes use of the Distributive Property.

$$a(b + c) = ab + ac$$

The Distributive Property is used to rewrite a variable expression without parentheses.

HOW TO 2   Solve: $4(3 + x) - 2 = 2(x - 4)$

$4(3 + x) - 2 = 2(x - 4)$	• The goal is to write the equation in the form *variable = constant*.
$12 + 4x - 2 = 2x - 8$	• Use the Distributive Property to rewrite the equation without parentheses.
$10 + 4x = 2x - 8$	• Combine like terms.
$10 + 4x - 2x = 2x - 2x - 8$	• Use the Addition Property of Equations.
$10 + 2x = -8$	Subtract $2x$ from each side of the equation.
$10 - 10 + 2x = -8 - 10$	• Use the Addition Property of Equations.
$2x = -18$	Subtract 10 from each side of the equation.
$\dfrac{2x}{2} = \dfrac{-18}{2}$	• Use the Multiplication Property of Equations. Divide each side of the equation by the
$x = -9$	numerical coefficient of the variable term.

Check:

$$
\begin{array}{c|c}
4(3 + x) - 2 & 2(x - 4) \\
\hline
4[3 + (-9)] - 2 & 2(-9 - 4) \\
4(-6) - 2 & 2(-13) \\
-24 - 2 & -26 \\
-26 = & -26
\end{array}
$$

• Check the solution.

• A true equation

The solution is -9.

The solution to HOW TO 2 illustrates the steps involved in solving first-degree equations.

Steps in Solving General First-Degree Equations

1. Use the Distributive Property to remove parentheses.
2. Combine like terms on each side of the equation.
3. Use the Addition Property of Equations to rewrite the equation with only one variable term.
4. Use the Addition Property of Equations to rewrite the equation with only one constant term.
5. Use the Multiplication Property of Equations to rewrite the equation so that the coefficient of the variable term is 1.

EXAMPLE 2

Solve: $3(x + 2) - x = 11$

Solution

$3(x + 2) - x = 11$

$3x + 6 - x = 11$ • Use the Distributive Property.

$2x + 6 = 11$ • Combine like terms on the left side.

$2x + 6 - 6 = 11 - 6$ • Use the Addition Property of Equations. Subtract 6 from each side.

$2x = 5$ • Combine like terms on each side.

$\dfrac{2x}{2} = \dfrac{5}{2}$ • Use the Multiplication Property. Divide both sides by 2.

$x = \dfrac{5}{2}$ • The solution checks.

The solution is $\dfrac{5}{2}$.

YOU TRY IT 2

Solve: $4(x - 1) - x = 5$

Your solution

EXAMPLE 3

Solve: $5x - 2(x - 3) = 6(x - 2)$

Solution

$5x - 2(x - 3) = 6(x - 2)$

$5x - 2x + 6 = 6x - 12$ • Distributive Property

$3x + 6 = 6x - 12$ • Combine like terms.

$3x - 6x + 6 = 6x - 6x - 12$ • Subtract $6x$ from each side.

$-3x + 6 = -12$ • Combine like terms.

$-3x + 6 - 6 = -12 - 6$ • Subtract 6 from each side.

$-3x = -18$ • Combine like terms.

$\dfrac{-3x}{-3} = \dfrac{-18}{-3}$ • Divide both sides by -3.

$x = 6$ • The solution checks.

The solution is 6.

YOU TRY IT 3

Solve: $2x - 7(3x + 1) = 5(5 - 3x)$

Your solution

Solutions on p. S27

5.3 EXERCISES

✔ Concept Check

1. To solve the equation $3x + 4 = 5x - 7$, Karl began by subtracting $5x$ from each side of the equation, and Maria began by subtracting 4 from each side of the equation. Was the first step taken by each student correct? If not, which student began correctly?

2. Here are the first several steps that a student used to solve the equation $3(2x - 6) + 5 = 2x - 3$. Are all of these steps correct? If not, which equation contains an error? What is the correct equation?
$$3(2x - 6) + 5 = 2x - 3$$
$$6x - 6 + 5 = 2x - 3$$
$$6x - 1 = 2x - 3$$
$$6x - 2x - 1 = 2x - 2x - 3$$
$$4x - 1 = -3$$

OBJECTIVE A   *To solve an equation of the form $ax + b = cx + d$*

For Exercises 3 to 56, solve.

3. $6x + 3 = 2x + 5$

4. $7x + 1 = x + 19$

5. $3x + 3 = 2x + 2$

6. $6x + 3 = 3x + 6$

7. $5x + 4 = x - 12$

8. $3x - 12 = x - 8$

9. $7b - 2 = 3b - 6$

10. $2d - 9 = d - 8$

11. $9n - 4 = 5n - 20$

12. $8x - 7 = 5x + 8$

13. $2x + 1 = 16 - 3x$

14. $3x + 2 = -23 - 2x$

15. $5x - 2 = -10 - 3x$

16. $4x - 3 = 7 - x$

17. $2x + 7 = 4x + 3$

18. $7m - 6 = 10m - 15$

19. $c + 4 = 6c - 11$

20. $t - 6 = 4t - 21$

21. $3x - 7 = x - 7$

22. $2x + 6 = 7x + 6$

23. $3 - 4x = 5 - 3x$

24. $6 - 2x = 9 - x$

25. $7 + 3x = 9 + 5x$

26. $12 + 5x = 9 - 3x$

27. $5 + 2y = 7 + 5y$

28. $9 + z = 2 + 3z$

29. $8 - 5w = 4 - 6w$

30. $9 - 4x = 11 - 5x$

31. $6x + 1 = 3x + 2$

32. $7x + 5 = 4x + 7$

33. $5x + 8 = x + 5$

34. $9x + 1 = 3x - 4$

35. $2x - 3 = 6x - 4$

36. $4 - 3x = 4 - 5x$

37. $6 - 3x = 6 - 5x$

38. $2x + 7 = 4x - 3$

39. $6x - 2 = 2x - 9$

40. $4x - 7 = -3x + 2$

41. $6x - 3 = -5x + 8$

42. $7y - 5 = 3y + 9$

43. $-6t - 2 = -8t - 4$

44. $-7w + 2 = 3w - 8$

45. $-3 - 4x = 7 - 2x$

46. $-8 + 5x = 8 + 6x$

47. $3 - 7x = -2 + 5x$

48. $3x - 2 = 7 - 5x$

49. $5x + 8 = 4 - 2x$

50. $4 - 3x = 6x - 8$

51. $12z - 9 = 3z + 12$

52. $4c + 13 = -6c + 9$

53. $\dfrac{5}{7}m - 3 = \dfrac{2}{7}m + 6$

54. $\dfrac{4}{5}x - 1 = \dfrac{1}{5}x + 5$

55. $\dfrac{3}{7}x + 5 = \dfrac{5}{7}x - 1$

56. $\dfrac{3}{4}x + 2 = \dfrac{1}{4}x - 9$

57. If a is a negative number, will solving the equation $-8x = a - 6x$ for x result in a positive solution or a negative solution?

58. If a is a positive number, will solving the equation $9x - a = 13x$ for x result in a positive solution or a negative solution?

OBJECTIVE B *To solve an equation containing parentheses*

59. Which of the following equations is equivalent to $9 - 2(4y - 1) = 6$?
   (i) $9 - 8y - 1 = 6$ **(ii)** $7(4y - 1) = 6$
   (iii) $9 - 8y - 2 = 6$ **(iv)** $9 - 8y + 2 = 6$

60. Which of the following equations is equivalent to $5x - 3(4x + 2) = 7(x + 3)$?
   (i) $2x(4x + 2) = 7x + 21$ **(ii)** $5x - 12x - 6 = 7x + 21$
   (iii) $5x - 12x - 6 = 7x + 3$ **(iv)** $5x(-12x - 6) = 7x + 21$

For Exercises 61 to 106, solve.

61. $6x + 2(x - 1) = 14$

62. $3x + 2(x + 4) = 13$

63. $-3 + 4(x + 3) = 5$

64. $8b - 3(b - 5) = 30$

65. $6 - 2(d + 4) = 6$

66. $5 - 3(n + 2) = 8$

67. $5 + 7(x + 3) = 20$

68. $6 - 3(x - 4) = 12$

69. $2x + 3(x - 5) = 10$

70. $3x - 4(x + 3) = 9$

71. $3(x - 4) + 2x = 3$

72. $4 + 3(x - 9) = -12$

73. $2x - 3(x - 4) = 12$

74. $4x - 2(x - 5) = 10$

75. $2x + 3(x + 4) = 7$

76. $3(x + 2) + 7 = 12$

77. $3(x - 2) + 5 = 5$

78. $4(x - 5) + 7 = 7$

79. $3y + 7(y - 2) = 5$

80. $-3z - 3(z - 3) = 3$

81. $4b - 2(b + 9) = 8$

82. $3x - 6(x - 3) = 9$

83. $3x + 5(x - 2) = 10$

84. $3x - 5(x - 1) = -5$

85. $3x + 4(x + 2) = 2(x + 9)$

86. $5x + 3(x + 4) = 4(x + 2)$

87. $2d - 3(d - 4) = 2(d + 6)$

88. $3t - 4(t - 1) = 3(t - 2)$

89. $7 - 2(x - 3) = 3(x - 1)$

90. $4 - 3(x + 2) = 2(x - 4)$

91. $6x - 2(x - 3) = 11(x - 2)$

92. $9x - 5(x - 3) = 5(x + 4)$

93. $6c - 3(c + 1) = 5(c + 2)$

94. $2w - 7(w - 2) = 3(w - 4)$

95. $7 - (x + 1) = 3(x + 3)$

96. $12 + 2(x - 9) = 3(x - 12)$

97. $2x - 3(x + 4) = 2(x - 5)$

98. $3x + 2(x - 7) = 7(x - 1)$

99. $x + 5(x - 4) = 3(x - 8) - 5$

100. $2x - 2(x - 1) = 3(x - 2) + 7$

101. $9b - 3(b - 4) = 13 + 2(b - 3)$

102. $3y - 4(y - 2) = 15 - 3(y - 2)$

103. $3(x - 4) + 3x = 7 - 2(x - 1)$

104. $2(x - 6) + 7x = 5 - 3(x - 2)$

105. $3.67x - 5.3(x - 1.932) = 6.9959$

106. $4.06x + 4.7(x + 3.22) = 1.775$

Critical Thinking

107. If $2x - 2 = 4x + 6$, what is the value of $3x^2$?

108. If $3 + 2(4a - 3) = 4$ and $4 - 3(2 - 3b) = 11$, which is larger, a or b?

Projects or Group Activities

109. ◣ The equation $x = x + 1$ has no solution, whereas the solution of the equation $2x + 3 = 3$ is zero. Is there a difference between no solution and a solution of zero? Explain.

5.4 Equations of the Form $ax + b = c$

OBJECTIVE A   *To solve equations of the form $ax + b = c$*

To solve an equation such as $3w - 5 = 16$, both the Addition and Multiplication Properties of Equations are used.

$$3w - 5 = 16$$

First add the opposite of the constant term -5 to each side of the equation.

$$3w - 5 + 5 = 16 + 5$$
$$3w = 21$$

Divide each side of the equation by the coefficient of w.

$$\frac{3w}{3} = \frac{21}{3}$$

The equation is in the form *variable = constant*.

$$w = 7$$

Check the solution.

Check:
$$\begin{array}{c|c} 3w - 5 = 16 \\ \hline 3(7) - 5 & 16 \\ 21 - 5 & 16 \\ 16 = 16 \end{array}$$

> **Take Note**
> Note that the Order of Operations Agreement applies when evaluating the expression $3(7) - 5$.

7 checks as the solution.

The solution is 7.

> **Tips for Success**
> When we suggest that you check a solution, substitute the solution into the *original* equation.

HOW TO 1   Solve: $8 = 4 - \frac{2}{3}x$

The variable is on the right side of the equation. Work toward the goal of *constant = variable*.

$$8 = 4 - \frac{2}{3}x$$

Subtract 4 from each side of the equation.

$$8 - 4 = 4 - 4 - \frac{2}{3}x$$

$$4 = -\frac{2}{3}x$$

> **Take Note**
> Always check the solution.
> Check:
> $$\begin{array}{c|c} 8 = 4 - \frac{2}{3}x \\ \hline 8 & 4 - \frac{2}{3}(-6) \\ 8 & 4 + 4 \\ 8 = 8 \end{array}$$

Multiply each side of the equation by $-\frac{3}{2}$.

$$-\frac{3}{2} \cdot 4 = \left(-\frac{3}{2}\right)\left(-\frac{2}{3}x\right)$$

The equation is in the form *constant = variable*.

$$-6 = x$$

You should check the solution.

The solution is -6.

EXAMPLE 1

Solve: $4m - 7 + m = 8$

Solution

$$4m - 7 + m = 8$$
$$5m - 7 = 8$$
$$5m - 7 + 7 = 8 + 7$$
$$5m = 15$$
$$m = 3$$

- Combine like terms.
- Add 7 to each side.

- Divide each side by 5.

The solution is 3.

YOU TRY IT 1

Solve: $5v + 3 - 9v = 9$

Your solution

Solution on p. S17

OBJECTIVE B *To solve application problems using formulas*

Some application problems can be solved by using a known formula. Here is an example.

You can afford a maximum monthly car payment of $250. Find the maximum loan amount you can afford. Use the formula $P = 0.02076L$, where P is the amount of a car payment on a 60-month loan at a 9% interest rate and L is the amount of the loan.

Strategy   To find the maximum loan amount, replace the variable P in the formula by its value (250) and solve for L.

Solution

$$P = 0.02076L$$

$$250 = 0.02076L$$ • Replace P by 250.

$$\frac{250}{0.02076} = \frac{0.02076L}{0.02076}$$ • Divide each side of the equation by 0.02076.

$$12{,}042.39 \approx L$$

The maximum loan amount you can afford is $12,042.39.

Integrating Technology

To solve for L, use your calculator: 250 ÷ 0.02076. Then round the answer to the nearest cent.

EXAMPLE 2

An accountant uses the straight-line depreciation equation $V = C - 4500t$ to determine the value V, after t years, of a company car that originally cost C dollars. Use this formula to determine in how many years a company car that originally cost $39,000 will be worth $25,500.

Strategy

To find the number of years, replace each of the variables by its value and solve for t. $V = 25{,}500$, $C = 39{,}000$

Solution

$$V = C - 4500t$$
$$25{,}500 = 39{,}000 - 4500t$$
$$25{,}500 - 39{,}000 = 39{,}000 - 39{,}000 - 4500t$$
$$-13{,}500 = -4500t$$
$$\frac{-13{,}500}{-4500} = \frac{-4500t}{-4500}$$
$$3 = t$$

In 3 years, the company car will have a value of $25,500.

YOU TRY IT 2

The pressure P, in pounds per square inch, at a certain depth in the ocean is approximated by the equation $P = 15 + \frac{1}{2}D$, where D is the depth in feet. Use this formula to find the depth when the pressure is 45 pounds per square inch.

Your strategy

Your solution

Solution on p. S17

5.4 EXERCISES

✔ Concept Check

1. The first step in solving the equation $5x - 3 = 27$ is to add _____ to each side of the equation. The second step is to divide each side of the equation by _____.

2. The first step in solving the equation $4 + 7x = 25$ is to subtract _____ from each side of the equation. The second step is to divide each side of the equation by _____.

OBJECTIVE A   *To solve equations of the form $ax + b = c$*

Solve.

3. $5y + 1 = 11$

4. $3x + 5 = 26$

5. $2z - 9 = 11$

6. $7p - 2 = 26$

7. $12 = 2 + 5a$

8. $29 = 1 + 7v$

9. $-5y + 8 = 13$

10. $-7p + 6 = -8$

11. $-12a - 1 = 23$

12. $-15y - 7 = 38$

13. $10 - c = 14$

14. $3 - x = 1$

15. $4 - 3x = -5$

16. $8 - 5x = -12$

17. $-33 = 3 - 4z$

18. $-41 = 7 - 8v$

19. $-4t + 16 = 0$

20. $-6p - 72 = 0$

21. $5a + 9 = 12$

22. $7c + 5 = 20$

23. $2t - 5 = 2$

24. $3v - 1 = 4$

25. $8x + 1 = 7$

26. $6y + 5 = 8$

27. $4z - 5 = 1$

28. $8 = 5 + 6p$

29. $25 = 11 + 8v$

30. $-4 = 11 + 6z$

31. $-3 = 7 + 4y$

32. $9w - 4 = 17$

33. $8a - 5 = 31$

34. $5 - 8x = 5$

35. $7 - 12y = 7$

36. $-3 - 8z = 11$

37. $-9 - 12y = 5$

38. $5n - \dfrac{2}{9} = \dfrac{43}{9}$

39. $6z - \dfrac{1}{3} = \dfrac{5}{3}$

40. $7y - \dfrac{2}{5} = \dfrac{12}{5}$

41. $3p - \dfrac{5}{8} = \dfrac{19}{8}$

42. $\dfrac{3}{4}x - 1 = 2$

43. $\dfrac{4}{5}y + 3 = 11$

44. $\dfrac{5t}{6} + 4 = -1$

45. $\dfrac{3v}{7} - 2 = 10$

46. $\dfrac{2a}{5} - 5 = 7$

47. $\dfrac{4z}{9} + 23 = 3$

48. $\dfrac{x}{3} + 6 = 1$

49. $\dfrac{y}{4} + 5 = 2$

50. $17 = 20 + \dfrac{3}{4}x$

51. $\dfrac{2}{5}y - 3 = 1$

52. $\dfrac{7}{3}v + 2 = 8$

53. $5 - \dfrac{7}{8}y = 2$

54. $3 - \dfrac{5}{2}z = 6$

55. $\dfrac{3}{5}y + \dfrac{1}{4} = \dfrac{3}{4}$

56. $\dfrac{5}{6}x - \dfrac{2}{3} = \dfrac{5}{3}$

57. $\dfrac{3}{5} = \dfrac{2}{7}t + \dfrac{1}{5}$

58. $\dfrac{10}{3} = \dfrac{9}{5}w - \dfrac{2}{3}$

59. $\dfrac{z}{3} - \dfrac{1}{2} = \dfrac{1}{4}$

60. $\dfrac{a}{6} + \dfrac{1}{4} = \dfrac{3}{8}$

61. $5.6t - 5.1 = 1.06$

62. $7.2 + 5.2z = 8.76$

63. $6.2 - 3.3t = -12.94$

64. $2.4 - 4.8v = 13.92$

65. $6c - 2 - 3c = 10$

66. $12t + 6 + 3t = 16$

67. $4y + 5 - 12y = -3$

68. $7m - 15 - 10m = 6$

69. $17 = 12p - 5 - 6p$

70. $3 = 6n + 23 - 10n$

Complete Exercises 71 and 72 without actually finding the solutions of the equations.

71. Is the solution of the equation $15x + 73 = -347$ positive or negative?

72. Is the solution of the equation $17 = 25 - 40a$ positive or negative?

OBJECTIVE B *To solve application problems using formulas*

Depreciation To determine the depreciated value of an X-ray machine, an accountant uses the formula $V = C - 5500t$, where V is the depreciated value of the machine in t years and C is the original cost. Use this formula for Exercises 73 and 74.

73. An X-ray machine originally cost $70,000. In how many years will the depreciated value be $48,000?

74. An X-ray machine originally cost $63,000. In how many years will the depreciated value be $47,500? Round to the nearest tenth.

● Champion Trees American Forests is an organization that maintains the National Register of Big Trees, a listing of the largest trees in the United States. The formula used to award points to a tree is $P = c + h + \frac{1}{4}s$, where P is the point total for a tree with a circumference of c inches, a height of h feet, and an average crown spread of s feet. Use this formula for Exercises 75 and 76. (*Source:* www.amfor.org)

75. Find the average crown spread of the baldcypress described in the article at the right.

76. One of the smallest trees in the United States is a Florida Crossopetalum in the Key Largo Hammocks State Botanical Site. This tree stands 11 ft tall, has a circumference of just 4.8 in., and scores 16.55 points using American Forests' formula. Find the tree's average crown spread. (*Source:* www.championtrees.org)

● Nutrition The formula $C = 9f + 4p + 4c$ gives the number of calories C in a serving of food that contains f grams of fat, p grams of protein, and c grams of carbohydrate. Use this formula for Exercises 77 and 78. (*Source:* www.nutristrategy.com)

77. Find the number of grams of protein in an 8-ounce serving of vanilla yogurt that contains 174 calories, 2 g of fat, and 30 g of carbohydrate.

78. Find the number of grams of fat in a serving of granola that contains 215 calories, 42 g of carbohydrate, and 5 g of protein.

Physics The distance s, in feet, that an object will fall in t seconds is given by the formula $s = 16t^2 + vt$, where v is the initial velocity of the object in feet per second. Use this equation for Exercises 79 and 80.

79. Find the initial velocity of an object that falls 80 ft in 2 s.

80. Find the initial velocity of an object that falls 144 ft in 3 s.

In the NEWS!

The Senator Is a Champion

Baldcypress trees are among the most ancient of North American trees. The 3500-year-old baldcypress known as the Senator was located in Big Tree Park, Longwood, and was the Florida Champion specimen of the species. With a circumference of 425 in. and a height of 118 ft, this king of the swamp forest earned a total of $557\frac{1}{4}$ points under the point system used for the National Register of Big Trees.
Source: www.championtrees.org

The Senator at Big Tree Park

Physics   Black ice is an ice covering on roads that is especially difficult to see and therefore extremely dangerous for motorists. The distance a car traveling 30 mph will slide after its brakes are applied is related to the outside air temperature by the formula $C = \frac{1}{4}D - 45$, where C is the Celsius temperature and D is the distance in feet the car will slide. Use this formula for Exercises 81 and 82.

81. Determine the distance a car will slide on black ice when the outside air temperature is $-3°C$.

82. Determine the distance a car will slide on black ice when the outside air temperature is $-11°C$.

83. 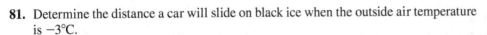 Which of the following equations is equivalent to the formula $V = C - 5500t$?

(i) $V - C = 5500t$ (ii) $V - C = -5500t$ (iii) $C - V = -5500t$ (iv) $C + V = -5500t$

Critical Thinking

84. Solve $3x + 4y = 13$ when $y = -2$.

85. Solve $2x - 3y = 8$ when $y = 0$.

86. Solve $-4x + 3y = 9$ when $x = 0$.

87. Solve $5x - 2y = -3$ when $x = -3$.

88. If $2x - 3 = 7$, evaluate $3x + 4$.

89. If $3x + 5 = -4$, evaluate $2x - 5$.

90. If $4 - 5x = -1$, evaluate $x^2 - 3x + 1$.

91. If $2 - 3x = 11$, evaluate $x^2 + 2x - 3$.

92. Solve: $x \div 28 = 1481$ remainder 25

93. Does the sentence "Solve $3x + 4(x - 3)$" make sense? Why or why not?

Projects or Group Activities

94. Make up an equation of the form $ax + b = c$ that has 5 as its solution.

95. Make up an equation of the form $ax + b = c$ that has -3 as its solution.

96. Explain in your own words the steps you would take to solve the equation $\frac{2}{3}x - 4 = 10$. State the property of real numbers or the property of equations that is used at each step.

5.5

Translating Verbal Expressions into Mathematical Expressions

OBJECTIVE A

To translate a verbal expression into a mathematical expression given the variable

One of the major skills required in applied mathematics is the ability to translate a verbal expression into a mathematical expression. Doing so requires recognizing the verbal phrases that translate into mathematical operations. Following is a partial list of the verbal phrases used to indicate the different mathematical operations.

Addition	more than	5 more than x	$x + 5$
	the sum of	the sum of w and 3	$w + 3$
	the total of	the total of 6 and z	$6 + z$
	increased by	x increased by 7	$x + 7$
Subtraction	less than	5 less than y	$y - 5$
	the difference between	the difference between w and 3	$w - 3$
	decreased by	8 decreased by a	$8 - a$
Multiplication	times	3 times c	$3c$
	the product of	the product of 4 and t	$4t$
	of	two-thirds of v	$\frac{2}{3}v$
	twice	twice d	$2d$
Division	divided by	n divided by 3	$\frac{n}{3}$
	the quotient of	the quotient of z and 4	$\frac{z}{4}$
	the ratio of	the ratio of s to 6	$\frac{s}{6}$

Translating phrases that contain the words *sum, difference, product,* and *quotient* can be challenging. In the examples at the right, note where the operation symbol is placed.

the *sum* of x and y $x + y$

the *difference* between x and y $x - y$

the *product* of x and y $x \cdot y$

the *quotient* of x and y $\dfrac{x}{y}$

Note where the fraction bar is placed when translating the word *ratio*.

the *ratio* of x to y $\dfrac{x}{y}$

HOW TO 1 Translate "the quotient of n and the sum of n and 6" into a mathematical expression.

the *quotient* of n and the *sum* of n and 6 $\dfrac{n}{n + 6}$

EXAMPLE 1

Translate "the sum of 5 and the product of 4 and n" into a mathematical expression.

Solution

$5 + 4n$

YOU TRY IT 1

Translate "the difference between 8 and twice t" into a mathematical expression.

Your solution

EXAMPLE 2

Translate "the product of 3 and the difference between z and 4" into a mathematical expression.

Solution

$3(z - 4)$

YOU TRY IT 2

Translate "the quotient of 5 and the product of 7 and x" into a mathematical expression.

Your solution

Solutions on p. S27

OBJECTIVE B

To translate a verbal expression into a mathematical expression by assigning the variable

In most applications that involve translating phrases into mathematical expressions, the variable to be used is not given. To translate these phrases, we must assign a variable to the unknown quantity before writing the mathematical expression.

HOW TO 2   Translate "the difference between seven and twice a number" into a mathematical expression.

The difference between seven and twice a number

• Identify the phrases that indicate the mathematical operations.

The unknown number: n

• Assign a variable to one of the unknown quantities.

Twice the number: $2n$

• Use the assigned variable to write an expression for any other unknown quantity.

$7 - 2n$

• Use the identified operations to write the mathematical expression.

EXAMPLE 3

Translate "the total of a number and the square of the number" into a mathematical expression.

Solution

The *total* of a number and the *square* of the number

The unknown number: x
The square of the number: x^2

$x + x^2$

YOU TRY IT 3

Translate "the product of a number and one-half of the number" into a mathematical expression.

Your solution

Solution on p. S27

5.5 EXERCISES

✔ Concept Check

1. Does the phrase "two times x plus three" translate into the same variable expression as the phrase "two times the sum of x and three?"

2. Does the phrase "the difference between three times y and three" translate into the same variable expression as the phrase "three less than three times y?"

OBJECTIVE A   *To translate a verbal expression into a mathematical expression given the variable*

For Exercises 3 to 22, translate into a mathematical expression.

3. 9 less than y

4. w divided by 7

5. z increased by 3

6. the product of -2 and x

7. the sum of two-thirds of n and n

8. the difference between the square of r and r

9. the quotient of m and the difference between m and 3

10. v increased by twice v

11. the product of 9 and 4 more than x

12. the difference between n and the product of 5 and n

13. x decreased by the quotient of x and 2

14. the product of c and one-fourth of c

15. the quotient of 3 less than z and z

16. the product of y and the sum of y and 4

17. 2 times the sum of t and 6

18. the quotient of r and the difference between 8 and r

19. x divided by the total of 9 and x

20. the sum of z and the product of 6 and z

21. 3 times the sum of b and 6

22. the ratio of w to the sum of w and 8

For Exercises 23 and 24, translate the mathematical expression into a verbal phrase.
Note: Answers will vary.

23. a. $2x + 3$

b. $2(x + 3)$

24. a. $\dfrac{2x}{7}$

b. $\dfrac{2 + x}{7}$

OBJECTIVE B *To translate a verbal expression into a mathematical expression by assigning the variable*

For Exercises 25 to 44, translate into a mathematical expression.

25. the square of a number

26. five less than some number

27. a number divided by twenty

28. the difference between a number and twelve

29. four times some number

30. the quotient of five and a number

31. three-fourths of a number

32. the sum of a number and seven

33. four increased by some number

34. the ratio of a number to nine

35. the difference between five times a number and the number

36. six less than the total of three and a number

37. the product of a number and two more than the number

38. the quotient of six and the sum of nine and a number

39. seven times the total of a number and eight

40. the difference between ten and the quotient of a number and two

41. the square of a number plus the product of three and the number

42. a number decreased by the product of five and the number

43. the sum of three more than a number and one-half of the number

44. eight more than twice the sum of a number and seven

For Exercises 45 and 46, determine whether the expression $4n^2 - 5$ is a correct translation of the given phrase.

45. five less than the square of the product of four and a number

46. the difference between five and the product of four and the square of a number

Critical Thinking

For Exercises 47 to 50, translate the phrase into a variable expression.

47. the quotient of the sum of a and 3 and 4

48. the sum of the product of 3 times x and y and negative 7

49. the difference between the quotient of 4 times c and 7 and 9

50. the product of the sum of 3 less than 4 times x plus y and 6

Projects or Group Activities

51. Chemistry The chemical formula for water is H_2O. This formula means that there are two hydrogen atoms and one oxygen atom in each molecule of water. If x represents the number of oxygen atoms in a glass of pure water, express the number of hydrogen atoms in the glass of water in terms of the number of oxygen atoms.

52. Chemistry The chemical formula for one molecule of glucose (sugar) is $C_6H_{12}O_6$, where C is carbon, H is hydrogen, and O is oxygen. The subscripts 6, 12, and 6 tell the numbers of atoms of each element that occur in one molecule of glucose. If x represents the number of hydrogen atoms in a sample of pure sugar, express the number of carbon atoms and the number of oxygen atoms in the sample in terms of x.

5.6 Translating Sentences into Equations and Solving

OBJECTIVE A *To translate a sentence into an equation and solve*

 Point of Interest

Number problems similar to the one on this page have appeared in textbooks for hundreds of years. Here is one from a first-century Chinese textbook: "When a number is divided by 3, the remainder is 2; when it is divided by 5, the remainder is 3; when it is divided by 7, the remainder is 2. Find the number." There are actually infinitely many solutions to this problem. See whether you can find one of them.

An equation states that two mathematical expressions are equal. Therefore, to translate a sentence into an equation, we must recognize the words or phrases that mean "equals." Some of these phrases are

$$\left.\begin{array}{l} \text{equals} \\ \text{is} \\ \text{is equal to} \\ \text{amounts to} \\ \text{represents} \end{array}\right\} \text{translate to } =$$

Once the sentence is translated into an equation, the equation can be simplified to one of the form *variable = constant*, and the solution can be found.

HOW TO 1 Translate "three more than twice a number is seventeen" into an equation and solve.

The unknown number: n

- Assign a variable to the unknown quantity.

| Three more than twice a number | is | seventeen |

- Find two verbal expressions for the same value.

$$\begin{aligned} 2n + 3 &= 17 \\ 2n + 3 - 3 &= 17 - 3 \\ 2n &= 14 \\ \frac{2n}{2} &= \frac{14}{2} \\ n &= 7 \end{aligned}$$

- Write a mathematical expression for each verbal expression. Write the equals sign. Solve the resulting equation.

The number is 7.

EXAMPLE 1

Translate "a number decreased by six equals fifteen" into an equation and solve.

Solution

The unknown number: x

| A number decreased by six | equals | fifteen |

$$\begin{aligned} x - 6 &= 15 \\ x - 6 + 6 &= 15 + 6 \\ x &= 21 \end{aligned}$$

The number is 21.

YOU TRY IT 1

Translate "a number increased by four equals twelve" into an equation and solve.

Your solution

Solution on p. S27

EXAMPLE 2

The quotient of a number and six is five. Find the number.

Solution

The unknown number: z

The quotient of a number and six	is	five

$$\frac{z}{6} = 5$$
$$6 \cdot \frac{z}{6} = 6 \cdot 5$$
$$z = 30$$

The number is 30.

YOU TRY IT 2

The product of two and a number is ten. Find the number.

Your solution

EXAMPLE 3

Eight decreased by twice a number is four. Find the number.

Solution

The unknown number: t

Eight decreased by twice a number	is	four

$$8 - 2t = 4$$
$$8 - 8 - 2t = 4 - 8$$
$$-2t = -4$$
$$\frac{-2t}{-2} = \frac{-4}{-2}$$
$$t = 2$$

The number is 2.

YOU TRY IT 3

The sum of three times a number and six equals four. Find the number.

Your solution

EXAMPLE 4

Three less than the ratio of a number to seven is one. Find the number.

Solution

The unknown number: x

Three less than the ratio of a number to seven	is	one

$$\frac{x}{7} - 3 = 1$$
$$\frac{x}{7} - 3 + 3 = 1 + 3$$
$$\frac{x}{7} = 4$$
$$7 \cdot \frac{x}{7} = 7 \cdot 4$$
$$x = 28$$

The number is 28.

YOU TRY IT 4

Three more than one-half of a number is nine. Find the number.

Your solution

Solutions on pp. S27–S28

OBJECTIVE B *To solve application problems*

EXAMPLE 5

The cost of a portable DVD player with carrying case is $187. This amount is $38 more than the cost of the DVD player without the carrying case. Find the cost of the DVD player without the carrying case.

Strategy

To find the cost of the DVD player without the carrying case, write and solve an equation using C to represent the cost of the DVD player without the carrying case.

Solution

| $187 | is | $38 more than the cost of the DVD player without the carrying case |

$$187 = C + 38$$
$$187 - 38 = C + 38 - 38$$
$$149 = C$$

The cost of the DVD player without the carrying case is $149.

YOU TRY IT 5

The sale price of a baseball jersey is $38.95. This amount is $11 less than the regular price. Find the regular price.

Your strategy

Your solution

EXAMPLE 6

By purchasing a fleet of cars, a company receives a discount of $1972 on each car purchased. This amount is 8% of the regular price. Find the regular price.

Strategy

To find the regular price, write and solve an equation using P to represent the regular price of each car.

Solution

| $1972 | is | 8% of the regular price |

$$1972 = 0.08P$$
$$\frac{1972}{0.08} = \frac{0.08P}{0.08}$$
$$24{,}650 = P$$

The regular price is $24,650.

YOU TRY IT 6

At a certain speed, the engine rpm (revolutions per minute) of a car in fourth gear is 2500. This is two-thirds of the engine rpm in third gear. Find the engine rpm when the engine is in third gear.

Your strategy

Your solution

Solutions on p. S28

EXAMPLE 7

Plumber Ron Sierra charged $1775 for plumbing repairs in an office building. This charge included $180 for parts and $55 per hour for labor. Find the number of hours Ron worked in the office building.

Strategy

To find the number of hours worked, write and solve an equation using N to represent the number of hours worked.

Solution

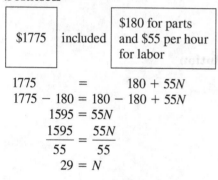

$$1775 = 180 + 55N$$
$$1775 - 180 = 180 - 180 + 55N$$
$$1595 = 55N$$
$$\frac{1595}{55} = \frac{55N}{55}$$
$$29 = N$$

Ron worked 29 h.

EXAMPLE 8

Tim Fong paid $256 in state income tax last month. This amount is $5 more than 8% of his monthly salary. Find Tim's monthly salary.

Strategy

To find Tim's monthly salary, write and solve an equation using S to represent his monthly salary.

Solution

$256	is	$5 more than 8% of the monthly salary

$$256 = 0.08S + 5$$
$$256 - 5 = 0.08S + 5 - 5$$
$$251 = 0.08S$$
$$\frac{251}{0.08} = \frac{0.08S}{0.08}$$
$$3137.50 = S$$

Tim's monthly salary is $3137.50.

YOU TRY IT 7

The total cost to make a model Z100 television is $492. The cost includes $100 for materials plus $24.50 per hour for labor. How many hours of labor are required to make a model Z100 television?

Your strategy

Your solution

YOU TRY IT 8

Natalie Adams earned $2500 last month for temporary work. This amount was the sum of a base monthly salary of $800 and an 8% commission on total sales. Find Natalie's total sales for the month.

Your strategy

Your solution

Solutions on p. S28

5.6 EXERCISES

✔ Concept Check

1. Does the phrase "four times the sum of x and three" translate into an equation? If so, identify the word that translates as "equals."

2. Does the phrase "the difference between three times a number and seven is four more than the number" translate into an equation? If so, identify the word that translates as "equals."

OBJECTIVE A   *To translate a sentence into an equation and solve*

For Exercises 3 to 28, write an equation and solve.

3. The sum of a number and seven is twelve. Find the number.

4. A number decreased by seven is five. Find the number.

5. The product of three and a number is eighteen. Find the number.

6. The quotient of a number and three is one. Find the number.

7. Five more than a number is three. Find the number.

8. A number divided by four is six. Find the number.

9. Six times a number is fourteen. Find the number.

10. Seven less than a number is three. Find the number.

11. Five-sixths of a number is fifteen. Find the number.

12. The total of twenty and a number is five. Find the number.

13. The sum of three times a number and four is eight. Find the number.

14. The sum of one-third of a number and seven is twelve. Find the number.

15. Seven less than one-fourth of a number is nine. Find the number.

16. The total of a number divided by four and nine is two. Find the number.

17. The ratio of a number to nine is fourteen. Find the number.

18. Five increased by the product of five and a number is equal to 30. Find the number.

19. Six less than the quotient of a number and four is equal to negative two. Find the number.

20. The product of a number plus three and two is eight. Find the number.

21. The difference between seven and twice a number is thirteen. Find the number.

22. Five more than the product of three and a number is eight. Find the number.

23. Nine decreased by the quotient of a number and two is five. Find the number.

24. The total of ten times a number and seven is twenty-seven. Find the number.

25. The sum of three-fifths of a number and eight is two. Find the number.

26. Five less than two-thirds of a number is three. Find the number.

27. The difference between a number divided by 4.18 and 7.92 is 12.52. Find the number.

28. The total of 5.68 times a number and 132.7 is the number minus 29.228. Find the number.

For Exercises 29 and 30, determine whether the equation $5 - 7x = 9$ is a correct translation of the given sentence.

29. Five less than the product of seven and a number is equal to nine.

30. The difference between five and the product of seven and a number is nine.

OBJECTIVE B *To solve application problems*

31. A student writes the equation $221,800 = n - 19,100$ to represent the situation described in Exercise 34. What does n represent in this equation?

32. A student writes the equation $1991 = x + 1505$ to represent the situation described in Exercise 33. What does x represent in this equation?

SeanPavonePhoto/Shutterstock.com

Akashi Kaikyo Bridge

33. ◗ **Bridges** The length of the Akashi Kaikyo Bridge is 1991 m. This is 1505 m greater than the length of the Brooklyn Bridge. Find the length of the Brooklyn Bridge.

34. ◗ **Housing** The median price of a house in 2010 was $221,800. This price is $19,100 less than the median price of a house in 2005. (*Source:* U.S. Census Bureau) Find the median price of a house in 2005.

35. ◗ **The Military** See the news clipping at the right. Find the amount the Army plans to pay in re-enlistment bonuses in 2010.

36. **Real Estate** This year, the value of a lakefront summer home is $525,000. This amount is twice the value of the home 6 years ago. What was the home's value 6 years ago?

In the NEWS!

Army to Reduce Bonus Budget

The Army expects to spend less on recruitment and re-enlistment bonuses in 2010. Recent budget plans show that the $626 million spent in 2009 on re-enlistment bonuses is $182 million more than the amount currently budgeted for 2010.

Source: www.armytimes.com

37. Depreciation   The value of a sport utility vehicle this year is $16,000, which is four-fifths of its value last year. Find the value of the vehicle last year.

38. Energy Consumption   The projected world energy consumption in 2018 is 600 quadrillion Btu, which is one-twelfth the expected world energy consumption in 2030. (*Source:* U.S. Energy Information Administration) What is the expected world energy consumption in 2030?

39. ◗ Sleep   First- through fifth-graders get an average of 9.5 h of sleep daily. This is three-fourths the number of hours infants aged 3 months to 11 months sleep each day. (*Source:* National Sleep Foundation) How many hours do infants aged 3 months to 11 months sleep each day? Round to the nearest tenth.

40. Finances   Each month the Manzanares family spends $1360 for their house payment and utilities, which amounts to one-fourth of the family's monthly income. Find the family's monthly income.

41. Consumerism   The cost of a graphing calculator today is three-fourths of the cost of the calculator 5 years ago. The cost of the graphing calculator today is $72. Find the cost of the calculator 5 years ago.

42. ◗ Sports   The average number of home runs per major league game in a recent year was 1.90. This represents 108% of the average number of home runs per game in 1970. (*Source:* Elias Sports Bureau) Find the average number of home runs per game in 1970. Round to the nearest hundredth.

43. ◗ Nutrition   The nutrition label on a bag of Baked Tostitos tortilla chips lists the sodium content of one serving as 200 mg, which is 8% of the recommended daily allowance of sodium. What is the recommended daily allowance of sodium? Express the answer in grams.

44. ◗ Language   See the news clipping at the right. Based on the information given, how many people speak Ojibwe?

45. ◗ Conservation   In a recent year, 1130 species of mammals were known to be at risk of extinction. This represented approximately 12.24% of all the species of animals known to be at risk of extinction on Earth. (*Source:* International Union for Conservation of Nature) Approximately how many species of animals were known to be at risk of extinction that year? Round to the nearest ten.

46. Compensation   Last month, Sandy's salary as a sales representative was $2580. This amount included her base monthly salary of $600 plus a 3% commission on total sales. Find her total sales for the month.

47. ◗ Diet   Americans consume 7 billion hot dogs from Memorial Day through Labor Day. This is 35% of the hot dogs consumed annually in the United States. (*Source:* National Hot Dog & Sausage Council; American Meat Institute) How many hot dogs do Americans consume annually?

In the NEWS!

Endangered Languages

There may be as many as 7000 "living" languages in the world today. Within 50 years, thousands of these languages may disappear as their remaining speakers die. For example, 8000 speakers of Ojibwe are over the age of 60—and they represent 80% of the people who speak Ojibwe.

Source: Bill Moyers Journal, www.pbs.com

48. ◐ **Insecticides**   Americans spend approximately $295 million a year on remedies for cockroaches. The table at the right shows the top U.S. cities for sales of roach insecticides. What percent of the total is spent in New York? Round to the nearest tenth of a percent.

City	Roach Insecticide Sales
Los Angeles	$16.8 million
New York	$9.8 million
Houston	$6.7 million

Source: IRI InfoScan for Combat

49. **Contractors**   Budget Plumbing charged $445 for a water softener and installation. The charge included $310 for the water softener and $45 per hour for labor. How many hours of labor were required for the job?

50. ◐ **Astronautics**   See the news clipping at the right. The number of men who have traveled into space is 25 more than 8 times the number of women who have traveled into space. How many women have traveled into space?

51. ◐ **Vacation Days**   In Italy, workers take an average of 42 vacation days per year. This number is 3 more than three times the average number of vacation days workers take each year in the United States. (*Source:* World Tourism Organization) On average, how many vacation days do U.S. workers take per year?

52. **Conservation**   A water flow restrictor has reduced the flow of water through a pipe to 2 gal/min. This rate is 1 gal/min less than three-fifths the original rate. Find the original rate.

53. **Compensation**   Assume that a sales executive receives a base monthly salary of $600 plus an 8.25% commission on total sales per month. Find the executive's total sales during a month in which she receives total compensation of $4109.55

In the NEWS!

NASA Website for Women

NASA has announced the launch of a new website, Women@NASA, aimed at promoting awareness of women's contributions to space travel. Men still far outnumber women in the realm of space travel. The number of women who have traveled into space is less than one-eighth of the number of men. To date, 465 men have traveled into space.

Source: www.space.com

Critical Thinking

Many applications in science, economics, and business require translating a relationship into an equation. For Exercises 54 to 57, translate the statement into an equation.

54. Because of depreciation, the value V of a car after t years of ownership is the difference between $28,000 and 2000 times t.

55. The reciprocal of the focal length f of a camera is equal to the sum of the reciprocal of the object distance o and the reciprocal of the image distance i.

56. The gravitational force F between two masses m and M equals the product of the masses divided by the square of the distance r between them.

57. The distance s an object falls in time t equals the product of 16 and the time squared.

Projects or Group Activities

58. A man's boyhood lasted $\frac{1}{6}$ of his life, he played football for the next $\frac{1}{8}$ of his life, and he married 5 years after quitting football. A daughter was born after he had been married $\frac{1}{12}$ of his life. The daughter lived $\frac{1}{2}$ as many years as her father. The man died 6 years after his daughter. How old was the man when he died? Use a number line to illustrate the time. Then write an equation and solve it.

CHAPTER

5   Summary

Key Words

Examples

A **variable** is a letter of the alphabet used to stand for a quantity that is unknown or that can change. An expression that contains one or more variables is a **variable expression.** Replacing the variable or variables in a variable expression and then simplifying the resulting numerical expression is called **evaluating the variable expression.**   [5.1A, p. 248]

Evaluate $5x^3 + 2y - 6$ when $x = -1$ and $y = 4$.
$5x^3 + 2y - 6$
$5(-1)^3 + 2(4) - 6 = 5(-1) + 2(4) - 6$
$\qquad\qquad\qquad\quad = -5 + 8 - 6$
$\qquad\qquad\qquad\quad = 3 - 6$
$\qquad\qquad\qquad\quad = 3 + (-6) = -3$

The **terms of a variable expression** are the addends of the expression. A **variable term** consists of a **numerical coefficient** and a **variable part.** A **constant term** has no variable part.   [5.1B, p. 249]

The variable expression $-3x^2 + 2x - 5$ has three terms: $-3x^2$, $2x$, and -5.
$-3x^2$ and $2x$ are variable terms.
-5 is a constant term.
For the term $-3x^2$, the coefficient is -3 and the variable part is x^2.

Like terms of a variable expression have the same variable part. Constant terms are considered like terms.   [5.1B, p. 249]

$-6a^3b^2$ and $4a^3b^2$ are like terms.

An **equation** expresses the equality of two mathematical expressions.   [5.2A, p. 260]

$5x + 6 = 7x - 3$
$y = 4x - 10$
$3a^2 - 6a + 4 = 0$

A **solution of an equation** is a number that, when substituted for the variable, results in a true equation.   [5.2A, p. 260]

6 is a solution of $x - 4 = 2$ because $6 - 4 = 2$ is a true equation.

Solving an equation means finding a solution of the equation. The goal is to rewrite the equation in the form **variable = constant.**   [5.2B, p. 261]

$x = 5$ is in the form *variable = constant*. The solution of the equation $x = 5$ is the constant 5 because $5 = 5$ is a true equation.

The **additive inverse,** or **opposite,** of a is $-a$. [5.2B, p. 261]

The additive inverse of 9 is -9.
The additive inverse of -5 is $-(-5)$, or 5.
The additive inverse of $3x$ is $-3x$.

A **formula** is an equation that expresses a relationship among variables.   [11.2D, p. 480]

The relationship between Celsius temperature and Fahrenheit temperature is given by the formula $F = \frac{9}{5}C + 32$, where F represents degrees Fahrenheit and C represents degrees Celsius.

Some of the words and phrases that translate to **equals** are **is, is equal to, amounts to,** and **represents.**   [5.6A, p. 285]

"Eight plus a number is ten" translates to $8 + x = 10$.

Essential Rules and Procedures	Examples
Commutative Property of Addition [5.1B, p. 249] $a + b = b + a$	$-9 + 5 = 5 + (-9)$
Associative Property of Addition [5.1B, p. 249] $(a + b) + c = a + (b + c)$	$(-6 + 4) + 2 = -6 + (4 + 2)$
Commutative Property of Multiplication [5.1C, p. 251] $a \cdot b = b \cdot a$	$-5(10) = 10(-5)$
Associative Property of Multiplication [5.1C, p. 251] $(a \cdot b) \cdot c = a \cdot (b \cdot c)$	$(-3 \cdot 4) \cdot 6 = -3 \cdot (4 \cdot 6)$
Distributive Property [5.1C, p. 251] $a(b + c) = ab + ac$ $a(b - c) = ab - ac$	$2(x + 7) = 2(x) + 2(7) = 2x + 14$ $5(4x - 3) = 5(4x) - 5(3) = 20x - 15$
Addition Property of Zero [5.2B, p. 261] $a + 0 = a$ or $0 + a = a$ The sum of a term and zero is the term.	$-16 + 0 = -16 \qquad 0 + 9 = 0$
Additive Inverse Property [5.2B, p. 261] $a + (-a) = 0$ and $-a + a = 0$ The sum of a number and its additive inverse (opposite) is zero.	$5 + (-5) = 0 \qquad -12 + 12 = 0$
Addition Property of Equations [5.2B, p. 261] If a, b, and c are algebraic expressions, then the equations $a = b$ and $a + c = b + c$ have the same solutions. The same number can be added to each side of an equation without changing the solution of the equation.	$x + 7 = 20$ $x + 7 + (-7) = 20 + (-7)$ $x = 13$
Multiplication Property of Reciprocals [11.2C, p. 477] For $a \neq 0$, $a \cdot \frac{1}{a} = 1$ and $\frac{1}{a} \cdot a = 1$. The product of a nonzero number and its reciprocal is 1.	$8 \cdot \frac{1}{8} = 1 \qquad -\frac{1}{4} \cdot (-4) = 1$
Multiplication Property of One [11.2C, p. 477] $a \cdot 1 = a$ and $1 \cdot a = a$ The product of a number and 1 is the number.	$-7(1) = -7 \qquad 1 \cdot 5 = 5$
Multiplication Property of Equations [11.2C, p. 478] If a, b, and c are algebraic expressions and $c \neq 0$, then the equation $a = b$ has the same solutions as the equation $ac = bc$. Each side of an equation can be multiplied by the same nonzero number without changing the solution of the equation.	$\frac{3}{4}x = 24$ $\frac{4}{3} \cdot \frac{3}{4}x = \frac{4}{3} \cdot 24$ $x = 32$

5 | Review Exercises

1. Simplify: $-2(a - b)$

2. Is -2 a solution of the equation
$3x - 2 = -8$?

3. Solve: $x - 3 = -7$

4. Solve: $-2x + 5 = -9$

5. Evaluate $a^2 - 3b$ when $a = 2$ and $b = -3$.

6. Solve: $-3x = 27$

7. Solve: $\frac{2}{3}x + 3 = -9$

8. Simplify: $3x - 2(3x - 2)$

9. Solve: $6x - 9 = -3x + 36$

10. Solve: $x + 3 = -2$

11. Is 5 a solution of the equation
$3x - 5 = -10$?

12. Evaluate $a^2 - (b \div c)$ when $a = -2$, $b = 8$, and
$c = -4$.

13. Solve: $3(x - 2) + 2 = 11$

14. Solve: $35 - 3x = 5$

15. Simplify: $6bc - 7bc + 2bc - 5bc$

16. Solve: $7 - 3x = 2 - 5x$

17. Solve: $-\frac{3}{8}x = -\frac{15}{32}$

18. Simplify: $\frac{1}{2}x^2 - \frac{1}{3}x^2 + \frac{1}{5}x^2 + 2x^2$

19. Solve: $5x - 3(1 - 2x) = 4(2x - 1)$

20. Solve: $\frac{5}{6}x - 4 = 5$

21. **Fuel Efficiency**   A tourist drove a rental car 621 mi on 27 gal of gas. Find the number of miles driven per gallon of gas. Use the formula $D = MG$, where D is distance, M is miles driven per gallon, and G is the number of gallons.

22. **Temperature Conversion**   Find the Celsius temperature when the Fahrenheit temperature is 100°. Use the formula $F = \frac{9}{5}C + 32$, where F is the Fahrenheit temperature and C is the Celsius temperature. Round to the nearest tenth.

23. Translate "the total of n and the quotient of n and 5" into a mathematical expression.

24. Translate "the sum of five more than a number and one-third of the number" into a mathematical expression.

25. The difference between nine and twice a number is five. Find the number.

26. The product of five and a number is fifty. Find the number.

27. **Discount**   A tablet PC is on sale for $392. This is 80% of the regular price. Find the regular price of the tablet PC.

28. **Agriculture**   A farmer harvested 28,336 bushels of corn. This amount represents a 12% increase over last year's crop. How many bushels of corn did the farmer harvest last year?

5   TEST

1. Solve: $\dfrac{x}{5} - 12 = 7$

2. Solve: $x - 12 = 14$

3. Simplify: $3y - 2x - 7y - 9x$

4. Solve: $8 - 3x = 2x - 8$

5. Solve: $3x - 12 = -18$

6. Evaluate $c^2 - (2a + b^2)$ when $a = 3$, $b = -6$, and $c = -2$.

7. Is 3 a solution of the equation $x^2 + 3x - 7 = 3x - 2$?

8. Simplify: $9 - 8ab - 6ab$

9. Solve: $-5x = 14$

10. Simplify: $3y + 5(y - 3) + 8$

11. Solve: $3x - 4(x - 2) = 8$

12. Solve: $5 = 3 - 4x$

13. Evaluate $\dfrac{x^2}{y} - \dfrac{y^2}{x}$ for $x = 3$ and $y = -2$.

14. Solve: $\dfrac{5}{8}x = -10$

15. Solve: $y - 4y + 3 = 12$

16. Solve: $2x + 4(x - 3) = 5x - 1$

17. Finance   A loan of $6600 is to be paid in 48 equal monthly installments. Find the monthly payment. Use the formula $L = PN$, where L is the loan amount, P is the monthly payment, and N is the number of months.

Caro Alamy

18. Manufacturing   A clock manufacturer's fixed costs per month are $5000. The unit cost for each clock is $15. Find the number of clocks made during a month in which the total cost was $65,000. Use the formula $T = UN + F$, where T is the total cost, U is the cost per unit, N is the number of units made, and F is the fixed costs.

19. Physics   Find the time required for a falling object to increase in velocity from 24 ft/s to 392 ft/s. Use the formula $V = V_0 + 32t$, where V is the final velocity of a falling object, V_0 is the starting velocity of the falling object, and t is the time for the object to fall.

20. Translate "the sum of x and one-third of x" into a mathematical expression.

21. Translate "five times the sum of a number and three" into a mathematical expression.

22. Translate "three less than two times a number is seven" into an equation and solve.

23. The total of five and three times a number is the number minus two. Find the number.

24. Compensation   Eduardo Santos earned $3600 last month. This salary is the sum of a base monthly salary of $1200 and a 6% commission on total sales. Find Eduardo's total sales for the month.

25. Consumerism   Your mechanic charges you $338 for performing a 30,000-mile checkup on your car. This charge includes $152 for parts and $62 per hour for labor. Find the number of hours the mechanic worked on your car.

Cumulative Review Exercises

1. Simplify: $6^2 - (18 - 6) \div 4 + 8$

2. Subtract: $3\frac{1}{6} - 1\frac{7}{15}$

3. Simplify: $\left(\frac{3}{8} - \frac{1}{4}\right) \div \frac{3}{4} + \frac{4}{9}$

4. Multiply: 9.67×0.0049

5. Write "$182 earned in 20 hours" as a unit rate.

6. Solve the proportion $\frac{2}{3} = \frac{n}{40}$. Round to the nearest hundredth.

7. Write $5\frac{1}{3}\%$ as a fraction.

8. What percent of 30 is 42?

9. 8 is 125% of what number?

10. Multiply: 3 ft 9 in. $\times$ 5

11. Convert $1\frac{3}{8}$ lb to ounces.

12. Convert 282 mg to grams.

13. Add: $-2 + 5 + (-8) + 4$

14. Find -6 less than 13.

15. Simplify: $(-2)^2 - (-8) \div (3 - 5)^2$

16. Evaluate $3ab - 2ac$ when $a = -2$, $b = 6$, and $c = -3$.

17. Simplify: $3z - 2x + 5z - 8x$

18. Simplify: $6y - 3(y - 5) + 8$

19. Solve: $2x - 5 = -7$

20. Solve: $7x - 3(x - 5) = -10$

21. Solve: $-\dfrac{2}{3}x = 5$

22. Solve: $\dfrac{x}{3} - 5 = -12$

23. Education In a mathematics class of 34 students, 6 received an A grade. Find the percent of students in the mathematics class who received an A grade. Round to the nearest tenth of a percent.

24. Markup The manager of a pottery store uses a markup rate of 40%. Find the price of a piece of pottery that cost the store $28.50.

25. Discount A laptop computer regularly priced at $450 is on sale for $369.
a. What is the discount?
b. What is the discount rate?

26. Simple Interest A toy store borrowed $80,000 at a simple interest rate of 11% for 4 months. What is the simple interest due on the loan? Round to the nearest cent.

27. ◗ **Smartphones** Use the information in the news clipping at the right. How many people participated in the survey described in the article? Round to the nearest whole number.

> **In the NEWS!**
>
> **Over One-Third of Adults Own a Smartphone**
> The results of a recent survey show that 35% of adult Americans now own a smartphone. During the survey, 797 people responded that they owned a smartphone.
> *Source:* www.pewinternet.org

28. Probability A tetrahedral die is one with four triangular sides numbered from 1 to 4. If two tetrahedral dice are rolled, what is the probability that the sum of the dots on the upward faces is 7?

29. Compensation Sunah Yee, a sales executive, receives a base salary of $800 plus an 8% commission on total sales. Find the total sales during a month in which Sunah earned $3400. Use the formula $M = SR + B$, where M is the monthly earnings, S is the total sales, R is the commission rate, and B is the base monthly salary.

30. Three less than eight times a number is three more than five times the number. Find the number.

Ratio and Proportion

6

Focus on Success

Are you making attending class a priority? Remember that to be successful, you must attend class. You need to be in class to hear your instructor's explanations and instructions, as well as to ask questions when something is unclear. Most students who miss a class fall behind and then find it very difficult to catch up. (See Class Time, page AIM-5.)

Monkey Business Images/shutterstock.com

Prep Test

Are you ready to succeed in this chapter? Take the Prep Test below to find out if you are ready to learn the new material.

1. Simplify: $\dfrac{8}{10}$

2. Simplify: $\dfrac{450}{650 + 250}$

3. Write $\dfrac{372}{15}$ as a terminating or repeating decimal.

4. Which is greater, 4×33 or 62×2?

5. Complete: $? \times 5 = 20$

SECTION

6.1   Ratio

OBJECTIVE A   *To write the ratio of two quantities in simplest form*

Quantities such as 3 feet, 12 cents, and 9 cars are number quantities written with units.

3 feet

12 cents   These are some examples of units. Shirts, dollars, trees, miles,

9 cars   and gallons are further examples.

↑

units

A **ratio** is a comparison of two quantities that have the *same* units. This comparison can be written in three different ways:

1. As a fraction

2. As two numbers separated by a colon (:)

3. As two numbers separated by the word *to*

The ratio of the lengths of two boards, one 8 feet long and the other 10 feet long, can be written as

1. $\dfrac{8 \text{ feet}}{10 \text{ feet}} = \dfrac{8}{10} = \dfrac{4}{5}$

2. 8 feet : 10 feet = 8 : 10 = 4 : 5

3. 8 feet to 10 feet = 8 to 10 = 4 to 5

Writing the **simplest form of a ratio** means writing it so that the two numbers have no common factor other than 1.

This ratio means that the smaller board is $\frac{4}{5}$ the length of the longer board.

EXAMPLE 1

Write the comparison $6 to $8 as a ratio in simplest form using a fraction, a colon, and the word *to*.

Solution $\dfrac{\$6}{\$8} = \dfrac{6}{8} = \dfrac{3}{4}$

$6 : $8 = 6 : 8 = 3 : 4

$6 to $8 = 6 to 8 = 3 to 4

YOU TRY IT 1

Write the comparison 20 pounds to 24 pounds as a ratio in simplest form using a fraction, a colon, and the word *to*.

Your solution

EXAMPLE 2

Write the comparison 18 quarts to 6 quarts as a ratio in simplest form using a fraction, a colon, and the word *to*.

Solution $\dfrac{18 \text{ quarts}}{6 \text{ quarts}} = \dfrac{18}{6} = \dfrac{3}{1}$

18 quarts : 6 quarts = 18 : 6 = 3 : 1

18 quarts to 6 quarts = 18 to 6
    = 3 to 1

YOU TRY IT 2

Write the comparison 64 miles to 8 miles as a ratio in simplest form using a fraction, a colon, and the word *to*.

Your solution

Solutions on p. S11

OBJECTIVE B *To solve application problems*

Christian Delbert/Shutterstock.com

The table below shows the number of board feet in stock at a lumber store for each of four types of wood. Use the table for Example 3 and You Try It 3.

Board Feet of Wood at a Lumber Store			
Pine	Ash	Oak	Cedar
20,000	18,000	10,000	12,000

EXAMPLE 3

Find, as a fraction in simplest form, the ratio of the number of board feet of pine to the number of board feet of oak.

Strategy

To find the ratio, write the ratio of board feet of pine (20,000) to board feet of oak (10,000) in simplest form.

Solution

$$\frac{20,000}{10,000} = \frac{2}{1}$$

The ratio is $\frac{2}{1}$.

YOU TRY IT 3

Find, as a fraction in simplest form, the ratio of the number of board feet of cedar to the number of board feet of ash.

Your strategy

Your solution

EXAMPLE 4

The cost of building a patio cover was $500 for labor and $700 for materials. What, as a fraction in simplest form, is the ratio of the cost of materials to the total cost for labor and materials?

Strategy

To find the ratio, write the ratio of the cost of materials ($700) to the total cost ($500 + $700) in simplest form.

Solution

$$\frac{\$700}{\$500 + \$700} = \frac{700}{1200} = \frac{7}{12}$$

The ratio is $\frac{7}{12}$.

YOU TRY IT 4

A company spends $600,000 a month for television advertising and $450,000 a month for radio advertising. What, as a fraction in simplest form, is the ratio of the cost of radio advertising to the total cost of radio and television advertising?

Your strategy

Your solution

Solutions on p. S11

6.1 EXERCISES

✔ Concept Check

1. How do you read $\frac{3}{8}$ as a ratio?

2. How do you read 8 : 3 as a ratio?

OBJECTIVE A *To write the ratio of two quantities in simplest form*

For Exercises 3 to 20, write the comparison as a ratio in simplest form using a fraction, a colon (:), and the word *to*.

3. 3 pints to 15 pints

4. 6 pounds to 8 pounds

5. $40 to $20

6. 10 feet to 2 feet

7. 3 miles to 8 miles

8. 2 hours to 3 hours

9. 6 minutes to 6 minutes

10. 8 days to 12 days

11. 35 cents to 50 cents

12. 28 inches to 36 inches

13. 30 minutes to 60 minutes

14. 25 cents to 100 cents

15. 32 ounces to 16 ounces

16. 12 quarts to 4 quarts

17. 30 yards to 12 yards

18. 12 quarts to 18 quarts

19. 20 gallons to 28 gallons

20. 14 days to 7 days

21. ⬚ To write a ratio that compares 3 days to 3 weeks, change 3 weeks into an equivalent number of _____.

22. ⬚ Is the ratio 3 : 4 the same as the ratio 4 : 3?

OBJECTIVE B *To solve application problems*

Budgets For Exercises 23 to 26, use the information in the table. Write ratios in simplest form using a fraction.

Family Budget						
Housing	Food	Transportation	Taxes	Utilities	Miscellaneous	Total
$1600	$800	$600	$700	$300	$800	$4800

23. Find the ratio of utilities costs to food costs.

24. Find the ratio of food costs to total expenses.

25. Find the ratio of housing costs to total expenses.

26. ⬚ Write a verbal description of two ratios represented by 1 : 2.

27. ● **Facial Hair**   Using the data in the news clipping at the right and the figure 110 million for the number of adult males in the United States, write the ratio of the number of men who participated in Movember to the number of adult males in the U.S. Write the ratio as a fraction in simplest form.

28. **Real Estate**   A house with an original value of $180,000 increased in value to $220,000 in 5 years. What is the ratio of the increase in value to the original value of the house?

29. **Energy Prices**   The price per gallon of gasoline rose from $2.70 to $3.24 in one year. What is the ratio of the increase in price to the original price?

30. ● **Sports**   National Collegiate Athletic Association (NCAA) statistics show that for every 75,000 high school seniors playing basketball, about 2250 play college basketball as first-year students. Write the ratio of the number of first-year students playing college basketball to the number of high school seniors playing basketball.

31. ● **Sports**   NCAA statistics show that of about 3750 college seniors playing college basketball, about 45 will play as rookies in the National Basketball Association. Write the ratio of the number of National Basketball Association rookies to the number of college seniors playing basketball.

32. ● **Consumerism**   In a recent year, women spent $2 million on swimwear and purchased 92,000 swimsuits. During the same year, men spent $500,000 on swimwear and purchased 37,000 swimsuits. (*Source:* NPD Group) **a.** Find the ratio of the amount men spent on swimwear to the amount women spent on swimwear. **b.** Find the ratio of the amount men spent on swimwear to the total amount men and women spent on swimwear. Write the ratios as fractions in simplest form.

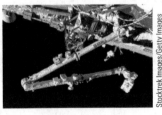

In the NEWS!

Grow a Mustache, Save a Life

Movember, a month-long mustache-growing event during November, raises money for the Prostate Cancer Foundation. Last year, 65,000 U.S. men took part in Movember, raising $7.5 million.
Source: The Sacramento Bee

Critical Thinking

33. ◥ Is the value of a ratio always less than 1? Explain.

Projects or Group Activities

34. Ratios can be extended to include more than two numbers. For instance, the ratio of the sides of the triangle at the right below can be written 3 : 4 : 5. The study of the ratios of the sides of a triangle is part of a branch of mathematics called **trigonometry,** which has important applications to science and engineering. The Canadarm2 uses trigonometry in the design of its robotic system on the international space station.
    a. Are the sides of a triangle whose sides measure 18 inches, 24 inches, and 30 inches in the ratio 3 : 4 : 5?
    b. Are the sides of a triangle whose sides measure 9 inches, 16 inches, and 25 inches in the ratio 3 : 4 : 5?
    c. For the triangle at the right, find the ratio of Side B to Side A.
    d. For the triangle at the right, find the ratio of Side B to Side C.
    e. For the triangle at the right, find the ratio of Side A to Side C.

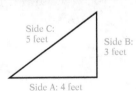

Side C: 5 feet

Side B: 3 feet

Side A: 4 feet

35. Get a large bag of M&Ms and find the ratio of the number of red, blue, green, yellow, and orange candies.

SECTION

6.2 Rates

OBJECTIVE A   *To write rates*

Point of Interest

Listed below are rates at which various crimes are committed in our nation.

Crime	Every
Larceny	4 seconds
Burglary	14 seconds
Robbery	60 seconds
Rape	6 minutes
Murder	31 minutes

A **rate** is a comparison of two quantities that have *different* units. A rate is written as a fraction.

A distance runner ran 26 miles in 4 hours. The distance-to-time rate is written

$$\frac{26 \text{ miles}}{4 \text{ hours}} = \frac{13 \text{ miles}}{2 \text{ hours}}$$

Notice that the above rate is written in simplest form. Writing the **simplest form of a rate** means writing it so that the two numbers that form the rate have no common factor other than 1.

EXAMPLE 1

Write "6 roof supports for every 9 feet" as a rate in simplest form.

Solution

$$\frac{6 \text{ supports}}{9 \text{ feet}} = \frac{2 \text{ supports}}{3 \text{ feet}}$$

YOU TRY IT 1

Write "15 pounds of fertilizer for 12 trees" as a rate in simplest form.

Your solution

Solution on p. S11

OBJECTIVE B   *To write unit rates*

Point of Interest

According to a Gallup Poll, women see doctors more often than men do. On average, men visit the doctor 3.8 times per year, whereas women go to the doctor 5.8 times per year.

A **unit rate** is a rate in which the number in the denominator is 1.

$$\frac{\$3.25}{1 \text{ pound}}$$ or \$3.25/pound is read "\$3.25 per pound."

To find a unit rate, divide the number in the numerator of the rate by the number in the denominator of the rate.

APPLY THE CONCEPT ....

A car was driven 344 miles on 16 gallons of gasoline. How many miles did the car travel on 1 gallon of gasoline?

The rate that compares miles to gallons is $\frac{344 \text{ miles}}{16 \text{ gallons}}$.

To find the miles per gallon (the unit rate), divide the numerator (344 miles) by the denominator (16 gallons).

344 miles ÷ 16 gallons = 21.5 miles/gallon

The car traveled 21.5 miles per gallon of gasoline.

EXAMPLE 2

Write "300 feet in 8 seconds" as a unit rate.

Solution

$$\frac{300 \text{ feet}}{8 \text{ seconds}} \qquad 8\overline{)300.0}^{\,37.5}$$

37.5 feet/second

YOU TRY IT 2

Write "260 miles in 8 hours" as a unit rate.

Your solution

Solution on p. S11

OBJECTIVE C   *To solve application problems*

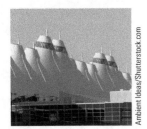

Denver Airport

Integrating Technology

To calculate the costs per mile using a calculator, perform four divisions:

683 ÷ 2475 =

536 ÷ 1464 =

525 ÷ 1302 =

483 ÷ 1050 =

In each case, round the number in the display to the nearest hundredth.

HOW TO 1   The table at the right shows miles flown and air fares for some routes in the continental United States. Determine the most expensive route and the least expensive route per mile.

Long Routes	Miles	Fare
New York–Los Angeles	2475	$683
San Francisco–Dallas	1464	$536
Denver–Pittsburgh	1302	$525
Minneapolis–Hartford	1050	$483

Strategy

Find the cost per mile for each route by dividing the fare by the miles flown. Compare the costs per mile to determine the most and least expensive routes.

Solution   New York–Los Angeles $\dfrac{683}{2475} \approx 0.28$

San Francisco–Dallas $\dfrac{536}{1464} \approx 0.37$

Denver–Pittsburgh $\dfrac{525}{1302} \approx 0.40$

Minneapolis–Hartford $\dfrac{483}{1050} = 0.46$

$0.28 < 0.37 < 0.40 < 0.46$

The Minneapolis–Hartford route is the most expensive per mile, and the New York–Los Angeles route is the least expensive per mile.

EXAMPLE 3

A motorcycle racer completed a 6-mile lap in 0.05 hour (3 minutes). Find the racer's speed in miles per hour.

Strategy

To find the speed in miles per hour, divide the length of the lap (6 miles) by the time (0.05 hour).

Solution

$$\frac{6 \text{ miles}}{0.05 \text{ hour}} = 120 \text{ miles/hour}$$

The racer's speed was 120 miles/hour.

YOU TRY IT 3

A landscape technician purchased 40 feet of $\frac{3}{4}$-inch PVC pipe for $22.40. What is the per-foot cost of the pipe?

Your strategy

Your solution

Solution on p. S11

6.2 EXERCISES

✔ Concept Check

1. ◥ What is the difference between a ratio and a rate?

2. ◥ How is a unit rate calculated?

OBJECTIVE A *To write rates*

For Exercises 3 to 10, write each phrase as a rate in simplest form.

3. 3 pounds of meat for 4 people

4. 30 ounces in 24 glasses

5. $80 for 12 boards

6. 84 cents for 3 candy bars

7. 300 miles on 15 gallons

8. 88 feet in 8 seconds

9. 16 gallons in 2 hours

10. 25 ounces in 5 minutes

11. ◈ If the rate at which water flows through a nozzle is given in gallons per minute, how do you find the rate in gallons per second?

OBJECTIVE B *To write unit rates*

◈ For Exercises 12 to 14, complete the unit rate.

12. 5 miles in ___ hour

13. 15 feet in ___ second

14. 5 grams of fat in ___ serving

For Exercises 15 to 24, write each phrase as a unit rate.

15. 10 feet in 4 seconds

16. 816 miles in 6 days

17. $3900 earned in 4 weeks

18. $51,000 earned in 12 months

19. 1100 trees planted on 10 acres

20. 3750 words on 15 pages

21. $131.88 earned in 7 hours

22. 628.8 miles in 12 hours

23. 409.4 miles on 11.5 gallons of gasoline

24. $11.05 for 3.4 pounds

25. Fuel Efficiency   A hybrid electric vehicle used 15 gallons of gasoline to travel 639 miles. How many miles per gallon did the car get?

26. Audio Technology   An audio-visual technician spent 2 hours preparing a surround sound recommendation for a homeowner. If the technician charged $99 for this service, what is the technician's hourly wage?

OBJECTIVE C   *To solve application problems*

Miles per Dollar   One measure of how expensive it is to drive your car is calculated as miles per dollar, which is the number of miles you drive on 1 dollar's worth of gasoline. Use this information for Exercises 27 and 28.

27. Suppose you get 26 miles per gallon of gasoline and gasoline costs $3.49 per gallon. Calculate your miles per dollar. Round to the nearest tenth.

28. Suppose you get 23 miles per gallon of gasoline and gasoline costs $3.15 per gallon. It costs you $44.10 to fill the tank. Calculate your miles per dollar. Round to the nearest tenth.

29. Bike Sharing   Use the information in the news clipping at the right. Find the average number of rides per day during the Hubway program's first month. Round to the nearest whole number of rides per day.

In the NEWS!

Hubway's First Month a Success

In recent years, bike sharing programs have been rolled out in cities across the United States and around the world. In its first 30 days of operation, Boston's Hubway program saw its bicycles used for 36,612 rides.
Source: boston.com

30. Construction   An architect designed a house that contains 1850 square feet. A home builder estimates that it will cost $172,050 to build the house. What is the estimated cost per square foot to build the house?

31. ● **Advertising**   The advertising fee for a 30-second spot for the 2011 Super Bowl was approximately $3 million. If 106 million viewers watched the Super Bowl, what is the advertiser's cost per viewer for a 30-second ad? Round to the nearest cent. (*Source:* money.cnn.com)

32. Air Flow A tire containing 732 cubic inches of air is punctured and begins a slow leak. After 4 hours, the tire is flat and there are 36 cubic inches of air remaining in the tire. What is the rate, in cubic feet per minute, at which air escaped from the tire?

33. Gas Pump A quality control inspector needs to measure the flow rate of a gasoline pump. The inspector pumps 10 gallons of gas into a container in 50 seconds. What is the rate, in gallons per minute, at which the pump dispenses gas?

Exchange Rates One application of rates is in the area of international trade. Suppose a company in Canada purchases a shipment of sneakers from an American company. The Canadian company must exchange Canadian dollars for U.S. dollars in order to pay for the order. The number of Canadian dollars that are equivalent to 1 U.S. dollar is called the **exchange rate.** The table at the right below shows the exchange rates per U.S. dollar for three foreign countries and for the euro at the time of this writing. Use this table for Exercises 34 to 36.

34. How many euros would be paid for an order of American computer hardware costing $120,000?

Exchange Rates per U.S. Dollar	
Russian Ruble	30.4006
Brazilian Real	1.9831
Japanese Yen	79.8700
Euro	0.7788

35. Calculate the cost, in Japanese yen, of an American car costing $34,000.

36. What does the quantity 1.9831 × 2500 represent?

37. Demography The table below shows the population and area of three countries. The population density of a country is the number of people per square mile.

Country	Population	Area (in square miles)
Australia	21,767,000	2,968,000
India	1,189,173,000	1,269,000
United States	311,051,000	3,619,000

a. Which country has the least population density?
b. How many more people per square mile are there in India than in the United States? Round to the nearest whole number.

Critical Thinking

38. Compensation You have a choice of receiving a wage of $34,000 per year, $2840 per month, $650 per week, or $18 per hour. Which pay choice would you take? Assume a 40-hour work week with 52 weeks of work per year.

39. The price–earnings ratio of a company's stock is one measure used by stock market analysts to assess the financial well-being of the company. Explain the meaning of the price–earnings ratio.

Projects or Group Activities

Other Bases for Rates   Some unit rates are so small that they are difficult to read, so a base other than 1 is used. Some common bases are 1000, 100,000, 1,000,000, and 1,000,000,000. For instance, a smog test on a car may be reported as 650 parts per million, abbreviated 650 ppm. This means that there are 650 smog molecules (such as nitrogen dioxide or carbon monoxide) per million molecules of exhaust. This rate is easier to understand than a unit rate of $\frac{650}{1,000,000} = 0.00065$ smog molecule per 1 molecule of exhaust.

40. Infant mortality rates are reported in deaths per 1000 live births. Work through the following steps to find the infant mortality rate in the United States for a recent year, given that there were 4,316,000 live births and 29,000 deaths.
   a. Divide the number of deaths by the number of live births.
   b. Multiply the answer by 1000. Round to the nearest tenth. This is the infant mortality rate per thousand.

41. The Environmental Projection Agency (EPA) has started using a new statistic on EPA fuel economy stickers—gallons of gas used per 100 miles driven. To find the number of gallons used per 100 miles, divide 100 by the car's miles-per-gallon (mpg) rating. What is the number of gallons per 100 miles for a car that has a rating of 28 mpg? Round to the nearest tenth.

42. The maximum amount of arsenic that is allowed in safe drinking water is 0.010 ppm. What is this amount in parts per billion (ppb)?

43. A safe level of beryllium in drinking water is set at 4 ppb. What is this amount in parts per million (ppm)?

✔ CHECK YOUR PROGRESS: CHAPTER 6

For Exercises 1 to 3, write the ratio in simplest form using a fraction and a colon.

1. 12 minutes to 48 minutes
2. 24 pounds to 36 pounds
3. 25 miles to 60 miles

For Exercises 4 to 6, write the rate as a unit rate. Round to the nearest tenth.

4. $96 in 4 hours
5. 100 yards in 9.6 seconds
6. 525 miles on 18 gallons of gasoline

7. Lawn Care   A fertilizer manufacturer recommends using 10 gallons of liquid fertilizer for every 400 square feet of lawn. What is the recommended amount of fertilizer per square foot of lawn?

8. Nutrition   There are 150 calories in an 8-ounce glass of whole milk. What is the number of calories per ounce in whole milk?

9. Consumerism   One dozen long-stemmed roses cost $51. What is the cost per rose?

10. Consumerism   A certain cyan print cartridge will print 2000 pages before it needs to be replaced. If the cost of the cartridge is $85, what is the cost per page for this cartridge?

SECTION

6.3   Proportions

OBJECTIVE A   *To determine whether a proportion is true*

 Point of Interest

Proportions were studied by the earliest mathematicians. Clay tablets uncovered by archaeologists show evidence of proportions in Egyptian and Babylonian cultures dating from 1800 B.C.

A **proportion** is an expression of the equality of two ratios or rates.

$$\frac{50 \text{ miles}}{4 \text{ gallons}} = \frac{25 \text{ miles}}{2 \text{ gallons}}$$

Note that the units of the numerators are the same and the units of the denominators are the same.

$$\frac{3}{6} = \frac{1}{2}$$

This is the equality of two ratios.

A proportion is **true** if the fractions are equal when written in simplest form. In any true proportion, the **cross products** are equal.

HOW TO 1   Is $\frac{2}{3} = \frac{8}{12}$ a true proportion?

$$\frac{2}{3} \asymp \frac{8}{12} \quad\longrightarrow\quad \begin{array}{l} 3 \times 8 = 24 \\ 2 \times 12 = 24 \end{array}$$

The cross products *are* equal.

$\frac{2}{3} = \frac{8}{12}$ is a true proportion.

A proportion is **not true** if the fractions are not equal when reduced to simplest form. If the cross products are not equal, then the proportion is not true.

HOW TO 2   Is $\frac{4}{5} = \frac{8}{9}$ a true proportion?

$$\frac{4}{5} \asymp \frac{8}{9} \quad\longrightarrow\quad \begin{array}{l} 5 \times 8 = 40 \\ 4 \times 9 = 36 \end{array}$$

The cross products *are not* equal.

$\frac{4}{5} = \frac{8}{9}$ is not a true proportion.

EXAMPLE 1

Is $\frac{5}{8} = \frac{10}{16}$ a true proportion?

Solution

$$\frac{5}{8} \asymp \frac{10}{16} \quad\longrightarrow\quad \begin{array}{l} 8 \times 10 = 80 \\ 5 \times 16 = 80 \end{array}$$

The cross products are equal.
The proportion is true.

YOU TRY IT 1

Is $\frac{6}{10} = \frac{9}{15}$ a true proportion?

Your solution

EXAMPLE 2

Is $\frac{62 \text{ miles}}{4 \text{ gallons}} = \frac{33 \text{ miles}}{2 \text{ gallons}}$ a true proportion?

Solution

$$\frac{62}{4} \asymp \frac{33}{2} \quad\longrightarrow\quad \begin{array}{l} 4 \times 33 = 132 \\ 62 \times 2 = 124 \end{array}$$

The cross products are not equal.
The proportion is not true.

YOU TRY IT 2

Is $\frac{\$32}{6 \text{ hours}} = \frac{\$90}{8 \text{ hours}}$ a true proportion?

Your solution

Solutions on p. S11

OBJECTIVE B   *To solve proportions*

Sometimes one of the numbers in a proportion is unknown. In this case, it is necessary to *solve* the proportion.

To **solve a proportion,** find a number to replace the unknown so that the proportion is true.

HOW TO 3   Solve: $\dfrac{9}{6} = \dfrac{3}{n}$

$$\frac{9}{6} = \frac{3}{n}$$

$9 \times n = 6 \times 3$ • Find the cross products.

$9 \times n = 18$

$n = 18 \div 9$ • Think of $9 \times n = 18$ as $9\overline{)18}$.

$n = 2$

Check:

$\dfrac{9}{6} \diagtimes \dfrac{3}{2}$ → $6 \times 3 = 18$

→ $9 \times 2 = 18$

EXAMPLE 3

Solve $\dfrac{n}{12} = \dfrac{25}{60}$ and check.

Solution

$n \times 60 = 12 \times 25$ • Find the cross

$n \times 60 = 300$ products. Then

$n = 300 \div 60$ solve for n.

$n = 5$

Check:

$\dfrac{5}{12} \diagtimes \dfrac{25}{60}$ → $12 \times 25 = 300$

→ $5 \times 60 = 300$

YOU TRY IT 3

Solve $\dfrac{n}{14} = \dfrac{3}{7}$ and check.

Your solution

EXAMPLE 4

Solve $\dfrac{4}{9} = \dfrac{n}{16}$. Round to the nearest tenth.

Solution

$4 \times 16 = 9 \times n$ • Find the cross

$64 = 9 \times n$ products. Then

$64 \div 9 = n$ solve for n.

$7.1 \approx n$

Note: A rounded answer is an approximation. Therefore, the answer to a check will not be exact.

YOU TRY IT 4

Solve $\dfrac{5}{7} = \dfrac{n}{20}$. Round to the nearest tenth.

Your solution

Solutions on pp. S11–S12

<table>
<tr><td>

EXAMPLE 5

Solve $\frac{28}{52} = \frac{7}{n}$ and check.

Solution

$28 \times n = 52 \times 7$ • Find the cross
$28 \times n = 364$ products. Then
     $n = 364 \div 28$ solve for n.
     $n = 13$

Check:

$$\frac{28}{52} \diagdown\!\!\!\diagup \frac{7}{13} \longrightarrow \begin{array}{l} 52 \times 7 = 364 \\ 28 \times 13 = 364 \end{array}$$

</td><td>

YOU TRY IT 5

Solve $\frac{15}{20} = \frac{12}{n}$ and check.

Your solution

</td></tr>
<tr><td>

EXAMPLE 6

Solve $\frac{15}{n} = \frac{8}{3}$. Round to the nearest hundredth.

Solution

$15 \times 3 = n \times 8$
     $45 = n \times 8$
$45 \div 8 = n$
  $5.63 \approx n$

</td><td>

YOU TRY IT 6

Solve $\frac{12}{n} = \frac{7}{4}$. Round to the nearest hundredth.

Your solution

</td></tr>
<tr><td>

EXAMPLE 7

Solve $\frac{n}{9} = \frac{3}{1}$ and check.

Solution

$n \times 1 = 9 \times 3$
$n \times 1 = 27$
     $n = 27 \div 1$
     $n = 27$

Check:

$$\frac{27}{9} \diagdown\!\!\!\diagup \frac{3}{1} \longrightarrow \begin{array}{l} 9 \times 3 = 27 \\ 27 \times 1 = 27 \end{array}$$

</td><td>

YOU TRY IT 7

Solve $\frac{n}{12} = \frac{4}{1}$ and check.

Your solution

</td></tr>
</table>

Solutions on p. S12

OBJECTIVE C *To solve application problems*

The application problems in this objective require you to write and solve a proportion. When setting up a proportion, remember to keep the same units in the numerators and the same units in the denominators.

EXAMPLE 8

The dosage of a certain medication is 2 ounces for every 50 pounds of body weight. How many ounces of this medication are required for a person who weighs 175 pounds?

Strategy

To find the number of ounces of medication for a person weighing 175 pounds, write and solve a proportion using n to represent the number of ounces of medication for a 175-pound person.

Solution

$$\frac{2 \text{ ounces}}{50 \text{ pounds}} = \frac{n \text{ ounces}}{175 \text{ pounds}}$$

• The unit "ounces" is in the numerator. The unit "pounds" is in the denominator.

$$2 \times 175 = 50 \times n$$
$$350 = 50 \times n$$
$$350 \div 50 = n$$
$$7 = n$$

A 175-pound person requires 7 ounces of medication.

YOU TRY IT 8

Three tablespoons of a liquid plant fertilizer are to be added to every 4 gallons of water. How many tablespoons of fertilizer are required for 10 gallons of water?

Your strategy

Your solution

EXAMPLE 9

A mason determines that 9 cement blocks are required for a retaining wall that is 2 feet long. At this rate, how many cement blocks are required for a retaining wall that is 24 feet long?

Strategy

To find the number of cement blocks required for a retaining wall that is 24 feet long, write and solve a proportion using n to represent the number of blocks required.

Solution

$$\frac{9 \text{ cement blocks}}{2 \text{ feet}} = \frac{n \text{ cement blocks}}{24 \text{ feet}}$$

$$9 \times 24 = 2 \times n$$
$$216 = 2 \times n$$
$$216 \div 2 = n$$
$$108 = n$$

A 24-foot retaining wall requires 108 cement blocks.

YOU TRY IT 9

Twenty-four jars can be packed in 6 identical boxes. At this rate, how many jars can be packed in 15 boxes?

Your strategy

Your solution

Solutions on p. S12

6.3 EXERCISES

✔ Concept Check

Solving a proportion requires rewriting a multiplication problem as a division problem. For instance, the multiplication problem $7 \times 9 = 63$ has the related division problems $63 \div 9 = 7$ and $63 \div 7 = 9$. For Exercises 1 to 4, rewrite the given multiplication problem as a division problem whose quotient is n.

1. $n \times 15 = 45$ **2.** $12 \times n = 60$ **3.** $72 = n \times 9$ **4.** $54 = 6 \times n$

OBJECTIVE A   *To determine whether a proportion is true*

For Exercises 5 to 22, determine whether the proportion is true or not true.

5. $\dfrac{4}{8} = \dfrac{10}{20}$ **6.** $\dfrac{39}{48} = \dfrac{13}{16}$ **7.** $\dfrac{7}{8} = \dfrac{11}{12}$ **8.** $\dfrac{15}{7} = \dfrac{17}{8}$

9. $\dfrac{27}{8} = \dfrac{9}{4}$ **10.** $\dfrac{3}{18} = \dfrac{4}{19}$ **11.** $\dfrac{45}{135} = \dfrac{3}{9}$ **12.** $\dfrac{3}{4} = \dfrac{54}{72}$

13. $\dfrac{50 \text{ miles}}{2 \text{ gallons}} = \dfrac{25 \text{ miles}}{1 \text{ gallon}}$ **14.** $\dfrac{16 \text{ feet}}{10 \text{ seconds}} = \dfrac{24 \text{ feet}}{15 \text{ seconds}}$

15. $\dfrac{6 \text{ minutes}}{5 \text{ cents}} = \dfrac{30 \text{ minutes}}{25 \text{ cents}}$ **16.** $\dfrac{16 \text{ pounds}}{12 \text{ days}} = \dfrac{20 \text{ pounds}}{14 \text{ days}}$

17. $\dfrac{\$15}{4 \text{ pounds}} = \dfrac{\$45}{12 \text{ pounds}}$ **18.** $\dfrac{270 \text{ trees}}{6 \text{ acres}} = \dfrac{90 \text{ trees}}{2 \text{ acres}}$

19. $\dfrac{300 \text{ feet}}{4 \text{ rolls}} = \dfrac{450 \text{ feet}}{7 \text{ rolls}}$ **20.** $\dfrac{1 \text{ gallon}}{4 \text{ quarts}} = \dfrac{7 \text{ gallons}}{28 \text{ quarts}}$

21. $\dfrac{\$65}{5 \text{ days}} = \dfrac{\$26}{2 \text{ days}}$ **22.** $\dfrac{80 \text{ miles}}{2 \text{ hours}} = \dfrac{110 \text{ miles}}{3 \text{ hours}}$

23. 🖋 Suppose in a true proportion you switch the numerator of the first fraction with the denominator of the second fraction. Must the result be another true proportion?

24. 🖋 Write a true proportion in which the cross products are equal to 36.

OBJECTIVE B   *To solve proportions*

25. [icon] Consider the proportion $\frac{n}{7} = \frac{9}{21}$ in Exercise 27. The simplest form of the ratio $\frac{9}{21}$ is $\frac{3}{7}$. Will solving the proportion $\frac{n}{7} = \frac{3}{7}$ give the same result for n as found in Exercise 27?

For Exercises 26 to 45, solve. Round to the nearest hundredth, if necessary.

26. $\frac{n}{4} = \frac{6}{8}$

27. $\frac{n}{7} = \frac{9}{21}$

28. $\frac{12}{18} = \frac{n}{9}$

29. $\frac{7}{21} = \frac{35}{n}$

30. $\frac{6}{n} = \frac{24}{36}$

31. $\frac{3}{n} = \frac{15}{10}$

32. $\frac{n}{6} = \frac{2}{3}$

33. $\frac{5}{12} = \frac{n}{144}$

34. $\frac{n}{5} = \frac{7}{8}$

35. $\frac{4}{n} = \frac{9}{5}$

36. $\frac{5}{12} = \frac{n}{8}$

37. $\frac{36}{20} = \frac{12}{n}$

38. $\frac{n}{15} = \frac{21}{12}$

39. $\frac{40}{n} = \frac{15}{8}$

40. $\frac{28}{8} = \frac{12}{n}$

41. $\frac{n}{30} = \frac{65}{120}$

42. $\frac{0.3}{5.6} = \frac{n}{25}$

43. $\frac{1.3}{16} = \frac{n}{30}$

44. $\frac{0.7}{9.8} = \frac{3.6}{n}$

45. $\frac{1.9}{7} = \frac{13}{n}$

OBJECTIVE C   *To solve application problems*

46. [icon] Jesse walked 3 miles in 40 minutes. Let n be the number of miles Jesse can walk in 60 minutes at the same rate. To determine how many miles Jesse can walk in 60 minutes, a student used the proportion $\frac{40}{3} = \frac{60}{n}$. Is this a valid proportion to use in solving this problem?

47. **Nutrition**   A 6-ounce package of Puffed Wheat contains 600 calories. How many calories are contained in a 0.5-ounce serving of the cereal?

48. [icon] **Health**   Using the information in the news clipping at the right and a figure of 309 million for the number of Americans, determine the number of **a.** overweight Americans and **b.** obese Americans.

49. **Fuel Efficiency**   A car travels 70.5 miles on 3 gallons of gas. Find the distance the car can travel on 14 gallons of gas.

In the NEWS!

Small Gains in Obesity Battle

A recent study shows a small but encouraging increase in the number of Americans of normal weight. Still, obesity remains a major health problem in the United States, with approximately 1 in 3 Americans falling in the overweight category, and 1 in 4 in the obese category.

Source: msnbc.com

50. **Landscaping** Ron Stokes uses 2 pounds of fertilizer for every 100 square feet of lawn for landscape maintenance. At this rate, how many pounds of fertilizer did he use on a lawn that measures 3500 square feet?

51. **Gardening** A nursery prepares a liquid plant food by adding 1 gallon of water for each 2 ounces of plant food. At this rate, how many gallons of water are required for 25 ounces of plant food?

52. **Masonry** A brick wall 20 feet in length contains 1040 bricks. At the same rate, how many bricks would it take to build a wall 48 feet in length?

53. **Cartography** The scale on the map at the right is "1.25 inches equals 10 miles." Find the distance between Carlsbad and Del Mar, which are 2 inches apart on the map.

54. **Architecture** The scale on the plans for a new house is "1 inch equals 3 feet." Find the width and the length of a room that measures 5 inches by 8 inches on the drawing.

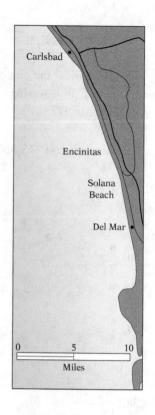

55. **Medicine** The dosage for a medication is $\frac{1}{3}$ ounce for every 40 pounds of body weight. At this rate, how many ounces of medication should a physician prescribe for a patient who weighs 150 pounds? Write the answer as a decimal.

56. **Banking** A bank requires a monthly payment of $33.45 on a $2500 loan. At the same rate, find the monthly payment on a $10,000 loan.

57. **Elections** A pre-election survey showed that 2 out of every 3 eligible voters would cast ballots in the county election. At this rate, how many people in a county of 240,000 eligible voters would vote in the election?

58. **Interior Design** A paint manufacturer suggests using 1 gallon of paint for every 400 square feet of wall. At this rate, how many gallons of paint would be required for a room that has 1400 square feet of wall?

59. **Insurance** A 60-year-old male can obtain $10,000 of life insurance for $35.35 per month. At this rate, what is the monthly cost for $50,000 of life insurance?

60. ● **Food Waste** At the rate given in the news clipping, find the cost of food wasted yearly by **a.** the average family of three and **b.** the average family of five.

In the NEWS!

How Much Food Do You Waste?

In the United States, the estimated cost of food wasted each year by the average family of four is $590.

Source: University of Arizona

61. **Manufacturing** Suppose a computer chip manufacturer knows that in an average production run of 2000 circuit boards, 60 will be defective. How many defective circuit boards are expected in a run of 25,000 circuit boards?

62. **Investments** You own 240 shares of stock in a computer company. The company declares a stock split of 5 shares for every 3 owned. How many shares of stock will you own after the stock split?

63. ● **Physics** The ratio of weight on the moon to weight on Earth is 1:6. If a bowling ball weighs 16 pounds on Earth, what would it weigh on the moon? Round to the nearest hundredth of a pound.

Michael Dunning/Getty Images

64. **Automobiles** When engineers designed a new car, they first built a model of the car. The ratio of the size of a part on the model to the actual size of the part is 2:5. If a door is 1.3 feet long on the model, what is the length of the door on the car?

65. **Investments** Carlos Capasso owns 50 shares of Texas Utilities that pay dividends of $153. At this rate, what dividend would Carlos receive after buying 300 additional shares of Texas Utilities?

Critical Thinking

66. ◼ ● **Gaming** Use the information in the news clipping at the right. Explain how a proportion can be used to determine the number of Nintendo DS systems sold given the number of Nintendo 3DS systems sold.

67. ◼ ● **Social Security** According to the Social Security Administration, the numbers of workers per retiree in the future are expected to be as given in the table below.
Why is the shrinking number of workers per retiree of importance to the Social Security Administration?

Year	2020	2030	2040
Number of workers per retiree	2.5	2.1	2.0

68. ◼ **Elections** A survey of voters in a city claimed that 2 people of every 5 who voted cast a ballot in favor of city amendment A and that 3 people of every 4 who voted cast a ballot against amendment A. Is this possible? Explain your answer.

Projects or Group Activities

69. **Anatomy** The average circumference (the distance around an object) of a baby's head at birth is approximately 13.7 inches. The average length of a baby at birth is approximately 20 inches. Measure the circumference of your head and your height in inches. Is the ratio of a baby's head circumference at birth to your head circumference equal to the ratio of a baby's length at birth to your height? Based on your findings, does the circumference of a person's head grow more slowly or more quickly than the person's height?

70. **Biology** One way biologists measure a wildlife population is by capturing a certain species of animal, tagging it, and then releasing it back into the wild. Suppose a biologist captures 100 trout from a lake, tags them, and releases them back into the water. One month later, the biologist captures 50 trout from the same lake and finds that 3 trout have tags. Based on this information, approximate the number of trout in the lake.

CHAPTER

6 | Summary

Key Words | Examples

A **ratio** is the comparison of two quantities with the same units. A ratio can be written in three ways: as a fraction, as two numbers separated by a colon (:), or as two numbers separated by the word *to*. A ratio is in **simplest form** when the two numbers do not have a common factor other than 1. [6.1A, p. 302]

The comparison 16 to 24 ounces can be written as a ratio in simplest form as $\frac{2}{3}$, 2 : 3, or 2 to 3.

A **rate** is the comparison of two quantities with different units. A rate is written as a fraction. A rate is in **simplest form** when the numbers that form the rate do not have a common factor other than 1. [6.2A, p. 306]

You earned $63 for working 6 hours. The rate is written in simplest form as $\frac{\$21}{2\text{ hours}}$.

A **unit rate** is a rate in which the number in the denominator is 1. [6.2B, p. 306]

You traveled 144 miles in 3 hours. The unit rate is 48 miles per hour.

A **proportion** is an expression of the equality of two ratios or rates. A proportion is true if the fractions are equal when written in simplest form; in any true proportion, the **cross products** are equal. A proportion is not true if the fractions are not equal when written in simplest form; if the cross products are not equal, the proportion is not true. [6.3A, p. 312]

The proportion $\frac{3}{5} = \frac{12}{20}$ is true because the cross products are equal:
$3 \times 20 = 5 \times 12$.

The proportion $\frac{3}{4} = \frac{12}{20}$ is not true because the cross products are not equal:
$3 \times 20 \neq 4 \times 12$.

Essential Rules and Procedures | Examples

To find a unit rate, divide the number in the numerator of the rate by the number in the denominator of the rate. [6.2B, p. 306]

You earned $41 for working 4 hours.

$$\frac{41}{4} = 41 \div 4 = 10.25$$

The unit rate is $10.25/hour.

To solve a proportion, find a number to replace the unknown so that the proportion is true. [6.3B, p. 313]

$$\frac{6}{24} = \frac{9}{n}$$

$6 \times n = 24 \times 9$ • Find the cross products.

$6 \times n = 216$
$n = 216 \div 6$
$n = 36$

To set up a proportion, keep the same units in the numerators and the same units in the denominators. [6.3C, p. 314]

Three machines fill 5 cereal boxes per minute. How many boxes can 8 machines fill per minute?

$$\frac{3\text{ machines}}{5\text{ cereal boxes}} = \frac{8\text{ machines}}{n\text{ cereal boxes}}$$

6 | Review Exercises

1. Is $\frac{2}{9} = \frac{10}{45}$ a true proportion?

2. Write the comparison 32 dollars to 80 dollars as a ratio in simplest form using a fraction, a colon (:), and the word *to*.

3. Write "250 miles in 4 hours" as a unit rate.

4. Is $\frac{8}{15} = \frac{32}{60}$ a true proportion?

5. Solve the proportion.
$$\frac{16}{n} = \frac{4}{17}$$

6. Write "$500 earned in 40 hours" as a unit rate.

7. Write "$8.75 for 5 pounds" as a unit rate.

8. Write the comparison 8 feet to 28 feet as a ratio in simplest form using a fraction, a colon (:), and the word *to*.

9. Solve the proportion.
$$\frac{n}{8} = \frac{9}{2}$$

10. Solve the proportion. Round to the nearest hundredth.
$$\frac{18}{35} = \frac{10}{n}$$

11. Write the comparison 6 inches to 15 inches as a ratio in simplest form using a fraction, a colon (:), and the word *to*.

12. Is $\frac{3}{8} = \frac{10}{24}$ a true proportion?

13. Write "$35 in 4 hours" as a rate in simplest form.

14. Write "326.4 miles on 12 gallons" as a unit rate.

15. Write the comparison 12 days to 12 days as a ratio in simplest form using a fraction, a colon (:), and the word *to*.

16. Is $\frac{5}{7} = \frac{25}{35}$ a true proportion?

17. Solve the proportion. Round to the nearest hundredth.

$$\frac{24}{11} = \frac{n}{30}$$

18. Write "100 miles in 3 hours" as a rate in simplest form.

19. **Business** In 5 years, the price of a calculator went from $80 to $48. What is the ratio, as a fraction in simplest form, of the decrease in price to the original price?

20. **Taxes** The property tax on a $245,000 home is $4900. At the same rate, what is the property tax on a home valued at $320,000?

21. **Consumerism** Rita Sterling bought a computer system for $2400. Five years later, she sold the computer for $900. Find the ratio of the amount she received for the computer to the cost of the computer.

22. **Manufacturing** The total cost of manufacturing 1000 camera phones was $36,600. Of the phones made, 24 did not pass inspection. What is the cost per phone of the phones that *did* pass inspection?

23. **Masonry** A brick wall 40 feet in length contains 448 concrete blocks. At the same rate, how many blocks would it take to build a wall that is 120 feet in length?

24. **Advertising** A retail computer store spends $30,000 a year on radio advertising and $12,000 on newspaper advertising. Find the ratio, as a fraction in simplest form, of radio advertising to newspaper advertising.

25. **Consumerism** A 15-pound turkey costs $13.95. What is the cost per pound?

26. **Travel** Mahesh drove 198.8 miles in 3.5 hours. Find the average number of miles he drove per hour.

27. **Insurance** An insurance policy costs $9.87 for every $1000 of insurance. At this rate, what is the cost of $50,000 of insurance?

28. **Investments** Pascal Hollis purchased 80 shares of stock for $3580. What was the cost per share?

29. **Landscaping** Monique uses 1.5 pounds of fertilizer for every 200 square feet of lawn. How many pounds of fertilizer will she have to use on a lawn that measures 3000 square feet?

30. **Real Estate** A house had an original value of $160,000, but its value increased to $240,000 in 2 years. Find the ratio, as a fraction in simplest form, of the increase to the original value.

6 TEST

1. Write "$46,036.80 earned in 12 months" as a unit rate.

2. Write the comparison 40 miles to 240 miles as a ratio in simplest form using a fraction, a colon (:), and the word *to*.

3. Write "18 supports for every 8 feet" as a rate in simplest form.

4. Is $\frac{40}{125} = \frac{5}{25}$ a true proportion?

5. Write the comparison 12 days to 4 days as a ratio in simplest form using a fraction, a colon (:), and the word *to*.

6. Solve the proportion.
$$\frac{5}{12} = \frac{60}{n}$$

7. Write "256.2 miles on 8.4 gallons of gas" as a unit rate.

8. Write the comparison 27 dollars to 81 dollars as a ratio in simplest form using a fraction, a colon (:), and the word *to*.

9. Is $\frac{5}{14} = \frac{25}{70}$ a true proportion?

10. Solve the proportion.
$$\frac{n}{18} = \frac{9}{4}$$

11. Write "9 feet for 6 boards" as a rate in simplest form.

12. Write the comparison 18 feet to 30 feet as a ratio in simplest form using a fraction, a colon (:), and the word *to*.

13. Investments   Fifty shares of a utility stock pay a dividend of $62.50. At the same rate, what is the dividend paid on 500 shares of the utility stock?

14. Electricity   A transformer has 40 turns in the primary coil and 480 turns in the secondary coil. State the ratio of the number of turns in the primary coil to the number of turns in the secondary coil.

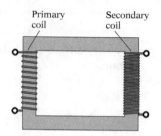

Primary coil   Secondary coil

15. Travel   A plane travels 2421 miles in 4.5 hours. Find the plane's speed in miles per hour.

16. Physiology   A research scientist estimates that the human body contains 88 pounds of water for every 100 pounds of body weight. At this rate, estimate the number of pounds of water in a college student who weighs 150 pounds.

17. Business   If 40 feet of lumber costs $69.20, what is the per-foot cost of the lumber?

18. Medicine   The dosage of a certain medication is $\frac{1}{4}$ ounce for every 50 pounds of body weight. How many ounces of this medication are required for a person who weighs 175 pounds? Write the answer as a decimal.

19. Sports   A basketball team won 20 games and lost 5 games during the season. Write, as a fraction in simplest form, the ratio of the number of games won to the total number of games played.

20. Manufacturing   A computer manufacturer discovers through experience that an average of 3 defective hard drives are found in every 100 hard drives manufactured. How many defective hard drives are expected to be found in the production of 1200 hard drives?

Cumulative Review Exercises

1. Subtract: $\begin{array}{r} 20{,}095 \\ -\ 10{,}937 \end{array}$

2. Write $2 \cdot 2 \cdot 2 \cdot 2 \cdot 3 \cdot 3 \cdot 3$ in exponential notation.

3. Simplify: $4 - (5 - 2)^2 \div 3 + 2$

4. Find the prime factorization of 160.

5. Find the LCM of 9, 12, and 18.

6. Find the GCF of 28 and 42.

7. Write $\frac{40}{64}$ in simplest form.

8. Find $4\frac{7}{15}$ more than $3\frac{5}{6}$.

9. What is $4\frac{5}{9}$ less than $10\frac{1}{6}$?

10. Multiply: $\frac{11}{12} \times 3\frac{1}{11}$

11. Find the quotient of $3\frac{1}{3}$ and $\frac{5}{7}$.

12. Simplify: $\left(\frac{2}{5} + \frac{3}{4} \right) \div \frac{3}{2}$

13. Write 4.0709 in words.

14. Round 2.09762 to the nearest hundredth.

15. Divide: $8.09\overline{)16.0976}$
Round to the nearest thousandth.

16. Convert 0.06 to a fraction.

17. Write the comparison 25 miles to 200 miles as a ratio in simplest form using a fraction.

18. Write "87 cents for 6 pencils" as a rate in simplest form.

19. Write "250.5 miles on 7.5 gallons of gas" as a unit rate.

20. Solve $\frac{40}{n} = \frac{160}{17}$.

21. Travel   A car traveled 457.6 miles in 8 hours. Find the car's speed in miles per hour.

22. Solve the proportion.
$\frac{12}{5} = \frac{n}{15}$

23. Banking   You had $1024 in your checking account. You then wrote checks for $192 and $88. What is your new checking account balance?

24. Finance   Malek Khatri buys a tractor for $32,360. A down payment of $5000 is required. The balance remaining is paid in 48 equal monthly installments. What is the monthly payment?

25. Homework Assignments   Yuko is assigned to read a book containing 175 pages. She reads $\frac{2}{5}$ of the book during Thanksgiving vacation. How many pages of the assignment remain to be read?

26. Real Estate   A building contractor bought $2\frac{1}{3}$ acres of land for $84,000. What was the cost of each acre?

27. Consumerism   Benjamin Eli bought a shirt for $45.58 and a tie for $19.18. He used a $100 bill to pay for the purchases. Find the amount of change.

28. Compensation   If you earn an annual salary of $41,619, what is your monthly salary?

29. Erosion   A soil conservationist estimates that a river bank is eroding at the rate of 3 inches every 6 months. At this rate, how many inches will be eroded in 50 months?

30. Medicine   The dosage of a certain medication is $\frac{1}{2}$ ounce for every 50 pounds of body weight. How many ounces of this medication are required for a person who weighs 160 pounds? Write the answer as a decimal.

Percents and Applications

OBJECTIVES

Focus on Success

What resources do you use when you need help in this course? You know to read and reread the text when you are having difficulty understanding a concept. Instructors are available to help you during their office hours. Most schools have a math center where students can get help. Some schools have a tutoring program. You might also ask a student who has been successful in this class for assistance. (See Habits of Successful Students, page AIM-6).

Monkey Business Images/Shutterstock.com

Prep Test

Are you ready to succeed in this chapter? Take the Prep Test below to find out if you are ready to learn the new material.

For Exercises 1 to 6, multiply or divide.

1. $19 \times \dfrac{1}{100}$

2. 23×0.01

3. 0.47×100

4. $0.06 \times 47{,}500$

5. $60 \div 0.015$

6. $8 \div \dfrac{1}{4}$

7. Multiply $\dfrac{5}{8} \times 100$. Write the answer as a decimal.

8. Write $\dfrac{200}{3}$ as a mixed number.

9. Divide $28 \div 16$. Write the answer as a decimal.

7.1   Introduction to Percents

OBJECTIVE A   *To write a percent as a decimal or a fraction*

Percent means "parts of 100." In the figure at the right, there are 100 parts. Because 13 of the 100 parts are shaded, 13% of the figure is shaded. The symbol % is the **percent sign**.

In most applied problems involving percents, it is necessary either to rewrite a percent as a decimal or a fraction or to rewrite a fraction or a decimal as a percent.

To write a percent as a decimal, remove the percent sign and multiply by 0.01.

$$13\% \quad = \quad 13 \times 0.01 \quad = \quad 0.13$$

> Move the decimal point two places to the left. Then remove the percent sign.

To write a percent as a fraction, remove the percent sign and multiply by $\frac{1}{100}$.

$$13\% = 13 \times \frac{1}{100} = \frac{13}{100}$$

> **Take Note**
> Recall that division is defined as multiplication by the reciprocal. Therefore, multiplying by $\frac{1}{100}$ is equivalent to dividing by 100.

EXAMPLE 1

Write each percent as a decimal and as a fraction.
a. 120%   **b.** 4.3%   **c.** 0.45%

Solution

a. $120\% = 120 \times 0.01 = 1.2$

$$120\% = 120 \times \frac{1}{100} = \frac{120}{100} = 1\frac{1}{5}$$

b. $4.3\% = 4.3 \times 0.01 = 0.043$

$$4.3\% = 4.3 \times \frac{1}{100}$$

$$= 4\frac{3}{10} \times \frac{1}{100}$$

$$= \frac{43}{10} \times \frac{1}{100} = \frac{43}{1000}$$

   • $4.3 = 4\frac{3}{10}$

   • Multiply the fractions.

c. $0.45\% = 0.45 \times 0.01 = 0.0045$

$$0.45\% = 0.45 \times \frac{1}{100}$$

$$= \frac{9}{20} \times \frac{1}{100}$$

$$= \frac{9}{2000}$$

   • $0.45 = \frac{45}{100} = \frac{9}{20}$

   • Multiply the fractions.

YOU TRY IT 1

Write each percent as a decimal and as a fraction.
a. 125%   **b.** 8.5%   **c.** 0.25%

Your solution

Solution on p. S12

EXAMPLE 2

Write $16\frac{2}{3}\%$ as a fraction.

Solution $16\frac{2}{3}\% = 16\frac{2}{3} \times \frac{1}{100}$

$$= \frac{50}{3} \times \frac{1}{100} = \frac{50}{300} = \frac{1}{6}$$

YOU TRY IT 2

Write $33\frac{1}{3}\%$ as a fraction.

Your solution

Solution on p. S12

OBJECTIVE B   *To write a decimal or a fraction as a percent*

A decimal or a fraction can be written as a percent by multiplying by 100%.

HOW TO 1   Write 0.37 as a percent.

$$0.37 \quad = \quad 0.37 \times 100\% \quad = \quad 37\%$$

Move the decimal point two places to the right. Then write the percent sign.

When changing a fraction to a percent, if the fraction can be written as a terminating decimal, the percent is written in decimal form. If the decimal representation of the fraction is a repeating decimal, the answer is written with a fraction.

 Take Note

The decimal form of $\frac{3}{8}$ terminates.

$$\begin{array}{r} 0.375 \\ 8{\overline{\smash{\big)}\,3.000}} \\ \underline{-2\,4} \\ 60 \\ \underline{-56} \\ 40 \\ \underline{-40} \\ 0 \end{array}$$

HOW TO 2   Write $\frac{3}{8}$ as a percent.

$$\frac{3}{8} = \frac{3}{8} \times \frac{100\%}{1}$$

$$= \frac{300\%}{8}$$

$$= 37.5\%$$

• $\frac{3}{8} = 0.375$ is a terminating decimal.

• The answer is written in decimal form.

Take Note

The decimal form of $\frac{1}{6}$ repeats.

$$\begin{array}{r} 0.16\overline{6} \\ 6{\overline{\smash{\big)}\,1.000}} \\ \underline{-6} \\ 40 \\ \underline{-36} \\ 40 \\ \underline{-36} \\ 4 \end{array}$$

HOW TO 3   Write $\frac{1}{6}$ as a percent.

$$\frac{1}{6} = \frac{1}{6} \times \frac{100\%}{1}$$

$$= \frac{100\%}{6}$$

$$= 16\frac{2}{3}\%$$

• $\frac{1}{6} = 0.1\overline{6}$ is a repeating decimal.

• The answer is written with a fraction.

EXAMPLE 3

Write 0.015 and 2.3 as percents.

Solution

$0.015 = 0.015 \times 100\%$
$\qquad = 1.5\%$

$2.3 = 2.3 \times 100\%$
$\quad\;\; = 230\%$

YOU TRY IT 3

Write 0.048 and 3.6 as percents.

Your solution

EXAMPLE 4

Write $\frac{19}{80}$ as a percent.

Solution

$\dfrac{19}{80} \times \dfrac{100\%}{1} = \dfrac{1900\%}{80}$

$\qquad\qquad\quad = 23.75\%$ • Write the answer in decimal form.

YOU TRY IT 4

Write $\frac{5}{16}$ as a percent.

Your solution

EXAMPLE 5

Write $\frac{2}{3}$ as a percent.

Solution

$\dfrac{2}{3} = \dfrac{2}{3} \times \dfrac{100\%}{1}$

$\quad = \dfrac{200\%}{3}$

$\quad = 66\dfrac{2}{3}\%$ • Write the answer with a fraction.

YOU TRY IT 5

Write $\frac{5}{6}$ as a percent.

Your solution

7.1 EXERCISES

✔ Concept Check

1. Percent means "parts of ____."

2. If you answered correctly 85% of the questions on a 100-question exam, how many questions did you answer correctly?

3. To change a percent to a decimal, remove the percent sign and move the decimal point two places to the _____.

4. To change a fraction to a percent, multiply the fraction by _____.

OBJECTIVE A *To write a percent as a decimal or a fraction*

For Exercises 5 to 26, write the percent as a decimal and as a fraction.

5. 72% **6.** 65% **7.** 23% **8.** 79% **9.** 36%

10. 69% **11.** 59% **12.** 24% **13.** 41% **14.** 25%

15. 25.4% **16.** 34% **17.** 57.9% **18.** 73.6%

19. 6.2% **20.** 6.9% **21.** 6.4% **22.** 7.5%

23. 0.25% **24.** 0.875% **25.** 0.55% **26.** 0.74%

For Exercises 27 to 38, write as a fraction.

27. $66\frac{2}{3}\%$ **28.** $12\frac{1}{2}\%$ **29.** $83\frac{1}{3}\%$ **30.** $3\frac{1}{8}\%$ **31.** $11\frac{1}{9}\%$ **32.** $\frac{3}{8}\%$

33. $45\frac{5}{11}\%$ **34.** $15\frac{3}{8}\%$ **35.** $4\frac{2}{7}\%$ **36.** $5\frac{3}{4}\%$ **37.** $6\frac{2}{3}\%$ **38.** $8\frac{2}{3}\%$

39. 🖊 When a certain percent is written as a fraction, the result is an improper fraction. Is the percent less than, equal to, or greater than 100%?

OBJECTIVE B *To write a decimal or a fraction as a percent*

For Exercises 40 to 51, write as a percent.

40. 0.16 **41.** 0.73 **42.** 0.05 **43.** 0.01 **44.** 1.07 **45.** 2.94

46. 0.004 **47.** 0.006 **48.** 1.012 **49.** 3.106 **50.** 0.8 **51.** 0.7

For Exercises 52 to 71, write as a percent.

52. $\dfrac{27}{50}$ **53.** $\dfrac{17}{20}$ **54.** $\dfrac{9}{16}$ **55.** $\dfrac{2}{5}$ **56.** $\dfrac{5}{8}$ **57.** $\dfrac{1}{8}$

58. $\dfrac{3}{40}$ **59.** $1\dfrac{1}{2}$ **60.** $\dfrac{7}{40}$ **61.** $\dfrac{9}{4}$ **62.** $\dfrac{16}{5}$ **63.** $\dfrac{7}{8}$

64. $\dfrac{15}{50}$ **65.** $\dfrac{12}{25}$ **66.** $\dfrac{7}{30}$ **67.** $\dfrac{4}{9}$

68. $\dfrac{7}{12}$ **69.** $1\dfrac{2}{3}$ **70.** $2\dfrac{1}{6}$ **71.** $\dfrac{7}{18}$

72. Does a mixed number represent a percent greater than 100% or less than 100%?

73. A decimal number less than 0 has zeros in the tenths and hundredths places. Does the decimal represent a percent greater than 1% or less than 1%?

74. Write the part of the square that is shaded as a fraction, as a decimal, and as a percent. Write the part of the square that is not shaded as a fraction, as a decimal, and as a percent.

Critical Thinking

75. The Food Industry In a survey conducted by Opinion Research Corp. for Lloyd's Barbeque Co., people were asked to name their favorite barbeque side dishes. 38% named corn on the cob, 35% named cole slaw, 11% named corn bread, and 10% named fries. What percent of those surveyed named something other than corn on the cob, cole slaw, corn bread, or fries?

76. Elections If $\frac{2}{5}$ of the population voted in an election, what percent of the population did not vote?

Projects or Group Activities

There is a quantity similar to percent ("per hundred") called *per mil*, which means *per thousand*. The symbol for per mil is ‰. Using this symbol, $7‰ = \frac{7}{1000} = 0.007$. For Exercises 77 to 80, write each per mil as a fraction in simplest form and as a decimal.

77. 53‰   **78.** 25‰   **79.** 150‰   **80.** 600‰

For Exercises 81 to 84, write each per mil as a percent.

81. 5‰   **82.** 45‰   **83.** 625‰   **84.** 1000‰

7.2   The Basic Percent Equation

OBJECTIVE A   *To use the basic percent equation*

What percent of the region shown below is shaded?

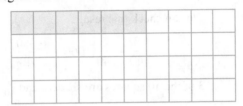

To answer this question, first determine what fraction of the region is shaded.

> There are a total of 40 squares in the region.
>
> 6 of the squares are shaded.
>
> $\dfrac{6}{40}$ of the region is shaded.

Now write the fraction $\frac{6}{40}$ as a percent.

$$\frac{6}{40} = \frac{6}{40}(100\%) = \frac{600}{40}\% = 15\%$$

15% of the region is shaded.

Now consider the question, "How many squares should be shaded if we want to shade 7.5% of the region shown below?"

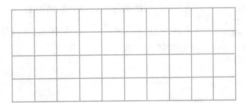

Determining the number of squares to be shaded requires answering the question

"7.5% of 40 is what number?"

This question can be translated into an equation and solved for the unknown number.

of	translates to	· (times)
is	translates to	= (equals)
what	translates to	*n* (the unknown number)

Here is the translation of "7.5% of 40 is what number?" Note that the percent is written as a decimal.

7.5%   of   40   is   what number?

0.075   ·   40   =   *n*

$$0.075 \cdot 40 = n \qquad \text{• Solve this equation for } n.$$
$$3 = n$$

If we shade 3 squares, 7.5% of the region will be shaded. **See the figure at the top of the next page.**

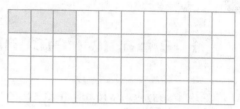

7.5% of the region is shaded.

We can check this result.

$$\frac{3}{40} = \frac{3}{40}(100\%) = \frac{300}{40}\% = 7.5\%$$

3 of the 40 squares are shaded, and $\frac{3}{40} = 7.5\%$. The solution checks.

We found the solution to this problem by solving the basic percent equation for *amount*.

The Basic Percent Equation

Percent · base = amount

In the example above, 7.5% is the percent, 40 is the base, and 3 is the amount.

Integrating Technology

The percent key % on a scientific calculator moves the decimal point two places to the left when pressed after a multiplication or division computation. For HOW TO 1 at the right, enter

800 ✕ 25 % =

The display reads 200.

HOW TO 1 What is 25% of 800?

Use the basic percent equation.

Percent = 25% = 0.25, base = 800, amount = n

Percent · base = amount

$$0.25 \cdot 800 = n$$

$$200 = n$$

25% of 800 is 200.

Notice from HOW TO 1 that the base in the basic percent equation follows the word *of*: 800 follows the word *of*, and 800 is the base in the basic percent equation. Look for the number or phrase that follows the word *of* when determining the base in the basic percent equation.

APPLY THE CONCEPT ··

A real estate broker receives a commission of 3% of the selling price of a house. Find the amount the broker receives on the sale of a $275,000 house.

Use the basic percent equation.

The base is the selling price of the house.
Percent = 3% = 0.03, base = 275,000, amount = n

Percent · base = amount

$$0.03 \cdot 275{,}000 = n$$

$$8250 = n$$

The broker receives a commission of $8250.

In most cases, the percent is written as a decimal before the basic percent equation is solved. However, some percents are more easily written as a fraction than as a decimal. For example,

$$33\frac{1}{3}\% = \frac{1}{3} \qquad 66\frac{2}{3}\% = \frac{2}{3} \qquad 16\frac{2}{3}\% = \frac{1}{6} \qquad 83\frac{1}{3}\% = \frac{5}{6}$$

In HOW TO 2, the percent is written as a fraction rather than as a decimal.

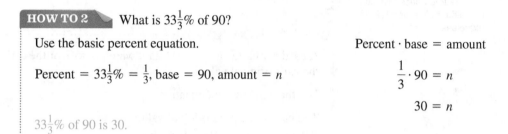

HOW TO 2   What is $33\frac{1}{3}\%$ of 90?

Use the basic percent equation.

Percent $= 33\frac{1}{3}\% = \frac{1}{3}$, base $= 90$, amount $= n$

Percent · base = amount

$$\frac{1}{3} \cdot 90 = n$$

$$30 = n$$

$33\frac{1}{3}\%$ of 90 is 30.

The three elements of the basic percent equation are the percent, the base, and the amount. If any two elements of the basic percent equation are given, the third element can be found.

In HOW TO 1 and HOW TO 2, the unknown was the amount. In HOW TO 3 below, the unknown is the percent. In HOW TO 4, the unknown is the base.

HOW TO 3   20 is what percent of 32?

Use the basic percent equation.

Percent $= n$, base $= 32$, amount $= 20$

Solve for n by dividing each side of the equation by 32.

Write the decimal as a percent.

Percent · base = amount

$$n \cdot 32 = 20$$

$$\frac{32n}{32} = \frac{20}{32}$$

$$n = 0.625$$

$$n = 62.5\%$$

20 is 62.5% of 32.

APPLY THE CONCEPT ··

You correctly answered 96 of the 120 questions on an exam. What percent of the questions did you answer correctly?

Use the basic percent equation.

Percent $= n$, base $= 120$, amount $= 96$

Solve for n by dividing each side of the equation by 120.

Write the decimal as a percent.

Percent · base = amount

$$n \cdot 120 = 96$$

$$\frac{120n}{120} = \frac{96}{120}$$

$$n = 0.8$$

$$n = 80\%$$

You answered 80% of the questions correctly.

HOW TO 4 60% of what number is 300?

Use the basic percent equation.

Percent = 60% = 0.60, base = n, amount = 300

Solve for n by dividing each side of the equation by 0.60.

60% of 500 is 300.

$$\text{Percent} \cdot \text{base} = \text{amount}$$
$$0.60 \cdot n = 300$$
$$\frac{0.60n}{0.60} = \frac{300}{0.60}$$
$$n = 500$$

APPLY THE CONCEPT ···

A used car has a value of $11,250, which is 45% of the car's original value. What was the car's original value?

Use the basic percent equation.

The base is the car's original value.
Percent = 45% = 0.45, base = n,
amount = 11,250

Solve for n by dividing each side of the equation by 0.45.

The car's original value was $25,000.

$$\text{Percent} \cdot \text{base} = \text{amount}$$
$$0.45 \cdot n = 11{,}250$$
$$\frac{0.45n}{0.45} = \frac{11{,}250}{0.45}$$
$$n = 25{,}000$$

EXAMPLE 1

Find 9.4% of 240.

Solution

Use the basic percent equation.
Percent = 9.4% = 0.094, base = 240,
amount = n

Percent · base = amount
  0.094 · 240 = n
     22.56 = n

9.4% of 240 is 22.56.

YOU TRY IT 1

Find $66\frac{2}{3}$% of 45.

Your solution

EXAMPLE 2

What percent of 30 is 12?

Solution

Use the basic percent equation.
Percent = n, base = 30, amount = 12

Percent · base = amount
  $n \cdot 30 = 12$
  $\frac{30n}{30} = \frac{12}{30}$
  $n = 0.4 = 40\%$

12 is 40% of 30.

YOU TRY IT 2

25 is what percent of 40?

Your solution

Solutions on p. S23

EXAMPLE 3

60 is 2.5% of what?

Solution

Use the basic percent equation.

Percent = 2.5% = 0.025, base = n,
amount = 60

$$\text{Percent} \cdot \text{base} = \text{amount}$$
$$0.025 \cdot n = 60$$
$$\frac{0.025n}{0.025} = \frac{60}{0.025}$$
$$n = 2400$$

60 is 2.5% of 2400.

YOU TRY IT 3

$16\frac{2}{3}\%$ of what is 15?

Your solution

Solution on p. S23

OBJECTIVE B   *To solve percent problems using proportions*

Problems that can be solved using the basic percent equation can also be solved using proportions.

The proportion method is based on writing two ratios . One ratio is the percent ratio, written as $\frac{\text{percent}}{100}$. The second ratio is the amount-to-base ratio, written as $\frac{\text{amount}}{\text{base}}$. These two ratios form the proportion

$$\frac{\textbf{percent}}{\textbf{100}} = \frac{\textbf{amount}}{\textbf{base}}$$

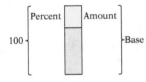

The proportion method can be illustrated by a diagram. The rectangle at the left is divided into two parts. On the left-hand side, the whole rectangle is represented by 100 and the part by the percent. On the right-hand side, the whole rectangle is represented by the base and the part by the amount. The ratio of the percent to 100 is equal to the ratio of the amount to the base.

When solving a percent problem using the basic percent equation, we first have to identify the percent, the base, and the amount. The same is true when solving a percent problem using the proportion method. Remember that the base usually follows the word *of.*

HOW TO 5   What is 32% of 85?

Use the proportion method.

Look at the diagram at the left.
Percent = 32, base = 85, amount = n

Solve the proportion for n.

$$\frac{\text{percent}}{100} = \frac{\text{amount}}{\text{base}}$$
$$\frac{32}{100} = \frac{n}{85}$$
$$100 \cdot n = 32 \cdot 85$$
$$100n = 2720$$
$$\frac{100n}{100} = \frac{2720}{100}$$
$$n = 27.2$$

32% of 85 is 27.2.

EXAMPLE 4

24% of what is 16? Round to the nearest hundredth.

Solution

$$\frac{\text{percent}}{100} = \frac{\text{amount}}{\text{base}}$$

$$\frac{24}{100} = \frac{16}{n}$$

$$24 \cdot n = 100 \cdot 16$$

$$24n = 1600$$

$$n = \frac{1600}{24} \approx 66.67$$

16 is approximately 24% of 66.67.

YOU TRY IT 4

8 is 25% of what?

Your solution

EXAMPLE 5

Find 1.2% of 42.

Solution

$$\frac{\text{percent}}{100} = \frac{\text{amount}}{\text{base}}$$

$$\frac{1.2}{100} = \frac{n}{42}$$

$$1.2 \cdot 42 = 100 \cdot n$$

$$50.4 = 100n$$

$$\frac{50.4}{100} = \frac{100n}{100}$$

$$0.504 = n$$

1.2% of 42 is 0.504.

YOU TRY IT 5

Find 0.74% of 1200.

Your solution

EXAMPLE 6

What percent of 52 is 13?

Solution

$$\frac{\text{percent}}{100} = \frac{\text{amount}}{\text{base}}$$

$$\frac{n}{100} = \frac{13}{52}$$

$$n \cdot 52 = 100 \cdot 13$$

$$52n = 1300$$

$$\frac{52n}{52} = \frac{1300}{52}$$

$$n = 25$$

25% of 52 is 13.

YOU TRY IT 6

What percent of 180 is 54?

Your solution

OBJECTIVE C   *To solve application problems*

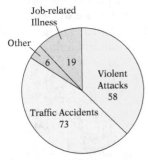

Figure 7.1 Causes of Death for Police Officers Killed in the Line of Duty
Source: International Union of Police Associations

HOW TO 6   The circle graph at the left shows the causes of death for all police officers who died while on duty during a recent year. What percent of the deaths were due to traffic accidents? Round to the nearest tenth of a percent.

Strategy   To find the percent:
- Find the total number of officers who died in the line of duty.
- Use the basic percent equation.
  Percent = n, base = total number killed,
  amount = number of deaths due to traffic accidents = 73

Solution $58 + 73 + 6 + 19 = 156$ • Total number killed

$$\text{Percent} \cdot \text{base} = \text{amount}$$
$$n \cdot 156 = 73$$
$$\frac{156n}{156} = \frac{73}{156}$$
$$n \approx 0.468$$
$$n \approx 46.8\%$$

46.8% of the deaths were due to traffic accidents.

EXAMPLE 7

During a recent year, 276 billion product coupons were issued by manufacturers. Shoppers redeemed 4.8 billion of these coupons. (*Source:* NCH NuWorld Consumer Behavior Study, America Coupon Council) What percent of the coupons issued were redeemed by customers? Round to the nearest tenth of a percent.

Strategy

To find the percent, use the basic percent equation.
Percent = n, base = number of coupons issued = 276 billion, amount = number of coupons redeemed = 4.8 billion

Solution

$$\text{Percent} \cdot \text{base} = \text{amount}$$
$$n \cdot 276 = 4.8$$
$$\frac{276n}{276} = \frac{4.8}{276}$$
$$n \approx 0.017$$
$$n \approx 1.7\%$$

Of the product coupons issued, 1.7% were redeemed by customers.

YOU TRY IT 7

An instructor receives a monthly salary of $4330, and $649.50 is deducted for income tax. Find the percent of the instructor's salary that is deducted for income tax.

Your strategy

Your solution

Solution on p. S24

EXAMPLE 8

A taxpayer pays a tax rate of 35% for state and federal taxes. The taxpayer has an income of $47,500. Find the amount of state and federal taxes paid by the taxpayer.

Strategy

To find the amount, use the basic percent equation.
Percent = 35% = 0.35, base = 47,500, amount = n

Solution

Percent · base = amount
0.35 · 47,500 = n
16,625 = n

The amount of taxes paid is $16,625.

According to Board-Trac, approximately 19% of the country's 2.4 million surfers are women. Estimate the number of female surfers in this country. Write the number in standard form.

Your strategy

Your solution

EXAMPLE 9

A department store has a blue blazer on sale for $114, which is 60% of the original price. What is the difference between the original price and the sale price?

Strategy

To find the difference between the original price and the sale price:

• Find the original price. Use the basic percent equation.
   Percent = 60% = 0.60,
   amount = 114, base = n
• Subtract the sale price from the original price.

Solution

Percent · base = amount
0.60 · n = 114
$\dfrac{0.60n}{0.60} = \dfrac{114}{0.60}$
$n = 190$ • The original price

190 − 114 = 76   • Subtract the sale price.

The difference in price is $76.

An electrician's wage this year is $30.13 per hour, which is 115% of last year's hourly wage. What is the increase in the hourly wage over the past year?

Your strategy

Your solution

Solutions on p. S24

7.2 EXERCISES

✔ Concept Check

For Exercises 1 to 4, state the number or variable that will replace each word in the basic percent equation, percent · base = amount. If the percent is known, write the percent as a decimal.

1. 12% of what is 68?

percent = _____   base = _____   amount = _____

2. What percent of 64 is 16?

percent = _____   base = _____   amount = _____

3. What is 8% of 450?

percent = _____   base = _____   amount = _____

4. 32 is what percent of 96?

percent = _____   base = _____   amount = _____

For Exercises 5 and 6, state the number or variable that will replace each word in the proportion $\frac{percent}{100} = \frac{amount}{base}$.

5. What is 36% of 25?

percent = _____   amount = _____   base = _____

6. 89% of what is 1780?

percent = _____   amount = _____   base = _____

OBJECTIVE A   *To use the basic percent equation*

7. Shade 70% of the region at the right.

8. Shade 45% of the region at the right.

9. Shade 62.5% of the region at the right.

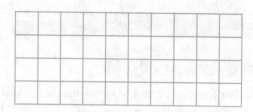

10. Shade 37.5% of the region at the right.

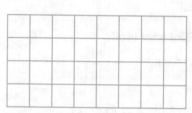

11. Shade $16\frac{2}{3}$% of the region at the right.

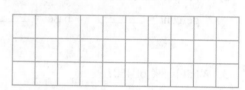

12. Circle 12.5% of the 80 people pictured at the right.

13. Circle 56.25% of the people pictured at the right.

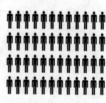

14. Circle $33\frac{1}{3}$% of the people pictured at the right.

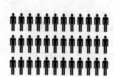

Solve. Use the basic percent equation.

15. 8% of 100 is what?

16. 16% of 50 is what?

17. 0.05% of 150 is what?

18. 0.075% of 625 is what?

19. 15 is what percent of 90?

20. 24 is what percent of 60?

21. What percent of 16 is 6?

22. What percent of 24 is 18?

23. 10 is 10% of what?

24. 37 is 37% of what?

25. 2.5% of what is 30?

26. 10.4% of what is 52?

27. Find 10.7% of 485.

28. Find 12.8% of 625.

29. 80% of 16.25 is what?

30. 26% of 19.5 is what?

31. 54 is what percent of 2000?

32. 8 is what percent of 2500?

33. 16.4 is what percent of 4.1?

34. 5.3 is what percent of 50?

35. 18 is 240% of what?

36. 24 is 320% of what?

37. **Entertainment** A usatoday.com online poll asked 8878 Internet users, "Would you use software to cut out objectionable parts of movies?" 29.8% of the respondents answered yes. How many respondents did not answer yes to the question? Round to the nearest whole number.

38. **Sociology** In a survey, 1236 adults nationwide were asked, "What irks you most about the actions of other motorists?" The response "tailgaters" was given by 293 people. (*Source:* Reuters/Zogby) What percent of those surveyed were most irked by tailgaters? Round to the nearest tenth of a percent.

39. **Travel** Of the travelers who, during a recent year, allowed their children to miss school to go on a trip, approximately 1.738 million allowed their children to miss school for more than a week. This represented 11% of the travelers who allowed their children to miss school. (*Source:* Travel Industry Association) About how many travelers allowed their children to miss school to go on a trip?

40. Given that 25% of x equals y, is $x < y$ or is $x > y$?

41. Given that 200% of x equals y, is $x < y$ or is $x > y$?

OBJECTIVE B   *To solve percent problems using proportions*

Solve. Use the proportion method.

42. 26% of 250 is what?

43. Find 18% of 150.

44. 37 is what percent of 148?

45. What percent of 150 is 33?

46. 68% of what is 51?

47. 126 is 84% of what?

48. What percent of 344 is 43?

49. 750 is what percent of 50?

50. 82 is 20.5% of what?

51. 2.4% of what is 21?

52. What is 6.5% of 300?

53. Find 96% of 75.

54. 7.4 is what percent of 50?

55. What percent of 1500 is 693?

56. Find 50.5% of 124.

57. What is 87.4% of 225?

58. 120% of what is 6?

59. 14 is 175% of what?

60. What is 250% of 18?

61. 325% of 4.4 is what?

62. 87 is what percent of 29?

63. What percent of 38 is 95?

64. ◗ **Email** The number of email messages sent each day has risen to 171 billion, of which 71% are spam. (*Source:* FeedsFarm.com) How many email messages sent per day are not spam?

65. ◗ **Wind Energy** In a recent year, wind machines in the United States generated 17.8 billion kilowatt-hours of electricity, enough to serve over 1.6 million households. The nation's total electricity production that year was 4450 billion kilowatt-hours. (*Source:* Energy Information Administration) What percent of the total energy production was generated by wind machines?

66. ◗ **Taxes** A TurboTax online survey asked people how they planned to use their tax refunds. Seven hundred forty people, or 22% of the respondents, said they would save the money. How many people responded to the survey?

67. For $\frac{1}{4}\%$, the percent ratio is the ratio $\dfrac{\frac{1}{4}}{100}$. Which of the following fractions is equivalent to this ratio?

    (i) $\dfrac{1}{25}$ (ii) $\dfrac{1}{400}$ (iii) $\dfrac{25}{1}$

68. For 0.75%, the percent ratio is the ratio $\dfrac{0.75}{100}$. Which of the following fractions are equivalent to this ratio?

    (i) $\dfrac{3}{4}$ (ii) $\dfrac{3}{400}$ (iii) $\dfrac{75}{10,000}$

69. True or false? For all positive values of N, 20% of N is equal to $N\%$ of 20.

OBJECTIVE C   *To solve application problems*

70. **Automotive Technology**   A mechanic estimates that the brakes of an RV still have 6000 mi of wear. This amount is 12% of the estimated safe-life use of the brakes. What is the estimated safe-life use of the brakes?

71. **Fireworks**   The value of the fireworks imported to the United States in a recent year was $163.1 million. During that year, the value of the fireworks imported from China was $157.2 million. (*Source:* www.census.gov) What percent of the value of the fireworks imported to the United States was the value of the fireworks imported from China? Round to the nearest tenth of a percent.

72. **Fire Science**   A fire department received 24 false alarms out of a total of 200 alarms received. What percent of the alarms received were false alarms?

73. **Fire Science**   The graph at the right shows firefighter deaths by type of duty for a recent year. What percent of the deaths occurred during training? Round to the nearest tenth of a percent.

74. **Lobsters**   Each year, 183 million pounds of lobster are caught in the United States and Canada. Twenty-five percent of this amount is sold live. (*Source:* Lobster Institute at the University of Maine) How many pounds of lobster are sold live each year in the United States and Canada?

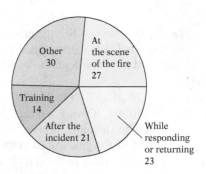

Firefighter Deaths
Source: U.S. Fire Administration

75. **Home Schooling**   In a recent year, 1.1 million students were home-schooled. This was 2.2% of all students in the United States. (*Source:* Home Schooling in the United States; U.S. Department of Education) Find the number of students in the United States that year.

76. ⬤ **Wind-Powered Ships** Using the information in the news clipping at the right, calculate the cargo ship's daily fuel bill.

HERO LANG/AFP/Getty Images

77. ⬤ **Lifestyles** There are 114 million households in the United States. Opposite-sex cohabiting couples comprise 4.4% of these households. (*Source:* Families and Living Arrangements) Find the number of opposite-sex cohabiting couples who maintain households in the United States. Round to the nearest million.

78. **Jewelry** Fourteen-carat yellow gold contains 58.5% gold, 17.5% silver, and 24% copper. If a jeweler has a 50-gram piece of 14-carat yellow gold, how many grams of gold, silver, and copper are in the piece?

79. ⬤ **Girl Scout Cookies** Using the information in the news clipping at the right, calculate the cash generated annually from sales of **a.** Thin Mints and **b.** Trefoil shortbread cookies.

80. ⬤ **Charities** The American Red Cross spent $185,048,179 for administrative expenses. This amount was 3.16% of its total revenue. Find the American Red Cross's total revenue. Round to the nearest hundred million.

Jeff Greenberg/AGEFotostock

81. ⬤ **Agriculture** Of the 572 million pounds of cranberries grown in the United States in a recent year, Wisconsin growers produced 291.72 million pounds. What percent of the total cranberry crop was produced in Wisconsin?

82. ⬤ **Education** See the news clipping at the right. What percent of the baby boomers living in the United States have some college experience but have not earned a college degree? Round to the nearest tenth of a percent.

83. ⬤ **Mining** During a recent year, approximately 2,240,000 oz of gold were used in the manufacturing of electronic equipment in the United States. This is 16% of all the gold mined in the United States that year. How many ounces of gold were mined in the United States that year?

84. ⬤ **Demography** According to a 25-city survey on the status of hunger and homelessness by the U.S. Conference of Mayors, 41% of the homeless in the United States are single men, 41% are families with children, 13% are single women, and 5% are unaccompanied minors. How many homeless people in the United States are single men?

In the NEWS!

Kite-Powered Cargo Ships

In January 2008, the first cargo ship partially powered by a giant kite set sail from Germany bound for Venezuela. The 1722-square-foot kite helped to propel the ship, which consequently used 20% less fuel, cutting approximately $1600 from the ship's daily fuel bill.

Source: The Internal Revenue Service; TSN Financial Services

In the NEWS!

Thin Mints Biggest Seller

Every year, sales from all the Girl Scout cookies sold by about 2.7 million girls total $700 million. The most popular cookie is Thin Mints, which earn 25% of total sales. Sales of Trefoil shortbread cookies represent only 9% of total sales.

Source: Southwest Airlines Spirit Magazine 2007

In the NEWS!

Over Half of Baby Boomers Have College Experience

Of the 78 million baby boomers living in the United States, 45 million have some college experience but no college degree. Twenty million baby boomers have one or more college degrees.

Sources: The National Center for Education Statistics; U.S. Census Bureau; *McCook Daily Gazette*

85. 🔵 **Pets**   The average costs associated with owning a dog over an average 11-year life span are shown in the graph at the right. These costs do not include the price of the puppy when purchased. The category labeled "Other" includes such expenses as fencing and repairing furniture damaged by the pet. What percent of the total cost is spent on food? Round to the nearest tenth of a percent.

86. 🔵 **Agriculture**   According to the U.S. Department of Agriculture, of the 63 billion pounds of vegetables produced in the United States in one year, 16 billion pounds were wasted. What percent of the vegetables produced were wasted? Round to the nearest tenth of a percent.

87. 🔵 **Health Insurance**   Approximately 30% of the 44 million people in the United States who do not have health insurance are between the ages of 18 and 24. (*Source:* U.S. Census Bureau) About how many people in the United States aged 18 to 24 do not have health insurance?

88. 🔵 **e-Filed Tax Returns**   See the news clipping at the right. How many of the 128 million returns were filed electronically? Round to the nearest million.

89. 🔵 **Diabetes**   Approximately 7% of the American population has diabetes. Within this group, 14.6 million are diagnosed, while 6.2 million are undiagnosed. (*Source:* The National Diabetes Education Program) What percent of Americans with diabetes have not been diagnosed with the disease? Round to the nearest tenth of a percent.

🔵 **Politics**   The results of a survey in which 32,840 full-time college and university faculty members were asked to describe their political views are shown at the right. Use these data for Exercises 90 and 91.

90. How many more faculty members described their political views as liberal than described their views as far-left?

91. How many fewer faculty members described their political views as conservative than described their views as middle-of-the-road?

Cost of Owning a Dog
Source: American Kennel Club, *USA Today* research

In the NEWS!

More Taxpayers Filing Electronically

The IRS reported that, as of May 4, it has received 128 million returns. Sixty percent of the returns were filed electronically.
Source: IRS

Political View	Percent of Faculty Members Responding
Far left	5.3%
Liberal	42.3%
Middle-of-the-road	34.3%
Conservative	17.7%
Far right	0.3%

Source: Higher Education Research Institute, UCLA

Critical Thinking

92. 🔲 Find 10% of a number and subtract it from the original number. Now take 10% of the new number and subtract it from the new number. Is this the same as taking 20% of the original number? Explain.

93. 🔲 Increase a number by 10%. Now decrease the new number by 10%. Is the result the original number? Explain.

94. **Compensation**   Your employer agrees to give you a 5% raise after one year on the job, a 6% raise the next year, and a 7% raise the following year. Is your salary after the third year greater than, less than, or the same as it would be if you had received a 6% raise each year?

Projects or Group Activities

95. The grid at the right contains 100 squares and represents 100 lb.
  a. What weight does one square represent?
  b. What is 1% of 100 lb?
  c. What weight does 50 squares represent?
  d. What is 50% of 100 lb?
  e. If 25 squares were shaded, what weight would that represent?
  f. What is 25% of 100?
  g. Shade the number of squares that corresponds to a weight of 70 lb.
  h. What percent of 100 lb is 70 lb?

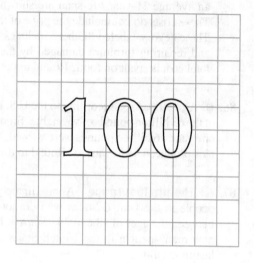

96. The grid at the right contains 100 squares and represents 200 lb.
  a. What weight does one square represent?
  b. What is 1% of 200 lb?
  c. What weight does 50 squares represent?
  d. What is 50% of 200 lb?
  e. If 25 squares were shaded, what weight would that represent?
  f. What is 25% of 200?
  g. Shade the number of squares that corresponds to a weight of 60 lb.
  h. What percent of 200 lb is 60 lb?

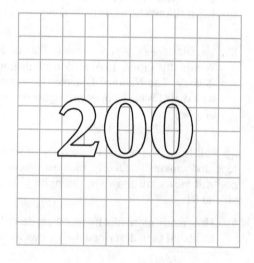

97. The grid at the right contains 100 squares and represents 20 lb.
  a. What weight does one square represent?
  b. What is 1% of 20 lb?
  c. What weight does 50 squares represent?
  d. What is 50% of 20 lb?
  e. If 25 squares were shaded, what weight would that represent?
  f. What is 25% of 20?
  g. Shade the number of squares that corresponds to a weight of 8 lb.
  h. What percent of 20 lb is 8 lb?

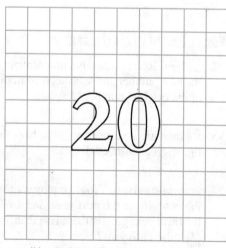

SECTION

7.3

Percent Increase and Percent Decrease

To solve percent increase problems

Point of Interest

According to the U.S. Census Bureau, the population of Arizona rose from 5,130,632 in 2000 to 6,392,017 in 2010, an increase of 24.6%.

Percent increase is used to show how much a quantity has increased over its original value. The statements "health care costs increased 4.8% last year" and "employees received an 8% pay increase" are illustrations of the use of percent increase.

HOW TO 1 ● According to the Energy Information Administration, the number of alternative-fuel vehicles increased from approximately 277,000 to approximately 352,000 in four years. Find the percent increase in the number of alternative-fuel vehicles. Round to the nearest percent.

Take Note

In solving percent increase and percent decrease problems, remember that the base in the basic percent equation is always the quantity *before* the increase or decrease. That is, it is the *original value*. For HOW TO 1 at the right, the base is 277,000—the quantity before the increase.

Strategy   To find the percent increase:
- Find the increase in the number of alternative-fuel vehicles.
- Use the basic percent equation.
  Percent = n, base = 277,000, amount = the amount of increase

Solution $352,000 - 277,000 = 75,000$ • The amount of increase

Percent · base = amount
$n \cdot 277,000 = 75,000$ • The base is the original value.
                             The amount is the amount of increase.

$$\frac{277,000n}{277,000} = \frac{75,000}{277,000}$$

$$n \approx 0.27$$

The number of alternative-fuel vehicles increased by approximately 27%.

EXAMPLE 1

A sales associate was earning $11.60 per hour before an 8% increase in pay. What is the new hourly wage? Round to the nearest cent.

Strategy

To find the new hourly wage:

- Use the basic percent equation to find the increase in pay.
  Percent = 8% = 0.08, base = 11.60,
  amount = n
- Add the amount of increase to the original wage.

Solution

Percent · base = amount
$0.08 \cdot 11.60 = n$
$0.93 \approx n$ • Increase in pay

$11.60 + \$.93 = \$12.53$ • Add the increase to the original wage.

The new hourly wage is $12.53.

YOU TRY IT 1

An automobile manufacturer increased the average mileage on a car from 17.5 mi/gal to 18.2 mi/gal. Find the percent increase in mileage.

Your strategy

Your solution

Solution on p. S24

OBJECTIVE B   *To solve percent decrease problems*

 Point of Interest

According to the U.S. Census Bureau, the population of Michigan dropped from 9,938,444 in 2000 to 9,883,640 in 2010, a decrease of 0.6%.

Percent decrease is used to show how much a quantity has decreased from its original value. The statements "the number of family farms decreased 2% last year" and "the president's approval rating has decreased 9% over the last month" are illustrations of the use of percent decrease.

HOW TO 2   During a 2-year period, the value of U.S. agricultural exports decreased from approximately \$60.6 billion to approximately \$52.0 billion. Find the percent decrease in the value of U. S. agricultural exports. Round to the nearest tenth of a percent.

Strategy   To find the percent decrease:
- Find the decrease in the value of agricultural exports.
- Use the basic percent equation.
  Percent = n, base = 60.6, amount = the amount of decrease

Solution $60.6 - 52.0 = 8.6$ • The amount of decrease

$$\text{Percent} \cdot \text{base} = \text{amount}$$
$$n \cdot 60.6 = 8.6$$

• The base is the original value. The amount is the amount of decrease.

$$\frac{60.6n}{60.6} = \frac{8.6}{60.6}$$
$$n \approx 0.142$$

The value of agricultural exports decreased by approximately 14.2%.

📋 **Take Note**

Remember that the base in the basic percent equation is the *original value*—that is, the quantity *before* the decrease. For HOW TO 2 at the right, the base is 60.6.

EXAMPLE 2

During a recent year, violent crime in a small city decreased from 27 crimes per 1000 people to 24 crimes per 1000 people. Find the percent decrease in violent crime. Round to the nearest tenth of a percent.

Strategy

To find the percent decrease in crime:
- Find the decrease in the number of crimes.
- Use the basic percent equation to find the percent decrease in crime.

Solution

$27 - 24 = 3$ • Amount of decrease

$$\text{Percent} \cdot \text{base} = \text{amount}$$
$$n \cdot 27 = 3$$

• The amount is the amount of decrease.

$$n = \frac{3}{27} \approx 0.111$$

Violent crime decreased by approximately 11.1% during the year.

YOU TRY IT 2

The market value of a luxury car decreased by 24% during the past year. Find the market value of a luxury car that cost \$47,000 last year. Round to the nearest dollar.

Your strategy

Your solution

Solution on p. S24

7.3 EXERCISES

✔ Concept Check

1. Suppose the price of an item increases from $15 to $18.

   a. Fill in each blank with *original* or *new:* The amount of increase is found by subtracting the _____ price from the _____ price.

   The amount of increase is $_____ − $_____ = $_____.

   b. To find the percent increase in price, use the basic percent equation. Let n represent the unknown percent.

   base = the original price = $_____; amount = amount of increase = $_____

2. Suppose the price of an item decreases from $48 to $38.

   a. Fill in each blank with *original* or *new:* The amount of decrease is found by subtracting the _____ price from the _____ price.

   The amount of decrease is $_____ − $_____ = $_____.

   b. To find the percent decrease in price, use the basic percent equation. Let n represent the unknown percent.

   base = the original price = $_____; amount = amount of decrease = $_____

OBJECTIVE A *To solve percent increase problems*

Solve. If necessary, round percents to the nearest tenth.

3. ● **Bison** See the news clipping at the right. Find the percent increase in human consumption of bison from 2005 to the date of this news article.

4. **Fuel Efficiency** An automobile manufacturer increased the average mileage on a car from 17.5 mi/gal to 18.2 mi/gal. Find the percent increase in mileage.

5. ● **Sports** In 1924, the number of events in the Winter Olympics was 14. The 2010 Winter Olympics in Salt Lake City included 86 medal events. (*Sources:* David Wallenchinsky's *The Complete Book of the Winter Olympics*; Wikipedia) Find the percent increase in the number of events in the Winter Olympics from 1924 to 2010.

6. ● **Wealth** The table at the right shows the numbers of millionaire households in the United States for selected years. Find the percent increase in the number of millionaire households from 1975 to 2010.

7. ● **Poverty** According to the Census Bureau, there were 32.9 million Americans living in poverty in 2001. By 2009, the number had increased to 43.6 million. Find the percent increase in the number of Americans living in poverty from 2001 to 2009.

In the NEWS!

A Taste for Bison

In 2005, the meat of 17,674 bison was consumed in the United States. This year, that number will reach 50,000. However, the consumption of bison is still a small fraction of beef consumption. Every day, the meat of 90,000 cattle is consumed in this country.

Source: Time, March 26, 2007

Year	Number of Households Containing Millionaires
1975	350,000
1997	3,500,000
2010	8,400,000

Source: Affluent Market Institute; CNNMoney.com

8. ◗ **Education**   In the 1990–1991 school year, the average cost for tuition, fees, and room and board at a private college was $13,476. In the 2009–2010 school year, the cost had risen to $26,273. (*Source:* The College Board) Find the percent increase in the average cost of attending a private college.

9. ◗ **Education**   In the 1990–1991 school year, the average cost for tuition, fees, and room and board at a public college was $5074. In the 2009–2010 school year, the cost had risen to $7020. (*Source:* The College Board) Find the percent increase in the average cost of attending a public college.

10. ◗ **Public Service**   Read the news clipping at the right. What is the percent increase in the number of applicants for AmeriCorps?

11. ◗ **Public Service**   Read the news clipping at the right. Find the percent increase in the number of applications for Teach for America.

12. ◗ **Housing**   The average size of a home in the United States in the 1960s was 1200 ft^2. That average grew to 1710 ft^2 in the 1980s and then 2330 ft^2 in the 2000s. (*Source:* finance.yahoo.com) Find the percent increase in the size of a home in the United States from the 1960s to the 2000s.

13. ◗ **Wages**   A welder earning $12 per hour is given a 10% raise. To find the new wage, we can multiply $12 by 0.10 and add the product to $12. Can the new wage be found by multiplying $12 by 1.10?

In the NEWS!

More College Grads Apply for Public Service Jobs

With jobs harder to find, there is a renewed interest in public service positions. The number of applicants for AmeriCorps rose from 91,399 in 2008 to 258,829 in 2010. Applications for Teach for America increased to 46,359 in 2010, from 35,120 a year earlier.

Source: topics.nytimes.com

OBJECTIVE B   *To solve percent decrease problems*

Solve. If necessary, round percents to the nearest tenth.

14. **Food Bills**   A family reduced its normal monthly food bill of $320 by $50. What percent decrease does this represent?

15. ◗ **Passports**   The graph at the right shows the numbers of passports, in millions, issued to U.S. citizens each year from 2007 to 2010. Find the percent decrease in the number of passports issued from 2007 to 2010.

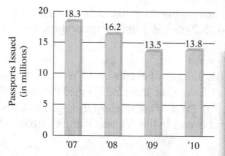

Passports Issued to U.S. Citizens
Source: State Department

16. **Manufacturing**   A new production method reduced the time needed to clean a piece of metal from 8 min to 5 min. What percent decrease does this represent?

17. **Demographics**   Read the news clipping at the right. Find the percent decrease in the size of the average U.S. household from 1960 to 2010.

In the NEWS!

Average Number of People in U.S. Households Decreasing

In 1960, the size of the average American household was 3.3 persons. By 2010, that number had decreased to 2.6 persons.

Source: Time, November 29, 2010

18. Customer Service As a result of an increased number of service lines at a grocery store, the average amount of time a customer waits in line has decreased from 3.8 min to 2.5 min. Find the percent decrease.

19. ● **Law School** Use the news clipping at the right to find the percent decrease in the number of people who took the LSATs in the last three years.

20. Finance Juanita's average monthly expense for gasoline was $176. After joining a carpool, she was able to reduce the expense by 20%.
a. What was the amount of decrease?
b. What is Juanita's average monthly gasoline bill now?

21. Depreciation It is estimated that the value of a new car is reduced 30% after one year of ownership. Find the value of a $21,900 new car after one year.

In the NEWS!

Fewer Students Take LSATs

This year, 137,444 people took the Law School Admission Test (LSAT). Three years ago, the LSATs were administered to 148,014 people.
Source: Law School Admission Council

22. Employment A department store employs 1200 people during the holidays. At the end of the holiday season, the store reduces the number of employees by 45%. What is the decrease in the number of employees?

23. ● **The Military** The graph at the right shows the numbers of active-duty U.S. military personnel, in thousands, in 1990 and in 2009. Which branch of the military had the greatest percent decrease in personnel from 1990 to 2009? What was the percent decrease for this branch of the service?

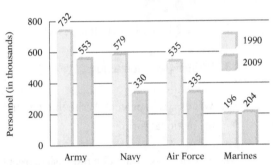

Number of Active-Duty U.S. Military Personnel
Source: Department of Defense

24. ⬚ In a math class, the average grade on the second test was 5% lower than the average grade on the first test. What should you multiply the first test average by to find the difference between the average grades on the two tests?

Critical Thinking

25. ◤ What is the difference between amount of increase and percent increase?

26. ◤ Explain how to find the new value when you are given the original value and the percent increase.

27. ◤ What is the difference between amount of decrease and percent decrease?

28. ◤ Explain how to find the amount of decrease when you are given the original value and the percent decrease.

29. ◤ Explain how to find the new value when you are given the original value and the amount of decrease.

30. ◤ Explain how to find the new value when you are given the original value and the percent decrease.

Projects or Group Activities

31. 📐 **Consumerism** A department store gives you three discount coupons: a 10% discount, a 20% discount, and a 30% discount off any item. You have decided to purchase a digital camera costing $225, and you plan to use all three coupons. Is there a particular order in which you should ask to have the discount coupons applied to your purchase so that your purchase price is as low as possible? Explain.

32. Consumerism A 3D TV costing $3000 was on sale for 30% off. An additional 10% off the sale price was offered to customers who paid using a store-issued credit card. Calculate the sales price after the two discounts. Is this the same as a discount of 40%? Find the single discount equal to the successive discounts.

✔ CHECK YOUR PROGRESS: CHAPTER 7

1. Write 38.7% as a decimal.

2. Write 44% as a fraction.

3. Write $5\frac{1}{3}$% as a fraction.

4. Write 0.725 as a percent.

5. Write $\frac{7}{12}$ as a percent. Write the remainder in fractional form.

6. Write $\frac{9}{16}$ as a percent. Round to the nearest tenth of a percent.

7. 21% of 50 is what? Use the basic percent equation.

8. What percent of 80 is 50? Use the basic percent equation.

9. 15% of what number is 30? Use the basic percent equation.

10. Find 18% of 425. Use the proportion method.

11. 38 is what percent of 95? Use the proportion method.

12. 56 is 140% of what number? Use the proportion method.

13. Taxes A consumer paid sales tax of $180 on a purchase of $4500. What percent of the purchase price is the sales tax?

14. ⬤ **Arctic Ice Cap** Read the news clipping at the right. What is the percent decrease in the area of the Arctic ice cap from 2000 to 2010? Round to the nearest tenth of a percent.

15. Business A company "plowed back" 54% of the $800,000 it earned one year into research and development. How much of the money the company earned that year was reinvested in research and development?

16. ⬤ **Movie Rentals** Netflix's revenue in 2004 was $506 million. Its revenue in 2009 was $1.67 billion. Find the percent increase in Netflix's revenue from 2004 to 2009. Round to the nearest tenth of a percent.

17. Car Purchases You made a down payment of $4110 on a new car. The down payment was 15% of the purchase price of the car. Find the purchase price of the car.

In the NEWS!

Arctic Ice Cap Melting

The Arctic sea ice is significantly smaller than it was a decade ago. In 2000, its area was 2.7 million square miles. By 2010, its area had decreased to 1.9 million square miles. Some scientists report that the smaller ice cap will reflect less sunlight, which will lead to warmer global temperatures.

Source: Time, December 6, 2010

7.4 | Markup and Discount

OBJECTIVE A   *To solve markup problems*

Cost is the amount a merchandising business or retailer pays for a product. **Selling price,** or **retail price,** is the price for which a merchandising business or retailer sells a product to a customer.

The difference between selling price and cost is called **markup.** Markup is added to cost to cover the expenses of operating a business and to provide a profit to the owners.

Markup can be expressed as a percent of the cost, or it can be expressed as a percent of the selling price. Here we present markup as a percent of the cost, which is the most common practice.

The percent markup is called the **markup rate,** and it is expressed as the markup based on the cost.

A diagram is useful for expressing the markup equations. In the diagram at the left, the total length is the selling price. One part of the diagram is the cost, and the other part is the markup.

Markup · Selling Price · Cost

Take Note

If C is added to both sides of the first equation, $M = P - C$, the result is the second equation listed, $P = C + M$.

The Markup Equations

$$M = P - C$$
$$P = C + M$$
$$M = r \cdot C$$

where

M = markup
P = selling price
C = cost
r = markup rate

EXAMPLE

A book costs a store $20. The markup rate is 50%.
$C = \$20, r = 50\% = 0.5$
Markup $= M = r \cdot C = 0.5(\$20) = \$10$
Selling price $= P = C + M = \$20 + \$10 = \$30$

HOW TO 1   The manager of a clothing store buys a fleece tracksuit for $80 and sells the tracksuit for $116. Find the markup rate.

Strategy   To find the markup rate:

- Find the markup by solving the formula $M = P - C$ for M. $P = 116$, $C = 80$
- Solve the formula $M = r \cdot C$ for r. M = the markup, $C = 80$

Solution

$M = P - C$
$M = 116 - 80$
$M = 36$

$M = r \cdot C$
$36 = r \cdot 80$

$$\frac{36}{80} = \frac{80r}{80}$$

$0.45 = r$

The markup rate is 45%.

M · 80 · 116

EXAMPLE 1

A convertible soft top that costs a dealer $250 has a markup rate of 35%. Find the markup.

Strategy

To find the markup, solve the formula $M = r \cdot C$ for M.
$r = 35\% = 0.35$, $C = 250$

Solution

$M = r \cdot C$

$M = 0.35 \cdot 250$ • $r = 0.35$, $C = 250$

$M = 87.50$

The markup is $87.50.

YOU TRY IT 1

An outboard motor costing $650 has a markup rate of 45%. Find the markup.

Your strategy

Your solution

EXAMPLE 2

A graphing calculator costing $45 is sold for $80. Find the markup rate. Round to the nearest tenth of a percent.

Strategy

To find the markup rate:

• Find the markup by solving the formula $M = P - C$ for M.
  $P = 80$, $C = 45$
• Solve the formula $M = r \cdot C$ for r.
  M = the markup, $C = 45$

Solution

$M = P - C$

$M = 80 - 45$

$M = 35$ • The markup is $35.

$M = r \cdot C$

$35 = r \cdot 45$ • $M = 35$, $C = 45$

$\dfrac{35}{45} = \dfrac{45r}{45}$

$0.778 \approx r$

The markup rate is 77.8%.

YOU TRY IT 2

A photo printer costing $950 is sold for $1450. Find the markup rate. Round to the nearest tenth of a percent.

Your strategy

Your solution

Solutions on pp. S24–S25

EXAMPLE 3

A fishing reel with a cost of $50 has a markup rate of 22%. Find the selling price.

Strategy

To find the selling price:

• Find the markup by solving the equation
  $M = r \cdot C$ for M.
  $r = 22\% = 0.22, C = 50$
• Solve the formula $P = C + M$ for P.
  $C = 50, M =$ the markup

Solution

$M = r \cdot C$
$M = 0.22 \cdot 50$
$M = 11$ • The markup is $11.

$P = C + M$
$P = 50 + 11$ • $C = 50, M = 11$
$P = 61$

The selling price is $61.

YOU TRY IT 3

A basketball with a cost of $82.50 has a markup rate of 42%. Find the selling price.

Your strategy

Your solution

Solution on p. S25

OBJECTIVE B   *To solve discount problems*

A retailer may reduce the regular price of a product for a promotional sale because the product is damaged, an odd size or color, or a discontinued item. The **discount,** or **markdown,** is the amount by which a retailer reduces the regular price of a product.

The percent discount is called the **discount rate** and is usually expressed as a percent of the original price (the regular selling price).

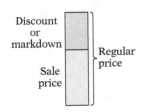

Discount or markdown
Sale price
Regular price

The Discount Equations

$D = R - S$	where	$D =$ discount or markdown
$D = r \cdot R$		$S =$ sale price
$S = (1 - r)R$		$R =$ regular price
		$r =$ discount rate

EXAMPLE

A book that regularly sells for $20 is on sale for 25% off the regular price.

$R = \$20, r = 25\% = 0.25$

Sale price $= S = (1 - r)R = (1 - 0.25)(\$20) = 0.75(\$20) = \$15$

Discount $= D = R - S = \$20 - \$15 = \$5$

EXAMPLE 4

A graphics tablet that regularly sells for $1850 is on sale for $1480. Find the discount rate.

Strategy

To find the discount rate:

- Find the discount by solving the formula $D = R - S$ for D. $R = 1850$, $S = 1480$
- Solve the formula $D = r \cdot R$ for r. $D =$ the discount, $R = 1850$

Solution

$$D = R - S \qquad\qquad D = r \cdot R$$
$$D = 1850 - 1480 \qquad 370 = r \cdot 1850$$
$$D = 370 \qquad\qquad \frac{370}{1850} = \frac{1850r}{1850}$$
$$0.2 = r$$

The discount rate is 20%.

YOU TRY IT 4

A camera has a regular price of $325. It is currently on sale for $253.50. Find the discount rate.

Your strategy

Your solution

EXAMPLE 5

A necklace with a regular price of $450 is on sale for 32% off the regular price. Find the sale price.

Strategy

To find the sale price, solve the formula $S = (1 - r)R$ for S. $r = 32\% = 0.32$, $R = 450$

Solution

$$S = (1 - r)R$$
$$S = (1 - 0.32)450$$
$$S = (0.68)450$$
$$S = 306$$

The sale price is $306.

YOU TRY IT 5

A GPS regularly priced at $234 is on sale for 25% off the regular price. Find the sale price.

Your strategy

Your solution

EXAMPLE 6

An iPod docking system is on sale for $104 after a markdown of 35%. Find the regular price.

Strategy

To find the regular price, solve the formula $S = (1 - r)R$ for R. $S = 104$, $r = 35\% = 0.35$

Solution

$$S = (1 - r)R$$
$$104 = (1 - 0.35)R$$
$$104 = 0.65R$$
$$\frac{104}{0.65} = \frac{0.65R}{0.65}$$
$$160 = R$$

The regular price is $160.

YOU TRY IT 6

A large-screen TV, marked down 35%, is on sale for $1495. Find the regular price.

Your strategy

Your solution

7.4 EXERCISES

✔ Concept Check

1. Fill in the blank with *sells a product for* or *pays for a product*.

   Cost is the amount of money a business _____.

2. Fill in each blank with *an amount of money* or *a percent*.

   A *markup* is _____. A *markup rate* is _____.

3. Fill in each blank with *cost* or *selling price*.

   The markup is the difference between the _____ and the

   _____.

   The markup rate is the markup expressed as a percent of the _____.

4. Two words for the amount by which a seller reduces the price of a product are

   _____ and _____.

5. Fill in each blank with *an amount of money* or *a percent*.

   A *markdown* is _____. A *discount rate* is

   _____.

6. Fill in each blank with *sale price* or *regular price*.

   The markdown is the difference between the _____ and the

   _____.

   The discount rate is the markdown expressed as a percent of the

   _____.

OBJECTIVE A   *To solve markup problems*

7. 🖐 The markup equations are $M = P - C$, $P = C + M$, and $M = r \cdot C$. List, in
   the order in which they will be used, the equations needed to solve each problem.
   Do not solve.
   a. A CD that costs $8 is sold for $12. Find the markup.
   b. A sweater that cost the seller $50 is being sold for $65. Find the markup rate.
   c. A camera that costs $230 has a markup rate of 35%. Find the selling price.

Solve.

8. A camcorder costing $110 has a markup rate of 55%. Find the markup.

9. A television set costing $315 has a markup rate of 30%. Find the markup.

10. A watch that cost $98 is being sold for $156.80. Find the markup rate.

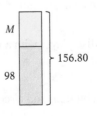

11. A set of golf clubs costing $360 is sold for $630. Find the markup rate.

12. A freezer selling for $520 cost the appliance dealer $360. Find the markup rate. Round to the nearest tenth of a percent.

13. A digital camera costing $320 is sold for $479. What is the markup rate on the digital camera? Round to the nearest tenth of a percent.

14. A markup rate of 25% is applied to a printer costing $1750. Find the selling price.

15. A flat of strawberries costing $7.60 has a markup rate of 125%. Find the selling price.

16. A video game costing $47 has a markup rate of 75%. Find the selling price.

17. A markup rate of 58% is applied to a leather jacket costing $225. Find the selling price.

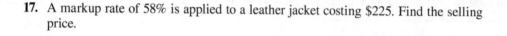

OBJECTIVE B   *To solve discount problems*

18. The discount equations are $D = R - S$, $D = r \cdot R$, and $S = (1 - r)R$. List, in the order in which they will be used, the equations needed to solve each problem. Do not solve.
   a. A gallon of milk that regularly sells for $3.69 is on sale for $2.19. Find the markdown.
   b. A television with a regular price of $429 is on sale for $379. Find the discount rate.
   c. A jacket with a regular price of $95 is on sale for 25% off the regular price. Find the sale price.

Solve.

19. An exercise bicycle that regularly sells for $460 is on sale for $350. Find the markdown.

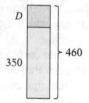

20. A smartphone with a regular price of $179 is on sale for $119. Find the markdown.

21. Find the markdown rate on a round-trip ticket to Paris that has a regular price of $1295 and is on sale for $995. Round to the nearest tenth of a percent.

22. A bicycle with a regular price of $495 is on sale for $380. Find the markdown rate. Round to the nearest tenth of a percent.

23. A compact disc player with a regular price of $162.50 is on sale for $94.25. Find the discount rate.

24. Find the discount rate on a scooter that has a regular price of $178 and is on sale for $103.24.

25. A memory foam mattress with a regular price of $1995 is on sale for 30% off the regular price. Find the sale price.

26. What is the sale price on a painting that has a regular price of $1600 and is on sale for 45% off the regular price?

27. A soccer ball that has a regular price of $42 is on sale for 40% off the regular price. What is the sale price of the soccer ball?

28. A gold ring with a regular price of $415 is on sale for 55% off the regular price. Find the sale price.

29. A mechanic's tool set is on sale for $180 after a markdown of 40% off the regular price. Find the regular price.

30. A battery with a discount price of $65 is on sale for 22% off the regular price. Find the regular price. Round to the nearest cent.

31. A cell phone that is on sale for $80 has a markdown of 35% off the regular price. What is the regular price of the cell phone? Round to the nearest cent.

Critical Thinking

32. A media center is on sale for 20% off the regular price of $5500. An additional 10% discount on the sale price is offered. Is the result a 30% discount? What is the single discount that would give the same sale price?

33. ◣ A promotional sale at a department store offers 25% off the sale price of merchandise that has already been discounted 25% off the regular price. Is this the same as a sale that offers 50% off the regular price? If not, which sale price gives the lower price? Explain your answer.

Projects or Group Activities

34. A lamp, originally priced at under $100, was on sale for 25% off the regular price. When the regular price, a whole number of dollars, was discounted, the discounted price was also a whole number of dollars. Find the largest possible number of dollars in the regular price of the lamp.

35. ◣ Write an application problem involving a discount rate of 35%. Choose a product and its regular price. Determine the sale price. Use complete sentences.

36. ◣ Write a report on series trade discounts. Explain how to convert a series discount to a single-discount equivalent.

CHAPTER

7 | Review Exercises

1. Write 32% as a fraction.

2. Write 22% as a decimal.

3. Write 25% as a fraction and as a decimal.

4. Write $3\frac{2}{5}$% as a fraction.

5. Write $\frac{7}{40}$ as a percent.

6. Write $1\frac{2}{7}$ as a percent. Round to the nearest tenth of a percent.

7. Write 2.8 as a percent.

8. 42% of 50 is what?

9. What percent of 3 is 15?

10. 12 is what percent of 18? Round to the nearest tenth of a percent.

11. 150% of 20 is what number?

12. Find 18% of 85.

13. 32% of what number is 180?

14. 4.5 is what percent of 80?

15. Find 0.58% of 2.54.

16. 0.0048 is 0.05% of what number?

17. ⬤ Tourism   The table at the right shows the countries with the highest projected numbers of tourists visiting in 2020. What percent of the tourists projected to visit these countries will be visiting China? Round to the nearest tenth of a percent.

Country	Projected Number of Tourists in 2020
China	137 million
France	93 million
Spain	71 million
USA	102 million

Source: The State of the World Atlas by Dan Smith

18. Advertising   A company spent 7% of its $120,000 budget on advertising. How much did the company spend on advertising?

19. Manufacturing   A quality control inspector found that 1.2% of 4000 cellular telephones were defective. How many of the phones were not defective?

20. ⬤ Television   According to the Cabletelevision Advertising Bureau, cable households watch an average of 61.35 h of television per week. On average, what percent of the week do cable households spend watching TV? Round to the nearest tenth of a percent.

21. **Business**   A resort lodge expects to make a profit of 22% of total income. What is the expected profit on $750,000 of income?

22. **Sports**   A basketball auditorium increased its 9000-person seating capacity by 18%. How many seats were added to the auditorium?

23. **The Airline Industry**   An airline knowingly overbooks flights by selling 12% more tickets than there are seats available. How many tickets would this airline sell for an airplane that has 175 seats?

24. **Elections**   In a recent city election, 25,400 out of 112,000 registered voters voted. What percent of the registered voters voted in the election? Round to the nearest tenth of a percent.

25. **Wages**   A sales clerk was earning $10.50 an hour before an 8% increase in pay. What is the clerk's new hourly wage?

26. **Consumerism**   A media system that sold for $2400 one year ago can now be bought for $1800. What percent decrease does this represent?

27. **Markup**   A car dealer advertises a 6% markup rate on a car that cost the dealer $18,500. Find the selling price of the car.

28. **Markup**   A parka costing $110 is sold for $181.50. Find the markup rate.

29. **Discount**   A tennis racket that regularly sells for $80 is on sale for 30% off the regular price. Find the sale price.

30. **Discount**   An airline is offering a 40% discount on round-trip air fares. Find the sale price of a round-trip ticket that normally sells for $650.

31. **Simple Interest**   Find the simple interest due on a 45-day loan of $3000 at an annual simple interest rate of 8.6%.

32. **Simple Interest**   A corporation borrowed $500,000 for 60 days and paid $7397.26 in simple interest. What annual simple interest rate did the corporation pay on the loan? Round to the nearest hundredth of a percent.

33. **Simple Interest**   A realtor took out a $10,000 loan at a 5.4% annual simple interest rate for 9 months. Find the maturity value of the loan.

7 | TEST

1. Write 86.4% as a decimal.

2. Write 0.4 as a percent.

3. Write $\frac{5}{4}$ as a percent.

4. Write $83\frac{1}{3}\%$ as a fraction.

5. Write 32% as a fraction.

6. Write 1.18 as a percent.

7. 18 is 20% of what number?

8. What is 68% of 73?

9. What percent of 320 is 180?

10. 28 is 14% of what number?

11. Industrial Accidents   An insurance company expects that 2.2% of a company's employees will have an industrial accident. How many accidents are expected for a company that employs 1500 people?

12. Test Scores   A student missed 16 questions on a history exam of 90 questions. What percent of the questions did the student answer correctly? Round to the nearest tenth.

13. Wages   An administrative assistant has a wage of $480 per week. This is 120% of last year's weekly wage. What is the dollar increase in the assistant's weekly wage over last year?

14. ◗ **Education**   The table at the right shows the average cost of tuition, room, and board at both public and private colleges in the United States. What is the percent increase in cost for a student who goes from a public college to a private college? Round to the nearest tenth of a percent.

Average Tuition, Room, and Board	
Public college	$12,127
Private college	$29,026

Source: The College Board

15. Management   The number of management trainees working for a company has increased from 36 to 42. What percent increase does this represent?

16. ● **Nutrition** The table at the right shows the fat, saturated fat, cholesterol, and calorie content in a 90-gram ground-beef burger and in a 90-gram soy burger.

	Beef Burger	Soy Burger
Fat	24 g	4 g
Saturated Fat	10 g	1.5 g
Cholesterol	75 mg	0 mg
Calories	280	140

    a. As compared with the beef burger, by what percent is the fat content decreased in the soy burger?

    b. What is the percent decrease in cholesterol in the soy burger as compared with the beef burger?

    c. Calculate the percent decrease in calories in the soy burger as compared with the beef burger.

17. **Travel Expenses** Last year, a company's travel expenses totaled $25,000. This year, the travel expenses totaled $23,000. What percent decrease does this represent?

18. **Art** A painting has a value of $1500. This is 125% of the painting's value last year. What is the dollar increase in the value of the painting?

19. **Markup** The manager of a stationery store uses a markup rate of 60%. What is the markup on a box of notepaper that costs the store $21?

20. **Markup** An electric keyboard costing $225 is sold for $349. Find the markup rate on the keyboard. Round to the nearest tenth of a percent.

21. **Discount** A telescope is on sale for $180 after a markdown of 40% off the regular price. Find the regular price.

22. **Discount** The regular price of a 10-foot by 10-foot dome tent is $370. The tent is now marked down $51.80. Find the discount rate on the tent.

23. **Simple Interest** Find the simple interest due on a 9-month loan of $5000 when the annual interest rate is 5.4%.

24. **Simple Interest** Maribeth Bakke took out a 150-day, $40,000 business loan that had an annual simple interest rate of 6.25%. Find the maturity value of the loan.

25. **Simple Interest** Gene Connery paid $672 in simple interest on an 8-month loan of $12,000. Find the simple interest rate on the loan.

Monomials, Measurement, and Radicals

8

Focus on Success

Are you using the features of this text to learn the concepts being presented? The HOW TO feature includes a step-by-step solution to the types of exercises you will be working in your homework assignments and on exams. A numbered Example provides you with a fully-worked-out solution. After studying the Example, try completing the You Try It to the right of the Example. A complete solution to the You Try It is given in the back of the text. (See Use the Interactive Method, page AIM-8.)

Helder Almeida/Shutterstock.com

Prep Test

Are you ready to succeed in this chapter? Take the Prep Test below to find out if you are ready to learn the new material.

1. Place the correct symbol, $<$ or $>$, between the two numbers.

54   45

For Exercises 2 to 6, add, subtract, multiply, or divide.

2. $-19 + 8$

3. $26 - 38$

4. $-2(44)$

5. $-\dfrac{3}{4}(-8)$

6. $3.97 \cdot 10^4$

7. Simplify: $(-3)^2$

8. Simplify: $(8 - 6)^2 + 12 \div 4 \cdot 3^2$

8.1 Multiplication of Monomials

OBJECTIVE A   *To multiply monomials*

Recall that in the exponential expression 3^4, 3 is the base and 4 is the exponent. The exponential expression 3^4 means to multiply 3, the base, 4 times. Therefore, $3^4 = 3 \cdot 3 \cdot 3 \cdot 3 = 81$.

For the variable exponential expression x^6, x is the base and 6 is the exponent. The exponent indicates the number of times the base occurs as a factor. Therefore,

$$\overbrace{}^{\text{Multiply } x \text{ 6 times.}}$$
$$x^6 = x \cdot x \cdot x \cdot x \cdot x \cdot x$$

The product of exponential expressions with the *same* base can be simplified by writing each expression in factored form and then writing the result with an exponent.

$$x^3 \cdot x^2 = \overbrace{(x \cdot x \cdot x)}^{\text{3 factors}} \cdot \overbrace{(x \cdot x)}^{\text{2 factors}}$$
$$\underbrace{}_{\text{5 factors}}$$
$$= x \cdot x \cdot x \cdot x \cdot x$$
$$= x^5$$

Note that adding the exponents results in the same product.

$$x^3 \cdot x^2 = x^{3+2} = x^5$$

This suggests the following rule for multiplying exponential expressions.

Rule for Multiplying Exponential Expressions

If m and n are positive integers, then $x^m \cdot x^n = x^{m+n}$.

EXAMPLE

Simplify: $a^4 \cdot a^5$

$a^4 \cdot a^5 = a^{4+5}$ • This is the product of two exponential expressions with the same base. Add the exponents.

$ = a^9$

HOW TO 1   Simplify: $c^3 \cdot c^4 \cdot c$

The bases are the same.
Add the exponents. Note that $c = c^1$.

$c^3 \cdot c^4 \cdot c = c^{3+4+1}$
$ = c^8$

HOW TO 2   Simplify: $x^5 y^3$

The bases are *not* the same. The exponential expression is in simplest form.

$x^5 y^3$ is in simplest form.

> **HOW TO 3** Simplify: $(4x^3)(2x^2)$

Use the Commutative and Associative Properties of Multiplication to rearrange and group like factors.

$$(4x^3)(2x^2) = (4 \cdot 2)(x^3 \cdot x^2)$$

Multiply the coefficients. Multiply variables with the same base by adding the exponents.

$$= 8x^{3+2}$$
$$= 8x^5$$

> **HOW TO 4** Simplify: $(a^3b^2)(a^4)$

Multiply variables with the same base by adding the exponents.

$$(a^3b^2)(a^4) = a^{3+4}b^2$$
$$= a^7b^2$$

> **HOW TO 5** Simplify: $(-2v^3z^5)(5v^2z^6)$

Multiply the coefficients of the monomials. Multiply variables with the same base by adding the exponents.

$$(-2v^3z^5)(5v^2z^6) = [(-2)5](v^{3+2})(z^{5+6})$$
$$= -10v^5z^{11}$$

EXAMPLE 1

Simplify: $(-6c^5)(7c^8)$

Solution
$$(-6c^5)(7c^8)$$
$$= [(-6)7](c^{5+8})$$
$$= -42c^{13}$$

• The bases are the same. Add the exponents.

YOU TRY IT 1

Simplify: $(-7a^4)(4a^2)$

Your solution

EXAMPLE 2

Simplify: $(-5ab^3)(4a^5)$

Solution
$$(-5ab^3)(4a^5)$$
$$= (-5 \cdot 4)(a \cdot a^5)b^3$$
$$= -20a^{1+5}b^3$$
$$= -20a^6b^3$$

• Add the exponents on variables with the same base.

YOU TRY IT 2

Simplify: $(8m^3n)(-3n^5)$

Your solution

EXAMPLE 3

Simplify: $(6x^3y^2)(4x^4y^5)$

Solution
$$(6x^3y^2)(4x^4y^5)$$
$$= (6 \cdot 4)(x^3 \cdot x^4)(y^2 \cdot y^5)$$
$$= 24x^{3+4}y^{2+5}$$
$$= 24x^7y^7$$

YOU TRY IT 3

Simplify: $(12p^4q^3)(-3p^5q^2)$

Your solution

Solutions on p. S16

OBJECTIVE B *To simplify powers of monomials*

The expression $(x^4)^3$ is an example of a *power of a monomial;* the monomial x^4 is raised to the third (3) power.

The power of a monomial can be simplified by writing the power in factored form and then using the Rule for Multiplying Exponential Expressions.

$$(x^4)^3 = x^4 \cdot x^4 \cdot x^4$$
$$= x^{4+4+4} = x^{12}$$

Note that multiplying the exponent inside the parentheses by the exponent outside the parentheses results in the same product.

$$(x^4)^3 = x^{4 \cdot 3} = x^{12}$$

This suggests the following rule for simplifying powers of monomials.

Rule for Simplifying the Power of an Exponential Expression

If m and n are positive integers, then $(x^m)^n = x^{m \cdot n}$.

EXAMPLE

Simplify: $(z^2)^5$

$(z^2)^5 = z^{2 \cdot 5}$ • This is the power of an exponential expression. Multiply the exponents.
$\quad\quad\quad = z^{10}$

The expression $(a^2b^3)^2$ is the *power of the product* of the two exponential expressions a^2 and b^3. The power of a product of exponential expressions can be simplified by writing the product in factored form and then using the Rule for Multiplying Exponential Expressions.

Write the power of the product of the monomial in factored form.
Use the Rule for Multiplying Exponential Expressions.

$$(a^2b^3)^2 = (a^2b^3)(a^2b^3)$$
$$= a^{2+2}b^{3+3}$$
$$= a^4b^6$$

Note that multiplying each exponent inside the parentheses by the exponent outside the parentheses results in the same product.

$$(a^2b^3)^2 = a^{2 \cdot 2}b^{3 \cdot 2}$$
$$= a^4b^6$$

Rule for Simplifying Powers of Products

If m, n, and p are positive integers, then $(x^my^n)^p = x^{m \cdot p}y^{n \cdot p}$.

EXAMPLE

Simplify: $(x^4y)^6$

$(x^4y)^6 = x^{4 \cdot 6}y^{1 \cdot 6}$ • This is a power of a product of exponential expressions. Multiply each exponent inside the parentheses by the exponent outside the parentheses.

$= x^{24}y^6$

HOW TO 6   Simplify: $(5x^2)^3$

Multiply each exponent inside the parentheses by the exponent outside the parentheses.
Note that $5 = 5^1$.

Evaluate 5^3.

$(5x^2)^3 = 5^{1 \cdot 3}x^{2 \cdot 3}$

$= 5^3x^6$

$= 125x^6$

HOW TO 7   Simplify: $(-a^5)^4$

Multiply each exponent inside the parentheses by the exponent outside the parentheses. Note that $-a^5 = (-1)a^5 = (-1)^1a^5$.

$(-a^5)^4 = (-1)^{1 \cdot 4}a^{5 \cdot 4}$

$= (-1)^4a^{20}$

$= 1a^{20} = a^{20}$

HOW TO 8   Simplify: $(3m^5p^2)^4$

Multiply each exponent inside the parentheses by the exponent outside the parentheses.

Evaluate 3^4.

$(3m^5p^2)^4 = 3^{1 \cdot 4}m^{5 \cdot 4}p^{2 \cdot 4}$

$= 3^4m^{20}p^8$

$= 81m^{20}p^8$

EXAMPLE 4

Simplify: $(-2x^4)^3$

Solution $(-2x^4)^3$

$= (-2)^{1 \cdot 3}x^{4 \cdot 3}$ • Multiply each exponent inside the parentheses by 3.

$= (-2)^3x^{12}$

$= -8x^{12}$

YOU TRY IT 4

Simplify: $(-y^4)^5$

Your solution

EXAMPLE 5

Simplify: $(-2p^3r)^4$

Solution $(-2p^3r)^4$

$= (-2)^{1 \cdot 4}p^{3 \cdot 4}r^{1 \cdot 4}$ • Multiply each exponent inside the parentheses by 4.

$= (-2)^4p^{12}r^4$

$= 16p^{12}r^4$

YOU TRY IT 5

Simplify: $(-3a^4bc^2)^3$

Your solution

Solutions on p. S16

8.1 EXERCISES

✔ Concept Check

1. Use the Rule for Multiplying Exponential Expressions:
$x^6 \cdot x^3 = x$———— $+$ ———— $=$ ————.

2. To multiply $(4a^3)(7a^5)$, use the Commutative and Associative Properties of
———————— to rearrange and group like factors. Then multiply the coefficients and
multiply variables with the same base by ———————— the exponents:

$(4a^3)(7a^5) = (4 \cdot$ ————$)(a^3 \cdot$ ————$) = ($————$)(a$————$^+$————$) = $————

3. Use the Rule for Simplifying the Power of an Exponential Expression:
$(x^3)^4 = x$———— $\cdot$ ———— $=$ ————.

4. The Rule for Simplifying Powers of Products states that we raise a product to a
power by multiplying each exponent ———————— the parentheses by the exponent
———————— the parentheses.

For example, $(x^3y)^4 = (x$———— $\cdot$ ————$)(y$———— $\cdot$ ————$) = $————.

OBJECTIVE A   *To multiply monomials*

📝 For Exercises 5 to 8, state whether the expression can be simplified using the Rule for
Multiplying Exponential Expressions.

5. $a^3 + a^4$

6. a^3a^4

7. a^3b^3

8. $a^3 + a^3$

Multiply.

9. $a^4 \cdot a^5$

10. $y^5 \cdot y^8$

11. $x^9 \cdot x^7$

12. $d^6 \cdot d$

13. $n^4 \cdot n^2$

14. $p^7 \cdot p^3$

15. $z^3 \cdot z \cdot z^4$

16. $b \cdot b^2 \cdot b^6$

17. $(a^3b^2)(a^5b)$

18. $(xy^5)(x^3y^7)$

19. $(-m^3n)(m^6n^2)$

20. $(-r^4t^3)(r^2t^9)$

21. $(2x^3)(5x^4)$

22. $(6x^3)(9x)$

23. $(8x^2y)(xy^5)$

24. $(4a^3b^4)(3ab^5)$

25. $(-4m^3)(3m^4)$

26. $(6r^2)(-4r)$

27. $(7v^3)(-2w)$

28. $(-9a^3)(4b^2)$

29. $(ab^2c^3)(-2b^3c^2)$

30. $(4x^2y^3)(-5x^5)$

31. $(4b^4c^2)(6a^3b)$

32. $(3xy^5)(5y^2z)$

33. $(-8r^2t^3)(-5rt^4v)$ **34.** $(-4ab^3c^2)(b^3c)$ **35.** $(9mn^4p)(-3mp^2)$ **36.** $(-3v^2wz)(-4vz^4)$

37. $(2x)(3x^2)(4x^4)$ **38.** $(5a^2)(4a)(3a^5)$ **39.** $(3ab)(2a^2b^3)(a^3b)$ **40.** $(4x^2y)(3xy^5)(2x^2y^2)$

OBJECTIVE B   *To simplify powers of monomials*

For Exercises 41 to 44, state whether the expression can be simplified using one of the rules presented in this section.

41. $(xy)^3$ **42.** $(x+y)^3$ **43.** $(a^3+b^4)^2$ **44.** $(a^3b^4)^2$

Simplify.

45. $(p^3)^5$ **46.** $(x^3)^5$ **47.** $(b^2)^4$ **48.** $(z^6)^3$ **49.** $(p^4)^7$

50. $(y^{10})^2$ **51.** $(c^7)^4$ **52.** $(d^9)^2$ **53.** $(3x)^2$ **54.** $(2y)^3$

55. $(x^2y^3)^6$ **56.** $(m^4n^2)^3$ **57.** $(r^3t)^4$ **58.** $(a^2b)^5$ **59.** $(-y^2)^2$

60. $(-z^3)^2$ **61.** $(2x^4)^3$ **62.** $(3n^3)^3$ **63.** $(-2a^2)^3$ **64.** $(-3b^3)^2$

65. $(3x^2y)^2$ **66.** $(4a^4b^5)^3$ **67.** $(2a^3bc^2)^3$ **68.** $(4xy^3z^2)^2$ **69.** $(-mn^5p^3)^4$

Critical Thinking

70. **Geometry** Find the area of the rectangle shown at the right. The dimensions given are in feet. Use the formula $A = LW$.

$3a^2b^5$

a^4b

71. **Geometry** Find the area of the square shown at the right. The dimensions given are in centimeters. Use the formula $A = s^2$.

$7y^5$

Projects or Group Activities

72. Let $x_1 = -1x^1$ and, for $n \geq 1$, $x_n = -nx^n$. Calculate the product $(x_1)(x_2)(x_3)(x_4)(x_5)$.

73. a. Evaluate $(2^3)^2$ and $2^{(3^2)}$. Are the results the same? If not, which expression has the larger value?

b. What is the order of operations for the expression x^{m^n}?

SECTION

8.2 Division of Monomials

OBJECTIVE A *To divide monomials*

The quotient of two exponential expressions with the *same base* can be simplified by writing each expression in factored form, dividing by the common factors, and then writing the result with an exponent.

$$\frac{x^6}{x^2} = \frac{\overset{1}{\cancel{x}} \cdot \overset{1}{\cancel{x}} \cdot x \cdot x \cdot x \cdot x}{\underset{1}{\cancel{x}} \cdot \underset{1}{\cancel{x}}} = x^4$$

Note that subtracting the exponents results in the same quotient.

$$\frac{x^6}{x^2} = x^{6-2} = x^4$$

This example suggests that to divide monomials with like bases, subtract the exponents.

Rule for Dividing Exponential Expressions

If m and n are positive integers and $x \neq 0$, then $\frac{x^m}{x^n} = x^{m-n}$.

EXAMPLE

Simplify: $\dfrac{c^8}{c^5}$

$\dfrac{c^8}{c^5} = c^{8-5}$ • This is the quotient of two exponential
expressions with the same base.
Subtract the exponents.

$\phantom{\dfrac{c^8}{c^5}} = c^3$

HOW TO 1 Simplify: $\dfrac{x^5 y^7}{x^4 y^2}$

Use the Rule for Dividing Exponential Expressions by subtracting the exponents of the like bases. Note that $x^{5-4} = x^1$ but the exponent 1 is not written.

$$\frac{x^5 y^7}{x^4 y^2} = x^{5-4} y^{7-2} = xy^5$$

The expression at the right has been simplified in two ways: by dividing by common factors, and by using the Rule for Dividing Exponential Expressions.

$$\frac{x^3}{x^3} = \frac{\overset{1}{\cancel{x}} \cdot \overset{1}{\cancel{x}} \cdot \overset{1}{\cancel{x}}}{\underset{1}{\cancel{x}} \cdot \underset{1}{\cancel{x}} \cdot \underset{1}{\cancel{x}}} = 1$$

$$\frac{x^3}{x^3} = x^{3-3} = x^0$$

Because $\frac{x^3}{x^3} = 1$ and $\frac{x^3}{x^3} = x^0$, 1 must equal x^0. Therefore, the following definition of zero as an exponent is used.

Zero as an Exponent

If $x \neq 0$, then $x^0 = 1$. The expression 0^0 is not defined.

EXAMPLE

Simplify: 15^0

$15^0 = 1$ • Any nonzero expression to the zero power is 1.

HOW TO 2 Simplify: $(4t^3)^0$, $t \neq 0$

Any nonzero expression to the zero power is 1. $\qquad\qquad (4t^3)^0 = 1$

HOW TO 3 Simplify: $-(2r)^0$, $r \neq 0$

Any nonzero expression to the zero power is 1.
Because the negative sign is in front of the parentheses,
the answer is -1. $\qquad\qquad -(2r)^0 = -1$

The expression at the right has been simplified in two
ways: by dividing by common factors, and by using the
Rule for Dividing Exponential Expressions.

$$\frac{x^3}{x^5} = \frac{\overset{1}{\cancel{x}} \cdot \overset{1}{\cancel{x}} \cdot \overset{1}{\cancel{x}}}{\underset{1}{\cancel{x}} \cdot \underset{1}{\cancel{x}} \cdot \underset{1}{\cancel{x}} \cdot x \cdot x} = \frac{1}{x^2}$$

$$\frac{x^3}{x^5} = x^{3-5} = x^{-2}$$

Because $\frac{x^3}{x^5} = \frac{1}{x^2}$ and $\frac{x^3}{x^5} = x^{-2}$, $\frac{1}{x^2}$ must equal x^{-2}. Therefore, the following definition
of a negative exponent is used.

Definition of Negative Exponents

If n is a positive integer and $x \neq 0$, then $x^{-n} = \frac{1}{x^n}$ and $\frac{1}{x^{-n}} = x^n$.

EXAMPLES

In each example below, the Definition of Negative Exponents is used to rewrite the
expression with a positive exponent.

1. $y^{-7} = \frac{1}{y^7}$ $\qquad$ **2.** $\frac{1}{c^{-4}} = c^4$

An exponential expression is in simplest form when there are no negative exponents in
the expression.

A numerical expression with a negative exponent can be evaluated by first rewriting the expression with a positive exponent.

 Take Note

Note from HOW TO 4 at the right that 2^{-3} is a *positive* number. A negative exponent does not indicate a negative number.

HOW TO 4   Evaluate: 2^{-3}

Use the Definition of Negative Exponents to write the expression with a positive exponent. Then simplify.

$$2^{-3} = \frac{1}{2^3} = \frac{1}{8}$$

Sometimes applying the Rule for Dividing Exponential Expressions results in a quotient that contains a negative exponent. If this happens, use the Definition of Negative Exponents to rewrite the expression with a positive exponent.

HOW TO 5   Simplify: $\dfrac{p^4}{p^7}$

Use the Rule for Dividing Exponential Expressions.

Use the Definition of Negative Exponents to rewrite the expression with a positive exponent.

$$\frac{p^4}{p^7} = p^{4-7}$$
$$= p^{-3}$$
$$= \frac{1}{p^3}$$

EXAMPLE 1

Simplify: **a.** $\dfrac{1}{a^{-8}}$ **b.** $\dfrac{b^2}{b^9}$

Solution   **a.** $\dfrac{1}{a^{-8}} = a^8$

b. $\dfrac{b^2}{b^9} = b^{2-9} = b^{-7} = \dfrac{1}{b^7}$

YOU TRY IT 1

Simplify: **a.** $\dfrac{1}{d^{-6}}$ **b.** $\dfrac{n^6}{n^{11}}$

Your solution

EXAMPLE 2

Simplify:
a. 3^{-4} **b.** $-(7z)^0, z \neq 0$

Solution   **a.** $3^{-4} = \dfrac{1}{3^4} = \dfrac{1}{81}$

b. $-(7z)^0 = -1$

YOU TRY IT 2

Simplify:
a. 4^{-2} **b.** $-8x^0, x \neq 0$

Your solution

OBJECTIVE B *To write numbers in scientific notation*

Very large and very small numbers are encountered in the natural sciences. For example, the mass of an electron is 0.00000000000000000000000000000911 kg. Numbers such as this are difficult to read, so they are written using a more convenient system called **scientific notation.** In scientific notation, a number is expressed as the product of two factors, one a number between 1 and 10, and the other a power of 10.

To express a number in scientific notation, write it in the form $a \times 10^n$, where a is a number between 1 and 10, and n is an integer.

Take Note
There are two steps involved in writing a number in scientific notation:
(1) determine the number between 1 and 10, and
(2) determine the exponent on 10.

For numbers greater than 10, move the decimal point to the right of the first digit. The exponent n is positive and equal to the number of places the decimal point has been moved.

$240{,}000 = 2.4 \times 10^5$

$93{,}000{,}000 = 9.3 \times 10^7$

For numbers less than 1, move the decimal point to the right of the first nonzero digit. The exponent n is negative. The absolute value of the exponent is equal to the number of places the decimal point has been moved.

$0.0003 = 3.0 \times 10^{-4}$

$0.0000832 = 8.32 \times 10^{-5}$

Changing a number written in scientific notation to decimal notation also requires moving the decimal point.

When the exponent is positive, move the decimal point to the right the same number of places as the exponent.

$3.45 \times 10^6 = 3{,}450{,}000$

$2.3 \times 10^8 = 230{,}000{,}000$

When the exponent is negative, move the decimal point to the left the same number of places as the absolute value of the exponent.

$8.1 \times 10^{-3} = 0.0081$

$6.34 \times 10^{-7} = 0.000000634$

EXAMPLE 3

Write 824,300,000,000 in scientific notation.

Solution The number is greater than 10. Move the decimal point 11 places to the left. The exponent on 10 is 11.

$824{,}300{,}000{,}000 = 8.243 \times 10^{11}$

YOU TRY IT 3

Write 0.000000961 in scientific notation.

Your solution

EXAMPLE 4

Write 6.8×10^{-10} in decimal notation.

Solution The exponent on 10 is negative. Move the decimal point 10 places to the left.

$6.8 \times 10^{-10} = 0.00000000068$

YOU TRY IT 4

Write 7.329×10^6 in decimal notation.

Your solution

Solutions on p. S16

8.2 EXERCISES

✔ Concept Check

1. As long as x is not zero, x^0 is defined to be equal to _____. Using this definition, $3^0 = $ _____ and $(7x^3)^0 = $ _____.

2. Use the Rule for Dividing Exponential Expressions:
   $$\frac{p^6}{p^2} = p^{\underline{} - \underline{}} = \underline{}.$$

3. A number is written in scientific notation if it is written as the product of a number between _____ and _____ and a power of _____.

4. To write the number 354,000,000 in scientific notation, move the decimal point _____ places to the _____. The exponent on 10 is _____.

5. To write the number 0.0000000086 in scientific notation, move the decimal point _____ places to the _____. The exponent on 10 is _____.

6. For the number 2.8×10^7, the exponent on 10 is _____. To write this number in decimal notation, move the decimal point _____ places to the _____.

OBJECTIVE A *To divide monomials*

For Exercises 7 to 10, state whether the expression can be simplified using the Rule for Dividing Exponential Expressions.

7. $a^4 - a^2$

8. $\dfrac{a^4}{a^2}$

9. $\dfrac{a^4}{b^2}$

10. $\dfrac{4}{2}$

Simplify.

11. 27^0

12. $(3x)^0$

13. $-(17)^0$

14. $-(2a)^0$

15. 3^{-2}

16. 4^{-3}

17. 2^{-3}

18. 5^{-2}

19. x^{-5}

20. v^{-3}

21. w^{-8}

22. m^{-9}

23. y^{-1}

24. d^{-4}

25. $\dfrac{1}{a^{-5}}$

26. $\dfrac{1}{c^{-6}}$

27. $\dfrac{1}{b^{-3}}$

28. $\dfrac{1}{y^{-7}}$

29. $\dfrac{a^8}{a^2}$

30. $\dfrac{c^{12}}{c^5}$

31. $\dfrac{q^5}{q}$

32. $\dfrac{r^{10}}{r}$

33. $\dfrac{m^4 n^7}{m^3 n^5}$

34. $\dfrac{a^5 b^6}{a^3 b^2}$

35. $\dfrac{t^4 u^8}{t^2 u^5}$

36. $\dfrac{b^{11} c^4}{b^4 c}$

37. $\dfrac{x^4}{x^9}$

38. $\dfrac{r^2}{r^5}$

39. $\dfrac{b}{b^5}$

40. $\dfrac{m^5}{m^8}$

OBJECTIVE B *To write numbers in scientific notation*

Write the number in scientific notation.

41. 2,370,000

42. 75,000

43. 0.00045

44. 0.000076

45. 309,000

46. 819,000,000

47. 0.000000601

48. 0.00000000096

49. 57,000,000,000

50. 934,800,000,000

51. 0.000000017

52. 0.0000009217

Write the number in decimal notation.

53. 7.1×10^5

54. 2.3×10^7

55. 4.3×10^{-5}

56. 9.21×10^{-7}

57. 6.71×10^8

58. 5.75×10^9

59. 7.13×10^{-6}

60. 3.54×10^{-8}

61. 5×10^{12}

62. 1.0987×10^{11}

63. 8.01×10^{-3}

64. 4.0162×10^{-9}

For Exercises 65 to 68, determine whether the number is written in scientific notation. If not, explain why not.

65. 84.3×10^{-3}

66. 0.97×10^4

67. $6.4 \times 10^{2.5}$

68. 4×10^{-297}

69. **Technology** See the news clipping at the right. Express in scientific notation the thickness, in meters, of the memristor.

70. **Astronomy** Astrophysicists estimate that the radius of the Milky Way galaxy is 1,000,000,000,000,000,000,000 m. Write this number in scientific notation.

71. **Geology** The mass of Earth is 5,980,000,000,000,000,000,000,000 kg. Write this number in scientific notation.

72. **Physics** Carbon nanotubes are extremely strong cylinders of carbon atoms that have remarkable properties. Some nanotubes with a diameter of 0.0000000004 m have been created. Write this number in scientific notation.

73. **Biology** The weight of a single *E. coli* bacterium is 0.000000000000665 g. Write this number in scientific notation.

74. **Archeology** The weight of the Great Pyramid of Khufu is estimated to be 12,000,000,000 lb. Write this number in scientific notation.

75. **Food Science** The frequency (in oscillations per second) of a microwave generated by a microwave oven is approximately 2,450,000,000 hertz. (One hertz is one oscillation in 1 s.) Write this number in scientific notation.

76. **Astronomy** One light-year is the distance traveled by light in one year. One light-year is 5,880,000,000,000 mi. Write this number in scientific notation.

77. **Biophysics** Biologists and physicists are working together to measure the mass of a virus. Currently, a virus with a mass of 0.00000000000000000039 g can be measured. Write this number in scientific notation.

78. **Astronomy** See the news clipping at the right. WASP-12b orbits a star that is 5.1156×10^{15} mi from Earth. Write this number in decimal notation.

79. **Physics** The length of an infrared light wave is approximately 0.0000037 m. Write this number in scientific notation.

80. $m \times 10^8$ and $n \times 10^6$ are numbers written in scientific notation. Place the correct symbol, $<$ or $>$, between these two numbers.

81. $m \times 10^{-5}$ and $n \times 10^{-3}$ are numbers written in scientific notation. Place the correct symbol, $<$ or $>$, between these two numbers.

In the NEWS!

HP Introduces the Memristor

Hewlett Packard has announced the design of the *memristor*, a new memory technology with the potential to be much smaller than the memory chips used in today's computers. HP has made a memristor with a thickness of 0.000000015 m (15 nanometers).
Source: The New York Times

Great Pyramid of Khufu

Julia Chernikova/Shutterstock.com

In the NEWS!

Hottest Planet Ever Discovered

A planet called WASP-12b is the hottest planet ever discovered, at about 4000°F. It orbits its star faster than any other known planet, completing one revolution each day.
Source: news.yahoo.com

Critical Thinking

82. Place the correct symbol, $<$ or $>$, between the two numbers.
   a. 3.45×10^{-14} _____ 6.45×10^{-15} **b.** 5.23×10^{18} _____ 5.23×10^{17}
   c. 3.12×10^{12} _____ 4.23×10^{11} **d.** -6.81×10^{-24} _____ -9.37×10^{-25}

83. **a.** Evaluate 3^{-x} when $x = -2, -1, 0, 1,$ and 2.
   b. Evaluate 2^{-x} when $x = -2, -1, 0, 1,$ and 2.

Evaluate.

84. $8^{-2} + 2^{-5}$

85. $9^{-2} + 3^{-3}$

Write in decimal notation.

86. 2^{-4}

87. 25^{-2}

Complete.

88. If $m = n$ and $a \neq 0$, then $\dfrac{a^m}{a^n} =$ _____.

89. If $m = n + 1$ and $a \neq 0$, then $\dfrac{a^m}{a^n} =$ _____.

Solve.

90. $(-4.8)^x = 1$

91. $-6.3^x = -1$

Projects or Group Activities

92. **Population and Land Allocation** In this project, you are asked to determine hypothetical land allocation for the world's population today. Use the figure 7×10^9 for the current world population and the figure 3.1×10^8 for the current U.S. population. (*Source:* www.infoplease.com) One square mile is approximately 2.8×10^7 ft^2.

Texas

Rhode Island

   a. If every person in the world moved to Texas and each person were given an equal amount of land, how many square feet of land would each person have? The area of Texas is 2.619×10^5 mi^2.
   b. If every person in the United States moved to Rhode Island and each person were given an equal amount of land, how many square feet of land would each person have? The area of Rhode Island is 1.0×10^3 mi^2. Round to the nearest whole number.
   c. Suppose every person in the world were given a plot of land the size of a two-car garage (22 ft $\times$ 22 ft).
      i. How many people would fit in a square mile? Round to the nearest hundred.
      ii. How many square miles would be required to accommodate the entire world population? Round to the nearest hundred.
   d. If the total land area of Earth were divided equally, how many acres of land would each person be allocated? Use a figure of 5.7×10^7 mi^2 for the land area of Earth. One acre is 43,560 ft^2. Round to the nearest tenth.
   e. If every person on Earth were given a plot of land the size of a two-car garage, what would be the carrying capacity of Earth? Round to the nearest hundred billion.

8.3 The Metric System of Measurement

OBJECTIVE A *To use units of measurement in the metric system*

In 1789, an attempt was made to standardize units of measurement internationally in order to simplify trade and commerce among nations. A commission in France developed a system of measurement known as the **metric system.** Today, almost all countries use the metric system as their sole system of measurement. The United States is one of only a few countries that have not converted to the metric system as their official system of measurement.

In this section, we present the metric system of measurement and explain how to convert between different units.

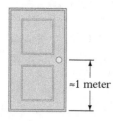

≈1 meter

The basic unit of *length,* or distance, in the metric system is the **meter** (m). One meter is approximately the distance from a doorknob to the floor. All units of length in the metric system are derived from the meter. Prefixes to the basic unit denote the length of each unit. For example, the prefix "centi-" means one-hundredth; therefore, 1 centimeter is 1 one-hundredth of a meter (0.01 m).

kilo-	= 1 000	1 kilometer (km)	= 1 000 meters (m)
hecto-	= 100	1 hectometer (hm)	= 100 m
deca-	= 10	1 decameter (dam)	= 10 m
		1 meter (m)	= 1 m
deci-	= 0.1	1 decimeter (dm)	= 0.1 m
centi-	= 0.01	1 centimeter (cm)	= 0.01 m
milli-	= 0.001	1 millimeter (mm)	= 0.001 m

Point of Interest

Originally the meter (spelled *metre* in some countries) was defined as $\frac{1}{10,000,000}$ of the distance from the equator to the North Pole. Modern scientists have redefined the meter as 1,650,753.73 wavelengths of the orange-red light given off by the element krypton.

Note that in this list, 1000 is written as 1 000, with a space between the 1 and the zeros. When writing numbers using metric units, separate each group of three numbers by a space instead of a comma. A space is also used after each group of three numbers to the right of a decimal point. For example, 31,245.2976 is written 31 245.297 6 in metric notation.

Mass and weight are closely related. *Weight* is a measure of how strongly gravity is pulling on an object. Therefore, an object weighs less in space than on Earth's surface. However, the amount of material in the object, its *mass,* remains the same. On the surface of Earth, the terms *mass* and *weight* can be used interchangeably.

The basic unit of mass in the metric system is the **gram** (g). If a box that is 1 centimeter long on each side is filled with water, the mass of that water is 1 gram.

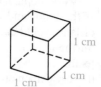

1 cm
1 cm
1 cm

1 gram = the mass of water in a box that is 1 centimeter long on each side

The units of mass in the metric system have the same prefixes as the units of length.

$$
\begin{array}{ll}
1 \text{ kilogram (kg)} & = 1\ 000 \text{ grams (g)} \\
1 \text{ hectogram (hg)} & = 100 \text{ g} \\
1 \text{ decagram (dag)} & = 10 \text{ g} \\
1 \text{ gram (g)} & = 1 \text{ g} \\
1 \text{ decigram (dg)} & = 0.1 \text{ g} \\
1 \text{ centigram (cg)} & = 0.01 \text{ g} \\
1 \text{ milligram (mg)} & = 0.001 \text{ g}
\end{array}
$$

Weight ≈ 1 gram

The gram is a very small unit of mass. A paperclip weighs about 1 gram. In applications, the kilogram (1 000 grams) is a more useful unit of mass. This textbook weighs about 1 kilogram.

Liquid substances are measured in units of *capacity*.

The basic unit of capacity in the metric system is the **liter** (L). One liter is defined as the capacity of a box that is 10 centimeters long on each side.

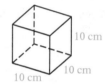

1 liter = the capacity of a box that is
10 centimeters long on each side

The units of capacity in the metric system have the same prefixes as the units of length.

$$
\begin{array}{ll}
1 \text{ kiloliter (kl)} & = 1\ 000 \text{ liters (L)} \\
1 \text{ hectoliter (hl)} & = 100 \text{ L} \\
1 \text{ decaliter (dal)} & = 10 \text{ L} \\
1 \text{ liter (L)} & = 1 \text{ L} \\
1 \text{ deciliter (dl)} & = 0.1 \text{ L} \\
1 \text{ centiliter (cl)} & = 0.01 \text{ L} \\
1 \text{ milliliter (ml)} & = 0.001 \text{ L}
\end{array}
$$

Converting between units in the metric system involves moving the decimal point to the right or to the left. Listing the units in order from largest to smallest will indicate how many places to move the decimal point and in which direction.

To convert 3 800 cm to meters, write the units of length in order from largest to smallest.

km   hm   dam   m   dm   cm   mm

2 positions

Converting from cm to m requires moving 2 places to the left.

3 800 cm = 38.00 m

2 places

Move the decimal point the same number of places and in the same direction.

Take Note

In the metric system, all prefixes represent powers of 10. Therefore, when converting between units, we are multiplying or dividing by a power of 10.

HOW TO 1 Convert 2.1 kg to grams.

kg hg dag g dg cg mg

3 positions

Write the units of mass in order from largest to smallest.

Converting from kg to g requires moving 3 positions to the right.

2.1 kg = 2 100 g

3 places

Move the decimal point the same number of places and in the same direction.

EXAMPLE 1

What unit in the metric system is used to measure the distance from San Francisco to Dallas?

Solution

The meter is the basic unit for measuring distance.

The distance from San Francisco to Dallas is measured in kilometers.

YOU TRY IT 1

What unit in the metric system is used to measure the amount of protein in a glass of milk?

Your solution

EXAMPLE 2

a. Convert 4.08 m to centimeters.
b. Convert 5.93 g to milligrams.
c. Convert 824 ml to liters.
d. Convert 9 kl to liters.

Solution

a. km hm dam (m) dm (cm) mm

Move the decimal point 2 places to the right.

4.08 m = 408 cm

b. kg hg dag (g) dg cg (mg)

Move the decimal point 3 places to the right.

5.93 g = 5 930 mg

c. kl hl dal (L) dl cl (ml)

Move the decimal point 3 places to the left.

824 ml = 0.824 L

d. (kl) hl dal (L) dl cl ml

Move the decimal point 3 places to the right.

9 kl = 9 000 L

YOU TRY IT 2

a. Convert 1 295 m to kilometers.
b. Convert 7 543 g to kilograms.
c. Convert 6.3 L to milliliters.
d. Convert 2 kl to liters.

Your solution

EXAMPLE 3

Find the cost of three packages of ground meat weighing 540 g, 670 g, and 890 g if the cost per kilogram is $9.89. Round to the nearest cent.

Strategy

To find the cost of the meat:

- Find the total weight of the three packages.
- Convert the total weight to kilograms.
- Multiply the weight by the cost per kilogram ($9.89).

Solution

540 g + 670 g + 890 g = 2 100 g   • Total weight
                                      in grams

2 100 g = 2.1 kg   • Total weight in kilograms

2.1 × 9.89 = 20.769   • Weight in kilograms times cost
                          per kilogram

The cost of the meat is $20.77.

YOU TRY IT 3

A bookcase 175 cm long has four shelves. Find the cost of the shelves when the cost of the lumber is $15.75 per meter.

Your strategy

Your solution

Solution on p. S20

As a result of technological advances in the computer industry, other prefixes in the metric system are becoming more common. For example,

tera-	= 1 000 000 000 000
giga-	= 1 000 000 000
mega-	= 1 000 000
micro-	= 0.000 001
nano-	= 0.000 000 001
pico-	= 0.000 000 000 001

The amount of memory in a computer hard drive is generally measured in gigabytes. The speed of a computer is measured in picoseconds.

Here are a few more examples of how these prefixes are used.

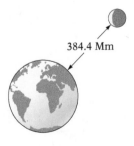

384.4 Mm

The mass of Earth gains 40 Gg (gigagrams) each year from captured meteorites and cosmic dust.

The average distance from Earth to the moon is 384.4 Mm (megameters), and the average distance from Earth to the sun is 149.5 Gm (gigameters).

The wavelength of yellow light is 590 nm (nanometers).

The diameter of a hydrogen atom is about 70 pm (picometers).

There are additional prefixes in the metric system, representing both larger and smaller units. We may hear them more and more often as computer chips hold more and more information, as computers get faster and faster, and as we learn more and more about objects in our universe that are great distances away.

8.3 EXERCISES

✔ Concept Check

1. ◣ In the metric system, what is the basic unit of length? Of liquid measure? Of weight?

2. ◣ a. Explain how to convert meters to centimeters.
   b. Explain how to convert milliliters to liters.

OBJECTIVE A *To use units of measurement in the metric system*

3. **a.** Complete the table.

Metric System Prefix	Symbol	Magnitude	Means Multiply the Basic Unit by:
tera-	T	10^{12}	1 000 000 000 000
giga-	G	_____	1 000 000 000
mega-	M	10^6	_____
kilo-	_____	_____	1 000
hecto-	h	_____	100
deca-	da	10^1	_____
deci-	d	$\dfrac{1}{10}$	_____
centi-	_____	$\dfrac{1}{10^2}$	_____
milli-	_____	_____	0.001
micro-	μ	$\dfrac{1}{10^6}$	_____
nano-	n	$\dfrac{1}{10^9}$	_____
pico-	p	_____	0.000 000 000 001

b. How can the magnitude column in the table above be used to determine how many places to move the decimal point when converting to the basic unit in the metric system?

Name the unit in the metric system that would be used to measure each of the following.

4. the distance from New York to London

5. the weight of a truck

6. a person's waist

7. the amount of coffee in a mug

8. the weight of a thumbtack

9. the amount of water in a swimming pool

10. the distance a baseball player hits a baseball

11. a person's hat size

12. the amount of fat in a slice of cheddar cheese

13. a person's weight

14. the amount of maple syrup served with pancakes

15. the amount of water in a watercooler

16. the amount of vitamin C in a vitamin tablet

17. a serving of cereal

18. the width of a hair

19. a person's height

20. the amount of medication in an aspirin

21. the weight of a lawn mower

22. the weight of a slice of bread

23. the contents of a bottle of salad dressing

24. the amount of water a family uses monthly

25. the weight of newspapers collected at a recycling center

26. the amount of liquid in a bowl of soup

27. the distance to the bank

Convert.

28. 42 cm = _____ mm

29. 91 cm = _____ mm

30. 360 g = _____ kg

31. 1 856 g = _____ kg

32. 5 194 ml = _____ L

33. 7 285 ml = _____ L

34. 2 m = _____ mm

35. 8 m = _____ mm

36. 217 mg = _____ g

37. 34 mg = _____ g

38. 4.52 L = _____ ml

39. 0.029 7 L = _____ ml

40. 8 406 m = _____ km

41. 7 530 m = _____ km

42. 2.4 kg = _____ g

43. 9.2 kg = _____ g

44. 6.18 kl = _____ L

45. 0.036 kl = _____ L

46. 9.612 km = _____ m

47. 2.35 km = _____ m

48. 0.24 g = _____ mg

49. 0.083 g = _____ mg

50. 298 cm = _____ m

51. 71.6 cm = _____ m

52. 4 231 L = _____ kl

53. 3 206 L = _____ kl

54. 5.84 m = _____ cm

55. 0.99 m = _____ cm

56. 87 mm = _____ cm

57. 605 mm = _____ cm

For Exercises 58 to 63, fill in the blank with the correct unit of measurement.

58. 8 750 cg = 87.5 _____

59. 0.05 m = 5 _____

60. 1.78 kl = 1 780 _____

61. 28 300 mg = 2 830 _____

62. 5 ml = 0.005 _____

63. 0.7 km = 70 000 _____

64. **Consumerism** A 1.19-kilogram container of Quaker Oats contains 30 servings. Find the number of grams in one serving of the oatmeal. Round to the nearest whole number.

65. **Nutrition** A patient is advised to supplement her diet with 2 g of calcium per day. The calcium tablets she purchases contain 500 mg of calcium per tablet. How many tablets per day should the patient take?

66. ● **Beverages** Read the news clipping at the right. How many 140-milliliter servings are in one carafe of Pure Premium?

67. **Chemistry** A chemistry experiment requires 12 ml of an acid solution. How many liters of acid should be ordered when 4 classes of 90 students each are going to perform the experiment? (The acid must be ordered by the whole liter).

68. **Fencing** You purchase a 50-meter roll of fencing, at a cost of $14.95 per meter, in order to build a dog run that is 340 cm wide and 1 380 cm long. After you cut the four pieces of fencing from the roll, how much fencing is left on the roll?

69. **Sports** A walk-a-thon had two checkpoints. One checkpoint was 1 400 m from the starting point. The second checkpoint was 1 200 m from the first checkpoint. The second checkpoint was 1 800 m from the finish line. How long was the walk? Express the answer in kilometers.

70. **Landscaping** Eighty grams of grass seed are used for every 100 m² of lawn. How many kilograms of grass seed are needed to cover 2 000 m²?

In the NEWS!

Tropicana Goes Metric

Tropicana has introduced metric-sized packaging. The first was the Pure Premium 1.75-liter carafe. Other sizes of packaging include 200 ml, 400 ml, 450 ml, and 1 L.

Source: www.gometric.us

71. **Measurements**   A trailer is loaded with nine automobiles weighing 1 405 kg each. Find the total weight of the automobiles.

72. **Consumerism**   A case of 12 one-liter bottles of apple juice costs $19.80. A case of 24 cans, each can containing 340 ml of apple juice, costs $14.50. Which case of apple juice is the better buy?

73. **Medicine**   A flu vaccine is being offered for the coming winter season. A medical corporation buys 12 L of flu vaccine. How many patients can be immunized if each person receives 3 cm³ of the vaccine?

74. **⬤ Astronomy**   The distance between Earth and the sun is 150 000 000 km. Light travels 300 000 000 m in 1 s. How long does it take for light to reach Earth from the sun?

75. **⬤ Adopt-A-Highway**   Use the news clipping at the right. Find the average number of meters adopted by a group in the Missouri Adopt-A-Highway program. Round to the nearest whole number.

76. **Business**   A health food store buys organic pumpkin seeds in 10-kilogram containers and repackages the seeds for resale. The store packages the seeds in 200-gram bags, costing $.04 each, and resells them for $3.89 per bag. Find the profit on a 10-kilogram container of organic pumpkin seeds costing $75.

77. **Business**   For $195, a pharmacist purchases 5 L of cough syrup and repackages it in 250-milliliter bottles. Each bottle costs the pharmacist $.55. Each bottle of cough syrup is sold for $23.89. Find the profit on the 5 L of cough syrup.

> **In the NEWS!**
>
> **Highway Adoption Proves Popular**
>
> The Missouri Adopt-A-Highway Program, which has been in existence for 20 years, currently has 3772 groups in the program. The groups have adopted 8 502 km along the roadways.
>
> *Source:* www.modot.org

78. **Business**   A wholesale distributor purchased 32 kl of cooking oil for $64,480. The wholesaler repackaged the cooking oil in 1.25-liter bottles. The bottles cost $.42 each. Each bottle of cooking oil was sold for $5.94. Find the distributor's profit on the 32 kl of cooking oil.

Critical Thinking

79. After a 280-milliliter serving is taken from a 3-liter bottle of water, how much water remains in the container? Write the answer in three different ways.

Projects or Group Activities

80. ◤ Discuss the advantages and disadvantages of the U.S. Customary System and the metric system of measurement.

8.4   Plane Geometric Figures

OBJECTIVE A   *To find the perimeter of plane geometric figures*

A **polygon** is a closed figure determined by three or more line segments that lie in a plane. The **sides of a polygon** are the line segments that form the polygon. The figures below are examples of polygons.

Point of Interest

Although a polygon is defined in terms of its *sides* (see the definition above), the word *polygon* actually comes from the Latin word *polygonum*, which means "having many *angles.*" This is certainly the case for a polygon.

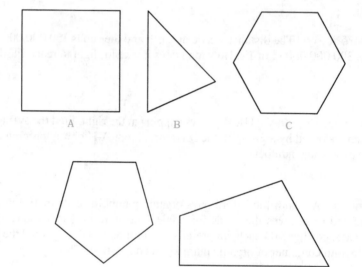

A **regular polygon** is one in which each side has the same length and each angle has the same measure. The polygons in Figures A, C, and D above are regular polygons.

The name of a polygon is based on the number of its sides. The table below lists the names of polygons that have from 3 to 10 sides.

The Pentagon in Arlington, Virginia

Number of Sides	Name of the Polygon
3	Triangle
4	Quadrilateral
5	Pentagon
6	Hexagon
7	Heptagon
8	Octagon
9	Nonagon
10	Decagon

Triangles and quadrilaterals are two of the most common types of polygons. Triangles are distinguished by the number of equal sides and also by the measures of their angles.

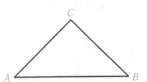

An **isosceles triangle** has two sides of equal length. The angles opposite each of the equal sides are of equal measure.

$AC = BC$
$\angle A = \angle B$

The three sides of an **equilateral triangle** are of equal length. The three angles are of equal measure.

$AB = BC = AC$
$\angle A = \angle B = \angle C$

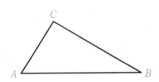

A **scalene triangle** has no two sides of equal length. No two angles are of equal measure.

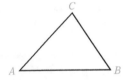

An **acute triangle** has three acute angles.

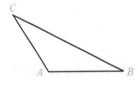

An **obtuse triangle** has one obtuse angle.

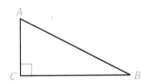

A **right triangle** has a right angle.

Quadrilaterals also are distinguished by their sides and angles, as shown below. Note that a rectangle, a square, and a rhombus are different forms of a parallelogram.

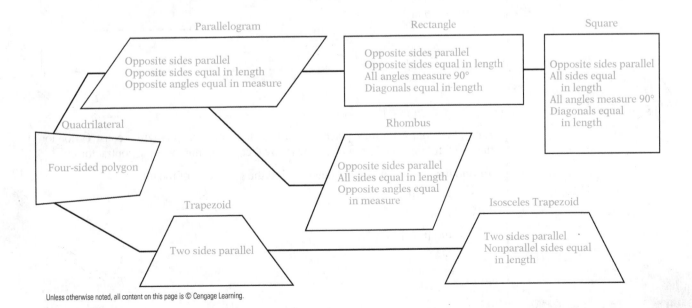

The **perimeter** of a plane geometric figure is a measure of the distance around the figure. The perimeter of a polygon is the sum of the lengths of its sides. Perimeter is used, for example, in buying fencing for a lawn or in determining how much baseboard is needed for a room.

Here are the perimeter formulas for some of the more common geometric figures.

Perimeter of a Triangle

Let a, b, and c be the lengths of the sides of a triangle.

The perimeter of the triangle is $P = a + b + c$.

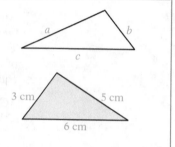

EXAMPLE

Find the perimeter of the triangle shown at the right.

$P = a + b + c$

$\quad = 3\text{ cm} + 5\text{ cm} + 6\text{ cm}$

$\quad = 14\text{ cm}$

The perimeter of the triangle is 14 cm.

Perimeter of a Rectangle

Let L be the length (usually the longer side) of a rectangle and W be the width (usually the shorter side) of a rectangle.

The perimeter of the rectangle is $P = 2L + 2W$.

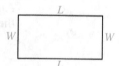

EXAMPLE

Find the perimeter of the rectangle shown at the right.

$P = 2L + 2W$

$\quad = 2(6\text{ m}) + 2(3\text{ m}) \qquad \bullet\ L = 6\text{ m}; W = 3\text{ m}$

$\quad = 12\text{ m} + 6\text{ m}$

$\quad = 18\text{ m}$

The perimeter of the rectangle is 18 m.

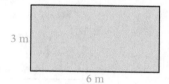

APPLY THE CONCEPT

A building contractor must place a security fence around a rectangular construction lot that is 95 ft long and 72 ft wide. How many feet of fencing must the contractor buy?

To find the amount of fencing needed, find the perimeter of the lot.

$P = 2L + 2W$

$\quad = 2(95\text{ ft}) + 2(72\text{ ft}) \qquad \bullet\ L = 95\text{ ft}; W = 72\text{ ft}$

$\quad = 190\text{ ft} + 144\text{ ft}$

$\quad = 334\text{ ft}$

The contractor must buy 334 ft of fencing.

Recall that a square is a rectangle in which all four sides are equal.

Perimeter of a Square

Let s be the length of a side of a square.

The perimeter of the square is $P = 4s$.

EXAMPLE

Find the perimeter of the square shown at the right.

$P = 4s$

$ = 4(3 \text{ ft}) \qquad \bullet \; s = 3 \text{ ft}$

$ = 12 \text{ ft}$

The perimeter of the square is 12 ft.

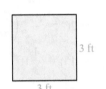

The perimeter of a circle is called its **circumference.** The circumference of a circle is equal to the product of pi (π) and the diameter. The value of π can be approximated as

$$\pi \approx 3.14 \text{ or } \pi \approx \frac{22}{7}$$

The π key on a calculator gives a more exact approximation of π.

Circumference of a Circle

Let d be the diameter of a circle.
The circumference of the circle is $C = \pi d$.
Because the diameter is twice the radius, the circumference is also given by $C = 2\pi r$.

EXAMPLE

Find the circumference of the circle shown at the right.

$C = 2\pi r$

$ = 2\pi(6 \text{ in.}) \qquad \bullet \; r = 6 \text{ in.}$

$ \approx 2(3.14)(6 \text{ in.})$

$ = 37.68 \text{ in.}$

The circumference of the circle is approximately 37.68 in.

APPLY THE CONCEPT

The diameter of a car tire is 16 in. If the tire makes two complete revolutions, what distance has the tire traveled? Use 3.14 for π.

To find the distance, first find the circumference of the tire. Because the tire makes two complete revolutions, multiply the circumference by 2.

$C = \pi d$

$ \approx 3.14(16 \text{ in.}) \qquad \bullet \; d = 16 \text{ in.}$

$ = 50.24 \text{ in.}$

The circumference of the tire is approximately 50.24 in.

$2 \times 50.24 = 100.48$

The tire has traveled a distance of 100.48 in.

EXAMPLE 1

Find the perimeter of a rectangle with a width of $\frac{2}{3}$ ft and a length of 2 ft.

Solution

2 ft
$\frac{2}{3}$ ft

$P = 2L + 2W$

$= 2(2 \text{ ft}) + 2\left(\frac{2}{3} \text{ ft}\right)$ • $L = 2$ ft, $W = \frac{2}{3}$ ft

$= 4 \text{ ft} + \frac{4}{3} \text{ ft}$

$= 5\frac{1}{3} \text{ ft}$

The perimeter of the rectangle is $5\frac{1}{3}$ ft.

YOU TRY IT 1

Find the perimeter of a rectangle with a length of 2 m and a width of 0.85 m.

Your solution

EXAMPLE 2

Find the perimeter of a triangle with sides of lengths 5 in., 7 in., and 8 in.

Solution

5 in.　7 in.
8 in.

$P = a + b + c$
$= 5 \text{ in.} + 7 \text{ in.} + 8 \text{ in.}$
$= 20 \text{ in.}$

The perimeter of the triangle is 20 in.

YOU TRY IT 2

Find the perimeter of a triangle with sides of lengths 12 cm, 15 cm, and 18 cm.

Your solution

EXAMPLE 3

Find the circumference of a circle with a radius of 18 cm. Use 3.14 for π.

Solution

18 cm

$C = 2\pi r$
$\approx 2 \cdot 3.14 \cdot 18 \text{ cm}$
$= 113.04 \text{ cm}$

The circumference is approximately 113.04 cm.

YOU TRY IT 3

Find the circumference of a circle with a diameter of 6 in. Use 3.14 for π.

Your solution

Solutions on p. S29

OBJECTIVE B   *To find the perimeter of composite geometric figures*

A **composite geometric figure** is a figure made from two or more geometric figures. The following composite is made from part of a rectangle and part of a circle:

Perimeter of the composite figure = 3 sides of a rectangle + $\frac{1}{2}$ the circumference of a circle

Perimeter of the composite figure = $2L + W + \frac{1}{2}\pi d$

The perimeter of the composite figure below is found by adding twice the length plus the width plus one-half the circumference of the circle.

$$P = 2L + W + \frac{1}{2}\pi d$$

$$\approx 2(12\text{ m}) + 4\text{ m} + \frac{1}{2}(3.14)(4\text{ m})$$ • $L = 12$ m, $W = 4$ m, $d = 4$ m. *Note:* The diameter of the circle is equal to the width of the rectangle.

$$= 34.28\text{ m}$$

The perimeter is approximately 34.28 m.

EXAMPLE 4

Find the perimeter of the composite figure. Use $\frac{22}{7}$ for π.

5 cm 5 cm
5 cm 5 cm
7 cm

Solution

$$\begin{array}{ccc}
\text{Perimeter} & \text{sum of} & \frac{1}{2}\text{ the} \\
\text{of} & \text{lengths} & + \quad \text{circumference} \\
\text{composite} = & \text{of the} & \text{of the circle} \\
\text{figure} & \text{four sides} &
\end{array}$$

$$P \;=\; 4s \;+\; \frac{1}{2}\pi d$$

$$\approx 4(5\text{ cm}) + \frac{1}{2}\left(\frac{22}{7}\right)(7\text{ cm})$$

$$= 20\text{ cm} + 11\text{ cm} = 31\text{ cm}$$

The perimeter is approximately 31 cm.

YOU TRY IT 4

Find the perimeter of the composite figure. Use 3.14 for π.

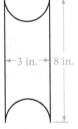

3 in.   8 in.

Your solution

Solution on p. S29

OBJECTIVE C   *To solve application problems*

EXAMPLE 5

The dimensions of a triangular sail are 18 ft, 11 ft, and 15 ft. What is the perimeter of the sail?

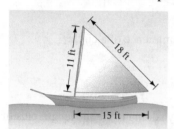

Strategy

To find the perimeter, use the formula for the perimeter of a triangle.

Solution

$P = a + b + c$
$= 18 \text{ ft} + 11 \text{ ft} + 15 \text{ ft} = 44 \text{ ft}$
The perimeter of the sail is 44 ft.

YOU TRY IT 5

What is the perimeter of a standard piece of computer paper that measures $8\frac{1}{2}$ in. by 11 in.?

Your strategy

Your solution

EXAMPLE 6

If fencing costs $6.75 per foot, how much will it cost to fence a rectangular lot that is 108 ft wide and 240 ft long?

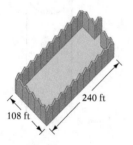

240 ft

108 ft

Strategy

To find the cost of the fence:

* Find the perimeter of the lot.
* Multiply the perimeter by the per-foot cost of the fencing.

Solution

$P = 2L + 2W$
$= 2(240 \text{ ft}) + 2(108 \text{ ft})$
$= 480 \text{ ft} + 216 \text{ ft} = 696 \text{ ft}$
Cost $= 696 \times 6.75 = 4698$

The cost to fence the lot is $4698.

YOU TRY IT 6

Metal stripping is being installed around a workbench that is 0.74 m wide and 3 m long. At $4.49 per meter, find the cost of the metal stripping. Round to the nearest cent.

Your strategy

Your solution

Solutions on p. S29

8.4 EXERCISES

✔ Concept Check

1. Complete each sentence with the name of a polygon or a number of sides.
   a. A _____ has three sides.
   b. A polygon with six sides is called a _____.
   c. A polygon with four equal sides is called a _____. If the polygon also has four equal angles, then it is called a _____.
   d. An isosceles triangle has _____ sides of equal length.

2. What is the perimeter of a circle called?

3. What is the formula for the perimeter of a rectangle?

4. What is the formula for the circumference of a circle?

OBJECTIVE A   *To find the perimeter of plane geometric figures*

For Exercises 5 to 12, find the perimeter or circumference of the given figure. Use 3.14 for π.

5.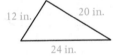
12 in.   20 in.   24 in.

6.
14 cm   13 cm   12 cm

7.
5 ft   5 ft

8.
2 m   2 m

9.
15 cm

10.
4 in.

11.
14 cm   32 cm

12.
5 ft   18 ft

13. Find the perimeter of a triangle with sides of lengths 2 ft 4 in., 3 ft, and 4 ft 6 in.

14. Find the perimeter of a rectangle with a length of 2 m and a width of 0.8 m.

15. Find the circumference of a circle with a radius of 8 cm. Use 3.14 for π.

16. Find the circumference of a circle with a diameter of 14 in. Use $\frac{22}{7}$ for π.

17. Find the perimeter of a square in which each side is 60 m.

18. Find the perimeter of a triangle in which each side is $1\frac{2}{3}$ ft.

19. Farming A horse trainer wants to build a rectangular corral that is 60 ft wide and 75 ft long. How many feet of fencing will the trainer need to build the corral?

20. Money The diameter of a quarter dollar is 24.26 mm. What is the circumference of a quarter dollar? Use 3.14 for π. Round to the nearest hundredth.

21. The length of a side of a square is equal to the diameter of a circle. Which is greater, the perimeter of the square or the circumference of the circle?

22. The length of a rectangle is equal to the diameter of a circle, and the width of the rectangle is equal to the radius of the same circle. Which is greater, the perimeter of the rectangle or the circumference of the circle?

OBJECTIVE B *To find the perimeter of composite geometric figures*

For Exercises 23 to 30, find the perimeter. Use 3.14 for π.

23.
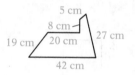

24.

25.

26.

27.

28.

29.
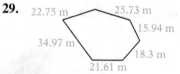

30.
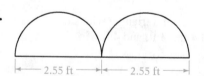

For Exercises 31 and 32, determine whether the perimeter of the given composite figure is less than, equal to, or greater than the perimeter of the figure shown at the right. The figure at the right is made up of a square and one-half a circle of diameter d.

31. A figure formed by an equilateral triangle and one-half a circle of diameter d

32. A figure formed by a square and one-half a circle of diameter d

OBJECTIVE C *To solve application problems*

33. Landscaping How many feet of fencing should be purchased to enclose a rectangular garden that is 18 ft long and 12 ft wide?

34. Interior Design Wall-to-wall carpeting is installed in a room that is 12 ft long and 10 ft wide. The edges of the carpet are nailed to the floor. Along how many feet must the carpet be nailed down?

35. Quilting How many feet of binding are required to bind the edge of a rectangular quilt that measures 3.5 ft by 8.5 ft?

36. Carpentry Find the length of molding needed to trim a circular table that is 3.8 ft in diameter. Use 3.14 for π.

37. ● **Race Tracks** The first circular dog race track opened in 1919 in Emeryville, California. The radius of the circular track was 157.64 ft. Find the circumference of the track. Use 3.14 for π. Round to the nearest whole number.

38. Landscaping The rectangular lot shown in the figure at the right is being fenced. The fencing along the road costs $6.20 per foot. The rest of the fencing costs $5.85 per foot. Find the total cost to fence the lot.

800 ft

1250 ft

39. Sewing Bias binding is to be sewed around the edge of a rectangular quilt measuring 72 in. by 45 in. Each package of bias binding costs $5.50 and contains 15 ft of binding. How many packages of bias binding are needed for the quilt?

40. Travel A bicycle tire has a diameter of 24 in. How many feet does the bicycle travel when the wheel makes five revolutions? Use 3.14 for π.

41. Travel A tricycle tire has a diameter of 12 in. How many feet does the tricycle travel when the wheel makes eight revolutions? Use 3.14 for π.

Architecture For Exercises 42 and 43, use the floor plan of a roller rink shown at the right.

25 m

10 m

42. 🖋 Use estimation to determine whether the perimeter is less than 70 m or greater than 70 m.

43. Calculate the perimeter of the roller rink. Use 3.14 for π.

44. Home Improvement A rain gutter is being installed on a home that has the dimensions shown in the figure at the right. At a cost of $11.30 per meter, how much will it cost to install the rain gutter?

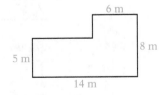

6 m

8 m

5 m

14 m

45. Home Improvement Find the length of weather stripping installed around the arched door shown in the figure at the right. Use 3.14 for π.

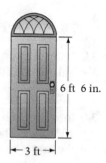

6 ft 6 in.

← 3 ft →

46. **Astronomy** The distance from Earth to the sun is 93,000,000 mi. Approximate the distance Earth travels in making one revolution about the sun. Use 3.14 for π.

Critical Thinking

47. a. If the diameter of a circle is doubled, how many times larger is the resulting circumference?

   b. If the radius of a circle is doubled, how many times larger is the resulting circumference?

48. Geometry In the pattern below, the length of one side of a square is 1 unit. Find the perimeter of the eighth figure in the pattern.

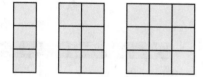

49. ◥ **Forestry** A forest ranger must determine the diameter of a redwood tree. Explain how the ranger could do this without cutting down the tree.

Projects or Group Activities

50. Fractals The diagrams below show the first three stages of the Sierpinski Triangle, a pattern in Italian mosaics that dates from the 13th century. The pattern is named for the Polish mathematician Waclaw Sierpinski, who studied the design and its properties in the early part of the 20th century.

To create the design, first place an equilateral triangle inside another equilateral triangle, as shown in Figure A. Then place three more equilateral triangles inside the unshaded triangles of Figure A, forming Figure B. Repeat this process again to make Figure C from Figure B. The process can be repeated indefinitely.

Determine the sum of the perimeters of all the shaded triangles in Figure C.

← 2 cm →

Figure A   Figure B   Figure C

8.5 | Area

OBJECTIVE A | *To find the area of geometric figures*

Area is a measure of the amount of surface in a region. Area can be used to describe, for example, the size of a rug, a parking lot, a farm, or a national park. Area is measured in square units.

A square that measures 1 in. on each side has an area of 1 square inch, which is written $1\ \text{in}^2$.

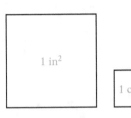

A square that measures 1 cm on each side has an area of 1 square centimeter, which is written $1\ \text{cm}^2$.

Larger areas can be measured in square feet (ft^2), square meters (m^2), square miles (mi^2), acres ($43{,}560\ \text{ft}^2$), or any other square unit.

The area of a geometric figure is the number of squares that are necessary to cover the figure. In the figures below, two rectangles have been drawn and covered with squares. In the figure on the left, 12 squares, each of area $1\ \text{cm}^2$, were used to cover the rectangle. The area of the rectangle is $12\ \text{cm}^2$. In the figure on the right, 6 squares, each of area $1\ \text{in}^2$, were used to cover the rectangle. The area of the rectangle is $6\ \text{in}^2$.

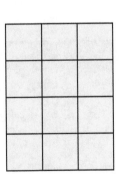

The area of the rectangle is 12 cm².

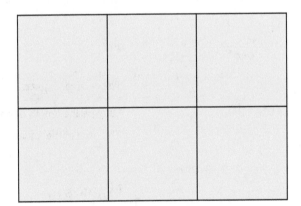

The area of the rectangle is 6 in².

Note from the above figures that the area of a rectangle can be found by multiplying the length of the rectangle by its width.

Area of a Rectangle

Let *L* be the length of a rectangle and *W* be the width of a rectangle.

The area of the rectangle is $A = LW$.

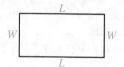

EXAMPLE

Find the area of the rectangle shown at the right.

$A = LW$

$\quad = (8 \text{ ft})(5 \text{ ft}) \quad \cdot L = 8 \text{ ft}, W = 5 \text{ ft}$

$\quad = 40 \text{ ft}^2$

The area of the rectangle is 40 ft².

APPLY THE CONCEPT

A carpet installer charges $.30 per square foot to install wall-to-wall carpeting. How much would the installer charge to install wall-to-wall carpeting in a rectangular room that measures 12 ft by 14 ft?

To find the cost, first find the area of the room. Then multiply the area by the cost per square foot.

$A = LW$

$\quad = (14 \text{ ft})(12 \text{ ft}) \quad \cdot L = 14 \text{ ft}, W = 12 \text{ ft}$

$\quad = 168 \text{ ft}^2$

The area of the room is 168 ft².

$\quad \text{Cost} = 168 \cdot 0.30 = 50.40$

The installer would charge $50.40 to install the carpet.

Area of a Square

Let *s* be the length of one side of a square.

The area of the square is $A = s^2$.

EXAMPLE

Find the area of the square shown at the right.

$A = s^2$

$\quad = (14 \text{ cm})^2 \quad \cdot s = 14 \text{ cm}$

$\quad = 196 \text{ cm}^2$

The area of the square is 196 cm².

Area of a Triangle

In the figure at the right, $\overline{AB}$ is the base b of the triangle, and $\overline{CD}$, which is perpendicular to the base b, is the height h.

The area of a triangle is $A = \frac{1}{2}bh$.

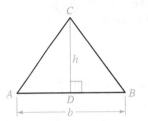

EXAMPLE

Find the area of the triangle shown at the right.

$A = \frac{1}{2}bh$

$\quad = \frac{1}{2}(20 \text{ m})(5 \text{ m})$ • $b = 20 \text{ m}, h = 5 \text{ m}$

$\quad = 50 \text{ m}^2$

The area of the triangle is 50 m².

Integrating Technology

To calculate the area of the triangle shown in the Example, you can enter

20 ✕ 5 ÷ 2 =

or

.5 ✕ 20 ✕ 5 =

Area of a Circle

Let r be the radius of a circle.

The area of the circle is $A = \pi r^2$.

EXAMPLE

Find the area of the circle shown at the right.

$A = \pi r^2$

$\quad = \pi(8 \text{ in.})^2 = 64\pi \text{ in}^2$

$\quad \approx 64 \cdot 3.14 \text{ in}^2 = 200.96 \text{ in}^2$

The area is exactly 64π in².

The area is approximately 200.96 in².

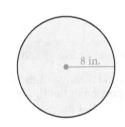

Take Note

Note that we gave two answers for the area of the circle. The *exact* answer, which includes the symbol for π, and an *approximate* answer, which uses an approximation for π.

APPLY THE CONCEPT

The bottom of a circular children's wading pool has a diameter of 5 ft. What is the area of the bottom of the pool?

To find the area, first find the radius of the bottom of the pool. Then use the equation $A = \pi r^2$ to find the area. Use 3.14 for π.

$$r = \frac{\text{diameter}}{2} = \frac{5 \text{ ft}}{2} = 2.5 \text{ ft}$$

$A = \pi r^2$

$\quad = \pi(2.5 \text{ ft})^2$

$\quad \approx 3.14(2.5 \text{ ft})^2$

$\quad = 19.625 \text{ ft}^2$

The area of the bottom of the pool is 19.625 ft².

EXAMPLE 1

Find the area of a circle with a diameter of 9 cm.
Use 3.14 for π.

Solution

$$r = \frac{1}{2}d = \frac{1}{2}(9 \text{ cm}) = 4.5 \text{ cm}$$
$$A = \pi r^2$$
$$\approx 3.14(4.5 \text{ cm})^2 = 63.585 \text{ cm}^2$$

The area is approximately 63.585 cm².

YOU TRY IT 1

Find the area of a triangle with a base of 24 in.
and a height of 14 in.

Your solution

Solution on p. S29

OBJECTIVE B   *To find the area of composite geometric figures*

The area of the composite figure shown below is found by calculating the area of the
rectangle and then subtracting the area of the triangle.

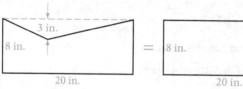

$$A = LW - \frac{1}{2}bh$$
$$= (20 \text{ in.})(8 \text{ in.}) - \frac{1}{2}(20 \text{ in.})(3 \text{ in.}) = 160 \text{ in}^2 - 30 \text{ in}^2 = 130 \text{ in}^2$$

EXAMPLE 2

Find the area of the shaded
portion of the figure.
Use 3.14 for π.

Solution

$$\begin{array}{l} \text{Area of} \\ \text{shaded} \\ \text{portion} \end{array} = \underbrace{\begin{array}{c}\text{area of}\\\text{square}\end{array}}_{} - \underbrace{\begin{array}{c}\text{area of}\\\text{circle}\end{array}}_{}$$

$$\begin{aligned}
A &= s^2 &- &\quad \pi r^2 \\
&= (8 \text{ m})^2 &- &\quad \pi (4 \text{ m})^2 \\
&\approx 64 \text{ m}^2 &- &\quad 3.14(16 \text{ m}^2) \\
&= 64 \text{ m}^2 &- &\quad 50.24 \text{ m}^2 = 13.76 \text{ m}^2
\end{aligned}$$

The area is approximately 13.76 m².

YOU TRY IT 2

Find the area of the
composite figure.

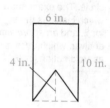

Your solution

Solution on p. S29

OBJECTIVE C   *To solve application problems*

EXAMPLE 3

A walkway 2 m wide is built along the front and along both sides of a building, as shown in the figure. Find the area of the walkway.

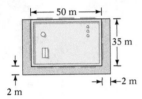

Strategy

To find the area of the walkway, add the area of the front section (54 m · 2 m) and the area of the two side sections (each 35 m · 2 m).

Solution

$$\text{Area of walkway} = \text{area of front section} + 2(\text{area of one side section})$$

$$A = (54\text{ m})(2\text{ m}) + 2(35\text{ m})(2\text{ m})$$
$$= 108\text{ m}^2 + 140\text{ m}^2$$
$$= 248\text{ m}^2$$

The area of the walkway is 248 m².

YOU TRY IT 3

New carpet is installed in a room measuring 9 ft by 12 ft. Find the area of the room in square yards. ($9\text{ ft}^2 = 1\text{ yd}^2$)

Your strategy

Your solution

Solution on p. S30

8.5 EXERCISES

✔ Concept Check

1. Give the formula for the area of each figure:
   a. Rectangle
   b. Circle

2. State whether each unit could be used to measure *perimeter* or *area*.
   a. mm
   b. ft^2
   c. mi
   d. km
   e. yd^2

OBJECTIVE A   *To find the area of geometric figures*

For Exercises 3 to 10, find the area of the given figure. Use 3.14 for π.

3.

6 ft
24 ft

4.
8 in.
18 in.

5.
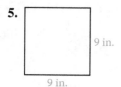
9 in.
9 in.

6.
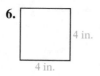
4 in.
4 in.

7.
4 ft

8.

3 cm

9.
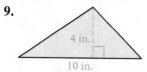
4 in.
10 in.

10.
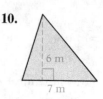
6 m
7 m

11. Find the area of a right triangle with a base of 3 cm and a height of 1.42 cm.

12. Find the area of a triangle with a base of 3 ft and a height of $\frac{2}{3}$ ft.

13. Find the area of a square with a side of 4 ft.

14. Find the area of a square with a side of 10 cm.

15. Find the area of a rectangle with a length of 43 in. and a width of 19 in.

16. Find the area of a rectangle with a length of 82 cm and a width of 20 cm.

17. Find the area of a circle with a radius of 7 in. Use $\frac{22}{7}$ for π.

18. Find the area of a circle with a diameter of 40 cm. Use 3.14 for π.

19. **Sports**   A square is formed by connecting the bases of a professional baseball field. The length of each side of the square is 90 ft. What is the area of the baseball field?

20. **Camping**   The back of a tent is in the shape of a triangle with a base of 6 ft and a height of 5 ft. What is the area of the back of the tent?

For Exercises 21 and 22, determine whether the area of the first figure is less than, equal to, or greater than the area of the second figure.

21.

22.

OBJECTIVE B   *To find the area of composite geometric figures*

For Exercises 23 to 30, find the area. Use 3.14 for π.

23.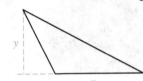

24.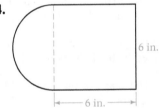

25.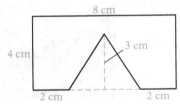

26.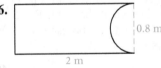

27.

28.

29.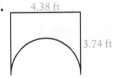

30.

31. Determine whether the area of Figure 1 below is less than, equal to, or greater than the area of Figure 2.

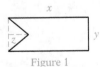
Figure 1

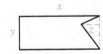
Figure 2

OBJECTIVE C *To solve application problems*

32. 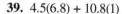 **Architecture** See the news clipping at the right. Use the dimensions given for the Yardmaster Building to estimate the cost of carpeting the two floors of office space if the cost of the carpet is $18 per square meter.

33. **Sports** Artificial turf is being used to cover a playing field. The field is rectangular with a length of 100 yd and a width of 75 yd. How much artificial turf must be purchased to cover the field?

34. **Telescopes** The telescope lens of the Hale telescope at Mount Palomar, California, has a diameter of 200 in. Find the area of the lens. Use 3.14 for π.

35. **Home Improvement** You plan to stain the wooden deck attached to your house. The deck measures 10 ft by 8 ft. A quart of stain will cost $11.87 and will cover 50 ft². How many quarts of stain should you buy?

36. **Interior Design** A fabric wall hanging is to fill a space that measures 5 m by 3.5 m. Allowing for 0.1 m of the fabric to be folded back along each edge, how much fabric must be purchased for the wall hanging?

37. **Agriculture** An irrigation system waters a circular field that has a 50-foot radius. Find the area watered by the irrigation system. Use 3.14 for π.

38. **Geography** The shape of the state of Massachusetts can be approximated by a rectangle with a length of 150 mi and a width of 70 mi. Use these dimensions to approximate the area of Massachusetts.

In the NEWS!

Railroad Building Stands Out

The new Yardmaster Building, home to railroad operation facilities in Melborne, Australia, makes a striking contrast to the surrounding railroad tracks. The unusual four-story rectangular building is about 30 m long and 10 m wide. Two of its four stories are devoted to office space.

Source: www.designboom.com

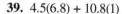 **Interior Design** A carpet is to be installed in one room and a hallway, as shown in the diagram at the right. For Exercises 39 to 42, state whether the given expression can be used to calculate the area of the carpet in square meters.

39. 4.5(6.8) + 10.8(1)

40. 4.5(10.8) − 3.5(4)

41. 10.8(1) + 3.5(6.8)

42. 4.5(6.8) + 1(4)

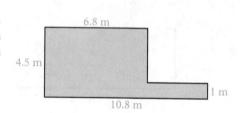

43. **Interior Design** Use the diagram for Exercises 39 to 42. At a cost of $28.50 per square meter, how much will it cost to carpet the area?

44. **Landscaping** Find the area of a concrete driveway with the measurements shown in the figure.

45. **Interior Design** You want to tile your kitchen floor. The floor measures 12 ft by 9 ft. How many tiles, each a square with side $1\frac{1}{2}$ ft, should you purchase for the job?

46. **Interior Design** You are wallpapering two walls of a child's room. One wall measures 9 ft by 8 ft, and the other measures 11 ft by 8 ft. The wallpaper costs $34.50 per roll, and each roll of the wallpaper will cover 40 ft². What is the cost to wallpaper the two walls?

47. Construction   Find the area of the 2-meter boundary around the swimming pool shown in the figure.

48. Parks   An urban renewal project involves reseeding a park that is in the shape of a square, 60 ft on each side. Each bag of grass seed costs $5.75 and will seed 1200 ft^2. How much money should be budgeted for buying grass seed for the park?

49. Architecture   The roller rink shown in the figure at the right is to be covered with hardwood flooring.
   a. Without doing the calculations, indicate whether the area of the rink is more than 8000 ft^2 or less than 8000 ft^2.
   b. Calculate how much hardwood flooring is needed to cover the roller rink. Use 3.14 for π.

50. Parks   Find the total area of the national park with the dimensions shown in the figure at the right. Use 3.14 for π.

51. Interior Design   Find the cost of plastering the walls of a room that is 22 ft wide, 25 ft 6 in. long, and 8 ft high. Subtract 120 ft^2 for windows and doors. The cost is $3 per square foot.

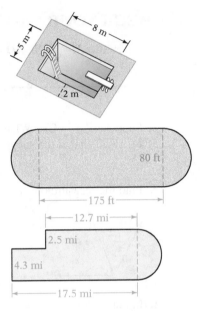

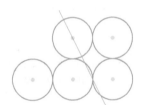

Critical Thinking

52. a. If both the length and the width of a rectangle are doubled, how many times larger is the area of the resulting rectangle?
   b. If the radius of a circle is doubled, what happens to the area?
   c. If the diameter of a circle is doubled, what happens to the area?

53. ◣ The circles at the right are identical. Is the area in the circles to the left of the line equal to, less than, or greater than the area in the circles to the right of the line? Explain your answer.

54. Determine whether the statement is always true, sometimes true, or never true.
   a. If two triangles have the same perimeter, then the triangles have the same area.
   b. If two rectangles have the same area, then the rectangles have the same perimeter.
   c. If two squares have the same area, then the sides of the squares have the same length.

Projects or Group Activities

55. ● **Lake Tahoe**   One way to measure the area of an irregular figure, such as a lake, is to divide the area into trapezoids that have the same height. Then measure the length of each base, calculate the area of each trapezoid, and add the areas. The figure at the right gives approximate dimensions for Lake Tahoe, which straddles the California and Nevada borders. Approximate the area of Lake Tahoe using the given trapezoids. Round to the nearest tenth. *Note:* The formula for the area A of a trapezoid is $A = \frac{1}{2}h(b_1 + b_2)$, where h is the height of the trapezoid and b_1 and b_2 are the lengths of the bases.

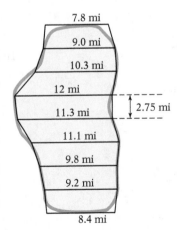

✔ CHECK YOUR PROGRESS: CHAPTER 8

1. Given that $MN = 20$, $NO = 24$, and $MP = 72$, find OP.

2. Suppose $\angle A = 27°$. What is the complement of $\angle A$? What is the supplement of $\angle A$?

3. Find the measure of $\angle a$.

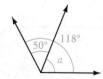

4. In the figure, $l_1 \parallel l_2$ and $\angle c = 120°$. Find the measures of $\angle a$ and $\angle b$.

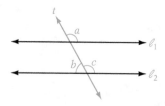

5. One angle of a right triangle measures 22°. What are the measures of the other two angles?

6. Two angles of a triangle measure 54° and 112°. What is the measure of the third angle?

7. In the figure, $\angle LON = 139°$ and $\angle MON = 86°$. Find the measure of $\angle LOM$.

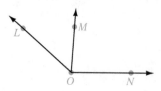

8. Find the measures of $\angle a$ and $\angle b$.

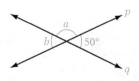

9. Find the perimeter of a rectangle with a length of 3.25 m and a width of 75 cm.

10. Find the circumference of a circle whose radius is 3.6 in. Use 3.14 for π.

11. Find the perimeter of the figure. Use 3.14 for π.

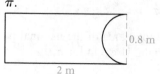

12. Find the area of the triangle.

13. Find the area of a circle whose diameter is 6 in. Use 3.14 for π.

14. Find the area of the figure. Use 3.14 for π.

15. **Carpeting** Wall-to-wall carpeting is being installed in a room that is 12 ft wide and 14 ft long. If the carpet costs $3.25 per square foot, what is the cost of the carpet?

16. **Landscaping** A circular brick walkway surrounds a garden as shown in the diagram at the right. What is the area of the brick walkway? Use 3.14 for π.

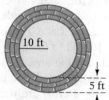

SECTION

8.6 | Volume

OBJECTIVE A   *To find the volume of geometric solids*

Volume is a measure of the amount of space inside a closed surface, or figure in space. Volume can be used to describe, for example, the amount of heating gas used for cooking, the amount of concrete delivered for the foundation of a house, or the amount of water in storage for a city's water supply.

A cube that is 1 ft on each side has a volume of 1 cubic foot, which is written 1 ft^3.

A cube that measures 1 cm on each side has a volume of 1 cubic centimeter, which is written 1 cm^3.

The volume of a solid is the number of cubes that are necessary to fill the solid exactly. The volume of the rectangular solid at the right is 24 cm^3 because it will hold exactly 24 cubes, each 1 cm on a side. Note that the volume can be found by multiplying the length times the width times the height.

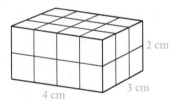

Volume of a Rectangular Solid

Let *L* be the length, *W* be the width, and *H* be the height of a rectangular solid.

The volume of the rectangular is $V = LWH$.

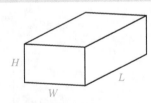

EXAMPLE

Find the volume of the rectangular solid shown at the right.

$V = LWH$

   $= (9 \text{ in.})(3 \text{ in.})(4 \text{ in.})$ • $L = 9$ in.,
                                 $W = 3$ in.,

   $= 108 \text{ in}^3$ $H = 4$ in.

The volume of the rectangular solid is 108 in^3.

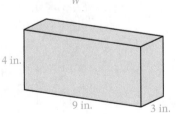

A **cube** is a rectangular solid for which the length, width, and height are all equal. The volume of a cube is found by multiplying the length of a side of the cube times itself three times ("side cubed").

Volume of a Cube

Let s be the length of one side of a cube.

The volume of the cube is $A = s^3$.

EXAMPLE

Find the volume of the cube shown at the right.

$$A = s^3$$
$$= (3 \text{ ft})^3 \qquad \bullet \; s = 3 \text{ ft}$$
$$= 27 \text{ ft}^3$$

The volume of the cube is 27 ft³.

Volume of a Sphere

Let r be the radius of a sphere.

The volume of the sphere is $V = \frac{4}{3}\pi r^3$.

EXAMPLE

Find the volume of the sphere shown at the right. Use 3.14 for π. Round to the nearest hundredth.

$$V = \frac{4}{3}\pi r^3$$
$$\approx \frac{4}{3}(3.14)(2 \text{ in.})^3 \qquad \bullet \; r = 2 \text{ in.}$$
$$= \frac{4}{3}(3.14)(8 \text{ in}^3)$$
$$\approx 33.49 \text{ in}^3$$

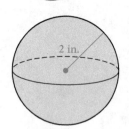

The volume is approximately 33.49 in³.

Volume of a Cylinder

Let r be the radius of a cylinder.

The volume of the cylinder is $V = \pi r^2 h$.

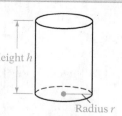

EXAMPLE

Find the volume of the cylinder shown below. Use 3.14 for π. Round to the nearest hundredth.

$$V = \pi r^2 h$$
$$\approx 3.14(3 \text{ cm})^2(8 \text{ cm}) \qquad \bullet \; r = 3 \text{ cm}, h = 8 \text{ cm}$$
$$= 3.14(9 \text{ cm}^2)(8 \text{ cm})$$
$$= 226.08 \text{ cm}^3$$

The volume of the cylinder is approximately 226.08 cm³.

EXAMPLE 1

Find the volume of a rectangular solid with a length of 3 ft, a width of 1.5 ft, and a height of 2 ft.

Solution

$V = LWH$
$= (3 \text{ ft})(1.5 \text{ ft})(2 \text{ ft})$
$= 9 \text{ ft}^3$

The volume is 9 ft³.

YOU TRY IT 1

Find the volume of a rectangular solid with a length of 8 cm, a width of 3.5 cm, and a height of 4 cm.

Your solution

EXAMPLE 2

Find the volume of a cube that has a side measuring 2.5 in.

Solution

$V = s^3$
$= (2.5 \text{ in.})^3$
$= 15.625 \text{ in}^3$

The volume is 15.625 in³.

YOU TRY IT 2

Find the volume of a cube with a side of length 5 cm.

Your solution

EXAMPLE 3

Find the volume of a cylinder with a radius of 12 cm and a height of 65 cm. Use 3.14 for π.

Solution

$V = \pi r^2 h$
$\approx 3.14(12 \text{ cm})^2(65 \text{ cm})$
$= 3.14(144 \text{ cm}^2)(65 \text{ cm})$
$= 29{,}390.4 \text{ cm}^3$

The volume is approximately 29,390.4 cm³.

YOU TRY IT 3

Find the volume of a cylinder with a diameter of 14 in. and a height of 15 in. Use $\frac{22}{7}$ for π.

Your solution

Solutions on p. S30

EXAMPLE 4

Find the volume of a sphere with a diameter of 12 in. Use 3.14 for π.

Solution

$r = \dfrac{1}{2}d = \dfrac{1}{2}(12 \text{ in.}) = 6 \text{ in.}$ • Find the radius.

$V = \dfrac{4}{3}\pi r^3$ • Use the formula for the volume of a sphere.

$\approx \dfrac{4}{3}(3.14)(6 \text{ in.})^3$

$= \dfrac{4}{3}(3.14)(216 \text{ in}^3)$

$= 904.32 \text{ in}^3$

The volume is approximately 904.32 in³.

YOU TRY IT 4

Find the volume of a sphere with a radius of 3 m. Use 3.14 for π.

Your solution

Solution on p. S30

OBJECTIVE B *To find the volume of composite geometric solids*

A **composite geometric solid** is a solid made from two or more geometric solids. The solid shown is made from a cylinder and one-half of a sphere.

Volume of the composite solid = volume of the cylinder + $\dfrac{1}{2}$ the volume of the sphere

HOW TO 1 Find the volume of the composite solid shown above if the radius of the base of the cylinder is 3 in. and the height of the cylinder is 10 in. Use 3.14 for π.

The volume equals the volume of a cylinder plus one-half the volume of a sphere. The radius of the sphere equals the radius of the base of the cylinder.

$V = \pi r^2 h + \dfrac{1}{2}\left(\dfrac{4}{3}\pi r^3\right)$

$\approx 3.14(3 \text{ in.})^2(10 \text{ in.}) + \dfrac{1}{2}\left(\dfrac{4}{3}\right)(3.14)(3 \text{ in.})^3$

$= 3.14(9 \text{ in}^2)(10 \text{ in.}) + \dfrac{1}{2}\left(\dfrac{4}{3}\right)(3.14)(27 \text{ in}^3)$

$= 282.6 \text{ in}^3 + 56.52 \text{ in}^3$

$= 339.12 \text{ in}^3$

The volume is approximately 339.12 in³.

EXAMPLE 5

Find the volume of the solid shown in the figure.
Use 3.14 for π.

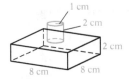

Solution

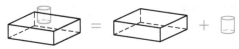

Volume of solid	=	volume of rectangular solid	+	volume of cylinder

$V = LWH + \pi r^2 h$
$\approx (8 \text{ cm})(8 \text{ cm})(2 \text{ cm}) + 3.14(1 \text{ cm})^2(2 \text{ cm})$
$= 128 \text{ cm}^3 + 6.28 \text{ cm}^3$
$= 134.28 \text{ cm}^3$

The volume is approximately 134.28 cm³.

Find the volume of the solid shown in the figure.
Use 3.14 for π.

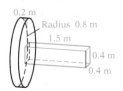

Your solution

EXAMPLE 6

Find the volume of the solid shown in the figure.
Use 3.14 for π.

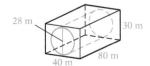

Solution

Volume of solid	=	volume of rectangular solid	−	volume of cylinder

$V = LWH - \pi r^2 h$
$\approx (80 \text{ m})(40 \text{ m})(30 \text{ m}) - 3.14(14 \text{ m})^2(80 \text{ m})$
$= 96,000 \text{ m}^3 - 49,235.2 \text{ m}^3$
$= 46,764.8 \text{ m}^3$

The volume is approximately 46,764.8 m³.

Find the volume of the solid shown in the figure.
Use 3.14 for π.

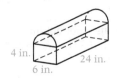

Your solution

Solutions on p. S30

OBJECTIVE C *To solve application problems*

EXAMPLE 7

An aquarium is 28 in. long, 14 in. wide, and 16 in. high. Find the volume of the aquarium.

Strategy

To find the volume of the aquarium, use the formula for the volume of a rectangular solid.

Solution

$V = LWH$

$= (28 \text{ in.})(14 \text{ in.})(16 \text{ in.})$

$= 6272 \text{ in}^3$

The volume of the aquarium is 6272 in^3.

YOU TRY IT 7

Find the volume of a freezer that is 7 ft long, 3 ft high, and 2.5 ft wide.

Your strategy

Your solution

EXAMPLE 8

Find the volume of the bushing shown in the figure below. Use 3.14 for π.

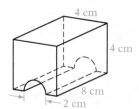

Strategy

To find the volume of the bushing, subtract the volume of the half-cylinder from the volume of the rectangular solid.

Solution

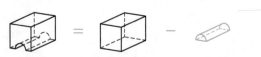

Volume of bushing $=$ volume of rectangular solid $-$ $\frac{1}{2}$ volume of cylinder

$V = LWH - \dfrac{1}{2}\pi r^2 h$

$\approx (8 \text{ cm})(4 \text{ cm})(4 \text{ cm}) - \dfrac{1}{2}(3.14)(1 \text{ cm})^2(8 \text{ cm})$

$= 128 \text{ cm}^3 - 12.56 \text{ cm}^3$

$= 115.44 \text{ cm}^3$

The volume of the bushing is approximately 115.44 cm^3.

YOU TRY IT 8

Find the volume of the channel iron shown in the figure below.

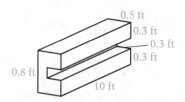

Your strategy

Your solution

Solutions on p. S30

8.6 EXERCISES

✔ Concept Check

1. Give the formula for the volume of each solid.
   a. Cube   **b.** Sphere   **c.** Cylinder

2. State whether each unit could be used to measure perimeter, area, or volume.
   a. km   **b.** yd^3 **c.** cm^3 **d.** mi^2
   e. mm^3 **f.** in.   **g.** dm   **h.** hm^2

OBJECTIVE A   *To find the volume of geometric solids*

For Exercises 3 to 10, find the volume. If necessary, round to the nearest hundredth. Use 3.14 for π.

3.
3 cm   12 cm   4 cm

4.
5 ft   6 ft   8 ft

5.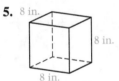
8 in.   8 in.   8 in.

6.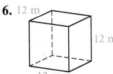
12 m   12 m   12 m

7.
8 in.

8.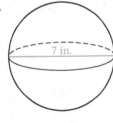
7 in.

9.
12 cm   2 cm

10.
8 ft   5 ft

11. Find the volume, in cubic meters, of a rectangular solid with a length of 2 m, a width of 80 cm, and a height of 4 m.

12. Find the volume, in cubic meters, of a rectangular solid with a length of 1.15 m, a width of 60 cm, and a height of 25 cm.

13. Find the volume of a sphere with an 11-millimeter radius. Use 3.14 for π. Round to the nearest hundredth.

14. Find the volume of a cube with a side of length 2.14 m. Round to the nearest tenth.

15. Find the volume of a cylinder with a diameter of 12 ft and a height of 30 ft. Use 3.14 for π.

16. Find the volume of a sphere with a 6-foot diameter. Use 3.14 for π.

17. Find the volume of a cube with a side of length $3\frac{1}{2}$ ft.

18. Find the volume of a cylinder with a radius of 7 cm and a height of 14 cm. Use $\frac{22}{7}$ for π.

19. The length of a side of a cube is equal to the radius of a sphere. Which solid has the greater volume?

20. A sphere and a cylinder have the same radius. The height of the cylinder is equal to the radius of its base. Which solid has the greater volume?

OBJECTIVE B *To find the volume of composite geometric solids*

For Exercises 21 to 26, find the volume. Use 3.14 for π.

21.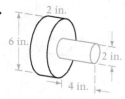

22.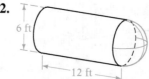

23.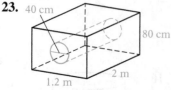

24.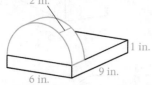

25.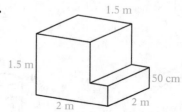

26.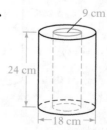

For Exercises 27 and 28, use the solid shown in Exercise 26. If the solid is changed as described, will its volume increase or decrease?

27. The outer cylinder is changed to a rectangular solid with a square base. The height and width of the outer solid remain the same.

28. The inner cylinder is changed to a rectangular solid with a square base. The height and width of the inner solid remain the same.

OBJECTIVE C   *To solve application problems*

For Exercises 29 to 42, solve. Use 3.14 for π.

29. **Fish Hatchery**   A rectangular tank at a fish hatchery is 9 m long, 3 m wide, and 1.5 m deep. Find the volume of the water in the tank when the tank is full.

30. **Rocketry**   A fuel tank in a booster rocket is a cylinder 10 ft in diameter and 52 ft high. Find the volume of the fuel tank.

31. **Ballooning**   A hot air balloon is in the shape of a sphere. Find the volume of a hot air balloon that is 32 ft in diameter. Round to the nearest hundredth.

32. **Petroleum**   An oil tank, which is in the shape of a cylinder, is 4 m high and has a diameter of 6 m. The oil tank is two-thirds full. Find the number of cubic meters of oil in the tank. Round to the nearest hundredth.

33. **Agriculture**   A silo, which is in the shape of a cylinder, is 16 ft in diameter and has a height of 30 ft. The silo is three-fourths full. Find the volume of the portion of the silo that is not being used for storage.

34. ● **Guacamole Consumption**   See the news clipping at the right. What is the volume, in cubic feet, of the guacamole eaten during the Super Bowl?

35. ● **Guacamole Consumption**   See the news clipping at the right. Assuming that each person eats 1 c of guacamole, how many people eat guacamole during the Super Bowl? $1 \text{ ft}^3 \approx 119.68 \text{ c}$.

36. ● **The Panama Canal**   The Gatun Lock of the Panama Canal is 1000 ft long, 110 ft wide, and 60 ft deep. Find the volume of the lock in cubic feet.

37. ● **The Panama Canal**   When the lock is full, the water in the Pedro Miguel Lock near the Pacific Ocean side of the Panama Canal fills a rectangular solid of dimensions 1000 ft long, 110 ft wide, and 43 ft deep. There are approximately 7.48 gal of water in each cubic foot. How many gallons of water are in the lock?

38. **Architecture**   An architect is designing the heating system for an auditorium and needs to know the volume of the structure. Find the volume of the auditorium with the measurements shown in the figure.

In the NEWS!

Super Bowl Win for Guacamole

Guacamole is the dish of choice at Super Bowl parties. If all the guacamole eaten during the Super Bowl were piled onto a football field—which, including endzones, is 360 ft long and 160 ft wide—it would cover the field to a depth of 3 ft!
Source: www.azcentral.com

Panama Canal

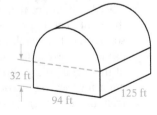

94 ft   125 ft   32 ft

39. Metal Works Find the volume of the bushing shown at the right.

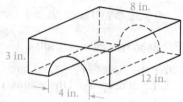

40. Aquariums How many gallons of water will fill a fish tank that is 12 in. long, 8 in. wide, and 9 in. high? Round to the nearest tenth. $(1 \text{ gal} = 231 \text{ in}^3)$

41. Aquariums How many gallons of water will fill an aquarium that is 12 in. wide, 18 in. long, and 16 in. high? Round to the nearest tenth. $(1 \text{ gal} = 231 \text{ in}^3)$

42. Petroleum A truck carrying an oil tank is shown in the figure at the right.

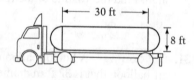

   a. Without doing the calculations, determine whether the volume of the oil tank is more than 240 ft^3 or less than 240 ft^3.

   b. If the tank is half full, how many cubic feet of oil is the truck carrying? Round to the nearest hundredth.

Construction For Exercises 43 to 46, use the diagram at the right showing the concrete floor of a building. State whether the given expression can be used to calculate the volume of the concrete floor in cubic feet.

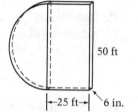

43. $(25)(50)(6) + (0.5)(3.14)(25^2)(6)$ **44.** $(25)(50)(0.5) + (0.5)(3.14)(25^2)(0.5)$

45. $0.5[(25)(50) + (0.5)(3.14)(25^2)]$ **46.** $(25)(50)(0.5) + (0.5)(3.14)(50^2)(0.5)$

47. Construction Use the diagram for Exercises 43 to 46. At a cost of $10 per cubic foot, find the cost of having the floor poured.

Critical Thinking

For Exercises 48 to 51, explain how you could cut through a cube so that the face of the resulting solid is the given geometric figure.

48. A square   **49.** An equilateral triangle

50. A trapezoid   **51.** A hexagon

Projects or Group Activities

52. Suppose a cylinder is cut into 16 equal pieces, which are then arranged as shown at the right. The figure resembles a rectangular solid. What variable expressions could be used to represent the length, width, and height of the rectangular solid? Explain how the formula for the volume of a cylinder is derived from this approach.

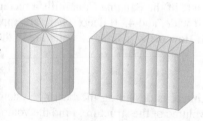

8.7 Radical Expressions

OBJECTIVE A *To find the square root of a perfect square*

Recall that the square of a number is equal to the number multiplied times itself.

$$3^2 = 3 \cdot 3 = 9$$

The square of an integer is called a **perfect square.**

9 is a perfect square because 9 is the square of 3: $3^2 = 9$.

The numbers 1, 4, 9, 16, 25, 36, 49, 64, 81, and 100 are perfect squares.

$$1^2 = 1$$
$$2^2 = 4$$
$$3^2 = 9$$
$$4^2 = 16$$
$$5^2 = 25$$
$$6^2 = 36$$
$$7^2 = 49$$
$$8^2 = 64$$
$$9^2 = 81$$
$$10^2 = 100$$

Larger perfect squares can be found by squaring 11, squaring 12, squaring 13, and so on.

Note that squaring the negative integers results in the same list of numbers.

$$(-1)^2 = 1$$
$$(-2)^2 = 4$$
$$(-3)^2 = 9$$
$$(-4)^2 = 16, \text{ and so on.}$$

Perfect squares are used in simplifying square roots. The symbol for square root is $\sqrt{}$.

Square Root

A **square root** of a positive number x is a number whose square is x.

If $a^2 = x$, then $\sqrt{x} = a$.

EXAMPLE

The expression $\sqrt{9}$, read "the square root of 9," is equal to the number that, when squared, is equal to 9.

Since $3^2 = 9$, $\sqrt{9} = 3$.

Every positive number has two square roots, one a positive number and one a negative number. The symbol $\sqrt{}$ is used to indicate the positive square root of a number. When the negative square root of a number is to be found, a negative sign is placed in front of the square root symbol. For example,

$$\sqrt{9} = 3 \quad \text{and} \quad -\sqrt{9} = -3$$

Point of Interest
The radical symbol was first used in 1525, when it was written as √. Some historians suggest that the radical symbol also developed into the symbols for "less than" and "greater than." Because typesetters of that time did not want to make additional symbols, the radical was rotated to the position ⟩ and used as the "greater than" symbol and rotated to ⟨ and used as the "less than" symbol. Other evidence, however, suggests that the "less than" and "greater than" symbols were developed independently of the radical symbol.

The square root symbol, $\sqrt{}$, is also called a **radical.** The number under the radical is called the **radicand.** In the radical expression $\sqrt{9}$, 9 is the radicand.

HOW TO 1   Simplify: $\sqrt{49}$

$\sqrt{49}$ is equal to the number that, when squared, equals 49. $7^2 = 49$.

$$\sqrt{49} = 7$$

HOW TO 2   Simplify: $-\sqrt{49}$

The negative sign in front of the square root symbol indicates the negative square root of 49. $(-7)^2 = 49$.

$$-\sqrt{49} = -7$$

HOW TO 3   Simplify: $\sqrt{25} + \sqrt{81}$

Simplify each radical expression.

Since $5^2 = 25$, $\sqrt{25} = 5$.

Since $9^2 = 81$, $\sqrt{81} = 9$.

Add.

$$\sqrt{25} + \sqrt{81} = 5 + 9$$
$$= 14$$

HOW TO 4   Simplify: $5\sqrt{64}$

The expression $5\sqrt{64}$ means 5 times $\sqrt{64}$.

Simplify $\sqrt{64}$.

Multiply.

$$5\sqrt{64} = 5 \cdot 8$$
$$= 40$$

HOW TO 5   Simplify: $6 + 4\sqrt{9}$

Simplify $\sqrt{9}$.

Use the Order of Operations Agreement.

$$6 + 4\sqrt{9} = 6 + 4 \cdot 3$$
$$= 6 + 12$$
$$= 18$$

HOW TO 6   Simplify: $\sqrt{\dfrac{1}{9}}$

$\sqrt{\dfrac{1}{9}}$ is equal to the number that, when squared, equals $\dfrac{1}{9}$. $\left(\dfrac{1}{3}\right)^2 = \dfrac{1}{9}$.

$$\sqrt{\dfrac{1}{9}} = \dfrac{1}{3}$$

Note that the square root of $\dfrac{1}{9}$ is equal to the square root of the numerator $\left(\sqrt{1} = 1\right)$ over the square root of the denominator $\left(\sqrt{9} = 3\right)$.

📋 **Take Note**

The radical is a grouping symbol. Therefore, when simplifying numerical expressions, simplify the radicand as part of Step 1 of the Order of Operations Agreement.

HOW TO 7 Evaluate $\sqrt{xy}$ when $x = 5$ and $y = 20$.

Replace x with 5 and y with 20.

Simplify under the radical.

Take the square root of 100. $10^2 = 100$.

$$\sqrt{xy}$$
$$\sqrt{5 \cdot 20}$$
$$= \sqrt{100}$$
$$= 10$$

EXAMPLE 1

Simplify: $\sqrt{121}$

Solution   Since $11^2 = 121$, $\sqrt{121} = 11$.

YOU TRY IT 1

Simplify: $-\sqrt{144}$

Your solution

EXAMPLE 2

Simplify: $\sqrt{\dfrac{4}{25}}$

Solution   Since $\left(\dfrac{2}{5}\right)^2 = \dfrac{4}{25}$, $\sqrt{\dfrac{4}{25}} = \dfrac{2}{5}$.

YOU TRY IT 2

Simplify: $\sqrt{\dfrac{81}{100}}$

Your solution

EXAMPLE 3

Simplify: $\sqrt{36} - 9\sqrt{4}$

Solution $\sqrt{36} - 9\sqrt{4} = 6 - 9 \cdot 2$
$$= 6 - 18$$
$$= 6 + (-18)$$
$$= -12$$

YOU TRY IT 3

Simplify: $4\sqrt{16} - \sqrt{9}$

Your solution

EXAMPLE 4

Evaluate $6\sqrt{ab}$ for $a = 2$ and $b = 8$.

Solution $6\sqrt{ab}$

$6\sqrt{2 \cdot 8} = 6\sqrt{16}$
$$= 6(4)$$
$$= 24$$

YOU TRY IT 4

Evaluate $5\sqrt{a + b}$ for $a = 17$ and $b = 19$.

Your solution

Solutions on p. S14

OBJECTIVE B   *To find the square root of a whole number*

In the last objective, the radicand in each radical expression was a perfect square. Since the square root of a perfect square is an integer, the exact value of each radical expression could be found.

If the radicand is not a perfect square, the square root can only be approximated. For example, the radicand in the radical expression $\sqrt{2}$ is 2, and 2 is not a perfect square. The square root of 2 can be approximated to any desired place value.

To the nearest tenth:	$\sqrt{2} \approx 1.4$	$(1.4)^2 = 1.96$
To the nearest hundredth:	$\sqrt{2} \approx 1.41$	$(1.41)^2 = 1.9881$
To the nearest thousandth:	$\sqrt{2} \approx 1.414$	$(1.414)^2 = 1.999396$
To the nearest ten-thousandth:	$\sqrt{2} \approx 1.4142$	$(1.4142)^2 = 1.99996164$

The square of each decimal approximation gets closer and closer to 2 as the number of place values in the approximation increases. But no matter how many place values are used to approximate $\sqrt{2}$, the digits never terminate or repeat. In general, the square root of any number that is not a perfect square can only be approximated.

HOW TO 8   Approximate $\sqrt{11}$ to the nearest ten-thousandth.

11 is not a perfect square.

Use a calculator to approximate $\sqrt{11}$. $\sqrt{11} \approx 3.3166$

HOW TO 9   Approximate $3\sqrt{5}$ to the nearest ten-thousandth.

$3\sqrt{5}$ means 3 times $\sqrt{5}$. $3\sqrt{5} \approx 6.7082$

HOW TO 10   Between what two whole numbers is the value of $\sqrt{41}$?

Since the number 41 is between the perfect squares 36 and 49, the value of $\sqrt{41}$ is between $\sqrt{36}$ and $\sqrt{49}$.

Because $\sqrt{36} = 6$ and $\sqrt{49} = 7$,

the value of $\sqrt{41}$ is between the whole numbers 6 and 7.

This can be written using inequality symbols as $6 < \sqrt{41} < 7$, which is read

"the square root of 41 is greater than 6 and less than 7."

Use a calculator to verify that $\sqrt{41} \approx 6.4$, which is between 6 and 7.

Sometimes we are not interested in an approximation of the square root of a number, but rather the exact value in simplest form.

A radical expression is in **simplest form** when the radicand contains no factor other than 1 that is a perfect square. The Product Property of Square Roots is used to simplify radical expressions.

Product Property of Square Roots

If a and b are positive numbers, then $\sqrt{a \cdot b} = \sqrt{a} \cdot \sqrt{b}$.

The Product Property of Square Roots states that the square root of a product is equal to the product of the square roots.

EXAMPLE

$\sqrt{4 \cdot 9} = \sqrt{4} \cdot \sqrt{9}$ • Note that $\sqrt{4 \cdot 9} = \sqrt{36} = 6$ and $\sqrt{4} \cdot \sqrt{9} = 2 \cdot 3 = 6.$

HOW TO 11 Simplify: $\sqrt{50}$

Think: What perfect square is a factor of 50?

Begin with a perfect square that is larger than 50.

Then test each successively smaller perfect square.

$8^2 = 64$; 64 is too big.
$7^2 = 49$; 49 is not a factor of 50.
$6^2 = 36$; 36 is not a factor of 50.
$5^2 = 25$; 25 is a factor of 50. ($50 = 25 \cdot 2$)

Write $\sqrt{50}$ as $\sqrt{25 \cdot 2}$.

Use the Product Property of Square Roots.

Simplify $\sqrt{25}$.

The radicand 2 contains no factor other than 1 that is a perfect square. The radical expression $5\sqrt{2}$ is in simplest form.

Remember that $5\sqrt{2}$ means 5 times $\sqrt{2}$. Using a calculator, $5\sqrt{2} \approx 5(1.4142) = 7.071$, and $\sqrt{50} \approx 7.071$.

$$\sqrt{50} = \sqrt{25 \cdot 2}$$
$$= \sqrt{25} \cdot \sqrt{2}$$
$$= 5 \cdot \sqrt{2}$$
$$= 5\sqrt{2}$$

Integrating Technology

The keystrokes to evaluate $5\sqrt{2}$ on a calculator are either

5 ☒ 2 √ =

or

5 √ 2 **ENTER**

Round the number in the display to the desired place value.

EXAMPLE 5

Approximate $4\sqrt{17}$ to the nearest ten-thousandth.

Solution

$4\sqrt{17} \approx 16.4924$ • Use a calculator.

YOU TRY IT 5

Approximate $5\sqrt{23}$ to the nearest ten-thousandth.

Your solution

Solution on p. S14

EXAMPLE 6

Between what two whole numbers is the value of $\sqrt{79}$?

Solution 79 is between the perfect squares 64 and 81.

$$\sqrt{64} = 8 \text{ and } \sqrt{81} = 9.$$

$$8 < \sqrt{79} < 9$$

YOU TRY IT 6

Between what two whole numbers is the value of $\sqrt{57}$?

Your solution

EXAMPLE 7

Simplify: $\sqrt{32}$

Solution $6^2 = 36$; 36 is too big.
$5^2 = 25$; 25 is not a factor of 32.
$4^2 = 16$; 16 is a factor of 32.

$$\sqrt{32} = \sqrt{16 \cdot 2}$$
$$= \sqrt{16} \cdot \sqrt{2}$$
$$= 4 \cdot \sqrt{2}$$
$$= 4\sqrt{2}$$

YOU TRY IT 7

Simplify: $\sqrt{80}$

Your solution

Solutions on p. S14

OBJECTIVE C *To solve application problems and use formulas*

EXAMPLE 8

Find the range of a submarine periscope that is 8 ft above the surface of the water. Use the formula $R = 1.4\sqrt{h}$, where R is the range in miles and h is the height in feet of the periscope above the surface of the water. Round to the nearest hundredth.

Strategy

To find the range, replace h by 8 in the given formula and solve for R.

Solution

$$R = 1.4\sqrt{h}$$
$$R = 1.4\sqrt{8}$$
$$R \approx 3.96 \qquad \bullet \text{ Use a calculator.}$$

The range of the periscope is 3.96 mi.

YOU TRY IT 8

Find the range of a submarine periscope that is 6 ft above the surface of the water. Use the formula $R = 1.4\sqrt{h}$, where R is the range in miles and h is the height in feet of the periscope above the surface of the water. Round to the nearest hundredth.

Your strategy

Your solution

Solution on p. S14

8.7 EXERCISES

✔ Concept Check

1. A perfect square is the square of an _____. Circle each number in the list below that is a perfect square.

   1   2   3   4   8   9   20   48   49   50   75   81   90   100

2. The expression $\sqrt{64}$ is read "the _____ of sixty-four." The symbol $\sqrt{}$ is called the _____, and 64 is called the _____.

3. **a.** The expression $\sqrt{64}$ is used to mean the positive number whose square is 64. The positive number whose square is 64 is _____, so we write $\sqrt{64} = $ _____.

   b. There is also a negative integer whose square is 64. This integer is _____. We write $-\sqrt{64} = $ _____.

4. Simplify: $\sqrt{81} - 3\sqrt{25}$

   a. Simplify each radical expression. Remember that $81 = ($_____$)^2$ and $25 = ($_____$)^2$.

   b. Use the Order of Operations Agreement. The next step is to _____.

   c. Subtract.

   $\sqrt{81} - 3\sqrt{25}$

   $= $ _____ $- 3 \cdot$ _____

   $= $ _____ $-$ _____

   $= $ _____

5. **a.** 33 is between the perfect squares _____ and _____, so $\sqrt{33}$ is between $\sqrt{} = $ _____ and $\sqrt{} = $ _____.

   b. Express the fact that $\sqrt{33}$ is between 5 and 6 as an inequality:

   _____ $<$ _____ $<$ _____

6. Simplify: $\sqrt{128}$

   a. Write 128 as the product of a perfect-square factor and a factor that does not contain a perfect square.

   b. Use the Product Property of Square Roots to write the expression as the product of two square roots.

   c. Simplify $\sqrt{64}$.

   $\sqrt{128}$

   $= \sqrt{} \cdot 2$

   $= \sqrt{} \cdot \sqrt{}$

   $= $ _____ $\cdot \sqrt{2} = $ _____

7. ▧ Describe **a.** how to find the square root of a perfect square and **b.** how to simplify the square root of a number that is not a perfect square.

8. ▧ Explain why $2\sqrt{2}$ is in simplest form and $\sqrt{8}$ is not in simplest form.

Simplify.

9. $\sqrt{36}$

10. $\sqrt{1}$

11. $-\sqrt{9}$

12. $-\sqrt{1}$

13. $\sqrt{169}$

14. $\sqrt{196}$

15. $\sqrt{225}$

16. $\sqrt{81}$

17. $-\sqrt{25}$

18. $-\sqrt{64}$

19. $-\sqrt{100}$

20. $-\sqrt{4}$

21. $\sqrt{8 + 17}$

22. $\sqrt{40 + 24}$

23. $\sqrt{49} + \sqrt{9}$

24. $\sqrt{100} + \sqrt{16}$

25. $\sqrt{121} - \sqrt{4}$

26. $\sqrt{144} - \sqrt{25}$

27. $3\sqrt{81}$

28. $8\sqrt{36}$

29. $-2\sqrt{49}$

30. $-6\sqrt{121}$

31. $5\sqrt{16} - 4$

32. $7\sqrt{64} + 9$

33. $3 + 10\sqrt{1}$

34. $14 - 3\sqrt{144}$

35. $\sqrt{4} - 2\sqrt{16}$

36. $\sqrt{144} + 3\sqrt{9}$

37. $5\sqrt{25} + \sqrt{49}$

38. $20\sqrt{1} - \sqrt{36}$

39. $\sqrt{\dfrac{1}{100}}$

40. $\sqrt{\dfrac{1}{81}}$

41. $\sqrt{\dfrac{9}{16}}$

42. $\sqrt{\dfrac{25}{49}}$

43. $\sqrt{\dfrac{1}{4}} + \sqrt{\dfrac{1}{64}}$

44. $\sqrt{\dfrac{1}{36}} - \sqrt{\dfrac{1}{144}}$

Evaluate the expression for the given values of the variables.

45. $-4\sqrt{xy}$, for $x = 3$ and $y = 12$

46. $-3\sqrt{xy}$, for $x = 20$ and $y = 5$

47. $8\sqrt{x + y}$, for $x = 19$ and $y = 6$

48. $7\sqrt{x + y}$, for $x = 34$ and $y = 15$

49. $5 + 2\sqrt{ab}$, for $a = 27$ and $b = 3$

50. $6\sqrt{ab} - 9$, for $a = 2$ and $b = 32$

51. $\sqrt{a^2 + b^2}$, for $a = 3$ and $b = 4$

52. $\sqrt{c^2 - a^2}$, for $a = 6$ and $c = 10$

53. $\sqrt{c^2 - b^2}$, for $b = 12$ and $c = 13$

54. $\sqrt{b^2 - 4ac}$, for $a = 1$, $b = -4$, and $c = -5$

55. What is the sum of five and the square root of nine?

56. Find eight more than the square root of four.

57. Find the difference between six and the square root of twenty-five.

58. What is seven decreased by the square root of sixteen?

59. What is negative four times the square root of eighty-one?

60. Find the product of negative three and the square root of forty-nine.

61. Simplify. **a.** $\sqrt{\sqrt{16}}$ **b.** $-\sqrt{\sqrt{81}}$

62. Given that x is a positive number, state whether the expression represents a positive or a negative number.
a. $-3 - \sqrt{x}$ **b.** $-3(-\sqrt{x})$

OBJECTIVE B *To find the square root of a whole number*

Approximate to the nearest ten-thousandth.

63. $\sqrt{3}$ **64.** $\sqrt{7}$ **65.** $\sqrt{10}$ **66.** $\sqrt{19}$

67. $2\sqrt{6}$ **68.** $10\sqrt{21}$ **69.** $3\sqrt{14}$ **70.** $6\sqrt{15}$

71. $-4\sqrt{2}$ **72.** $-5\sqrt{13}$ **73.** $-8\sqrt{30}$ **74.** $-12\sqrt{53}$

Between what two whole numbers is the value of the radical expression?

75. $\sqrt{23}$

76. $\sqrt{47}$

77. $\sqrt{29}$

78. $\sqrt{71}$

79. $\sqrt{62}$

80. $\sqrt{103}$

81. $\sqrt{130}$

82. $\sqrt{95}$

Simplify.

83. $\sqrt{8}$

84. $\sqrt{12}$

85. $\sqrt{45}$

86. $\sqrt{18}$

87. $\sqrt{20}$

88. $\sqrt{44}$

89. $\sqrt{27}$

90. $\sqrt{56}$

91. $\sqrt{48}$

92. $\sqrt{28}$

93. $\sqrt{75}$

94. $\sqrt{96}$

95. $\sqrt{63}$

96. $\sqrt{72}$

97. $\sqrt{98}$

98. $\sqrt{108}$

99. $\sqrt{112}$

100. $\sqrt{200}$

101. $\sqrt{175}$

102. $\sqrt{180}$

103. True or false?
If $0 < \sqrt{a} < 1$, then $0 < a < 1$.

104. True or false?
For a positive number a, $\sqrt{a^3} = a\sqrt{a}$.

OBJECTIVE C   *To solve application problems and use formulas*

Tsunamis   A tsunami is a great wave produced by underwater earthquakes or volcanic eruption. For Exercises 105 and 106, use the formula $v = 3\sqrt{d}$, where v is the velocity in feet per second of a tsunami as it approaches land and d is the depth in feet of the water.

105. Find the velocity of a tsunami when the depth of the water is 100 ft.

106. Find the velocity of a tsunami when the depth of the water is 144 ft.

107. Is the formula used in Exercises 105 and 106 equivalent to the formula $v = \sqrt{9d}$?

Physics   For Exercises 108 and 109, use the formula $t = \sqrt{\frac{d}{16}}$, where t is the time in seconds that an object falls and d is the distance in feet that the object falls.

108. If an object is dropped from a plane, how long will it take for the object to fall 144 ft?

109. If an object is dropped from a plane, how long will it take for the object to fall 64 ft?

110. Is the formula used in Exercises 108 and 109 equivalent to the formula $t = \frac{\sqrt{d}}{4}$?

Astronautics   The weight of an object is related to its distance above Earth's surface. A formula for this relationship is $d = 4000\frac{\sqrt{E}}{\sqrt{S}} - 4000$, where E is the object's weight on the surface of Earth and S is the object's weight at a distance of d miles above Earth's surface. Use this formula for Exercises 111 and 112.

111. A space explorer who weighs 144 lb on the surface of Earth weighs 36 lb in space. How far above Earth's surface is the space explorer?

112. A space explorer who weighs 189 lb on the surface of Earth weighs 21 lb in space. How far above Earth's surface is the space explorer?

Critical Thinking

113. Simplify.   **a.** $\sqrt{0.81}$ **b.** $-\sqrt{0.64}$ **c.** $\sqrt{2\frac{7}{9}}$ **d.** $-\sqrt{3\frac{1}{16}}$

114. Use the expressions $\sqrt{16+9}$ and $\sqrt{16}+\sqrt{9}$ to show that $\sqrt{a+b} \neq \sqrt{a}+\sqrt{b}$.

115. Explain the difference between simplifying and approximating a principal square root. Then simplify $\sqrt{20}$ and approximate $\sqrt{20}$.

Projects or Group Activities

116. List the expressions $\sqrt{\frac{1}{4}+\frac{1}{8}}$, $\sqrt{\frac{1}{3}+\frac{1}{9}}$, and $\sqrt{\frac{1}{5}+\frac{1}{6}}$ in order from smallest to largest.

117. Find a perfect square that is between 350 and 400. Explain the strategy you used to find it.

Cumulative Review Exercises

1. Find the GCF of 96 and 144.

2. Add: $3\dfrac{5}{12} + 2\dfrac{9}{16} + 1\dfrac{7}{8}$

3. Find the quotient of $4\dfrac{1}{3}$ and $6\dfrac{2}{9}$.

4. Simplify: $\left(\dfrac{2}{3}\right)^2 \div \left(\dfrac{1}{3} + \dfrac{1}{2}\right) - \dfrac{2}{5}$

5. Simplify: $-\dfrac{2}{3} - \left(-\dfrac{5}{8}\right)$

6. Write "$348.80 earned in 20 hours" as a unit rate.

7. Solve the proportion $\dfrac{3}{8} = \dfrac{n}{100}$.

8. Write $37\dfrac{1}{2}\%$ as a fraction.

9. Evaluate $a^2 - (b^2 - c)$ when $a = 2$, $b = -2$, and $c = -4$.

10. 30.94 is 36.4% of what number?

11. Solve: $\dfrac{x}{3} + 3 = 1$

12. Solve: $2(x - 3) + 2 = 5x - 8$

13. Convert 32.5 km to meters.

14. Subtract: $32 \text{ m} - 42 \text{ cm}$

15. Solve: $\dfrac{2}{3}x = -10$

16. Solve: $2x - 4(x - 3) = 8$

17. Finance You bought a car for $26,488 and made a down payment of $1000. You paid the balance in 36 equal monthly installments. Find the monthly payment.

18. Taxes The sales tax on a color printer costing $175 is $6.75. At the same rate, find the sales tax on a home theater system costing $1220.

19. Compensation A heavy-equipment operator receives an hourly wage of $32.12 after receiving a 10% wage increase. Find the operator's hourly wage before the increase.

20. Discount A hardware store is advertising a discount rate of 55% on windows. Find the sale price of a window that has a regular price of $240.

21. Investments An IRA pays 7% annual interest, compounded daily. What will be the value of an investment of $25,000 after 20 years? Use the table in the Appendix.

22. Shipping A square tile measuring 4 in. by 4 in. weighs 6 oz. Find the weight, in pounds, of a package of 144 such tiles.

23. Metal Works Twenty rivets, in two rows, are used to fasten two steel plates together. The plates are 5.4 m long, and the rivets are equally spaced with a rivet at each end. Find the distance, in centimeters, between the rivets in one row.

24. Integer Problems The total of four times a number and two is negative six. Find the number.

25. The lines ℓ_1 and ℓ_2 in the figure below are parallel.
  a. Find the measure of angle a.
  b. Find the measure of angle b.

26. Find the perimeter of the composite figure. Use 3.14 for π.

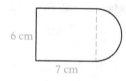

27. Find the area of the composite figure.

28. Find the volume of the composite figure. Use 3.14 for π.

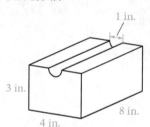

29. Find the unknown side of the triangle shown in the figure below. Round to the nearest hundredth.

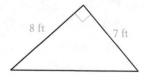

30. Triangles *ABC* and *FED* below are similar. Find the perimeter of *FED*.

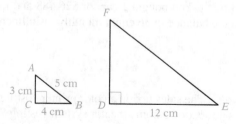

FINAL EXAM

1. Subtract: $100,914 - 97,655$

2. Find 34,821 divided by 657.

3. Find 90,001 decreased by 29,796.

4. Simplify: $3^2 \cdot (5 - 3)^2 \div 3 + 4$

5. Find the LCM of 9, 12, and 16.

6. Add: $\dfrac{3}{8} + \dfrac{5}{6} + \dfrac{1}{5}$

7. Subtract: $7\dfrac{5}{12} - 3\dfrac{13}{16}$

8. Find the product of $3\dfrac{5}{8}$ and $1\dfrac{5}{7}$.

9. Divide: $1\dfrac{2}{3} \div 3\dfrac{3}{4}$

10. Simplify: $\left(\dfrac{2}{3}\right)^3 \cdot \left(\dfrac{3}{4}\right)^2$

11. Simplify: $\left(\dfrac{2}{3}\right)^2 \div \left(\dfrac{3}{4} + \dfrac{1}{3}\right) - \dfrac{1}{3}$

12. Add:
$$\begin{array}{r} 4.972 \\ 28.6 \\ 1.88 \\ + \; 128.725 \\ \hline \end{array}$$

13. Multiply:
$$\begin{array}{r} 2.97 \\ \times \; 0.0094 \\ \hline \end{array}$$

14. Divide: $0.062\overline{)0.0426}$
Round to the nearest hundredth.

15. Convert 0.45 to a fraction in simplest form.

16. Write "323.4 miles on 13.2 gallons of gas" as a unit rate.

17. Solve the proportion $\frac{12}{35} = \frac{n}{160}$.
Round to the nearest tenth.

18. Write $22\frac{1}{2}\%$ as a fraction.

19. Write 1.35 as a percent.

20. Write $\frac{5}{4}$ as a percent.

21. Find 120% of 30.

22. 12 is what percent of 9?

23. 42 is 60% of what number?

24. Convert $1\frac{2}{3}$ ft to inches.

25. Subtract: 3 ft 2 in. − 1 ft 10 in.

26. Convert 40 oz to pounds.

27. Find the sum of 3 lb 12 oz and 2 lb 10 oz.

28. Convert 18 pt to gallons.

29. Divide: $3\overline{)5\ \text{gal}\ 1\ \text{qt}}$

30. Convert 2.48 m to centimeters.

31. Convert 4 m 62 cm to meters.

32. Convert 1 kg 614 g to kilograms.

33. Convert 2 L 67 ml to milliliters.

34. Convert 55 mi to kilometers. Round to the nearest hundredth. (1.61 km ≈ 1 mi)

35. Consumerism How much does it cost to run a 2400-watt air conditioner for 6 h at 8¢ per kilowatt-hour? Round to the nearest cent.

36. Write 0.0000000679 in scientific notation.

37. Find the perimeter of a rectangle with a length of 1.2 m and a width of 0.75 m.

38. Find the area of a rectangle with a length of 9 in. and a width of 5 in.

39. Find the volume of a box with a length of 20 cm, a width of 12 cm, and a height of 5 cm.

40. Add: $-2 + 8 + (-10)$

41. Subtract: $-30 - (-15)$

42. Multiply: $2\frac{1}{2} \times \left(-\frac{1}{5}\right)$

43. Find the quotient of $-1\frac{3}{8}$ and $5\frac{1}{2}$.

44. Simplify: $(-4)^2 \div (1 - 3)^2 - (-2)$

45. Simplify: $2x - 3(x - 4) + 5$

46. Solve: $\frac{2}{3}x = -12$

47. Solve: $3x - 5 = 10$

48. Solve: $8 - 3x = x + 4$

49. Banking You have $872.48 in a checking account. You write checks for $321.88 and $34.23 and then make a deposit of $443.56. Find your new checking account balance.

50. Elections On the basis of a pre-election survey, it is estimated that 5 out of 8 eligible voters will vote in an election. How many people will vote in an election with 102,000 eligible voters?

51. Investments This month, a company is paying its stockholders a dividend of $1.60 per share. This is 80% of the dividend per share one year ago. What was the dividend per share one year ago?

52. Compensation A sales executive received commissions of $4320, $3572, $2864, and $4420 during a 4-month period. Find the mean monthly income from commissions for the 4 months.

53. Simple Interest A contractor borrows $120,000 for 9 months at an annual interest rate of 8%. What is the simple interest due on the loan?

54. Probability If two dice are tossed, what is the probability that the sum of the dots on the upward faces is divisible by 3?

55. ◐ Wars The top four highest death counts, by country, for World War II are shown in the circle graph. What percent of the total death count for all four countries is the death count of China? Round to the nearest tenth of a percent.

Top Four Highest Death Counts in World War II (in thousands)
Source: U.S. Department of Defense

56. Discounts A pair of Bose headphones that regularly sells for $314.00 is on sale for $226.08. What is the discount rate?

57. Shipping A square tile measuring 8 in. by 8 in. weighs 9 oz. Find the weight, in pounds, of a box containing 144 tiles.

58. Find the perimeter of the composite figure. Use 3.14 for π.

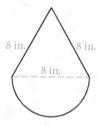

59. Find the area of the composite figure. Use 3.14 for π.

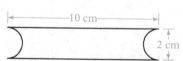

60. Integer Problems Five less than the quotient of a number and two is equal to three. Find the number.

FINAL EXAM

1. Estimate the sum of 672, 843, 509, and 417.

2. Simplify: $18 + 3(6 - 4)^2 \div 2$

3. Simplify: $-8 - (-13) - 10 + 7$

4. Evaluate $|a - b| - 3bc^3$ for $a = -2$, $b = 4$, and $c = -1$.

5. What is $5\frac{3}{8}$ minus $2\frac{11}{16}$?

6. Find the quotient of $\frac{7}{9}$ and $\frac{5}{6}$.

7. Simplify: $\dfrac{\dfrac{3}{4} - \dfrac{1}{2}}{\dfrac{5}{8} + \dfrac{1}{2}}$

8. Place the correct symbol, $<$ or $>$, between the two numbers.

$$\frac{5}{16} \qquad 0.313$$

9. Evaluate $-10qr$ for $q = -8.1$ and $r = -9.5$.

10. Divide and round to the nearest hundredth:
$-15.32 \div 4.67$

11. Is -0.5 a solution of the equation $-90y = 45$?

12. Simplify: $\sqrt{162}$

13. Graph $x \geq -4$.

14. Simplify: $-\dfrac{5}{6}(-12t)$

15. Simplify: $2(x - 3y) - 4(x + 2y)$

16. Subtract: $(5z^3 + 2z^2 - 1) - (4z^3 + 6z - 8)$

17. Multiply: $(4x^2)(2x^5y)$

18. Multiply: $2a^2b^2(5a^2 - 3ab + 4b^2)$

19. Multiply: $(3x - 2)(5x + 3)$

20. Simplify: $(3x^2y)^4$

21. Evaluate: 4^{-3}

22. Simplify: $\dfrac{m^5n^8}{m^3n^4}$

23. Solve: $2 - \dfrac{4}{3}y = 10$

24. Solve: $6z + 8 = 5 - 3z$

25. Solve: $8 + 2(6c - 7) = 4$

26. Convert 2.48 m to centimeters.

27. Convert 2.6 mi to feet.

28. Solve: $\dfrac{n + 2}{8} = \dfrac{5}{12}$

29. Given that $\ell_1 \parallel \ell_2$, find the measures of angles a and b.

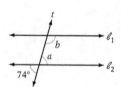

30. Find the unknown side of the triangle. Round to the nearest tenth.

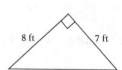

31. Find the perimeter of the rectangle.

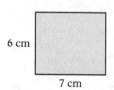

32. Find the volume of the rectangular solid.

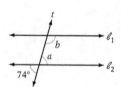

33. Graph $y = -2x + 3$.

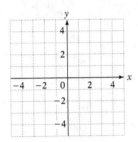

34. Graph $y = \frac{3}{5}x - 4$.

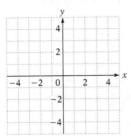

35. Air Travel Find the ground speed of an airplane traveling into a 22-mile-per-hour wind with an air speed of 386 mph. Use the formula $g = a - h$, where g is the ground speed, a is the air speed, and h is the speed of the headwind.

36. Manufacturing A factory worker can inspect a product in $1\frac{1}{2}$ min. How many products can the worker inspect during an 8-hour day?

37. ● **Chemistry** The boiling point of bromine is 58.78°C. The melting point of bromine is −7.2°C. Find the difference between the boiling point and the melting point of bromine.

38. Physics One light-year, which is the distance that light travels through empty space in one year, is approximately 5,880,000,000,000 mi. Write this number in scientific notation.

39. Physics Two children are sitting on a seesaw that is 10 ft long. One child weighs 50 lb and the second child weighs 75 lb. How far from the 50-pound child should the fulcrum be placed so that the seesaw balances? Use the formula $F_1 x = F_2(d - x)$.

40. Entertainment The fee charged by a ticketing agency for a concert is $10.50 plus $52.50 for each ticket purchased. If your total charge for tickets is $325.50, how many tickets are you purchasing?

41. Taxes The property tax on a $250,000 house is $3750. At this rate, what is the property tax on a home appraised at $314,000?

42. 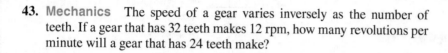 **Geography** The figure at the right represents the land area of the states in the United States. What percent of the states have a land area of 75,000 mi² or more?

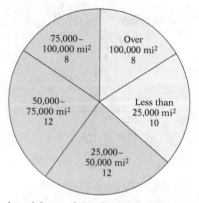

75,000–100,000 mi²
8

Over 100,000 mi²
8

50,000–75,000 mi²
12

Less than 25,000 mi²
10

25,000–50,000 mi²
12

Land Area of the States in the United States

43. **Mechanics** The speed of a gear varies inversely as the number of teeth. If a gear that has 32 teeth makes 12 rpm, how many revolutions per minute will a gear that has 24 teeth make?

44. **Taxes** A customer purchased a car for $32,500 and paid a sales tax of 5.5% of the cost. Find the total cost of the car including sales tax.

45. **Economics** Due to a recession, the number of housing starts in a community decreased from 124 to 96. What percent decrease does this represent? Round to the nearest tenth of a percent.

46. **Discounts** A necklace with a regular price of $245 is on sale for 35% off the regular price. Find the sale price.

47. **Simple Interest** Find the simple interest due on a 9-month loan of $25,000 at an annual interest rate of 8.6%.

48. **Labor Force** The numbers of hours per week that 80 twelfth-grade students spend at paid jobs are given in the figure at the right. What percent of the students work more than 15 h per week?

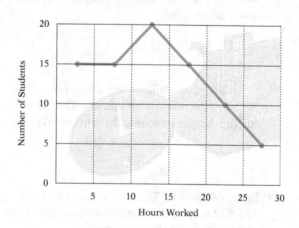

49. **Insurance** You requested rates for term life insurance from five different insurance companies. The annual premiums were $297, $425, $362, $281, and $309. Calculate the mean and median annual premiums for these five insurance companies.

50. **Probability** If two dice are tossed, what is the probability that the sum of the dots on the upward faces is divisible by 3?

Glossary

abscissa The first number in an ordered pair. It measures a horizontal distance and is also called the first coordinate. [6.5]

absolute value of a number The distance between zero and the number on the number line. [2.1]

acute angle An angle whose measure is between 0° and 90°. [9.1]

acute triangle A triangle that has three acute angles. [9.2]

addend In addition, one of the numbers added. [1.2]

addition The process of finding the total of two numbers. [1.2]

Addition Property of Equations The same number can be added to each side of an equation without changing the solution of the equation. [2.4]

Addition Property of Zero Zero added to a number does not change the number. [1.2]

additive inverses Numbers that are the same distance from zero on the number line, but on opposite sides; also called opposites. [2.2; 5.1]

adjacent angles Two angles that share a common side. [9.1]

alternate exterior angles Two nonadjacent angles that are on opposite sides of the transversal and outside the parallel lines. [9.1]

alternate interior angles Two nonadjacent angles that are on opposite sides of the transversal and between the parallel lines. [9.1]

angle An angle is formed when two rays start at the same point; it is measured in degrees. [1.2; 9.1]

approximation An estimated value obtained by rounding an exact value. [1.1]

area A measure of the amount of surface in a region. [1.3; 7.3; 9.2]

Associative Property of Addition Numbers to be added can be grouped (with parentheses, for example) in any order; the sum will be the same. [1.2]

Associative Property of Multiplication Numbers to be multiplied can be grouped (with parentheses, for example) in any order; the product will be the same. [1.3]

average One number that describes an entire collection of numbers. [10.2]

axes The two number lines that form a rectangular coordinate system; also called coordinate axes. [6.5]

bar graph A graph that represents data by the height of the bars. [1.1]

base In exponential form, the factor that is multiplied the number of times shown by the exponent. [1.3]

base of a triangle The side that the triangle rests on. [3.3; 9.2]

basic percent equation Percent times base equals amount. [8.2]

binomial A polynomial of two terms. [5.3]

borrowing In subtraction, taking a unit from the next larger place value in the minuend and adding it to the number in the given place value in order to make that number larger than the number to be subtracted from it. [1.2]

box-and-whiskers plot A graph that shows the smallest value in a set of numbers, the first quartile, the median, the third quartile, and the greatest value. [10.2]

broken-line graph A graph that represents data by the position of the lines and shows trends and comparisons. [1.1]

capacity A measure of liquid substances. [7.3]

carrying In addition, transferring a number to another column. [1.2]

center of a circle The point from which all points on the circle are equidistant. [9.2]

center of a sphere The point from which all points on the surface of the sphere are equidistant. [9.4]

circle A plane figure in which all points are the same distance from point O, which is called the center of the circle. [9.2]

circle graph A graph that represents data by the size of the sectors. [1.1]

circumference The distance around a circle. [9.2]

class frequency The number of occurrences of data in a class on a histogram; represented by the height of each bar. [10.1]

class midpoint The center of a class interval in a frequency polygon. [10.1]

class width Range of numbers represented by the width of a bar on a histogram. [10.1]

coefficient The number part of a variable term. [5.2]

combining like terms Using the Distributive Property to add the coefficients of like variable terms; adding like terms of a variable expression. [5.2]

common factor A number that is a factor of two or more numbers is a common factor of those numbers. [3.1]

common multiple A number that is a multiple of two or more numbers is a common multiple of those numbers. [3.1]

Commutative Property of Addition Two numbers can be added in either order; the sum will be the same. [1.2]

Commutative Property of Multiplication Two numbers can be multiplied in either order; the product will be the same. [1.3]

complementary angles Two angles whose sum is 90°. [9.1]

complex fraction A fraction whose numerator or denominator contains one or more fractions. [3.6]

composite number A number that has natural number factors besides 1 and itself. For instance, 18 is a composite number. [1.3]

congruent objects Objects that have the same shape and the same size. [9.3]

congruent triangles Triangles that have the same shape and the same size. [9.3]

constant of proportionality k in a variation equation; also called the constant of variation. [7.5]

constant of variation k in a variation equation; also called the constant of proportionality. [7.5]

constant term A term that includes no variable part; also called a constant. [5.2]

coordinate axes The two number lines that form a rectangular coordinate system; also simply called axes. [6.5]

coordinates of a point The numbers in an ordered pair that is associated with a point. [6.5]

corresponding angles Two angles that are on the same side of the transversal and are both acute angles or are both obtuse angles. [9.1]

cost The price that a business pays for a product. [5.3; 8.4]

counting numbers The numbers 1, 2, 3, 4, 5, ... [1.1]

cross product In a proportion, the product of the numerator on the left side of the proportion times the denominator on the right, and the product of the denominator on the left side of the proportion times the numerator on the right. [7.4]

cube A rectangular solid in which all six faces are squares. [9.4]

cylinder A geometric solid in which the bases are circles and are perpendicular to the height. [9.4]

decimal A number written in decimal notation. [4.1]

decimal notation Notation in which a number consists of a whole number part, a decimal point, and a decimal part. [4.1]

decimal part In decimal notation, that part of the number that appears to the right of the decimal point. [4.1]

decimal point In decimal notation, the point that separates the whole number part from the decimal part. [4.1]

degree Unit used to measure angles; one complete revolution is 360°. [1.2; 9.1]

denominator The part of a fraction that appears below the fraction bar. [3.2]

descending order The terms of a polynomial in one variable arranged so that the exponents on the variable decrease from left to right. The polynomial $9x^5 - 2x^4 + 7x^3 + x^2 - 8x + 1$ is in descending order. [5.3]

diameter of a circle A line segment with endpoints on the circle and going through the center. [9.2]

diameter of a sphere A line segment with endpoints on the sphere and going through the center. [9.4]

difference In subtraction, the result of subtracting two numbers. [1.2]

direct variation A special function that can be expressed as the equation $y = kx$, where k is a constant called the constant of variation or the constant of proportionality. [7.5]

discount The difference between the regular price and the sale price. [8.4]

discount rate The percent of a product's regular price that is represented by the discount. [8.4]

dividend In division, the number into which the divisor is divided to yield the quotient. [1.3]

division The process of finding the quotient of two numbers. [1.3]

divisor In division, the number that is divided into the dividend to yield the quotient. [1.3]

double-bar graph A graph used to display data for purposes of comparison. [1.1]

empirical probability The ratio of the number of observations of an event to the total number of observations. [10.3]

endpoint A point at which a ray starts. Either of two points marking the end of a line segment. [1.2]

equation A statement of the equality of two numerical or variable expressions. [1.2; 2.4; 6.1]

equilateral triangle A triangle that has three sides of equal length; the three angles are also of equal measure. [9.2]

equivalent fractions Equal fractions with different denominators. [3.2]

estimate An approximation. [1.2]

evaluating a variable expression Replacing the variable or variables with numbers and then simplifying the resulting numerical expression. [1.2]

event One or more outcomes of an experiment. [10.3]

expanded form The number 46,208 can be written in expanded form as $40,000 + 6000 + 200 + 8$. [1.1]

experiment Any activity that has an observable outcome. [10.3]

exponent In exponential form, the raised number that indicates how many times the base occurs in the multiplication. [1.3]

exponential form The expression 2^5 is in exponential form. [1.3]

exterior angle An angle adjacent to an interior angle in a triangle. [9.1]

extremes in a proportion The first and fourth terms in a proportion. [7.4]

factors In multiplication, the numbers that are multiplied. [1.3; 3.1]

factors of a number The natural number factors of a number divide that number evenly. [1.3]

favorable outcomes The outcomes of an experiment that satisfy the requirements of a particular event. [10.3]

first-degree equation in one variable An equation that has only one variable, and each instance of the variable is to the first power. [6.1]

first quartile In a set of numbers, the number below which one-quarter of the data lie. [10.2]

FOIL A method of finding the product of two binomials; the letters stand for First, Outer, Inner, and Last. [5.5]

fraction The notation used to represent the number of equal parts of a whole. [3.2]

fraction bar The bar that separates the numerator of a fraction from the denominator. [3.2]

frequency distribution A method of organizing the data collected from a population by dividing the data into classes. [10.1]

frequency polygon A graph that displays information similarly to a histogram. A dot is placed above the center of each class interval at a height corresponding to that class's frequency. [10.1]

geometric solid A figure in space. [9.4]

gram The basic unit of mass in the metric system. [7.1]

graph a point in the plane To place a dot at the location given by the ordered pair; also called plotting a point in the plane. [6.5]

graph of an equation in two variables A graph of the ordered-pair solutions of the equation. [6.6]

graph of an ordered pair The dot drawn at the coordinates of the point in the plane. [6.5]

graph of a whole number A heavy dot placed directly above that number on the number line. [1.1]

greater than A number that appears to the right of a given number on the number line is greater than the given number. [1.1]

greatest common factor (GCF) The largest common factor of two or more numbers. [3.1]

height of a parallelogram The distance between parallel sides. [9.2]

height of a triangle A line segment perpendicular to the base from the opposite vertex. [3.3; 9.2]

histogram A bar graph in which the width of each bar corresponds to a range of numbers called a class interval. [10.1]

hypotenuse The side opposite the right angle in a right triangle. [9.3]

improper fraction A fraction greater than or equal to 1. [3.2]

inequality An expression that contains the symbol $<$, $>$, $\geq$ (is greater than or equal to), or $\leq$ (is less than or equal to). [1.1; 4.6]

integers The numbers $\ldots, -3, -2, -1, 0, 1, 2, 3, \ldots$. [2.1]

interest Money paid for the privilege of using someone else's money. [8.5]

interest rate The percent used to determine the amount of interest. [8.5]

interior angles The angles within the region enclosed by a triangle. [9.1]

interquartile range The difference between the third quartile and the first quartile. [10.2]

intersecting lines Lines that cross at a point in the plane. [1.2; 9.1]

inverse variation A function that can be expressed as the equation $y = \dfrac{k}{x}$, where k is a constant. [7.5]

inverting a fraction Interchanging the numerator and denominator. [3.3]

irrational number The decimal representation of an irrational number never repeats or terminates and can only be approximated. [4.6]

isosceles triangle A triangle that has two sides of equal length; the angles opposite the equal sides are of equal measure. [9.2]

least common denominator (LCD) The least common multiple of denominators. [3.2; 3.4]

least common multiple (LCM) The smallest common multiple of two or more numbers. [3.1]

legs of a right triangle The two shortest sides of a right triangle. [9.3]

length A measure of distance. [7.1]

less than A number that appears to the left of a given number on the number line is less than the given number. [1.1]

like terms Terms of a variable expression that have the same variable part. [5.2]

line A line extends indefinitely in two directions in a plane; it has no width. [1.2; 9.1]

linear equation in two variables An equation of the form $y = mx + b$, where m is the coefficient of x and b is a constant. [6.6]

line segment Part of a line; it has two endpoints. [1.2; 9.1]

liter The basic unit of capacity in the metric system. [7.1]

markdown The amount by which a retailer reduces the regular price of a product. Also called the discount. [8.4]

markup The difference between selling price and cost. [8.4]

markup rate The percent of a product's cost that is represented by the markup. [8.4]

mass The amount of material in an object. On the surface of Earth, mass is the same as weight. [7.1]

maturity value of a loan The principal of a loan plus the interest owed on it. [8.5]

mean The sum of all values divided by the number of those values; also known as the average value. [10.2]

means in a proportion The second and third terms in a proportion. [7.4]

median The value that separates a list of values in such a way that there is the same number of values below the median as above it. [10.2]

meter The basic unit of length in the metric system. [7.1]

metric system A system of measurement based on the decimal system. [7.1]

minuend In subtraction, the number from which another number (the subtrahend) is subtracted. [1.2]

mixed number A number greater than 1 that has a whole number part and a fractional part. [3.2]

mode In a set of numbers, the value that occurs most frequently. [10.2]

monomial A number, a variable, or a product of numbers and variables; a polynomial of one term. [5.3]

multiples of a number The products of that number and the numbers 1, 2, 3, ... [3.1]

multiplication The process of finding the product of two numbers. [1.3]

Multiplication Property of Equations Each side of an equation can be multiplied by the same nonzero number without changing the solution of the equation. [3.5]

Multiplication Property of One The product of a number and one is the number. [1.3]

Multiplication Property of Zero The product of a number and zero is zero. [1.3]

multiplicative inverse The reciprocal of a number. [3.3; 5.1]

natural numbers The numbers 1, 2, 3, 4, 5, . . . [1.1]

negative integers The numbers . . . , -5, -4, -3, -2, -1. [2.1]

negative numbers Numbers less than zero. [2.1]

number line A line on which a number can be graphed; also called the real number line. [1.1; 4.6]

numerator The part of a fraction that appears above the fraction bar. [3.2]

numerical coefficient The number part of a variable term. When the numerical coefficient is 1 or -1, the 1 is usually not written. [5.2]

obtuse angle An angle whose measure is between 90° and 180°. [9.1]

obtuse triangle A triangle that has one obtuse angle. [9.2]

odds against an event The ratio of the number of unfavorable outcomes of an experiment to the number of favorable ones. [10.3]

odds in favor of an event The ratio of the number of favorable outcomes of an experiment to the number of unfavorable ones. [10.3]

opposite numbers Two numbers that are the same distance from zero on the number line, but on opposite sides. [2.1]

opposite of a polynomial The polynomial created when the sign of each term of the original polynomial is changed. [5.3]

Order of Operations Agreement A set of rules that tells us in what order to perform the operations that occur in a numerical expression. [1.5]

ordered pair Pair of numbers of the form (x, y) that can be used to identify a point in the plane determined by the axes of a rectangular coordinate system. [6.5]

ordinate The second number in an ordered pair. It measures a vertical distance and is also called the second coordinate. [6.5]

origin The point corresponding to 0 on the number line. Also the point of intersection of the two coordinate axes that form a rectangular coordinate system. [2.1; 6.5]

parallel lines Lines that never meet; the distance between them is always the same. [1.2; 9.1]

parallelogram A quadrilateral that has opposite sides equal and parallel. [9.2]

percent Parts per hundred. [8.1]

percent decrease A decrease of a quantity, expressed as a percent of its original value. [8.3]

percent increase An increase of a quantity, expressed as a percent of its original value. [8.3]

perfect square The square of an integer. [4.5]

perimeter The distance around a plane figure. [1.2; 9.2]

period In a number written in standard form, each group of digits separated from other digits by a comma or commas. [1.1]

perpendicular lines Intersecting lines that form right angles. [9.1]

pictograph A graph that uses symbols to represent information. [1.1]

place value The position of each digit in a number written in standard form determines that digit's place value. [1.1; 4.1]

place-value chart A chart that indicates the place value of every digit in a number. [1.1]

plane A flat surface. [1.2; 6.5; 9.1]

plane figures Figures that lie totally in a plane. [1.2; 9.1]

plot a point in the plane To place a dot at the location given by the ordered pair; to graph a point in the plane. [6.5]

polygon A closed figure determined by three or more line segments that lie in a plane. [1.2; 9.2]

polynomial A variable expression in which the terms are monomials. [5.3]

population The set of all observations of interest. [10.1]

positive integers The numbers 1, 2, 3, 4, 5, . . . ; also called the natural numbers. [2.1]

positive numbers Numbers greater than zero. [2.1]

prime factorization The expression of a number as the product of its prime factors. [1.3]

prime number A number whose only natural number factors are 1 and itself. For instance, 13 is a prime number. [1.3]

principal The amount of money originally deposited or borrowed. [8.5]

probability A number from 0 to 1 that tells us how likely it is that a certain outcome of an experiment will happen. [10.3]

product In multiplication, the result of multiplying two numbers. [1.3]

proper fraction A fraction less than 1. [3.2]

proportion An equation that states the equality of two ratios or rates. [7.4]

Pythagorean Theorem The square of the hypotenuse of a right triangle is equal to the sum of the squares of the two legs. [9.3]

quadrant One of the four regions into which the two axes of a rectangular coordinate system divide the plane. [6.5]

quadrilateral A four-sided polygon. [1.2; 9.2]

quotient In division, the result of dividing the divisor into the dividend. [1.3]

radical The symbol $\sqrt{}$, which is used to indicate the positive square root of a number. [4.5]

radicand In a radical expression, the expression under the radical sign. [4.5]

radius of a circle A line segment going from the center to a point on the circle. [9.2]

radius of a sphere A line segment going from the center to a point on the sphere. [9.4]

range In a set of numbers, the difference between the largest and smallest values. [10.1]

rate A comparison of two quantities that have different units. [7.2]

ratio A comparison of two quantities that have the same units. [7.2]

rational number A number that can be written in the form a/b, where a and b are integers and b is not equal to zero. [4.6]

ray A ray starts at a point and extends indefinitely in one direction. [1.2; 9.1]

real numbers The rational numbers and the irrational numbers. [4.6]

reciprocal of a fraction The fraction with the numerator and denominator interchanged. [3.3]

rectangle A quadrilateral in which opposite sides are parallel, opposite sides are equal in length, and all four angles are right angles. [1.2; 9.2]

rectangular coordinate system System formed by two number lines, one horizontal and one vertical, that intersect at the zero point of each line. [6.5]

rectangular solid A solid in which all six faces are rectangles. [9.4]

regular polygon A polygon in which each side has the same length and each angle has the same measure. [9.2]

remainder In division, the quantity left over when it is not possible to separate objects or numbers into a whole number of equal groups. [1.3]

repeating decimal A decimal in which a block of one or more digits repeats forever. [4.2]

right angle A 90° angle. [1.2; 9.1]

right triangle A triangle that contains one right angle. [9.2; 9.3]

rounding Giving an approximate value of an exact number. [1.1]

sample space All the possible outcomes of an experiment. [10.3]

scalene triangle A triangle that has no sides of equal length; no two of its angles are of equal measure. [9.2]

scatter diagram A graph of collected data as points in a coordinate system. [6.5]

scientific notation Notation in which a number is expressed as a product of two factors, one a number between 1 and 10 and the other a power of 10. [5.6]

selling price The price for which a business sells a product to a customer. [8.4]

sides of an angle The rays that form the angle. [9.1]

sides of a polygon The line segments that form the polygon. [1.2; 9.2]

similar objects Objects that have the same shape but not necessarily the same size. [9.3]

similar triangles Triangles that have the same shape but not necessarily the same size. [9.3]

simple interest Interest computed on the original principal. [8.5]

simplest form of a fraction A fraction is in simplest form when there are no common factors in the numerator and denominator. [3.2]

simplest form of a rate A rate is in simplest form when the numbers that make up the rate have no common factor. [7.2]

simplest form of a ratio A ratio is in simplest form when the two numbers do not have a common factor. [7.2]

solution of an equation A number that, when substituted for the variable, results in a true equation. [1.2; 1.4; 6.1]

solution of an equation in two variables An ordered pair whose coordinates make the equation a true statement. [6.6]

solving an equation Finding a solution of the equation. [1.4; 6.1]

sphere A solid in which all points are the same distance from point O, which is called the center of the sphere. [9.4]

square A rectangle that has four equal sides. [1.3; 9.2]

square root A square root of a positive number x is a number a for which $a^2 = x$. [4.5; 9.3]

standard deviation A measure of the consistency, or "clustering," of data near the mean. [10.2]

standard form A whole number is in standard form when it is written using the digits 0, 1, 2, . . . , 9. An example is 46,208. [1.1]

statistics The branch of mathematics concerned with data, or numerical information. [10.1]

straight angle A 180° angle. [9.1]

subtraction The process of finding the difference between two numbers. [1.2]

subtrahend In subtraction, the number that is subtracted from another number (the minuend). [1.2]

sum In addition, the total of the numbers added. [1.2]

supplementary angles Two angles whose sum is 180°. [9.1]

surface area The total area on the surface of a solid. [9.4]

terminating decimal A decimal that has a finite number of digits after the decimal point, which means that it comes to an end and does not go on forever. [4.2]

terms in a proportion Each of the four numbers in a proportion. [7.4]

terms of a variable expression The addends of the expression. [5.2]

theoretical probability A fraction with the number of favorable outcomes of an experiment in the numerator and the total number of possible outcomes of the experiment in the denominator. [10.3]

third quartile In a set of numbers, the number above which one-quarter of the data lie. [10.2]

transversal A line intersecting two other lines at two different points. [9.1]

triangle A three-sided polygon. [1.2; 9.1]

trinomial A polynomial of three terms. [5.3]

unit rate A rate in which the number in the denominator is 1. [7.2]

variable A letter used to stand for a quantity that is unknown or that can change. [1.2]

variable expression An expression that contains one or more variables. [1.2]

variable part In a variable term, the variable or variables and their exponents. [5.2]

variable term A term composed of a numerical coefficient and a variable part. [5.2]

vertex The common endpoint of two rays that form an angle. [9.1; 9.4]

vertical angles Two angles that are on opposite sides of the intersection of two lines. [9.1]

volume A measure of the amount of space inside a closed surface. [9.4]

weight A measure of how strongly Earth is pulling on an object. [7.3]

whole number part In decimal notation, that part of the number that appears to the left of the decimal point. [4.1]

whole numbers The whole numbers are 0, 1, 2, 3, ... [1.1]

x-coordinate The abscissa in an xy-coordinate system. [6.5]

y-coordinate The ordinate in an xy-coordinate system. [6.5]

Answers to
Selected Exercises

Answers to Chapter 1 Selected Exercises

PREP TEST
1. 8   **2.** 1 2 3 4 5 6 7 8 9 10   **3.** a and D; b and E; c and A; d and B; e and F; f and C

SECTION 1.1
1. a. False   **b.** True   **c.** True   **d.** True   **3.** ⊢──┼──●──┼──┼──┼──┼──┼──┼──┼──┼──┼──▶ 0 1 2 3 4 5 6 7 8 9 10 11 12   **5.** ⊢──┼──┼──┼──┼──┼──┼──┼──┼──●──┼──┼──▶ 0 1 2 3 4 5 6 7 8 9 10 11 12
7. $37 < 49$ **9.** $101 > 87$ **11.** $2701 > 2071$ **13.** $107 > 0$ **15.** Yes   **17.** Three thousand seven hundred ninety
19. Fifty-eight thousand four hundred seventy-three   **21.** Four hundred ninety-eight thousand five hundred twelve
23. Six million eight hundred forty-two thousand seven hundred fifteen   **25.** 357   **27.** 63,780   **29.** 7,024,709   **31.** $5000 + 200 + 80 + 7$
33. $50,000 + 8000 + 900 + 40 + 3$ **35.** $200,000 + 500 + 80 + 3$ **37.** $400,000 + 3000 + 700 + 5$ **39.** No   **41.** 850
43. 4000   **45.** 53,000   **47.** 630,000   **49.** 250,000   **51.** 72,000,000   **53.** No. Round 3846 to the nearest hundred.

SECTION 1.2
1. Addition Property of Zero   **3.** Associative Property of Addition   **5.** Commutative Property of Addition   **7.** 28   **9.** 125   **11.** 102
13. 154   **15.** 1489   **17.** 828   **19.** 1584   **21.** 102,317   **23.** 79,326   **25.** 1804   **27.** 1579   **29.** 19,740   **31.** 7420
33. 120,570   **35.** 207,453   **37.** 24,218   **39.** 11,974   **41.** 9323   **43.** 77,139   **45.** 14,383   **47.** 9473   **49.** 33,247   **51.** 5058
53. 1992   **55.** 68,263   **57.** Cal.: 17,754   **59.** Cal.: 2872   **61.** Cal.: 101,712   **63.** Cal.: 158,763   **65.** Cal.: 261,595
     Est.: 17,700   Est.: 2900   Est.: 101,000   Est.: 158,000   Est.: 260,000
67. Cal.: 946,718   **69.** Commutative Property of Addition   **71.** There were 144,928 multiple births during the year.
     Est.: 940,000
73. The total gross income from the eight *Harry Potter* movies was $2,390,100,000.   **75.** The total gross income from the two highest-grossing
Harry Potter movies was $698,600,000.   **77. a.** During the three days, 1285 miles will be driven.   **b.** At the end of the trip, the odometer will
read 69,977 miles.   **79.** 14,636,300 barrels of crude oil are produced and imported per day.   **81.** No. For example, $0 + 2 = 2$
85.

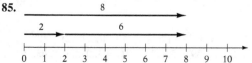

SECTION 1.3
1. $4; 5 + 4 = 9$ **3.** $11; 0 + 11 = 11$ **5.** 4   **7.** 9   **9.** 22   **11.** 60   **13.** 66   **15.** 31   **17.** 901   **19.** 791   **21.** 1125   **23.** 3131
25. 47   **27.** 925   **29.** 4561   **31.** 3205   **33.** 1222   **35.** 5 and 3   **37.** 53   **39.** 29   **41.** 8   **43.** 37   **45.** 58   **47.** 574
49. 337   **51.** 1423   **53.** 754   **55.** 2179   **57.** 6489   **59.** 889   **61.** 71,129   **63.** 698   **65.** 29,405   **67.** 49,624   **69.** 628
71. 6532   **73.** 4286   **75.** 4042   **77.** 5209   **79.** 10,378   **81.** ii and iii   **83.** 11,239   **85.** 8482   **87.** 625   **89.** 76,725
91. 23   **93.** 4648   **95.** Cal.: 29,837   **97.** Cal.: 36,668   **99.** Cal.: 101,998
     Est.: 30,000   Est.: 40,000   Est.: 100,000
101. a. The honey bee has 91 more smell genes than the mosquito.   **b.** The mosquito has eight more taste genes than the fruit fly.
c. The honey bee has the best sense of smell.   **d.** The honey bee has the worst sense of taste.   **103.** The difference between the maximum
eruption heights is 15 feet.   **105.** 202,345 more women than men earned a bachelor's degree.   **107. a.** The smallest expected increase occurs
from 2010 to 2012.   **b.** The greatest expected increase occurs from 2018 to 2020.   **109.** Your new credit card balance is $360.

CHECK YOUR PROGRESS: CHAPTER 1*

1.

|---+---+---+---+---+---+---+---●---+---+---+---+---+---+---→
 0   1   2   3   4   5   6   7   8   9 10 11 12 13 14

[1.1A]   **2.** $107 > 97$ [1.1A]   **3.** Eighty-two thousand seven hundred forty-three   [1.1B]   **4.** Two million five hundred thirty thousand twenty-one   [1.1B]   **5.** 23,401   [1.1B]   **6.** 903,003   [1.1B]
7. $60,000 + 3000 + 200 + 90 + 1$ [1.1C]   **8.** 592,000   [1.1D]   **9.** 46,000   [1.1D]   **10.** 843,995   [1.2A]   **11.** 14,632   [1.2A]
12. 197,523   [1.2A]   **13.** 7058   [1.3B]   **14.** 8538   [1.3B]   **15.** The national debt is about $14,800,000,000,000.   [1.1D]
16. Colonial Falls is 160 feet higher than Yosemite Falls.   [1.3C]   **17.** Janice contributed a total of $130.   [1.2B]   **18.** Boys grow 60 centimeters from birth to age 5.   [1.3C]   **19.** Girls grow the most between birth and age 1.   [1.3C]   **20.** The golfer's total score was 275.   [1.2B]

SECTION 1.4

1. 6×2 or $6 \cdot 2$ **3.** 4×7 or $4 \cdot 7$ **5.** Multiplication Property of One   **7.** Commutative Property of Multiplication   **9.** 12   **11.** 35
13. 25   **15.** 0   **17.** 72   **19.** 198   **21.** 335   **23.** 2492   **25.** 5463   **27.** 4200   **29.** 6327   **31.** 1896   **33.** 5056   **35.** 1685
37. 46,963   **39.** 59,976   **41.** 19,120   **43.** 19,790   **45.** 140   **47.** 22,456   **49.** 18,630   **51.** 336   **53.** 910   **55.** 63,063
57. 33,520   **59.** 380,834   **61.** 541,164   **63.** 400,995   **65.** 105,315   **67.** 428,770   **69.** 260,000   **71.** 344,463   **73.** 41,808
75. 189,500   **77.** 401,880   **79.** 1,052,763   **81.** 4,198,388   **83.** Answers will vary. For example, 5 and 20   **85.** 198,423
87. 18,834   **89.** 260,178   **91.** Cal.: 440,076   **93.** Cal.: 6,491,166   **95.** Cal.: 18,728,744   **97.** Cal.: 57,691,192
     Est.: 450,000   Est.: 6,300,000   Est.: 18,000,000   Est.: 54,000,000
99. The area is 2808 square feet.   **101.** The car could travel 516 miles on 12 gallons of gas.   **103. a.** eHarmony can take credit for 3794 marriages a week.   **b.** eHarmony can take credit for 197,830 marriages a year.   **105.** The estimated cost of the electricians' labor is $5100.   **107.** The total cost is $2138.   **109.** There are 12 accidental deaths each hour, 288 deaths each day, and 105,120 deaths each year.   **111.** $21,978 \times 4 = 87,912$

SECTION 1.5

1. 2; $2 \times 4 = 8$ **3.** 6; $6 \times 5 = 30$ **5.** 6   **7.** 12   **9.** 7   **11.** 16   **13.** 210   **15.** 44   **17.** 703   **19.** 910
21. 5006   **23.** 6050   **25.** 1075   **27.** 1   **29.** 3 r1   **31.** 9 r7   **33.** 16 r1   **35.** 10 r4   **37.** 90 r3   **39.** 120 r5
41. 309 r3   **43.** 1160 r4   **45.** 708 r2   **47.** 3825 r1   **49.** 5710 r3   **51.** 11,430   **53.** 510   **55.** False
57. 1 r38   **59.** 1 r26   **61.** 21 r21   **63.** 30 r22   **65.** 5 r40   **67.** 9 r17   **69.** 200 r21   **71.** 303 r1   **73.** 67 r13
75. 708 r49   **77.** 1086 r7   **79.** 5007 r55   **81.** 12 r456   **83.** 4 r160   **85.** 160 r27   **87.** 1669 r14   **89.** 7950
91. Cal.: 5129   **93.** Cal.: 21,968   **95.** Cal.: 24,596   **97.** Cal.: 2836   **99.** Cal.: 3024   **101.** Cal.: 32,036
     Est.: 5000   Est.: 20,000   Est.: 22,500   Est.: 3000   Est.: 3000   Est.: 30,000
103. Melissa's monthly salary is $5754.   **105.** The cost of the gold alloy in each necklace is $750.   **107.** The nursing student's average exam score was 88.   **109.** The monthly payment is $130.   **111.** The average monthly claim for theft was $25,000.   **113.** The average number of hours worked by employees in the United Kingdom is 33 hours.   **115.** Employees in the country with the most number of hours worked per year (Greece) work an average of 15 hours more per week than do employees in the country with the least number of hours worked per year (Germany).
117. On average, the U.S. Postal Service processed 390 million pieces of mail per day.   **119.** The total of the deductions is $350.
121. 49,500,000 more cases of eggs were sold by retail stores.   **123.** The average monthly expense for housing is $976.
125. The total amount paid is $11,860.   **127.** Subtraction   **129.** Division

SECTION 1.6

1. Five   **3.** i and iii   **5.** 2^3 **7.** $6^3 \cdot 7^4$ **9.** $2^3 \cdot 3^3$ **11.** $5 \cdot 7^5$ **13.** $3^3 \cdot 6^4$ **15.** $3^3 \cdot 5 \cdot 9^3$ **17.** 8   **19.** 400   **21.** 900
23. 972   **25.** 120   **27.** 360   **29.** 0   **31.** 90,000   **33.** 540   **35.** 4050   **37.** 11,025   **39.** 25,920   **41.** 4,320,000   **43.** 5
45. 23   **47.** 6   **49.** 5   **51.** 18   **53.** 10   **55.** 7   **57.** 8   **59.** 6   **61.** 52   **63.** 26   **65.** 52   **67.** 42   **69.** 16   **71.** 6
73. 8   **75.** 3   **77.** 4   **79.** 13   **81.** 0   **83.** $(2 \cdot 3 + 8) \cdot 4 - 2$ **85.** $2 \cdot (3 + 8 \cdot 4 - 2)$ **87.** No   **89.** No   **91. a.** 6561
b. 43,046,721   **c.** 43,046,721

SECTION 1.7

1. ii, iii, v, vi   **3.** 1, 2, 4   **5.** 1, 2, 5, 10   **7.** 1, 7   **9.** 1, 3, 9   **11.** 1, 13   **13.** 1, 2, 3, 6, 9, 18   **15.** 1, 2, 4, 7, 8, 14, 28, 56
17. 1, 3, 5, 9, 15, 45   **19.** 1, 29   **21.** 1, 2, 11, 22   **23.** 1, 2, 4, 13, 26, 52   **25.** 1, 2, 41, 82   **27.** 1, 3, 19, 57
29. 1, 2, 3, 4, 6, 8, 12, 16, 24, 48   **31.** 1, 5, 19, 95   **33.** 1, 2, 3, 6, 9, 18, 27, 54   **35.** 1, 2, 3, 6, 11, 22, 33, 66
37. 1, 2, 4, 5, 8, 10, 16, 20, 40, 80   **39.** 1, 2, 3, 4, 6, 8, 12, 16, 24, 32, 48, 96   **41.** 1, 2, 3, 5, 6, 9, 10, 15, 18, 30, 45, 90
43. True   **45.** $2 \cdot 3$ **47.** Prime   **49.** $2 \cdot 2 \cdot 2 \cdot 3$ **51.** $3 \cdot 3 \cdot 3$ **53.** $2 \cdot 2 \cdot 3 \cdot 3$ **55.** Prime   **57.** $2 \cdot 3 \cdot 3 \cdot 5$
59. $5 \cdot 23$ **61.** $2 \cdot 3 \cdot 3$ **63.** $2 \cdot 2 \cdot 7$ **65.** Prime   **67.** $2 \cdot 31$ **69.** $2 \cdot 11$ **71.** Prime   **73.** $2 \cdot 3 \cdot 11$
75. $2 \cdot 37$ **77.** Prime   **79.** $5 \cdot 11$ **81.** $2 \cdot 2 \cdot 2 \cdot 3 \cdot 5$ **83.** $2 \cdot 2 \cdot 2 \cdot 2 \cdot 2 \cdot 5$ **85.** $2 \cdot 2 \cdot 2 \cdot 3 \cdot 3 \cdot 3$
87. $5 \cdot 5 \cdot 5 \cdot 5$ **89.** False   **91.** Answers will vary. For example, 21, 33, 27, and 39

Note: The numbers in brackets following the answers to the Check Your Progress exercises are a reference to the objective that corresponds to that problem. For example, the reference [1.2A] stands for Section 1.2, Objective A. This notation will be used for all Prep Tests, Check Your Progress exercises, Chapter Reviews, Chapter Tests, and Cumulative Reviews throughout the text.

CHAPTER 1 REVIEW EXERCISES

1. 600 [1.6A]   **2.** 10,000 + 300 + 20 + 7 [1.1C]   **3.** 1, 2, 3, 6, 9, 18 [1.7A]   **4.** 12,493 [1.2A]   **5.** 1749 [1.3B]
6. 2135 [1.5A]   **7.** 101 > 87 [1.1A]   **8.** $5^2 \cdot 7^5$ [1.6A]   **9.** 619,833 [1.4B]   **10.** 5409 [1.3B]   **11.** 1081 [1.2A]
12. 2 [1.6B]   **13.** 45,700 [1.1D]   **14.** Two hundred seventy-six thousand fifty-seven [1.1B]   **15.** 1306 r59 [1.5C]
16. 2,011,044 [1.1B]   **17.** 488 r2 [1.5B]   **18.** 17 [1.6B]   **19.** 32 [1.6B]   **20.** $2 \cdot 2 \cdot 2 \cdot 3 \cdot 3$ [1.7B]
21. 2133 [1.3A]   **22.** 22,761 [1.4B]   **23.** The total pay for last week's work is $768. [1.4C]   **24.** He drove 27 miles
per gallon of gasoline. [1.5D]   **25.** Each monthly car payment is $560. [1.5D]   **26.** The total income from commissions
is $2567. [1.2B]   **27.** The total amount deposited is $301. The new checking account balance is $817. [1.2B]   **28.** The total
of the car payments is $2952. [1.4C]   **29.** More males were enrolled in U.S. colleges in 2009 than in 2005. [1.1A]
30. The difference between the numbers of males and females enrolled in U.S. colleges in 2005 is 2,575,625. [1.3C]   **31.** The number of
males enrolled in U.S. colleges increased by 1,313,579 students from 2005 to 2009. [1.3C]   **32.** 2,940,236 more students were enrolled
in U.S. colleges in 2009 than in 2005. [1.3C]

CHAPTER 1 TEST

1. 432 [1.6A; Example 3]   **2.** Two hundred seven thousand sixty-eight [1.1B; Example 3]   **3.** 15,069 [1.3B; Example 3]
4. 1, 2, 4, 5, 10, 20 [1.7A; Example 1]   **5.** 6,854,144 [1.4B; HOW TO 3]   **6.** 9 [1.6B; Example 4]
7. 900,000 + 6000 + 300 + 70 + 8 [1.1C; Example 6]   **8.** 75,000 [1.1D; Example 8]   **9.** 1121 r27 [1.5C; Example 8]
10. $3^3 \cdot 7^2$ [1.6A; Example 1]   **11.** 54,915 [1.2A; Example 1]   **12.** $2 \cdot 2 \cdot 3 \cdot 7$ [1.7B; Example 2]   **13.** 4
[1.6B; Example 4]   **14.** 726,104 [1.4A; Example 1]   **15.** 1,204,006 [1.1B; Example 4]   **16.** 8710 r2 [1.5B; Example 5]
17. 21 > 19 [1.1A; Example 2]   **18.** 703 [1.5A; Example 3]   **19.** 96,798 [1.2A; Example 3]   **20.** 19,922
[1.3B; Example 4]   **21.** The difference between projected total enrollment in 2016 and 2013 is 1,908,000 students. [1.3C; Example 6]
22. The projected enrollment in pre-kindergarten through grade 12 in 2016 is 59,781,000 students. [1.2B; HOW TO 4]
23. 3000 boxes were needed to pack the lemons. [1.5D; Example 10]   **24.** A hummingbird will beat its wings 46,800 times in 900 seconds.
[1.4C; You Try It 3]   **25.** The average speed was 66 miles per hour. [1.5D; HOW TO 3]

Answers to Chapter 2 Selected Exercises

PREP TEST

1. 20 [1.4A]   **2.** 120 [1.4A]   **3.** 9 [1.4A]   **4.** 10 [1.2A]   **5.** 7 [1.3A]   **6.** 2 r3 [1.5C]   **7.** 1, 2, 3, 4, 6, 12 [1.7A]
8. 59 [1.6B]   **9.** 7 [1.3A]   **10.** 44 < 48 [1.1A]

SECTION 2.1

1. 5, 10, 15, 20   **3.** 10, 20, 30, 40   **5.** Multiples of 6: 6, 12, 18, 24, 30, 36, 42, 48, 54, 60; multiples of 8: 8, 16, 24, 32, 40, 48, 56, 64, 72, 80;
common multiples: 24, 48; least common multiple: 24   **7.** 1, 2, 4, 5, 10, 20   **9.** 1, 2, 4, 7, 14, 28   **11.** 40   **13.** 24   **15.** 12
17. 24   **19.** 60   **21.** 56   **23.** 32   **25.** 36   **27.** 660   **29.** 9384   **31.** 24   **33.** 30   **35.** 24   **37.** 576   **39.** 420
41. True   **43.** 1   **45.** 3   **47.** 5   **49.** 25   **51.** 1   **53.** 4   **55.** 4   **57.** 4   **59.** 1   **61.** 7   **63.** 5   **65.** 8
67. 1   **69.** 25   **71.** 8   **73.** True   **75.** They will have another day off together in 12 days.   **79. a.** No **b.** Yes **c.** Yes **d.** Yes

SECTION 2.2

1. Improper fraction; greater than 1   **3.** Proper fraction; less than 1   **5.** $\frac{3}{4}$ **7.** $\frac{7}{8}$ **9.** $1\frac{1}{2}$ **11.** $2\frac{5}{8}$ **13.** $3\frac{3}{5}$ **15.** $\frac{5}{4}$

17. $\frac{8}{3}$ **19.** $\frac{27}{8}$ **21.**   **23.**   **25.** False   **27.** $5\frac{1}{3}$ **29.** 2   **31.** $3\frac{1}{4}$ **33.** $14\frac{1}{2}$ **35.** 17

37. $1\frac{7}{9}$ **39.** $1\frac{4}{5}$ **41.** 23   **43.** $1\frac{15}{16}$ **45.** $6\frac{1}{3}$ **47.** 5   **49.** 1   **51.** $\frac{14}{3}$ **53.** $\frac{26}{3}$ **55.** $\frac{59}{8}$ **57.** $\frac{25}{4}$ **59.** $\frac{121}{8}$

61. $\frac{41}{12}$ **63.** $\frac{34}{9}$ **65.** $\frac{38}{3}$ **67.** $\frac{38}{7}$ **69.** $\frac{63}{5}$ **71.** $\frac{41}{9}$ **73.** $\frac{117}{14}$ **77.** Answers will vary. For example, $\frac{17}{8}$

SECTION 2.3

1. No. 5 does not divide evenly into 7.   **3.** $\frac{5}{10}$ **5.** $\frac{9}{48}$ **7.** $\frac{12}{32}$ **9.** $\frac{9}{51}$ **11.** $\frac{12}{16}$ **13.** $\frac{27}{9}$ **15.** $\frac{20}{60}$ **17.** $\frac{44}{60}$

19. $\frac{12}{18}$ **21.** $\frac{35}{49}$ **23.** $\frac{10}{18}$ **25.** $\frac{21}{3}$ **27.** $\frac{35}{45}$ **29.** $\frac{60}{64}$ **31.** $\frac{21}{98}$ **33.** $\frac{30}{48}$ **35.** $\frac{15}{42}$ **37.** $\frac{102}{144}$ **39.** $\frac{1}{3}$

41. $\frac{1}{2}$ **43.** $\frac{1}{6}$ **45.** $1\frac{1}{9}$ **47.** 0   **49.** $\frac{9}{22}$ **51.** 3   **53.** $\frac{4}{21}$ **55.** $\frac{12}{35}$ **57.** $\frac{7}{11}$ **59.** $1\frac{1}{3}$ **61.** $\frac{3}{5}$ **63.** $\frac{1}{11}$

65. 4   **67.** $\frac{1}{3}$ **69.** $\frac{3}{5}$ **71.** $2\frac{1}{4}$ **73.** $\frac{1}{5}$ **75.** Answers will vary. For example, $\frac{4}{6}, \frac{6}{9}, \frac{8}{12}, \frac{10}{15}, \frac{12}{8}$.   **77. a.** $\frac{4}{25}$ **b.** $\frac{4}{25}$

SECTION 2.4

1. 2, 5, 7   **3.** 8   **5.** 18   **7.** $\frac{3}{7}$ **9.** $\frac{2}{3}$ **11.** $\frac{4}{7}$ **13.** 1   **15.** $1\frac{4}{11}$ **17.** $3\frac{2}{5}$ **19.** $1\frac{3}{8}$ **21.** $1\frac{7}{15}$ **23.** $1\frac{5}{12}$

25. A whole number other than 1   **27.** The number 1   **29.** $1\frac{1}{6}$ **31.** $\frac{13}{14}$ **33.** $\frac{53}{60}$ **35.** $1\frac{1}{56}$ **37.** $\frac{23}{60}$ **39.** $1\frac{17}{18}$

41. $1\frac{11}{48}$ **43.** $1\frac{9}{20}$ **45.** $2\frac{17}{120}$ **47.** $2\frac{5}{72}$ **49.** $\frac{39}{40}$ **51.** $1\frac{19}{24}$ **53.** ii   **55.** $10\frac{1}{12}$ **57.** $9\frac{2}{7}$ **59.** $9\frac{47}{48}$ **61.** $8\frac{3}{13}$

63. $16\frac{29}{120}$ **65.** $24\frac{29}{40}$ **67.** $33\frac{7}{24}$ **69.** $10\frac{5}{36}$ **71.** $10\frac{5}{12}$ **73.** $14\frac{73}{90}$ **75.** $10\frac{13}{48}$ **77.** The length of the pole is $9\frac{7}{8}$ feet.

79. $9\frac{5}{24}$ **81.** $14\frac{1}{18}$ **83.** $11\frac{11}{12}$ **85.** No   **87.** The length of the shaft is $8\frac{9}{16}$ inches.   **89.** The sum represents the height of the table.

91. The total length of the course is $10\frac{1}{2}$ miles.   **93.** The wall is $6\frac{5}{8}$ inches thick.

95. The minimum length of the bolt needed is $1\frac{3}{8}$ inches.   **97.** $\frac{1}{2}, \frac{1}{3}, \frac{1}{4}$ **99.** $\frac{1}{3} + \frac{1}{4}$ **101.** $\frac{1}{4} + \frac{1}{6}$

SECTION 2.5

1. 5, 3, 2   **3.** $\frac{11}{18}$ **5.** $\frac{2}{17}$ **7.** $\frac{1}{3}$ **9.** $\frac{1}{10}$ **11.** $\frac{5}{13}$ **13.** $\frac{1}{3}$ **15.** $\frac{4}{7}$ **17.** $\frac{1}{4}$ **19.** Yes   **21.** $\frac{1}{2}$ **23.** $\frac{19}{56}$

25. $\frac{1}{2}$ **27.** $\frac{11}{60}$ **29.** $\frac{1}{32}$ **31.** $\frac{19}{60}$ **33.** $\frac{5}{72}$ **35.** $\frac{11}{60}$ **37.** $\frac{29}{60}$ **39.** i   **41.** $5\frac{1}{5}$ **43.** $4\frac{7}{8}$ **45.** $\frac{16}{21}$ **47.** $5\frac{1}{2}$

49. $7\frac{5}{24}$ **51.** $1\frac{2}{5}$ **53.** $15\frac{11}{18}$ **55.** The distance is $21\frac{3}{4}$ inches.   **57.** $15\frac{11}{20}$ **59.** $4\frac{37}{45}$ **61.** No   **63.** The missing dimension

is $9\frac{1}{2}$ inches.   **65.** The desk is $\frac{3}{4}$ inch shorter than a standard size desk.   **67. a.** The hikers plan to travel $17\frac{17}{24}$ miles the first two days.

b. There will be $9\frac{19}{24}$ miles left to travel on the third day.   **69.** The difference represents how much farther the hikers plan to travel on the

second day than on the first day.   **71. a.** Yes   **b.** The wrestler needs to lose $3\frac{1}{4}$ pounds to reach the desired weight.

73. $\frac{11}{15}$ of the electrician's income is not spent on housing.   **75.** $6\frac{1}{8}$

CHECK YOUR PROGRESS: CHAPTER 2

1. 36 [2.1A]   **2.** 18 [2.1A]   **3.** 70 [2.1A]   **4.** 252 [2.1A]   **5.** 6 [2.1B]   **6.** 27 [2.1B]   **7.** 1 [2.1B]   **8.** 5 [2.1B]

9. $\frac{4}{5}$ [2.3B]   **10.** $\frac{1}{3}$ [2.3B]   **11.** Simplest form [2.3B]   **12.** 9 [2.3B]   **13.** $\frac{2}{3}$ [2.4A]   **14.** $\frac{1}{2}$ [2.5A]   **15.** $\frac{7}{18}$ [2.5B]

16. $\frac{3}{5}$ [2.4B]   **17.** $1\frac{25}{48}$ [2.4B]   **18.** $\frac{21}{52}$ [2.5B]   **19.** $\frac{23}{48}$ [2.5B]   **20.** $\frac{17}{20}$ [2.4B]   **21.** $9\frac{1}{6}$ [2.4C]   **22.** $18\frac{11}{18}$ [2.4C]

23. $6\frac{5}{14}$ [2.5C]   **24.** $2\frac{19}{56}$ [2.5C]   **25.** $13\frac{13}{18}$ [2.4C]   **26.** $17\frac{1}{20}$ [2.4C]   **27.** $3\frac{1}{4}$ [2.5C]   **28.** $2\frac{5}{12}$ [2.5C]

CHAPTER 2 REVIEW EXERCISES

1. $\frac{2}{3}$ [2.3B]   **2.** $\frac{3}{16}$ [2.8B]   **3.** $\frac{13}{4}$ [2.2A]   **4.** $\frac{32}{44}$ [2.3A]   **5.** $\frac{11}{18} < \frac{17}{24}$ [2.8A]   **6.** $14\frac{19}{42}$ [2.5C]   **7.** $\frac{5}{36}$ [2.8B]

8. $9\frac{1}{24}$ [2.6B]   **9.** 2 [2.7B]   **10.** $\frac{25}{48}$ [2.5B]   **11.** $3\frac{1}{3}$ [2.7B]   **12.** 4 [2.1B]   **13.** $\frac{24}{36}$ [2.3A]   **14.** $\frac{3}{4}$ [2.7A]

15. $1\frac{13}{18}$ [2.4B]   **16.** $16\frac{1}{2}$ [2.6B]   **17.** 36 [2.1A]   **18.** $\frac{4}{11}$ [2.3B]   **19.** $1\frac{1}{8}$ [2.4A]   **20.** $\frac{1}{8}$ [2.6A]   **21.** $18\frac{13}{54}$ [2.4C]

22. 5 [2.1B]   **23.** $3\frac{2}{5}$ [2.2B]   **24.** $\frac{1}{15}$ [2.8B]   **25.** $5\frac{7}{8}$ [2.4C]   **26.** 54 [2.1A]   **27.** $\frac{1}{3}$ [2.5A]   **28.** $\frac{19}{7}$ [2.2B]

29. 2 [2.7A]   **30.** $\frac{1}{15}$ [2.6A]   **31.** $10\frac{1}{8}$ [2.5C]   **32.** $1\frac{7}{8}$ [2.2A]   **33.** The total rainfall for the 3 months was $21\frac{7}{24}$ inches.

[2.4D]   **34.** The cost per acre was \$36,000. [2.7C]   **35.** The second checkpoint is $4\frac{3}{4}$ miles from the finish line. [2.5D]

36. The car can travel 243 miles. [2.6C]

CHAPTER 2 TEST

1. $\frac{4}{9}$ [2.6A; Example 1]   **2.** 8 [2.1B; Example 2]   **3.** $1\frac{3}{7}$ [2.7A; Example 2]   **4.** $\frac{7}{24}$ [2.8B; You Try It 2]

5. $\frac{49}{5}$ [2.2B; Example 5]   **6.** 8 [2.6B; Example 5]   **7.** $\frac{5}{8}$ [2.3B; Example 3]   **8.** $\frac{3}{8} < \frac{5}{12}$ [2.8A; Example 1]

9. $\frac{5}{6}$ [2.8B; Example 2]   **10.** 120 [2.1A; Example 1]   **11.** $\frac{1}{4}$ [2.5A; Example 1]   **12.** $3\frac{3}{5}$ [2.2B; Example 3]

13. $2\frac{2}{19}$ [2.7B; Example 4]   **14.** $\frac{45}{72}$ [2.3A; Example 1]   **15.** $1\frac{61}{90}$ [2.4B; Example 4]   **16.** $13\frac{81}{88}$ [2.5C; Example 4]

17. $\frac{7}{48}$ [2.5B; Example 2]   **18.** $\frac{19}{96}$ [2.8B; You Try It 2]   **19.** $1\frac{11}{12}$ [2.4A; Example 1]   **20.** $22\frac{4}{15}$ [2.4C; Example 7]

21. $\frac{11}{4}$ [2.2A; Example 2]   **22.** The electrician earns $840. [2.6C; Example 6]   **23.** 11 lots were available for sale. [2.7C; Example 8]

24. The actual length of wall A is $12\frac{1}{2}$ feet. The actual length of wall B is 18 feet. The actual length of wall C is $15\frac{3}{4}$ feet. [2.7C, Example 8]

25. The total rainfall for the 3-month period was $21\frac{11}{24}$ inches. [2.4D, Example 8]

CUMULATIVE REVIEW EXERCISES

1. 290,000 [1.1D]   **2.** 291,278 [1.3B]   **3.** 73,154 [1.4B]   **4.** 540 r12 [1.5C]   **5.** 1 [1.6B]   **6.** $2 \cdot 2 \cdot 11$ [1.7B]

7. 210 [2.1A]   **8.** 20 [2.1B]   **9.** $\frac{23}{3}$ [2.2B]   **10.** $6\frac{1}{4}$ [2.2B]   **11.** $\frac{15}{48}$ [2.3A]   **12.** $\frac{2}{5}$ [2.3B]   **13.** $1\frac{7}{48}$ [2.4B]

14. $14\frac{11}{48}$ [2.4C]   **15.** $\frac{13}{24}$ [2.5B]   **16.** $1\frac{7}{9}$ [2.5C]   **17.** $\frac{7}{20}$ [2.6A]   **18.** $7\frac{1}{2}$ [2.6B]   **19.** $1\frac{1}{20}$ [2.7A]   **20.** $2\frac{5}{8}$ [2.7B]

21. $\frac{1}{9}$ [2.8B]   **22.** $5\frac{5}{24}$ [2.8B]   **23.** The amount in the checking account at the end of the week was $862. [1.3C]   **24.** The total

income from the tickets was $1410. [1.4C]   **25.** The total weight is $12\frac{1}{24}$ pounds. [2.4D]   **26.** The length of the remaining piece is

$4\frac{17}{24}$ feet. [2.5D]   **27.** The car travels 225 miles on $8\frac{1}{3}$ gallons of gas. [2.6C]   **28.** 25 parcels can be sold from the remaining

land. [2.7C]

SECTION 3.1

1. -120 ft   **3.** Yes   **5.**   **7.**

9. $-2 > -5$ **11.** $-16 < 1$ **13.** $-11 < -8$ **15.** $-42 < 0$ **17.** $21 > -34$ **19.** $0 > -39$ **21.** $-87 < 63$
23. $-62 > -84$ **25.** 1   **27.** -1 **29.** 3   **31. a.** A is -4. **b.** C is -2.   **33. a.** A is -7. **b.** D is -4.   **35.** $-12°$ F
37. -42 ft   **39.** $-4, 0, 5, 9$ **41.** $-10, -7, -5, 4, 12$ **43.** $-11, -7, -2, 5, 10$ **45.** Always true   **47.** Sometimes true
49. -16 **51.** 3   **53.** 0   **55.** 59   **57.** 88   **59.** 4   **61.** 9   **63.** 11   **65.** 12   **67.** 2   **69.** 6   **71.** 16   **73.** 12
75. -29 **77.** -14 **79.** 15   **81.** -33 **83.** 32   **85.** -42 **87.** 61   **89.** -52 **91.** $|-12| > |8|$ **93.** $|6| < |13|$
95. $|-1| < |-17|$ **97.** $|17| = |-17|$ **99.** $-3, 22, -25, 37$ **101.** $10, -23, 42, -49$ **103.** $9, 23, -28, -40$
105. Positive integers   **107.** Negative integers   **109. a.** 8 and -2 are 5 units from 3. **b.** 2 and -4 are 3 units from -1.
111. -12 min and counting is closer to blastoff.   **113.** The loss was greater during the first quarter.

SECTION 3.2

1. $-14, -364$ **3.** Negative six minus positive four   **5.** Positive six minus negative four   **7.** -2 **9.** 20   **11.** -11 **13.** -9
15. -3 **17.** 1   **19.** -5 **21.** -30 **23.** 9   **25.** 1   **27.** -10 **29.** -28 **31.** -41 **33.** -392 **35.** -20 **37.** -23
39. -2 **41.** -6 **43.** -6 **45.** Always true   **47.** Sometimes true   **49.** 8   **51.** -7 **53.** -9 **55.** 36   **57.** -3 **59.** 18
61. -9 **63.** 11   **65.** 0   **67.** 11   **69.** 2   **71.** -138 **73.** 86   **75.** -337 **77.** 4   **79.** -12 **81.** -12 **83.** 3
85. Never true   **87.** Sometimes true   **89.** The difference between the temperatures is 44°C.   **91.** The temperature is $-1°C$.
93. The new temperature is above 0°C.   **95.** Nick's score was -15 points after his opponent shot the moon.   **97.** The change in the price of
the stock is -9 dollars.   **99.** The difference between the temperatures is 115°F.   **101.** The difference in elevation is 6051 m.
103. The largest difference that can be obtained is 22. The smallest positive difference is 2.   **105.** The possible pairs of integers are -7 and -1,
-6 and -2, -5 and -3, and -4 and -4.

SECTION 3.3

1. a. Positive **b.** Undefined **c.** Negative **d.** Zero **3.** 42 **5.** -24 **7.** 6 **9.** 18 **11.** -20 **13.** -16 **15.** 25 **17.** 0
19. 36 **21.** -8 **23.** 625 **25.** -228 **27.** -320 **29.** -156 **31.** -70 **33.** 162 **35.** 120 **37.** 36
39. 192 **41.** -108 **43.** -2100 **45.** 20 **47.** -48 **49.** 140 **51.** Negative **53.** Zero **55.** $3(-12) = -36$
57. $-5(11) = -55$ **59.** -2 **61.** 8 **63.** 0 **65.** -9 **67.** -9 **69.** 9 **71.** -24 **73.** -12 **75.** 31 **77.** 17
79. 15 **81.** -13 **83.** -18 **85.** 19 **87.** 13 **89.** -19 **91.** 17 **93.** 26 **95.** 23 **97.** 25 **99.** -34

101. 11 **103.** -13 **105.** 13 **107.** 12 **109.** -14 **111.** -14 **113.** -6 **115.** -4 **117.** Never true
119. Always true **121.** The average high temperature was $-4°F$. **123.** False **125.** The average score was -2.
127. The wind chill factor is $-45°F$. **129.** The student scored 71 points. **131. a.** True **b.** True

SECTION 3.4

1. 9^5 **3.** 7^n **5.** 36 **7.** -49 **9.** 9 **11.** 81 **13.** -256 **15.** 18 **17.** -27 **19.** 216 **21.** -12 **23.** -864
25. -1008 **27.** 72 **29.** Negative **31.** Negative **33.** 9 **35.** 12 **37.** 1 **39.** 8 **41.** -16 **43.** 12 **45.** 13
47. -36 **49.** 13 **51.** 4 **53.** 15 **55.** -1 **57.** 4 **59.** ii **61.** Column A; $1{,}000{,}000 = 100^3$

SECTION 3.5

1. $2x^2, 5x, \underline{-8}$ **3.** $-a^4, 6$ **5.** $7x^2y, 6xy^2$ **7.** $1, -9$ **9.** $1, -4, -1$ **13.** 10 **15.** 32 **17.** 21 **19.** 16
21. -9 **23.** 41 **25.** -7 **27.** 13 **29.** -15 **31.** 41 **33.** 1 **35.** 5 **37.** 1 **39.** 57 **41.** 5
43. 8 **45.** -3 **47.** -2 **49.** -4 **51.** Positive **53.** Negative **55.** 41 **57.** 1 **59.** -23
61a. 2 **b.** 5 **c.** 6 **d.** 7; $n^x > x^n$ if $x \geq n + 1$

SECTION 3.6

1a. can **b.** product; product **3.** $-\dfrac{6}{5}$ **5.** $246; 10\dfrac{1}{4}$ **7.** $\dfrac{3}{5}$ **9.** $-\dfrac{11}{14}$ **11.** $\dfrac{4}{5}$ **13.** 0 **15.** $\dfrac{1}{10}$ **17.** $-\dfrac{3}{8}$ **19.** $\dfrac{63}{xy}$
21. $-\dfrac{yz}{30}$ **23.** $\dfrac{1}{9}$ **25.** $-\dfrac{7}{30}$ **27.** $\dfrac{3}{16}$ **29.** 1 **31.** 6 **33.** $-7\dfrac{1}{2}$ **35.** $-3\dfrac{11}{15}$ **37.** 0 **39.** $\dfrac{1}{2}$ **41.** 19 **43.** $-2\dfrac{1}{3}$
45. 1 **47.** $7\dfrac{7}{9}$ **49.** -30 **51.** 42 **53.** $5\dfrac{1}{2}$ **55.** $\dfrac{7}{10}$ **57.** $-\dfrac{1}{12}$ **59.** $-\dfrac{1}{21}$ **61.** $1\dfrac{4}{5}$ **63.** $4\dfrac{1}{2}$

65. A typical U.S. household spends $13,000 on housing per year. **67.** $-\dfrac{7}{48}$ **69.** $3\dfrac{1}{2}$ **71.** $-17\dfrac{1}{2}$ **73.** -8 **75.** $\dfrac{1}{5}$ **77.** $\dfrac{1}{6}$

79. $-3\dfrac{2}{3}$ **81.** Yes **83.** No **85.** No **87.** Less than **89.** $1\dfrac{11}{14}$ **91.** -1 **93.** 0 **95.** $-\dfrac{2}{3}$ **97.** $\dfrac{5}{6}$ **99.** 0

101. 8 **103.** $-\dfrac{1}{8}$ **105.** Undefined **107.** $-\dfrac{8}{9}$ **109.** $\dfrac{1}{6}$ **111.** $-\dfrac{32}{xy}$ **113.** $\dfrac{bd}{30}$ **115.** $5\dfrac{1}{3}$ **117.** -8 **119.** $-\dfrac{6}{7}$

121. $\dfrac{1}{2}$ **123.** $5\dfrac{2}{7}$ **125.** -12 **127.** $1\dfrac{29}{31}$ **129.** There are 32 servings in a box of Kellogg Honey Crunch Corn Flakes. **131.** $1\dfrac{1}{5}$

133. $-1\dfrac{1}{24}$ **135.** $\dfrac{7}{26}$ **137.** $-\dfrac{10}{11}$ **139.** $\dfrac{1}{12}$ **141.** Undefined **143.** -48 **145.** $\dfrac{4}{29}$ **147.** $-1\dfrac{3}{5}$ **149.** 2

151. Greater than **153.** The length of time in four chukkers is 30 min. **155.** There are $16\dfrac{1}{2}$ ft in one rod; There are 198 in. in one rod.

157. The average couple spends 234 h per year cleaning house. **159.** The developer plans to build 30 houses. **161.** The asteroid's distance from Earth at its closest point is 225,000 mi. **163.** The area of the vegetable garden is $136\dfrac{1}{2}$ ft^2. **165.** Two bags of seed should be purchased.
167. The pressure on the diver is $21\dfrac{1}{4}$ pounds per square inch. **169.** There are 1250 mi between the two cities.

CHECK YOUR PROGRESS: CHAPTER 3

1. 50 [3.1A] **2.** 60 [3.1A] **3.** 26 [3.1B] **4.** 1 [3.1B] **5.** $3\dfrac{1}{3}$ [3.2A] **6.** 9 [3.2A] **7.** $\dfrac{13}{4}$ [3.2A] **8.** $\dfrac{17}{1}$ [3.2A]

9. $\dfrac{8}{12}$ [3.2B] **10.** $\dfrac{3}{8}$ [3.2B] **11.** $\dfrac{2}{3} > \dfrac{5}{8}$ [3.2C] **12.** $-\dfrac{1}{9}$ [3.3A] **13.** $2\dfrac{3}{4}$ [3.3A] **14.** $-\dfrac{1}{15}$ [3.3A] **15.** $-\dfrac{3}{4}$ [3.3B]

16. $-\dfrac{30}{mn}$ [3.3B] **17.** $\dfrac{1}{3}$ [3.3B] **18.** $-\dfrac{4}{5}$ [3.3A] **19.** $\dfrac{5}{9}$ [3.3A] **20.** No [3.3A] **21.** $-\dfrac{1}{2}$ [3.3B] **22.** $-\dfrac{6}{7}$ [3.3B]

23. 50 pairs of booties should be packaged together. [3.3C] **24.** 12 oz is equal to $\dfrac{3}{4}$ lb. [3.2D] **25.** The dimensions of the board are 14 in. by 7 in. by $1\dfrac{3}{4}$ in. [3.3C]

SECTION 3.7

1. denominators   **3a.** $\frac{1}{2}; \left(-\frac{3}{7}\right)$ **b.** $\frac{1}{2}; \frac{3}{7}$ **5.** subtraction   **7.** $\frac{9}{11}$ **9.** 1   **11.** $1\frac{2}{3}$ **13.** $1\frac{1}{6}$ **15.** $\frac{16}{b}$ **17.** $\frac{9}{c}$

19. $\frac{11}{x}$ **21.** $\frac{11}{12}$ **23.** $\frac{11}{12}$ **25.** $1\frac{7}{12}$ **27.** $2\frac{2}{15}$ **29.** $-\frac{1}{12}$ **31.** $-\frac{1}{3}$ **33.** $\frac{11}{24}$ **35.** $\frac{1}{12}$ **37.** $15\frac{2}{3}$ **39.** $5\frac{2}{3}$

41. $15\frac{1}{20}$ **43.** $10\frac{7}{36}$ **45.** $7\frac{5}{12}$ **47.** $-\frac{7}{18}$ **49.** $\frac{3}{4}$ **51.** $-1\frac{1}{2}$ **53.** $6\frac{5}{24}$ **55.** $1\frac{2}{5}$ **57.** $-\frac{1}{12}$ **59.** $1\frac{13}{18}$

61. $-\frac{19}{24}$ **63.** $1\frac{5}{24}$ **65.** $11\frac{2}{3}$ **67.** $14\frac{3}{4}$ **69.** Yes   **71.** Yes   **73.** $\frac{31}{50}$ of the money borrowed on home equity loans is

spent on debt consolidation and home improvement.   **75.** iii   **77.** $\frac{1}{6}$ **79.** $\frac{1}{6}$ **81.** $\frac{5}{d}$ **83.** $-\frac{5}{n}$ **85.** $\frac{1}{14}$ **87.** $\frac{1}{2}$ **89.** $\frac{1}{4}$

91. $-\frac{7}{8}$ **93.** $-1\frac{1}{10}$ **95.** $\frac{1}{4}$ **97.** $\frac{13}{36}$ **99.** $2\frac{1}{3}$ **101.** $6\frac{3}{4}$ **103.** $1\frac{1}{12}$ **105.** $3\frac{3}{8}$ **107.** $5\frac{1}{9}$ **109.** $2\frac{3}{4}$ **111.** $1\frac{17}{24}$

113. $4\frac{19}{24}$ **115.** $1\frac{7}{10}$ **117.** $-1\frac{13}{36}$ **119.** $-\frac{5}{24}$ **121.** $6\frac{5}{12}$ **123.** $\frac{1}{3}$ **125.** $-1\frac{1}{3}$ **127.** $\frac{1}{12}$ **129.** $\frac{1}{6}$ **131.** $1\frac{1}{9}$

133. $4\frac{2}{5}$ **135.** $2\frac{2}{9}$ **137.** $4\frac{11}{12}$ **139.** No   **141.** Yes   **143.** i   **145.** You own $1\frac{3}{4}$ acres.   **147.** You are still required to do $7\frac{3}{4}$ h

of community service.   **149.** $\frac{5}{12}$ of the job remains to be done. Yes, the roofer and the apprentice can complete the job in one more day.

151. The student earned $117 this week.   **153.** You need $29\frac{1}{2}$ ft of fencing.   **155.** The difference is $\frac{1}{32}$ in.

157. The boxer must gain $6\frac{3}{4}$ lb.   **159.** Answers will vary.   **161.** Not possible   **163.** A possible answer is $\frac{3}{4} + \left(-\frac{1}{2}\right) = \frac{1}{4}$.

165. A possible answer is $\frac{1}{2} - \frac{3}{4} = -\frac{1}{4}$.   **167.** Not possible

SECTION 3.8

1. four   **3.** $\frac{1}{3}; \frac{5}{6}$ **5.** $\frac{9}{16}$ **7.** $-\frac{1}{216}$ **9.** $\frac{5}{128}$ **11.** $-\frac{1}{10}$ **13.** $1\frac{1}{7}$ **15.** $-\frac{27}{49}$ **17.** $\frac{16}{81}$ **19.** $\frac{25}{144}$ **21.** $\frac{2}{3}$

23. True   **25.** $\frac{3}{4}$ **27.** $-\frac{8}{9}$ **29.** $\frac{1}{6}$ **31.** 6   **33.** $\frac{18}{35}$ **35.** $-\frac{1}{2}$ **37.** $1\frac{7}{25}$ **39.** $3\frac{3}{11}$ **41.** 17   **43.** $-\frac{4}{5}$ **45.** 1

47. 1   **49.** 0   **51.** Addition, division, subtraction   **53.** $\frac{2}{5}$ **55.** $\frac{5}{36}$ **57.** $\frac{11}{32}$ **59.** 1   **61.** 4   **63.** 0   **65.** $\frac{3}{10}$

67. $1\frac{1}{9}$ **69.** $1\frac{15}{16}$ **71.** $\frac{1}{2}$ **73.** 1   **75.** $\frac{11}{20}$ **77.**

$\frac{3}{8}$	$\frac{3}{4}$	$\frac{3}{4}$
1	$\frac{5}{8}$	$\frac{1}{4}$
$\frac{1}{2}$	$\frac{1}{2}$	$\frac{7}{8}$

CHAPTER 3 REVIEW EXERCISES

1. $9\frac{1}{2}$ [3.2A]   **2.** $2\frac{5}{6}$ [3.4B]   **3.** $1\frac{1}{2}$ [3.3B]   **4.** -1 [3.3A]   **5.** 2 [3.3B]   **6.** $2\frac{2}{3}$ [3.3A]   **7.** $2\frac{11}{12}$ [3.6B]

8. $\frac{3}{5} > \frac{7}{15}$ [3.2C]   **9.** 150 [3.1A]   **10.** $11\frac{13}{30}$ [3.4A]   **11.** $3\frac{1}{3}$ [3.3A]   **12.** $\frac{10}{7}; 1\frac{3}{7}$ [3.2A]   **13.** $\frac{7}{8} > \frac{17}{20}$ [3.2C]

14. $\frac{3}{5}$ [3.6B]   **15.** $\frac{32}{72}$ [3.2B]   **16.** $-\frac{1}{3}$ [3.6A]   **17.** $\frac{2}{7}$ [3.6C]   **18.** 21 [3.1B]   **19.** $\frac{33}{14}$ [3.2A]   **20.** $\frac{3}{8}$ [3.4A]

21. $-\frac{5}{6}$ [3.3B]   **22.** $1\frac{3}{40}$ [3.6C]   **23.** -14 [3.3A]   **24.** $\frac{1}{18}$ [3.4B]   **25.** $1\frac{17}{24}$ [3.4B]   **26.** $2\frac{1}{4}$ [3.6A]   **27.** $9\frac{1}{12}$ [3.4A]

28. $\frac{2}{7}$ [3.2B]   **29.** $4\frac{7}{10}$ [3.4B]   **30.** $-\frac{13}{18}$ [3.5A]   **31.** 40 min is $\frac{2}{3}$ of an hour. [3.2D]   **32.** The entire length is $68\frac{1}{6}$ yd.

[3.4C]   **33.** The wrestler must gain $6\frac{1}{4}$ lb. [3.4C]   **34.** The employee can assemble 192 units in an 8-hour day. [3.3C]

35. The employee's overtime pay is $150. [3.3C]   **36.** The final velocity is 496 ft/s. [3.3C]

CHAPTER 3 TEST

1. $2\frac{4}{7}$ [3.2A; Example 2] **2.** $3\frac{11}{12}$ [3.4B; HOW TO 13] **3.** $22\frac{1}{2}$ [3.3A; You Try It 6] **4.** $\frac{7}{12}$ [3.3A; HOW TO 2]

5. 90 [3.1A; HOW TO 1] **6.** $\frac{13}{24}$ [3.4A; HOW TO 3] **7.** $2\frac{11}{32}$ [3.6A; Example 2] **8.** $\frac{19}{5}$ [3.2A; You Try It 4]

9. $\frac{7}{9}$ [3.3B; Example 7] **10.** 2 [3.6C; Example 5] **11.** 7 [3.6B; You Try It 4] **12.** 18 [3.1B; HOW TO 2] **13.** $\frac{1}{6}$ [3.4B; HOW TO 8]

14. $\frac{4}{5}$ [3.2B; Example 8] **15.** $2\frac{17}{24}$ [3.4A; You Try It 5] **16.** $\frac{5}{6} > \frac{11}{15}$ [3.2C; Example 11] **17.** $3\frac{16}{25}$ [3.6C; HOW TO 8]

18. $\frac{5}{6}$ [3.6B; HOW TO 4] **19.** $\frac{1}{4}$ [3.6B; You Try It 4] **20.** $-1\frac{1}{2}$ [3.3B; Example 11] **21.** $-\frac{1}{2}$ [3.5A; HOW TO 3]

22. No [3.4A; HOW TO 5] **23.** $2\frac{1}{11}$ [3.3A; HOW TO 6] **24.** $\frac{1}{2}$ [3.5A; You Try It 1] **25.** $\frac{12}{28}$ [3.2B; Example 6]

26. The number is $\frac{5}{6}$. [3.5B; Example 3] **27.** 10 h is $\frac{5}{12}$ of a day. [3.2D; Example 13] **28.** The patient must lose $10\frac{5}{24}$ lb.
[3.4C; You Try It 10]

Answers to Chapter 4 Selected Exercises

PREP TEST

1. $\frac{3}{10}$ [3.2A] **2.** 36,900 [1.1C] **3.** four thousand seven hundred ninety-one [1.1B] **4.** 6842 [1.1B]
5. [number line from −6 to 6 with point at −3] [2.1A] **6.** 9311 [2.2A] **7.** 3168 [2.2B] **8.** 76,804 [2.3A]
9. 278 r18 [1.3C] **10.** 64 [1.3B]

SECTION 4.1

1. hundredths; thousandths; hundred-thousandths; millionths **3.** and; thousandths **5.** $<; <$ **7.** thousandths **9.** ten-thousandths
11. hundredths **13.** 0.3 **15.** 0.21 **17.** 0.461 **19.** 0.093 **21.** $\frac{1}{10}$ **23.** $\frac{47}{100}$ **25.** $\frac{289}{1000}$ **27.** $\frac{9}{100}$
29. thirty-seven hundredths **31.** nine and four tenths **33.** fifty-three ten-thousandths **35.** forty-five thousandths
37. twenty-six and four hundredths **39.** 3.0806 **41.** 407.03 **43.** 246.024 **45.** 73.02684 **47.** $0.7 > 0.56$
49. $3.605 > 3.065$ **51.** $9.004 < 9.04$ **53.** $9.31 > 9.031$ **55.** $4.6 < 40.6$ **57.** $0.07046 > 0.07036$
59. 0.609, 0.66, 0.696, 0.699 **61.** 1.237, 1.327, 1.372, 1.732 **63.** 21.78, 21.805, 21.87, 21.875 **65.** $0.62 > 0.062$ **67.** 5.4
69. 30.0 **71.** 413.60 **73.** 6.062 **75.** 97 **77.** 5440 **79.** 0.0236 **81a.** The cost to mint a penny is greater than the face value
of a penny. **b.** The cost to mint a penny is 2¢. **c.** The cost to mint a nickel is greater than the face value of a nickel.
d. The cost to mint a nickel is 8¢. **83.** An entrant who completes the Boston Marathon runs 26.2 mi. **85a.** The shipping cost is $2.40.
b. The shipping cost is $3.60. **c.** The shipping cost is $6.00. **d.** The shipping cost is $7.00. **e.** The shipping cost is $4.70.
f. The shipping cost is $2.40. **g.** The shipping cost is $2.40. **87.** Answers will vary. For example, **a.** 0.15 **b.** 1.05 **c.** 0.001

SECTION 4.2

1.
$$\begin{array}{r} 2.391 \\ 45. \\ + 13.0784 \\ \hline 60.4694 \end{array}$$
3. 65.9421 **5.** 190.857 **7.** 21.26 **9.** 21.26 **11.** 2.768 **13.** -50.7 **15.** -3.312 **17.** -5.905
19. -16.35 **21.** -9.55 **23.** -19.189 **25.** 56.361 **27.** 53.67 **29.** -98.38 **31.** -649.36 **33.** 31.09
35. 12.325; 12 **37.** 33.63; 40 **39.** 0.303; 0.3 **41.** 38.618; 40 **43a.** The total number of children in grades K–12 is 56.7 million.
b. There are 43.4 million more children in public school than in private school. **45.** -1.159 **47.** -25.665 **49.** 13.535 **51.** 28.3925
53. 10.737 **55.** -27.553 **57.** -1.412 **59.** Yes **61.** Yes **63.** iii **65a.** The expression represents the total amount of money
deposited in the account during the month. **b.** The expression represents the total amount of money withdrawn from the account during the
month. **c.** The expression represents the total amount of money in the account at the end of the month.
67. The temperature fell 26.11°C. **69.** The difference in net income was the greatest between 2008 and 2009. **71.** The new balance is $473.72.
73. The bill for the order is approximately $71. **75a.** Life expectancy has increased for both males and females with every 10-year period shown.
b. Females had a longer life expectancy in 2000; Females will live 5.8 years longer than males. **c.** The difference was the greatest in 1970.
77. The markup on the product is $578.62. **79.** The equity on the home is $57,146.75. **81.** $3.45 + 6.78 + 9.01 = 19.24$

SECTION 4.3

1. 1; 2; 3; 1.113   **3.** two; whole; $304.\overline{)364.8}^{\,1.2}$ **5.** 5; 4; terminating   **7.** multiplication   **9.** 1.70   **11.** 0.03316   **13.** 15.12
15. −5.46   **17.** −0.00786   **19.** −473   **21.** 4250   **23.** 67,100   **25.** 0.036   **27.** 7.5537; 8.0   **29.** 68.5936; 70
31. 32.1485; 30   **33.** 12,534 British pounds would be exchanged for 20,000 U.S. dollars.   **35.** 50.16   **37.** −48   **39.** −0.08338
41. 23.0867   **43.** Yes   **45.** No   **47.** Two   **49.** 32.3   **51.** −67.7   **53.** 4.14   **55.** −6.1   **57.** 6.3   **59.** 5.8
61. 0.81   **63.** −0.08   **65.** 5.278   **67.** 0.4805   **69.** −25.4   **71.** −0.5   **73.** 11.17; 10   **75.** 1.16; 1   **77.** 58.90; 50
79. 7.20; 6   **81.** The sales in 2010 were 8 times greater than in 1997.   **83.** 5.06   **85.** −0.24   **87.** 2.06   **89.** −6.1
91. Yes   **93.** No   **95.** Three   **97.** 0.375   **99.** $0.\overline{72}$ **101.** $0.58\overline{3}$ **103.** 1.75   **105.** 1.5   **107.** $4.1\overline{6}$ **109.** 2.25
111. $3.\overline{8}$ **113.** $\dfrac{1}{5}$ **115.** $\dfrac{3}{4}$ **117.** $\dfrac{1}{8}$ **119.** $2\dfrac{1}{2}$ **121.** $4\dfrac{11}{20}$ **123.** $1\dfrac{18}{25}$ **125.** $\dfrac{9}{200}$ **127.** $\dfrac{9}{10} > 0.89$
129. $\dfrac{4}{5} < 0.803$ **131.** $0.444 < \dfrac{4}{9}$ **133.** $0.13 > \dfrac{3}{25}$ **135.** $\dfrac{5}{16} > 0.312$ **137.** $\dfrac{10}{11} > 0.909$ **139.** $\dfrac{3}{5}$
141a. The expression represents the total cost of the sodas.   **b.** The expression represents the total cost of the meal.   **c.** The expression represents the total amount of money each friend will pay.   **143a.** The amount of the payments over 36 months is $17,982.
b. The total cost of the car is $22,982.   **145.** The average number of yards gained per carry is 6.23 yards.   **147.** A U.S. homeowner's average annual cost of electricity is $1147.92.   **149.** The amount received for the 400 cans is $14.06.   **151.** You will pay $5.83 in taxes.
153. The added cost to the government is $3,200,000.   **155.** Your family will use 0.1 ton of coal in one year.
157a. The reduction in solid waste per month would be 133,333,333 tons.   **b.** The reduction in greenhouse gas emissions per month would be 175,000 tons.   **159.** The profit on 5 L of cough syrup is $127.80.   **161.** The perimeter is 15.5 in.   **163.** The area is 14.625 in^2.
165. The perimeter is 13.95 m.   **167.** The force is −41.65 newtons.   **169.** $1.3 \times 2.31 = \dfrac{13}{20} \times \dfrac{231}{100} = \dfrac{3003}{1000} = 3.003$
171. $\times$ **173.** $\times$ **175.** $\div$

SECTION 4.4

1. Commutative   **3.** reciprocal (or multiplicative inverse)   **7.** $14x$ **9.** $5a$ **11.** $-6y$ **13.** $7 - 3b$ **15.** $5a$
17. $-2ab$ **19.** $5xy$ **21.** 0   **23.** $-\dfrac{5}{6}x$ **25.** $6.5x$ **27.** $0.45x$ **29.** $7a$ **31.** $-14x^2$ **33.** $-\dfrac{11}{24}x$ **35.** $17x - 3y$
37. $-2a - 6b$ **39.** $-3x - 8y$ **41.** $-4x^2 - 2x$ **43.** iv and v   **45.** $60x$ **47.** $-10a$ **49.** $30y$ **51.** $72x$ **53.** $-28a$
55. $108b$ **57.** $-56x^2$ **59.** x^2 **61.** x **63.** a **65.** b **67.** x **69.** n **71.** $2x$ **73.** $-2x$ **75.** $-15a^2$ **77.** $6y$
79. $3y$ **81.** $-2x$ **83.** $-9y$ **85.** $8x - 6$ **87.** $-2a - 14$ **89.** $-6y + 24$ **91.** $-x - 2$ **93.** $35 - 21b$ **95.** $2 - 5y$
97. $15x^2 + 6x$ **99.** $2y - 18$ **101.** $-15x - 30$ **103.** $-6x^2 - 28$ **105.** $-6y^2 + 21$ **107.** $3x^2 - 3y^2$ **109.** $-4x + 12y$
111. $-6a^2 + 7b^2$ **113.** $4x^2 - 12x + 20$ **115.** $\dfrac{3}{2}x - \dfrac{9}{2}y + 6$ **117.** $-12a^2 - 20a + 28$ **119.** $12x^2 - 9x + 12$
121. $10x^2 - 20xy - 5y^2$ **123.** $-8b^2 + 6b - 9$ **125.** iii   **127.** $a - 7$ **129.** $-11x + 13$ **131.** $-4y - 4$ **133.** $-2x - 16$
135. $14y - 45$ **137.** $a + 7b$ **139.** $6x + 28$ **141.** $5x - 75$ **143.** $4x - 4$ **145.** $2x - 9$ **147.** $1.24x + 0.36$
149. $-0.01x + 40$ **153a.** Yes; for example, $3 \otimes 2 = (3 \cdot 2) - (3 + 2) = 6 - 5 = 1$ and $2 \otimes 3 = (2 \cdot 3) - (2 + 3) = 6 - 5 = 1$.
b. No; for example, $[3 \otimes 2] \otimes 4 = 1 \otimes 4 = -1$ but $3 \otimes [2 \otimes 4] = 3 \otimes 2 = 1$.

Answers to Chapter 5 Selected Exercises

SECTION 5.1

1. a. Expression   **b.** Equation   **c.** Equation   **d.** Equation   **e.** Expression   **f.** Expression   **3.** Yes   **5.** No   **7.** Yes   **9.** Yes
11. Yes   **13.** Yes   **15.** Yes   **17.** Yes   **19.** No   **21.** True   **23.** 22   **25.** 1   **27.** −5   **29.** −4   **31.** 0   **33.** −3
35. −1   **37.** 15   **39.** 7   **41.** −1   **43.** −1   **45.** −1   **47.** $-\dfrac{5}{6}$ **49.** $-\dfrac{3}{4}$ **51.** The value of x must be negative.
53. The value of x must be positive.   **55.** 4   **57.** −4   **59.** −3   **61.** 8   **63.** 5   **65.** −6   **67.** 15   **69.** −8   **71.** −4   **73.** 6
75. −4   **77.** 6   **79.** 6   **81.** $-\dfrac{3}{7}$ **83.** $\dfrac{7}{2}$ **85.** 15   **87.** True   **89.** False   **91.** Julio used 22.2 gal of gasoline on the trip.
93. The hatchback gets 37.3 mi/gal.   **95.** The amount of the original investment was $15,000.   **97.** The value of the investment increased by $3420.   **99.** The tablet computer costs $324.   **101.** The crib costs $187.50.   **103.** −8   **105.** −4
107. 1   **111.** Answers will vary. For example, $x + 5 = 1$

SECTION 5.2

1. opposite; 20   **3.** 3   **5.** 5   **7.** −1   **9.** −4   **11.** 1   **13.** 3   **15.** −2   **17.** −3   **19.** −2   **21.** −1   **23.** 3   **25.** −1
27. 0   **29.** 2   **31.** $\dfrac{2}{3}$ **33.** $\dfrac{17}{6}$ **35.** 2   **37.** −2   **39.** 2   **41.** 1   **43.** 10   **45.** 5   **47.** −9   **49.** −16   **51.** −9
53. $-\dfrac{24}{5}$ **55.** $-\dfrac{35}{4}$ **57.** −18   **59.** 2   **61.** 4   **63.** 9   **65.** 4   **67.** 1   **69.** −9   **71.** The value of x must be negative.
73. The value of x must be positive.   **75.** The temperature is −40°C.   **77.** The time is 14.5 s.   **79.** 2500 units were made.
81. The total sales were $32,000.   **83.** Miguel's commission rate was 4.5%.

CHECK YOUR PROGRESS: CHAPTER 5

1. -48 [11.1A] **2.** -4 [11.1A] **3.** -7 [11.2B] **4.** 4 [11.2C] **5.** 4 [11.3A] **6.** $-\frac{1}{4}$ [11.3A] **7.** $6x$ [11.1C]
8. $10z - 15$ [11.1C] **9.** $-2ab + b$ [11.1B] **10.** 39 [11.1C] **11.** Commutative Property of Addition [11.1B]
12. Multiplication Property of Reciprocals [11.2C] **13.** The value of the investment after one year is $2100. [11.1A]

SECTION 5.3

1. Both students were correct. **3.** $\frac{1}{2}$ **5.** -1 **7.** -4 **9.** -1 **11.** -4 **13.** 3 **15.** -1 **17.** 2 **19.** 3 **21.** 0 **23.** -2
25. -1 **27.** $-\frac{2}{3}$ **29.** -4 **31.** $\frac{1}{3}$ **33.** $-\frac{3}{4}$ **35.** $\frac{1}{4}$ **37.** 0 **39.** $-\frac{7}{4}$ **41.** 1 **43.** -1 **45.** -5 **47.** $\frac{5}{12}$
49. $-\frac{4}{7}$ **51.** $\frac{7}{3}$ **53.** 21 **55.** 21 **57.** Positive **59.** iv **61.** 2 **63.** -1 **65.** -4 **67.** $-\frac{6}{7}$ **69.** 5
71. 3 **73.** 0 **75.** -1 **77.** 2 **79.** $\frac{19}{10}$ **81.** 13 **83.** $\frac{5}{2}$ **85.** 2 **87.** 0 **89.** $\frac{16}{5}$ **91.** 4 **93.** $-\frac{13}{2}$
95. $-\frac{3}{4}$ **97.** $-\frac{2}{3}$ **99.** -3 **101.** $-\frac{5}{4}$ **103.** $\frac{21}{8}$ **105.** 1.99 **107.** 48

SECTION 5.4

1. 3; 5 **3.** 2 **5.** 10 **7.** 2 **9.** -1 **11.** -2 **13.** -4 **15.** 3 **17.** 9 **19.** 4 **21.** $\frac{3}{5}$ **23.** $\frac{7}{2}$ **25.** $\frac{3}{4}$
27. $\frac{3}{2}$ **29.** $\frac{7}{4}$ **31.** $-\frac{5}{2}$ **33.** $\frac{9}{2}$ **35.** 0 **37.** $-\frac{7}{6}$ **39.** $\frac{1}{3}$ **41.** 1 **43.** 10 **45.** 28 **47.** -45 **49.** -12
51. 10 **53.** $\frac{24}{7}$ **55.** $\frac{5}{6}$ **57.** $\frac{7}{5}$ **59.** $\frac{9}{4}$ **61.** 1.1 **63.** 5.8 **65.** 4 **67.** 1 **69.** $\frac{11}{3}$ **71.** Negative
73. In 4 years, the depreciated value will be $48,000. **75.** The average crown spread of the baldcypress is 57 ft. **77.** The number of grams of
protein in the yogurt is 9 g. **79.** The initial velocity of the object is 8 ft/s. **81.** The car will slide 168 ft. **83.** ii **85.** $x = 4$
87. $y = -6$ **89.** -11 **91.** 0 **95.** Answers will vary. For example, $2x + 5 = -1$

SECTION 5.5

1. No **3.** $y - 9$ **5.** $z + 3$ **7.** $\frac{2}{3}n + n$ **9.** $\frac{m}{m - 3}$ **11.** $9(x + 4)$ **13.** $x - \frac{x}{2}$ **15.** $\frac{z - 3}{z}$ **17.** $2(t + 6)$ **19.** $\frac{x}{9 + x}$
21. $3(b + 6)$ **23. a.** 3 more than twice x **b.** Twice the sum of x and 3 **25.** x^2 **27.** $\frac{x}{20}$ **29.** $4x$ **31.** $\frac{3}{4}x$ **33.** $4 + x$
35. $5x - x$ **37.** $x(x + 2)$ **39.** $7(x + 8)$ **41.** $x^2 + 3x$ **43.** $(x + 3) + \frac{1}{2}x$ **45.** No **47.** $\frac{a + 3}{4}$ **49.** $\frac{4c}{7} - 9$ **51.** $2x$

SECTION 5.6

1. No **3.** $x + 7 = 12$; 5 **5.** $3x = 18$; 6 **7.** $x + 5 = 3$; -2 **9.** $6x = 14$; $\frac{7}{3}$ **11.** $\frac{5}{6}x = 15$; 18 **13.** $3x + 4 = 8$; $\frac{4}{3}$
15. $\frac{1}{4}x - 7 = 9$; 64 **17.** $\frac{x}{9} = 14$; 126 **19.** $\frac{x}{4} - 6 = -2$; 16 **21.** $7 - 2x = 13$; -3 **23.** $9 - \frac{x}{2} = 5$; 8
25. $\frac{3}{5}x + 8 = 2$; -10 **27.** $\frac{x}{4.18} - 7.92 = 12.52$; 85.4392 **29.** No **31.** n represents the median price of a house in 2005.
33. The length of the Brooklyn Bridge is 486 m. **35.** The Army paid $444 million in re-enlistment bonuses in 2010. **37.** The value of the
SUV last year was $20,000. **39.** Infants aged 3 months to 11 months sleep 12.7 h each day. **41.** Five years ago the calculator cost $96.
43. The recommended daily allowance of sodium is 2.5 g. **45.** About 9230 species of animals were known to be at risk of extinction.
47. Americans consume 20 billion hot dogs annually. **49.** It took 3 h to install the water softener. **51.** On average, U.S. workers take
13 vacation days per year. **53.** The total sales for the month were $42,540. **55.** $\frac{1}{f} = \frac{1}{o} + \frac{1}{i}$ **57.** $s = 16t^2$

CHAPTER 5 REVIEW EXERCISES

1. $-2a + 2b$ [11.1C] **2.** Yes [11.2A] **3.** -4 [11.2B] **4.** 7 [11.3A] **5.** 13 [11.1A] **6.** -9 [11.2C]
7. -18 [11.3A] **8.** $-3x + 4$ [11.1C] **9.** 5 [11.4A] **10.** -5 [11.2B] **11.** No [11.2A] **12.** 6 [11.1A]
13. 5 [11.4B] **14.** 10 [11.3A] **15.** $-4bc$ [11.1B] **16.** $-\frac{5}{2}$ [11.4A] **17.** $\frac{5}{4}$ [11.2C] **18.** $\frac{71}{30}x^2$ [11.1B]
19. $-\frac{1}{3}$ [11.4B] **20.** $\frac{54}{5}$ [11.3A] **21.** The car averaged 23 mi/gal. [11.2D] **22.** The temperature is 37.8°C. [11.3B]
23. $n + \frac{n}{5}$ [11.5A] **24.** $(n + 5) + \frac{1}{3}n$ [11.5B] **25.** The number is 2. [11.6A] **26.** The number is 10. [11.6A]
27. The regular price of the tablet PC is $490. [11.6B] **28.** Last year's crop was 25,300 bushels. [11.6B]

CHAPTER 5 TEST

1. 95 [11.3A; HOW TO 1] **2.** 26 [11.2B; HOW TO 2] **3.** $-11x - 4y$ [11.1B; HOW TO 3] **4.** $\frac{16}{5}$ [11.4A; HOW TO 1]
5. -2 [11.3A; Example 1] **6.** -38 [11.1A; HOW TO 1] **7.** No [11.2A; Example 2] **8.** $-14ab + 9$
[11.1B; HOW TO 2] **9.** $-\frac{14}{5}$ [11.2C; Example 6] **10.** $8y - 7$ [11.1C; Example 9] **11.** 0 [11.4B; Example 2]
12. $-\frac{1}{2}$ [11.3A; Example 2] **13.** $-\frac{35}{6}$ [11.1A; Example 4] **14.** -16 [11.2C; Example 7] **15.** -3 [11.3A; Example 2]
16. 11 [11.4B; Example 3] **17.** The monthly payment is $137.50. [11.2D; You Try It 10] **18.** 4000 clocks were made
during the month. [11.3B; Example 4] **19.** The time required is 11.5 s. [11.3B; Example 3] **20.** $x + \frac{1}{3}x$ [11.5A; Example 1]
21. $5(x + 3)$ [11.5B; HOW TO 2] **22.** $2x - 3 = 7$; 5 [11.6A; HOW TO 1] **23.** The number is $-\frac{7}{2}$. [11.6A; HOW TO 1]
24. Eduardo's total sales for the month were $40,000. [11.6B; You Try It 8] **25.** The mechanic worked for 3 h. [11.6B; Example 7]

Answers to Chapter 6 Selected Exercises

PREP TEST

1. $\frac{4}{5}$ [2.3B] **2.** $\frac{1}{2}$ [2.3B] **3.** 24.8 [3.6A] **4.** 4×33 [1.4A] **5.** 4 [1.5A]

SECTION 6.1

1. 3 to 8 **3.** $\frac{1}{5}$ 1:5 1 to 5 **5.** $\frac{2}{1}$ 2:1 2 to 1 **7.** $\frac{3}{8}$ 3:8 3 to 8 **9.** $\frac{1}{1}$ 1:1 1 to 1 **11.** $\frac{7}{10}$ 7:10 7 to 10 **13.** $\frac{1}{2}$ 1:2 1 to 2
15. $\frac{2}{1}$ 2:1 2 to 1 **17.** $\frac{5}{2}$ 5:2 5 to 2 **19.** $\frac{5}{7}$ 5:7 5 to 7 **21.** days **23.** The ratio is $\frac{3}{8}$. **25.** The ratio is $\frac{1}{3}$.
27. The ratio is $\frac{13}{22,000}$. **29.** The ratio is $\frac{1}{5}$. **31.** The ratio is $\frac{3}{250}$. **35.** Answers will vary.

SECTION 6.2

3. $\frac{3 \text{ pounds}}{4 \text{ people}}$ **5.** $\frac{\$20}{3 \text{ boards}}$ **7.** $\frac{20 \text{ miles}}{1 \text{ gallon}}$ **9.** $\frac{8 \text{ gallons}}{1 \text{ hour}}$ **11.** Divide the number of gallons per minute by 60. **13.** 1 **15.** 2.5 feet/second
17. \$975/week **19.** 110 trees/acre **21.** \$18.84/hour **23.** 35.6 miles/gallon **25.** The car got 42.6 miles/gallon.
27. The rate is 7.4 miles per dollar. **29.** The average number of rides per day was 1220. **31.** The cost per viewer is \$.03.
33. The rate is 12 gallons/minute. **35.** The cost is 2,715,580 yen. **37. a.** Australia has the least population density.
b. There are 851 more people per square mile in India than in the United States. **41.** The car gets about 3.6 gallons per 100 miles.
43. 0.004 ppm

CHECK YOUR PROGRESS: CHAPTER 6

1. $\frac{1}{4}$, 1:4 [4.1A] **2.** $\frac{2}{3}$, 2:3 [4.1A] **3.** $\frac{5}{12}$, 5:12 [4.1A] **4.** \$24/hour [4.2B] **5.** 10.4 yards/second [4.2B]
6. 29.2 miles/gallon [4.2B] **7.** The recommended amount of fertilizer is 0.025 gallon/square foot. [4.2C]
8. Whole milk has 18.75 calories/ounce. [4.2C] **9.** The cost per rose is \$4.25. [4.2C] **10.** The cost per page is \$.0425. [4.2C]

SECTION 6.3

1. $n = 45 \div 15$ **3.** $72 \div 9 = n$ **5.** True **7.** Not true **9.** Not true **11.** True **13.** True **15.** True **17.** True
19. Not true **21.** True **23.** Yes **25.** Yes **27.** 3 **29.** 105 **31.** 2 **33.** 60 **35.** 2.22 **37.** 6.67 **39.** 21.33
41. 16.25 **43.** 2.44 **45.** 47.89 **47.** A 0.5-ounce serving contains 50 calories. **49.** The car can travel 329 miles. **51.** 12.5 gallons
of water are required. **53.** The distance is 16 miles. **55.** 1.25 ounces are required. **57.** 160,000 people would vote.
59. The monthly payment is \$176.75. **61.** 750 defective circuit boards are expected in a run of 25,000. **63.** A bowling ball
would weigh about 2.67 pounds on the moon. **65.** The dividend would be \$1071.

CHAPTER 6 REVIEW EXERCISES

1. True [4.3A] **2.** $\frac{2}{5}$ 2:5 2 to 5 [4.1A] **3.** 62.5 miles/hour [4.2B] **4.** True [4.3A] **5.** 68 [4.3B]
6. \$12.50/hour [4.2B] **7.** \$1.75/pound [4.2B] **8.** $\frac{2}{7}$ 2:7 2 to 7 [4.1A] **9.** 36 [4.3B] **10.** 19.44 [4.3B]
11. $\frac{2}{5}$ 2:5 2 to 5 [4.1A] **12.** Not true [4.3A] **13.** $\frac{\$35}{4 \text{ hours}}$ [4.2A] **14.** 27.2 miles/gallon [4.2B]
15. $\frac{1}{1}$ 1:1 1 to 1 [4.1A] **16.** True [4.3A] **17.** 65.45 [4.3B] **18.** $\frac{100 \text{ miles}}{3 \text{ hours}}$ [4.2A] **19.** The ratio is $\frac{2}{5}$. [4.1B]
20. The property tax is \$6400. [4.3C] **21.** The ratio is $\frac{3}{8}$. [4.1B] **22.** The cost per phone is \$37.50. [4.2C]
23. 1344 blocks would be needed. [4.3C] **24.** The ratio is $\frac{5}{2}$. [4.1B] **25.** The turkey costs \$.93/pound. [4.2C]
26. The average was 56.8 miles/hour. [4.2C] **27.** The cost is \$493.50. [4.3C] **28.** The cost is \$44.75/share. [4.2C]
29. 22.5 pounds of fertilizer will be used. [4.3C] **30.** The ratio is $\frac{1}{2}$. [4.1B]

CHAPTER 6 TEST

1. \$3836.40/month [4.2B; Example 2] **2.** $\frac{1}{6}$ 1:6 1 to 6 [4.1A; You Try It 1] **3.** $\frac{9 \text{ supports}}{4 \text{ feet}}$ [4.2A; Example 1]
4. Not true [4.3A; Example 2] **5.** $\frac{3}{1}$ 3:1 3 to 1 [4.1A; Example 2] **6.** 144 [4.3B; HOW TO 3]
7. 30.5 miles/gallon [4.2B; Apply the Concept] **8.** $\frac{1}{3}$ 1:3 1 to 3 [4.1A; You Try It 1] **9.** True [4.3A; Example 1]
10. 40.5 [4.3B; Example 3] **11.** $\frac{3 \text{ feet}}{2 \text{ boards}}$ [4.2A; Example 1] **12.** $\frac{3}{5}$ 3:5 3 to 5 [4.1A; You Try It 1]
13. The dividend is \$625. [4.3C; Example 9] **14.** The ratio is $\frac{1}{12}$. [4.1B; Example 3] **15.** The plane's speed is
538 miles/hour. [4.2C; Example 3] **16.** The college student's body contains 132 pounds of water. [4.3C; Example 8]
17. The cost of the lumber is \$1.73/foot. [4.2C; You Try It 3] **18.** The amount of medication required is 0.875 ounce.
[4.3C; Example 8] **19.** The ratio is $\frac{4}{5}$. [4.1B; Example 4] **20.** 36 defective hard drives are expected to be found in the
production of 1200 hard drives. [4.3C; You Try It 9]

CUMULATIVE REVIEW EXERCISES

1. 9158 [1.3B]   **2.** $2^4 \cdot 3^3$ [1.6A]   **3.** 3 [1.6B]   **4.** $2 \cdot 2 \cdot 2 \cdot 2 \cdot 2 \cdot 5$ [1.7B]   **5.** 36 [2.1A]   **6.** 14 [2.1B]
7. $\frac{5}{8}$ [2.3B]   **8.** $8\frac{3}{10}$ [2.4C]   **9.** $5\frac{11}{18}$ [2.5C]   **10.** $2\frac{5}{6}$ [2.6B]   **11.** $4\frac{2}{3}$ [2.7B]   **12.** $\frac{23}{30}$ [2.8B]
13. Four and seven hundred nine ten-thousandths [3.1A]   **14.** 2.10 [3.1B]   **15.** 1.990 [3.5A]   **16.** $\frac{3}{50}$ [3.6B]
17. $\frac{1}{8}$ [4.1A]   **18.** $\frac{29¢}{2 \text{ pencils}}$ [4.2A]   **19.** 33.4 miles/gallon [4.2B]   **20.** 4.25 [4.3B]   **21.** The car's speed is
57.2 miles/hour. [4.2C]   **22.** 36 [4.3B]   **23.** Your new balance is $744. [1.3C]   **24.** The monthly payment is $570. [1.5D]
25. 105 pages remain to be read. [2.6C]   **26.** The cost per acre was $36,000. [2.7C]   **27.** The change was $35.24. [3.3B]
28. Your monthly salary is $3468.25. [3.5B]   **29.** 25 inches will erode in 50 months. [4.3C]   **30.** 1.6 ounces are required. [4.3C]

Answers to Chapter 7 Selected Exercises

PREP TEST

1. $\frac{19}{100}$ [2.6B]   **2.** 0.23 [3.4A]   **3.** 47 [3.4A]   **4.** 2850 [3.4A]   **5.** 4000 [3.5A]   **6.** 32 [2.7B]   **7.** 62.5 [3.6A]
8. $66\frac{2}{3}$ [2.2B]   **9.** 1.75 [3.5A]

SECTION 7.1

1. 100   **3.** left   **5.** 0.72, $\frac{18}{25}$ **7.** 0.23, $\frac{23}{100}$ **9.** 0.36, $\frac{9}{25}$ **11.** 0.59, $\frac{59}{100}$ **13.** 0.41, $\frac{41}{100}$ **15.** 0.254, $\frac{127}{500}$ **17.** 0.579, $\frac{579}{1000}$
19. 0.062, $\frac{31}{500}$ **21.** 0.064, $\frac{8}{125}$ **23.** 0.0025, $\frac{1}{400}$ **25.** 0.0055, $\frac{11}{2000}$ **27.** $\frac{2}{3}$ **29.** $\frac{5}{6}$ **31.** $\frac{1}{9}$ **33.** $\frac{5}{11}$ **35.** $\frac{3}{70}$ **37.** $\frac{1}{15}$
39. Greater than   **41.** 73%   **43.** 1%   **45.** 294%   **47.** 0.6%   **49.** 310.6%   **51.** 70%   **53.** 85%   **55.** 40%   **57.** 12.5%
59. 150%   **61.** 225%   **63.** 87.5%   **65.** 48%   **67.** $44\frac{4}{9}$%   **69.** $166\frac{2}{3}$%   **71.** $38\frac{8}{9}$%   **73.** Less than   **75.** 6% of those surveyed named
something other than corn on the cob, cole slaw, corn bread, or fries.   **77.** $\frac{53}{1000}$, 0.053   **79.** $\frac{3}{20}$, 0.15   **81.** 0.5%   **83.** 62.5%

SECTION 7.2

1. 0.12; n; 68   **3.** 0.08; 450; n **5.** 36; n; 25   **7.** 21 of the 30 squares should be shaded.   **9.** 25 of the 40 squares should be shaded.
11. 5 of the 30 squares should be shaded.   **13.** 27 of the 48 people should be circled.   **15.** 8   **17.** 0.075   **19.** $16\frac{2}{3}$%   **21.** 37.5%
23. 100   **25.** 1200   **27.** 51.895   **29.** 13   **31.** 2.7%   **33.** 400%   **35.** 7.5   **37.** 6232 respondents did not answer yes to the
question.   **39.** 15.8 million travelers allowed their children to miss school to go on a trip.   **41.** $x < y$ **43.** 27   **45.** 22%   **47.** 150
49. 1500%   **51.** 875   **53.** 72   **55.** 46.2%   **57.** 196.65   **59.** 8   **61.** 14.3   **63.** 250%   **65.** 0.4% of the total energy
production was generated by wind machines.   **67.** ii   **69.** True   **71.** The value of fireworks imported from China represented 96.4% of the
value of fireworks imported to the United States.   **73.** 12.2% of the deaths occurred during training.   **75.** There were 50 million students in
the United States that year.   **77.** There are 5 million opposite-sex cohabitating couples who maintain households in the United States.
79a. $175 million is generated from the sales of Thin Mints.   **b.** $63 million is generated from the sales of Trefoil shortbread cookies.
81. 51% of the total cranberry crop was produced in Wisconsin.   **83.** 14,000,000 oz of gold were mined in the United States that year.
85. 27.5% is spent on food.   **87.** Approximately 13.2 million people in the United States aged 18 to 24 do not have health insurance.
89. 29.8% of Americans with diabetes have not been diagnosed with the disease.   **91.** 5451 fewer faculty members described their views as
conservative than as middle-of-the-road.   **93.** No   **95a.** 1 lb   **b.** 1 lb   **c.** 50 lb   **d.** 50 lb   **e.** 25 lb   **f.** 25
g. 70 squares should be shaded.   **h.** 70%   **97a.** 0.2 lb   **b.** 0.2 lb   **c.** 10 lb   **d.** 10 lb   **e.** 5 lb   **f.** 5
g. 40 squares should be shaded.   **h.** 40%

SECTION 7.3

1a. original; new; 18; 15; 3   **b.** 15; 3   **3.** The percent increase is 182.9%.   **5.** The percent increase is 514.3%.
7. The percent increase is 32.5%.   **9.** The percent increase is 38.4%.   **11.** The percent increase is 32.0%.   **13.** Yes, the new wage can be
found by multiplying $12 by 1.10.   **15.** The percent decrease is 24.6%.   **17.** The percent decrease is 21.2%.
19. The percent decrease is 7.1%.   **21.** The value of a $21,900 new car after one year is $15,330.   **23.** The Navy had the greatest percent
decrease in personnel from 1990 to 2009; the percent decrease was 43.0%.

CHECK YOUR PROGRESS: CHAPTER 7

1. 0.387 [8.1A]   **2.** $\frac{11}{25}$ [8.1A]   **3.** $\frac{4}{75}$ [8.1A]   **4.** 72.5% [8.1B]   **5.** $58\frac{1}{3}$% [8.1B]   **6.** 56.3% [8.1B]   **7.** 10.5 [8.2A]
8. 62.5% [8.2A]   **9.** 200 [8.2A]   **10.** 76.5 [8.2B]   **11.** 40% [8.2B]   **12.** 40 [8.2B]   **13.** The sales tax is 4% of the purchase price.
[8.2C]   **14.** The percent decrease is 29.6%. [8.3B]   **15.** $432,000 of the money earned that year was reinvested in research and development.
[8.2C]   **16.** The percent increase is 230.0%. [8.3A]   **17.** The purchase price of the car was $27,400. [8.2C]

SECTION 7.4

1. pays for a product **3.** selling price; cost; cost **5.** an amount of money; a percent **7a.** $M = P - C$ **b.** $M = P - C; M = r \cdot C$
c. $M = r \cdot C; P = C + M$ **9.** The markup is \$94.50. **11.** The markup rate is 75%. **13.** The markup rate is 49.7%.
15. The selling price is \$17.10. **17.** The selling price is \$355.50. **19.** The markdown is \$110. **21.** The markdown rate is 23.2%.
23. The discount rate is 42%. **25.** The sale price is \$1396.50. **27.** The sale price is \$25.20. **29.** The regular price is \$300.
31. The regular price is \$123.08.

CHAPTER 7 REVIEW EXERCISES

1. $\frac{8}{25}$ [8.1A] **2.** 0.22 [8.1A] **3.** $\frac{1}{4}$, 0.25 [8.1A] **4.** $\frac{17}{500}$ [8.1A] **5.** 17.5% [8.1B] **6.** 128.6% [8.1B] **7.** 280% [8.1B]
8. 21 [8.2A/8.2B] **9.** 500% [8.2A/8.2B] **10.** 66.7% [8.2A/8.2B] **11.** 30 [8.2A/8.2B] **12.** 15.3 [8.2A/8.2B]
13. 562.5 [8.2A/8.2B] **14.** 5.625% [8.2A/8.2B] **15.** 0.014732 [8.2A/8.2B] **16.** 9.6 [8.2A/8.2B]

17. 34.0% of the tourists projected to visit the listed countries will be visiting China. [8.2C] **18.** The company spent \$8400 on advertising. [8.2C]
19. 3952 telephones were not defective. [8.2C] **20.** Cable households spend 36.5% of the week watching TV. [8.2C]
21. The expected profit is \$165,000. [8.2C] **22.** 1620 seats were added to the auditorium. [8.2C] **23.** The airline would sell 196 tickets for
an airplane that has 175 seats. [8.2C] **24.** 22.7% of the registered voters voted in the election. [8.2C] **25.** The clerk's new hourly wage is
\$11.34. [8.3A] **26.** The percent decrease is 25%. [8.3B] **27.** The selling price of the car is \$19,610. [8.4A] **28.** The markup rate is 65%.
[8.4A] **29.** The sale price is \$56. [8.4B] **30.** The sale price is \$390. [8.4B] **31.** The simple interest due on the loan is \$31.81. [8.5A]
32. The corporation paid a 9.00% annual simple interest rate. [8.5A] **33.** The maturity value of the loan is \$10,405. [8.5A]

CHAPTER 7 TEST

1. 0.864 [8.1A; Example 4] **2.** 40% [8.1B; HOW TO 4] **3.** 125% [8.1B; You Try It 6] **4.** $\frac{5}{6}$ [8.1A; Example 3]
5. $\frac{8}{25}$ [8.1A; HOW TO 1] **6.** 118% [8.1B; Example 8] **7.** 90 [8.2A/8.2B; Example 3] **8.** 49.64 [8.2A/8.2B; HOW TO 1]
9. 56.25% [8.2A/8.2B; Example 2] **10.** 200 [8.2A/8.2B; You Try It 4] **11.** 33 accidents are expected for a company that employs
1500 people. [8.2C; You Try It 8] **12.** The student answered 82.2% of the questions correctly. [8.2C; Example 7]
13. The increase in the assistant's weekly wage over last year is \$80. [8.2C; You Try It 9] **14.** The percent increase in cost is 139.4%.
[8.3A; You Try It 1] **15.** The percent increase is $16\frac{2}{3}$%. [8.3A; HOW TO 1] **16a.** The fat content in the soy burger is decreased by $83\frac{1}{3}$%.
b. The percent decrease in cholesterol is 100%. **c.** The percent decrease in calories is 50%. [8.3B; HOW TO 2]
17. The percent decrease in travel expenses is 8%. [8.3B; Example 2] **18.** The dollar increase in the value of the painting is \$300.
[8.2C; You Try It 9] **19.** The markup is \$12.60. [8.4A; Example 1] **20.** The markup rate is 55.1%. [8.4A; You Try It 2]
21. The regular price is \$300. [8.4B; Example 6] **22.** The discount rate is 14%. [8.4B; Example 4] **23.** The simple interest due on the loan
is \$202.50. [8.5A; HOW TO 1] **24.** The maturity value of the loan is \$41,027.40. [8.5A; Example 1] **25.** The simple interest rate on the loan
is 8.4%. [8.5A; HOW TO 2]

CUMULATIVE REVIEW EXERCISES

1. 24.954 [4.2A] **2.** 625 [1.3B] **3.** 14.04269 [4.3A] **4.** $4x^2 - 16x + 15$ [5.5B] **5.** $1\frac{25}{62}$ [3.3B]

6. $6a^3b^3 - 8a^4b^4 + 2a^3b^4$ [5.5A] **7.** 42 [8.2A/8.2B] **8.** -3 [6.1A] **9.** 100,500 [4.3A] **10.** $\frac{23}{24}$ [3.4B] **11.** $1\frac{23}{28}$ [3.6B]

12. $-12a^7b^5$ [5.4A] **13.** [6.6B] **14.** [6.6B]

15. $2\frac{4}{5}$ [3.3B] **16.** 4 [2.2B] **17.** -12 [6.1B] **18.** 5 [6.3A] **19.** 64.48 mph [7.2A] **20.** 44.8 [7.4A] **21.** 8.3% [8.2A/8.2B]
22. 67.2 [8.2A/8.2B] **23.** 58 [2.5A] **24.** 5 [6.3B] **25.** $\frac{1}{10}$ of the population aged 75–84 is affected by Alzheimer's disease. [8.1A]
26. The sale price is \$129.60. [8.4B] **27.** The cost of the graphing calculator is \$42. [8.4A] **28.** The team will win 117 games. [7.4B]
29. The wrestler must lose $2\frac{1}{4}$ lb. [3.4C] **30.** The speed of an object that has fallen 81 ft is 72 ft/s. [4.5C] **31.** The sliders' speed was
36.11 m/s. [7.1A] **32.** The plumber worked 36 h on the medical building. [6.4B] **33.** The resistance is 5 ohms. [7.5B]

Answers to Chapter 8 Selected Exercises

SECTION 8.1

1. 6; 3; x^9 **3.** 3; 4; x^{12} **5.** No **7.** No **9.** a^9 **11.** x^{16} **13.** n^6 **15.** z^8 **17.** a^8b^3 **19.** $-m^9n^3$ **21.** $10x^7$ **23.** $8x^3y^6$ **25.** $-12m^7$ **27.** $-14v^3w$ **29.** $-2ab^5c^5$ **31.** $24a^3b^5c^2$ **33.** $40r^3t^7v$ **35.** $-27m^2n^4p^3$ **37.** $24x^7$ **39.** $6a^6b^5$ **41.** Yes **43.** No **45.** p^{15} **47.** b^8 **49.** p^{28} **51.** c^{28} **53.** $9x^2$ **55.** $x^{12}y^{18}$ **57.** $r^{12}t^4$ **59.** y^4 **61.** $8x^{12}$ **63.** $-8a^6$ **65.** $9x^4y^2$ **67.** $8a^9b^3c^6$ **69.** $m^4n^{20}p^{12}$ **71.** The area of the square is $(49y^{10})$ cm^2. **73a.** No; $2^{(3^2)}$ is larger. $(2^3)^2 = 8^2 = 64$; $2^{(3^2)} = 2^9 = 512$. **b.** The order of operations is $x^{(m^n)}$.

SECTION 8.2

1. 1; 1; 1 **3.** 1; 10; 10 **5.** 9; right; -9 **7.** No **9.** No **11.** 1 **13.** -1 **15.** $\dfrac{1}{9}$ **17.** $\dfrac{1}{8}$ **19.** $\dfrac{1}{x^5}$ **21.** $\dfrac{1}{w^8}$ **23.** $\dfrac{1}{y}$ **25.** a^5 **27.** b^3 **29.** a^6 **31.** q^4 **33.** mn^2 **35.** t^2u^3 **37.** $\dfrac{1}{x^5}$ **39.** $\dfrac{1}{b^4}$ **41.** 2.37×10^6 **43.** 4.5×10^{-4} **45.** 3.09×10^5 **47.** 6.01×10^{-7} **49.** 5.7×10^{10} **51.** 1.7×10^{-8} **53.** 710,000 **55.** 0.000043 **57.** 671,000,000 **59.** 0.00000713 **61.** 5,000,000,000,000 **63.** 0.00801 **65.** No. 84.3 is not a number between 1 and 10. **67.** No. 2.5 is not an integer. **69.** The memristor is 1.5×10^{-8} m thick. **71.** The mass of the Earth is 5.98×10^{24} kg. **73.** The weight of a single *E. coli* bacterium is 6.65×10^{-13} g. **75.** The frequency of a microwave is 2.45×10^9 hertz. **77.** A virus with a mass of 3.9×10^{-19} g can be measured. **79.** The length of an infrared light wave is approximately 3.7×10^{-6} m. **81.** $m \times 10^{-5} < n \times 10^{-3}$ **83a.** 9, 3, 1, $\dfrac{1}{3}, \dfrac{1}{9}$ **b.** 4, 2, 1, $\dfrac{1}{2}, \dfrac{1}{4}$ **85.** $\dfrac{4}{81}$ **87.** 0.0016 **89.** a **91.** 0

SECTION 8.3

3a. Row 2: 10^9; row 3: 1 000 000; row 4: k, 10^3; row 5: 10^2; row 6: 10; row 7: 0.1; row 8: c, 0.01; row 9: m, $\dfrac{1}{10^3}$; row 10: 0.000 001; row 11: 0.000 000 001; row 12: $\dfrac{1}{10^{12}}$ **b.** The exponent on 10 indicates the number of places to move the decimal point. For the prefixes tera-, giga-, mega-, kilo-, hecto-, and deca-, move the decimal point to the right. For the other prefixes shown, move the decimal point to the left. **5.** kilogram **7.** milliliter **9.** kiloliter **11.** centimeter **13.** kilogram **15.** liter **17.** gram **19.** meter or centimeter **21.** kilogram **23.** milliliter **25.** kilogram **27.** kilometer **29.** 910 mm **31.** 1.856 kg **33.** 7.285 L **35.** 8 000 mm **37.** 0.034 g **39.** 29.7 ml **41.** 7.530 km **43.** 9 200 g **45.** 36 L **47.** 2 350 m **49.** 83 mg **51.** 0.716 m **53.** 3.206 kl **55.** 99 cm **57.** 60.5 cm **59.** cm **61.** cg **63.** cm **65.** The patient should take 4 tablets per day. **67.** 5 L of the acid solution should be ordered for the 4 classes of students. **69.** The walk was 4.4 km. **71.** The total weight of the automobiles is 12 645 kg. **73.** 4000 patients can be immunized. **75.** The average number of meters adopted by a group in the Missouri Adopt-a-Highway program is 2 254 m. **77.** The profit on 5 L of cough syrup is $271.80. **79.** 2 720 ml; 2.72 L; 2 L 720 ml

SECTION 8.4

1. a. triangle **b.** hexagon **c.** rhombus; square **d.** two **3.** $P = 2L + 2W$ **5.** 56 in. **7.** 20 ft **9.** 47.1 cm **11.** 92 cm **13.** 9 ft 10 in. **15.** 50.24 cm **17.** 240 m **19.** The trainer will need 270 ft of fencing. **21.** Perimeter of the square **23.** 121 cm **25.** 50.56 m **27.** 3.57 ft **29.** 139.3 m **31.** Less than **33.** The amount of fencing needed is 60 ft. **35.** The amount of binding needed is 24 ft. **37.** The circumferene of the track was 990 ft. **39.** Two packages of bias binding are needed. **41.** The tricycle travels 25.12 ft. **43.** The perimeter of the roller rink is 81.4 m. **45.** The length of the weather stripping is 20.71 ft. **47. a.** The circumference is two times larger. **b.** The circumference is two times larger.

SECTION 8.5

1. a. $A = LW$ **b.** $A = \pi r^2$ **3.** 144 ft^2 **5.** 81 in^2 **7.** 50.24 ft^2 **9.** 20 in^2 **11.** 2.13 cm^2 **13.** 16 ft^2 **15.** 817 in^2 **17.** 154 in^2 **19.** The area is 8100 ft^2. **21.** Equal to **23.** 26 cm^2 **25.** 2220 cm^2 **27.** 150.72 in^2 **29.** 8.851323 ft^2 **31.** Equal to **33.** 7500 yd^2 of artificial turf must be purchased. **35.** You should buy 2 qt of stain. **37.** The area watered by the irrigation system is approximately 7850 ft^2. **39.** No, the expression cannot be used to calculate the area of the carpet. **41.** Yes, the expression can be used to calculate the area of the carpet. **43.** It will cost $986.10 to carpet the area. **45.** You should purchase 48 tiles. **47.** The area is 68 m^2. **49. a.** The area of the rink is more than 8000 ft^2. **b.** 19,024 ft^2 of hardwood flooring is needed to cover the rink. **51.** The cost is $1920. **55.** The area of Lake Tahoe is approximately 222.2 mi^2.

CHECK YOUR PROGRESS: CHAPTER 8

1. 28 [12.1A] **2.** 63°; 153° [12.1A] **3.** 68° [12.1A] **4.** $\angle a = 120°$, $\angle b = 60°$ [12.1C] **5.** 68° and 90° [12.1B] **6.** 14° [12.1B] **7.** 53° [12.1A] **8.** $\angle a = 130°$, $\angle b = 50°$ [12.1C] **9.** 8 m [12.2A] **10.** 22.608 in. [12.2A] **11.** 6.056 m [12.2B] **12.** 6 m^2 [12.3A] **13.** 28.26 in^2 [12.3A] **14.** 41.12 cm^2 [12.3B] **15.** The cost of the carpet is $546. [12.2C] **16.** The area of the walkway is 392.5 ft^2. [12.3C]

SECTION 8.6

1. a. $V = s^3$ **b.** $V = \frac{4}{3}\pi r^3$ **c.** $V = \pi r^2 h$ **3.** 144 cm³   **5.** 512 in³   **7.** 2143.57 in³   **9.** 150.72 cm³   **11.** 6.4 m³   **13.** 5572.45 mm³
15. 3391.2 ft³   **17.** $42\frac{7}{8}$ ft³   **19.** Sphere   **21.** 82.26 in³   **23.** 1.6688 m³   **25.** 69.08 in³   **27.** Increase   **29.** The volume of the water in the tank is 40.5 m³.   **31.** The volume of the hot air balloon is approximately 17,148.59 ft³.   **33.** The volume of the portion of the silo not being used for storage is 1507.2 ft³.   **35.** 20,680,704 people eat guacamole during the Super Bowl.   **37.** The lock contains 35,380,400 gal of water.   **39.** The volume of the bushing is approximately 212.64 in³.   **41.** The tank will hold 15.0 gal.   **43.** No, the expression cannot be used to calculate the volume of the concrete floor.   **45.** Yes, the expression can be used to calculate the volume of the concrete floor.   **47.** The cost of having the floor poured is $11,156.25.

SECTION 8.7

1. integer; 1, 4, 9, 49, 81, 100   **3a.** 8; 8   **b.** −8; −8   **5a.** 25; 36; 25; 5; 36; 6   **b.** $5 < \sqrt{33} < 6$ **9.** 6   **11.** −3   **13.** 13
15. 15   **17.** −5   **19.** −10   **21.** 5   **23.** 10   **25.** 9   **27.** 27   **29.** −14   **31.** 16   **33.** 13   **35.** −6   **37.** 32
39. $\frac{1}{10}$ **41.** $\frac{3}{4}$ **43.** $\frac{5}{8}$ **45.** −24   **47.** 40   **49.** 23   **51.** 5   **53.** 5   **55.** 8   **57.** 1   **59.** −36   **61a.** 2   **b.** −3
63. 1.7321   **65.** 3.1623   **67.** 4.8990   **69.** 11.2250   **71.** −5.6569   **73.** −43.8178   **75.** 4 and 5   **77.** 5 and 6   **79.** 7 and 8
81. 11 and 12   **83.** $2\sqrt{2}$ **85.** $3\sqrt{5}$ **87.** $2\sqrt{5}$ **89.** $3\sqrt{3}$ **91.** $4\sqrt{3}$ **93.** $5\sqrt{3}$ **95.** $3\sqrt{7}$ **97.** $7\sqrt{2}$ **99.** $4\sqrt{7}$
101. $5\sqrt{7}$ **103.** True   **105.** The velocity of the tsunami is 30 ft/s.   **107.** Yes, the formulas are equivalent.
109. It will take 2 s for the object to fall 64 ft.   **111.** The space explorer is 4000 mi above Earth's surface.   **113a.** 0.9   **b.** −0.8
c. $1\frac{2}{3}$ **d.** $-1\frac{3}{4}$

CUMULATIVE REVIEW EXERCISES

1. 48   [2.1B]   **2.** $7\frac{41}{48}$ [2.4C]   **3.** $\frac{39}{56}$ [2.7B]   **4.** $\frac{2}{15}$ [2.8B]   **5.** $-\frac{1}{24}$ [10.4A]   **6.** $17.44/h   [4.2B]   **7.** 37.5   [4.3B]
8. $\frac{3}{8}$ [5.1A]   **9.** −4   [11.1A]   **10.** 85   [5.4A]   **11.** −6   [11.3A]   **12.** $\frac{4}{3}$ [11.4B]   **13.** 32,500 m   [9.1A]   **14.** 31.58 m   [9.1A]
15. −15   [11.2C]   **16.** 2   [11.4B]   **17.** The monthly payment is $708.   [1.5D]   **18.** The sales tax on the home theater system is $47.06. [4.3C]   **19.** The original hourly wage was $29.20.   [5.4B]   **20.** The sale price of the window is $108.   [6.2D]   **21.** The value of the investment after 20 years will be $101,366.50.   [6.3C]   **22.** The weight of the package is 54 lb.   [8.2C]   **23.** The distance between the rivets is 60 cm.   [9.1B]   **24.** The number is −2.   [11.6A]   **25. a.** 74°   **b.** 106°   [12.1C]   **26.** 29.42 cm   [12.2B]   **27.** 50 in²   [12.3B]
28. 92.86 in³   [12.4B]   **29.** 10.63 ft   [12.5B]   **30.** 36 cm   [12.6B]

FINAL EXAM

1. 3259   [1.3B]   **2.** 53   [1.5C]   **3.** 60,205   [1.3B]   **4.** 16   [1.6B]   **5.** 144   [2.1A]   **6.** $1\frac{49}{120}$ [2.4B]   **7.** $3\frac{29}{48}$ [2.5C]
8. $6\frac{3}{14}$ [2.6B]   **9.** $\frac{4}{9}$ [2.7B]   **10.** $\frac{1}{6}$ [2.8B]   **11.** $\frac{1}{13}$ [2.8B]   **12.** 164.177   [3.2A]   **13.** 0.027918   [3.4A]   **14.** 0.69   [3.5A]
15. $\frac{9}{20}$ [3.6B]   **16.** 24.5 mi/gal   [4.2B]   **17.** 54.9   [4.3B]   **18.** $\frac{9}{40}$ [5.1A]   **19.** 135%   [5.1B]   **20.** 125%   [5.1B]
21. 36   [5.2A]   **22.** $133\frac{1}{3}$%   [5.3A]   **23.** 70   [5.4A]   **24.** 20 in.   [8.1A]   **25.** 1 ft 4 in.   [8.1B]   **26.** 2.5 lb   [8.2A]
27. 6 lb 6 oz   [8.2B]   **28.** 2.25 gal   [8.3A]   **29.** 1 gal 3 qt   [8.3B]   **30.** 248 cm   [9.1A]   **31.** 4.62 m   [9.1A]   **32.** 1.614 kg   [9.2A]
33. 2067 ml   [9.3A]   **34.** 88.55 km   [9.5A]   **35.** The cost is $1.15.   [9.4A]   **36.** 6.79×10^{-8} [10.5A]   **37.** 3.9 m   [12.2A]
38. 45 in²   [12.3A]   **39.** 1200 cm³   [12.4A]   **40.** −4   [10.2A]   **41.** −15   [10.2B]   **42.** $-\frac{1}{2}$ [10.4B]   **43.** $-\frac{1}{4}$ [10.4B]
44. 6   [10.5B]   **45.** $-x + 17$ [11.1C]   **46.** −18   [11.2C]   **47.** 5   [11.3B]   **48.** 1   [11.4B]   **49.** Your new balance is $959.93.   [6.7A]   **50.** 63,750 people will vote.   [4.3C]   **51.** One year ago, the dividend per share was $2.00.   [5.4B]   **52.** The average monthly income is $3794.   [7.4A]   **53.** The simple interest due is $7200.   [6.3A]   **54.** The probability is $\frac{1}{3}$.   [7.5A]   **55.** The death count of China is 6.7% of the death count of the four countries.   [7.1B]   **56.** The discount rate for the Bose headphones is 28%.   [6.2D]
57. The weight of the box is 81 lb.   [8.2C]   **58.** The perimeter is approximately 28.56 in.   [12.2B]   **59.** The area is approximately 16.86 cm².   [12.3B]   **60.** The number is 16.   [11.6A]

Answers to Final Exam

1. 2400 [1.2A]   **2.** 24 [1.5A]   **3.** 2 [2.2B]   **4.** 18 [2.5A]   **5.** $2\frac{11}{16}$ [3.4B]   **6.** $\frac{14}{15}$ [3.3B]   **7.** $\frac{2}{9}$ [3.6B]   **8.** $\frac{5}{16} < 0.313$ [4.3C]

9. -769.5 [4.3A]   **10.** -3.28 [4.3B]   **11.** Yes [4.3A]   **12.** $9\sqrt{2}$ [4.5B]

13. 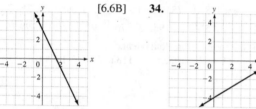 [4.6B]   **14.** $10t$ [5.1A]   **15.** $-2x - 14y$ [5.2B]   **16.** $z^3 + 2z^2 - 6z + 7$ [5.3B]

17. $8x^7y$ [5.4A]   **18.** $10a^4b^2 - 6a^3b^3 + 8a^2b^4$ [5.5A]   **19.** $15x^2 - x - 6$ [5.5B]   **20.** $81x^8y^4$ [5.4B]   **21.** $\frac{1}{64}$ [5.6A]

22. m^2n^4 [5.6A]   **23.** -6 [6.2A]   **24.** $-\frac{1}{3}$ [6.3A]   **25.** $\frac{5}{6}$ [6.3B]   **26.** 248 cm [7.1A]   **27.** 13,728 ft [7.3A]

28. $\frac{4}{3}$ [7.4A]   **29.** $\angle a = 74°; \angle b = 106°$ [9.1B]   **30.** 10.6 ft [9.3A]   **31.** The perimeter is 26 cm. [9.2A]   **32.** The volume is 96 in³. [9.4A]

33.   [6.6B]   **34.**   [6.6B]   **35.** The ground speed of the airplane is 364 mph. [1.2C]

36. The worker can inspect 320 products. [3.3C]   **37.** The difference is 65.98°C. [4.2B]   **38.** 5.88×10^{12} [5.6B]

39. The fulcrum should be placed 6 ft from the 50-pound child. [6.3C]   **40.** You are purchasing 6 tickets. [6.4B]

41. The property tax is $4710. [7.4B]   **42.** 32% of the states have a land area of 75,000 mi² or more. [8.2C]

43. The gear will make 16 rpm. [7.5B]   **44.** The total cost of the car is $34,287.50. [8.2C]   **45.** The percent decrease is 22.6%. [8.3B]   **46.** The sale price is $159.25. [8.4B]   **47.** The simple interest due is $1612.50. [8.5A]   **48.** 37.5% of the students work more than 15 h per week. [10.1C]   **49.** The mean annual premium is $334.80. The median annual premium is $309. [10.2A]   **50.** $\frac{1}{3}$ [10.3A]